INTRODUCTION TO INTEGRATIVE ENGINEERING

INTRODUCTION TO INTEGRATIVE ENGINEERING

A COMPUTATIONAL APPROACH TO BIOMEDICAL PROBLEMS

Guigen Zhang

CRC Press
Taylor & Francis Group
Boca Raton London New York

CRC Press is an imprint of the
Taylor & Francis Group, an **informa** business

CRC Press
Taylor & Francis Group
6000 Broken Sound Parkway NW, Suite 300
Boca Raton, FL 33487-2742

CRC Press is an imprint of Taylor & Francis Group, an Informa business

Printed on acid-free paper

International Standard Book Number-13: 978-1-4665-7228-7 (Hardback)

Library of Congress Cataloging-in-Publication Data

Names: Zhang, Guigen, author.
Title: Introduction to integrative engineering : a computational approach to biomedical problems / by Guigen Zhang.
Description: New York : CRC Press, [2017] | Includes bibliographical references and index.
Identifiers: LCCN 2016026224| ISBN 9781466572287 (hardback : alk. paper) | ISBN 9781315388465 (ebook)
Subjects: | MESH: Biomedical Engineering--methods | Computational Biology | Computer Simulation | Models, Theoretical
Classification: LCC R855.5 | NLM QT 36 | DDC 610.28--dc23
LC record available at https://lccn.loc.gov/2016026224

Visit the Taylor & Francis Web site at
http://www.taylorandfrancis.com

and the CRC Press Web site at
http://www.crcpress.com

I would like to dedicate this book to my parents, from whom I learned the importance of learning how *beyond* learning that *at a very young age (although I did not know the exact literary terms back then), and to my wife, for keeping me in check all these years whenever I wandered into foolishness.*

Contents

Preface

This book has been developed based on my years of firsthand experiences in teaching *computational modeling of multidisciplinary problems* with the motivation to encourage transdisciplinary learning, integrative thinking, and holistic problem solving. The structure of this book is shaped by my philosophic views toward learning and teaching. These views include mainly that (1) an integrative transdisciplinary approach, rather than a reductive compartmentalized one, should be pursued in today's teaching and learning in order to equip students and engineers to take on the twenty-first-century challenges and (2) knowing how our minds function differently in *learning that* and *learning how*, it is feasible to devise ways to stimulate *learning how* besides *learning that* to cultivate and develop critical and creative minds in students within the time frame of current curricula.

With its sight set on encouraging *learning how*, this book introduces a systemic look into the blackbox of how the engineering world is linked to differential equations, and how these differential equations are solved by computer-based approximate methods through domain discretization, field quantity interpolations, weighted integral of residue evaluations, linearization of differential equations into matrix algebraic equations, Gauss quadrature and numerical integrations, and minimization of approximation errors, among other topics.

Through hands-on experiences in the process of *learning that* and developing crucial hard skills, students and readers will find it not only feasible but also practical to examine and solve engineering problems in a holistic way by taking advantage of a computational tool. With this approach, real-world problems exhibiting mechanical, electrical, thermal, electrochemical, and mass transport phenomena, either individually or combined, will be dealt with in a coupled multidisciplinary (i.e., transdisciplinary) way, rather than in the conventional single-discipline (i.e., compartmentalized disciplinary) way. I hope that this practice, in the long run, will help set future modelers and engineers on a journey of integrative learning and problem solving.

Although this book will discuss procedures used in the finite element method (FEM), it is not like any other books on FEM. It aims to introduce a computational modeling approach based on FEM for facilitating integrative learning through consolidation of commonalities in various compartmentalized disciplines, and for gaining a deep understanding of how this "intricate machinery" of computational modeling operates to encourage *learning how* beyond *learning that.* It aims to pave some groundwork toward restructuring the engineering curriculum with the assistance of a computational modeling–based investigative tool, to promote integrative thinking and transdisciplinary reasoning in hypothesis testing, problem solving, inventing, designing, prototyping, and testing, among others, for the generation of novel solutions and cultivation of senses of unlimited possibilities in engineering research and industrial R&D activities. Such a journey is, of course, expected to be a long road. In its first edition, this book aims to lay the foundation. In future revisions, more and more integrated problems as case studies will be presented and discussed.

This book is designed for junior and senior undergraduate students in bioengineering and other related fields of engineering and applied sciences, and graduate students and practicing engineers in industry R&D labs and other consultancies. It was developed to suit the needs of not only novice modelers but also experienced ones. It is necessary that the reader has some basic understanding of elementary calculus and differential equations. Some knowledge with one or more of the following science and engineering disciplines would also be helpful: physics; chemistry; computer science; mechanical, electrical, chemical, biomedical, and materials science; and electrochemical, civil, and environmental engineering.

This book is structured in four parts. In Part I, the need for converting from a compartmentalized disciplinary to a transdisciplinary approach in education is argued for, for the purpose of promoting integrative rather than reductive learning. In Part II, a systemic discussion on the ins and outs of computational modeling procedures is presented, starting from the facts that the engineering world is linked to differential equations; where differential equations come from; how they are solved by computer-based approximate methods through domain discretization, field quantity interpolations, weighted integral of residue evaluations, and linearization of differential equations into matrix algebraic equations; how numerical integrations are performed using Gauss quadrature; and how minimization of approximation errors is ensured, among others. In Part III, the modeling environments of some common software, including COMSOL, ABAQUS, and ANSYS, are discussed, with the connections between software settings and the FEM fundamentals highlighted. Moreover, methods to develop hands-on practical skills in performing computational modeling and practical issues concerning image-based modeling, as well as the standardization and regulatory processes, are discussed. In Part IV, useful knowledge in the mechanics of materials and mathematics is provided as extra "just-in-time" learning and referencing materials.

Guigen Zhang
Clemson University

MATLAB® is a registered trademark of The MathWorks, Inc. For product information, please contact:

The MathWorks, Inc.
3 Apple Hill Drive
Natick, MA 01760-2098 USA
Tel: 508-647-7000
Fax: 508-647-7001
E-mail: info@mathworks.com
Web: www.mathworks.com

Acknowledgments

My interest in promoting *integrative engineering* did not come from any engineering textbooks. Instead, it came from my curious reading of articles in business, management, philosophy, history, and other engineering profession–related works over the years. For example, the writings by Mencius, Daisetz Suzuki, Gilbert Ryle, Peter Drucker, James March, Roger Martin, and Samuel Florman played certain roles in shaping my views toward learning and innovation in relation to engineering. Moreover, my active participation in *advancing engineering education in a liberal arts environment* at the University of Georgia, Athens, in the early 2000s (while I was on the faculty there) also helped shape my views.

My motivation for writing this textbook is to reflect the ideas I have developed over the years in my journey of searching for a practical strategy to update engineering curricula and make them relevant to our time. I developed it in the spirit of encouraging integrative learning, questioning, hypothesis testing, problem solving, inventing, designing, prototyping, and testing by linking commonalities across compartmentalized disciplines based on the underlying mathematics for the generation of novel solutions and cultivation of senses of limitless possibilities in engineering research and industrial R&D activities. Moreover, I structured it to promote transdisciplinary reasoning and encourage *learning how* besides *learning that.* It is my hope that such an integrative approach will also help make some curricular room for incorporating more relevant content of liberal arts and humanities in the engineering curricula.

As you will note from reading the book, iconic figures like Steve Jobs also had some influence on me, not just in the words I quoted from him, but also in his elegance to instill artistic beauty in whatever he touched. In my way of imitating, I pushed myself to learn and create my own graphic illustrations throughout the book to convey, with visualization, many of the mathematic and engineering concepts from a teacher's perspective. Of course, this is only possible thanks to the open-source codes of LaTeX and companion packages such as TikZ and PGF, allowing me to create illustrative graphics using mathematic equations (my way of linking math and engineering to graphic arts).

Many of the examples discussed in Chapters 14 through 16 are works of collaborations with many colleagues, associates, postdocs, graduate students, and undergraduate students. Although there are too many to list, I would particularly like to thank Mark Haidekker, Andrew Zhang, and Yutaka Takahashi for their contributions and constructive discussions on the denture project; Walter Schmidt (the hip and knee projects); Samuel Bearden (the spine project); Mike Jaeggli (the stent project); Larry Alvord, Jordan Hall, David Keyes, Courtney Morgan, and Lynn Winterton (the cornea project); and all the students in my classes over the years for their constructive feedback and suggestions.

Author

Guigen Zhang, PhD, is a professor of bioengineering and a professor of electrical and computer engineering at Clemson University, South Carolina. He is also the executive director of the Institute for Biological Interfaces of Engineering, a research and education/training institute designated by the South Carolina Commission on Higher Education. Professor Zhang is a fellow of the American Institute for Medical and Biological Engineering. He has published extensively in the areas of biosensors, biomechanics, biomaterials, and computational modeling. Over the years, his research has been funded by diverse funding sources, ranging from federal agencies such as the National Institutes of Health and National Science Foundation, to private foundations like the Bill and Melinda Gates Foundation, to venture groups and state-level start-up funds, as well as industries in the health care, semiconductors, and data storage sectors. Professor Zhang holds numerous patents in nanotechnology-enhanced structures and biosensors. Aside from his services on the editorial boards of numerous scientific journals, Professor Zhang is active in leadership roles in professional societies. He is currently the executive editor of the Biomaterials Forum of the Society for Biomaterials, and president of the Institute of Biological Engineering, a professional society that supports the community of scientists and engineers who are at the forefront of creating new linkages between biology and engineering and seeking new opportunities through *biology-inspired* engineering.

Part I

Readying the Integrative Mindset

1

From Compartmentalized Disciplines to Transdiscipline

Disciplines are not products of universities. They precede the founding of the first university back in the Middle Ages. Today, the word *discipline* often means a field of study or a trade in which a set of rules, codes, or way of doing things is imparted from teachers to students. The origin of disciplines is likely the result of our cognitive dealing with the world we live in, through a reductive process. Reductive thinking helps reduce a complex issue into small independent pieces by neglecting and discarding as much as possible any factors and issues that we have no knowledge or comprehension of at the moment. Doing so, we can avoid complexity and ambiguity, and gain the comfort of simplicity and clarity, as Roger Martin put it. The formation of disciplines not only makes the simplification of complex phenomena possible, but also offers compartmentalized frameworks and guidelines through which we explore, understand, and interact with the world.

1.1 Reductive Specialization for the Twentieth Century

As a tool for facilitating learning, disciplines have characterized higher education since the beginning of academic life. Even to this day, we still describe universities in terms of traditional disciplines, such as physics, chemistry, mathematics, medicine, biosciences, finances, social science, and engineering. Take engineering; the word has its lexiconic root in the Latin word *ingenium*, which means "innate quality, intelligence, natural capacity" to build and create. So engineering is all about creation and innovation. By today's definition, engineering often refers to the practice of exploiting basic laws and principles of science to design and construct tools and objects of certain utility. According to this definition, engineering practices can be dated back to the beginning of human history as humans devised fundamental tools for survival needs.

To facilitate learning, impart skills, and encourage specialized practices, the engineering field has witnessed, over the past century, subdivisions of the field into many specialized areas, such as mechanical, agricultural, materials, civil, electrical, chemical, industrial, computer, biomedical, and environmental. The benefit of such a compartmentalized division of disciplines is that in each discipline, certain selected or specialized knowledge, ways of thinking, procedures, and practices can be emphasized and imparted to students. This practice has proven useful in the past centuries, as engineers played many crucial roles in bringing on the industrial as well as digital revolution.

1.2 Integrative Problem Solving for the Twenty-First Century

But time has changed and we live in a different world now. With the disappearing of so-called "low-hanging fruits" in innovation, we can no longer ignore the complex and interwoven issues. Evidence is emerging that traditional compartmentalized disciplinary approaches are becoming insufficient for dealing with the unknowns and uncertainties of the real world, because our attention to simplicity has also made us unable to see the interconnectedness in the systems of the problems. Future innovation will require a strategy that encourages integrative knowledge acquisition at the convergence of biological, health, and behavioral sciences; physical sciences; engineering; and beyond, rather than reductive knowledge acquisition. Lately, a growing sense of calling for transdisciplinary approaches is emerging in all these traditional disciplines. Here, *transdiscipline* refers to a strategy that goes across and beyond disciplinary boundaries to seek a holistic understanding of the world around us from all possible angles and aspects, technical and beyond. The design and production of tomorrow's systems and products will require such a transdisciplinary way of practice.

A transdisciplinary approach encourages knowledge integration rather than reduction. Integrative learning and thinking require one to actively seek commonalities and patterns from various different angles to sort out potentially relevant factors; embrace complexity; welcome missing links; consider multidirectional, multivariable, and nonlinear relationships and interdependencies; see all factors in a systems view; and perform integrative investigations on how one possibility might affect another.

Bioengineering, or biomedical engineering, is a field that exemplifies the essence of transdisciplinary needs. In bioengineering, problems are solved based on myriad laws of physics and thermodynamics, as well as biochemistry and biology, among others. At a population level, statistical rules (e.g., Bayesian probability) may play an influential role as well. Over the past decades, advances in bioengineering have contributed to numerous innovations and developments of medical devices, sensors, implants, prostheses, and so forth, and they have resulted in significant improvement in our quality of life. However, one of the major challenges facing the field of bioengineering is its reliance on the knowledge and investigative approaches developed through the reductive method in the traditional compartmentalized disciplines. A case in point: Metal-on-metal articulating implants, such as total hip and knee joints made of alloys, are thought to be superior to metal-on-polymer implants in resisting wear, but the corrosion processes (an electrochemical phenomenon) of two alloys are much more active than those of an alloy and a polymer. Since wear is a mechanical and material issue and corrosion is an electrochemical problem, they are seldom dealt with in the same context. Because of this, serious corrosion-related problems have been coming to light recently for those metallic implants thought to provide better wear resistance.

This is just one example of the consequences of our reductive way of dealing with the real world. Looking around us, we can find similar problems in almost all traditional engineering fields and beyond. "Can anything be done about it?" you may ask. The answer depends on who you ask.

1.3 Jack of All Trades, Master of None?

In an effort to gage students' views on how they would react to an integrative and transdisciplinary way of learning, I found myself in a debate over whether one should be a "jack of all trades" or a "master of one trade." These phrases prompted me to recall the debate we had some 20 years ago concerning the nascent field of biomedical engineering. Back then, the phrase was "being a bioengineer is like becoming a jack of all trades and a master of none!" According to Wikipedia, "jack of all trades, master of none" is a phrase used with negative connotation in reference to a person who is competent with many skills, but spends so little time learning each skill in depth that he or she cannot become an expert in any particular one. William Shakespeare (1564–1616) was dismissively referred to as a "jack of all trades and master of none" by Robert Greene in his 1592 booklet "Greene's Groats-Worth of Wit." Of course, the students in the camp of jack of all trades do not regard themselves negatively. Instead, they believe being a jack of all trades is like being a generalist in the field of medicine and they can fulfill an important role in the field of biomedical engineering. On the other hand, the students in the camp of master of one trade believe that it is necessary to specialize in a particular area, like athletes, so that they can gain entrance to a collaborative team.

Looking back upon the phrase "jack of all trades, master of none," I can only speculate that it might have been the creation of people who were trained in these traditional disciplines—people who would regard themselves as the ones on a path to becoming an expert, or a master, of their trade. But knowing the fact that their disciplines are compartmentalized, how does one think of such a master? Do you recall the fabled story of the blind men and an elephant that you might have heard as a child? In case you forgot, here is a shortened version from Wikipedia: a group of blind men (or men in the dark) touch an elephant to learn what it is like. Each one feels a different part, but only one part, such as the side or the tusk. They then tell their individual "knowledge" of the elephant. As you can imagine, they ended with complete disagreements; although they were not wrong in a reductive way, none was complete, and hence none was correct.

1.4 Venturing Out of Our Comfort Zones

If a master of incompleteness is not what you aspire to, a complete way of inquiry may be what you need to develop. To be complete, we have to exercise integrative learning rather than reductive learning. Instead of narrowing our focus onto a specific aspect of a problem, we need to examine the problem from all possible angles.

Does this way of "integrative learning" require us to rethink and restructure the way of educating future engineers? Indeed, to alter the way engineering is taught and to connect engineering education to real-world applications, in the early 2000s, the University of Georgia established the Faculty of Engineering and Harvard University created the School of Engineering and Applied Sciences, both aiming to take a transdisciplinary approach to structure their engineering education with more broad connections with liberal arts, humanities, and biological sciences. Resistance to this way of reengineering can be attributed mainly to the worry of not equipping students with sufficient specialty knowledge, again, the worry of producing jacks of all trades and masters of none.

Even without a restructured engineering curriculum, one can still consciously develop the trait of integrative thinking as a habit of thought, as Martin suggested. To start, all you need is a willingness to venture out of your comfort zones, or develop a sense of "technology foolishness," in James March's words. According to March, a certain amount of technology foolishness is necessary to make you creative and cross-disciplinary. Using a scenario we are familiar with, technology foolishness refers to "stealing" ideas from one field and applying them to another with a certain degree of twisting and straining. Of course, please do not get carried away. "The chance that someone who knows no physics will be usefully creative in physics must be so close to zero as to be indistinguishable from it," as March also warned us. But applying some borrowed ideas from a domain you barely know to a field you know well may lead to breakthrough developments, as long as you can find the delicate balance "between how much foolishness is good for knowledge and how much knowledge is good for foolishness."

1.5 Difference in *Learning That* and *Learning How*

Finding the delicate balance between knowledge and foolishness is actually not as easy as it seems. For example, consider the fool in the fabled story about a hungry man and five pancakes; can you see any wisdom? One after another, the man kept buying and eating pancakes until he felt his stomach full after the fifth one. He then concluded that the fifth one made him full and he was so sorry that he had wasted the money on the previous four: "Had I known that, I should have bought only the fifth one."

The antifoolishness moral of this story has taught humankind the lesson that proper accumulation is necessary, whether being the food we eat or the knowledge we acquire. We accept this notion as if once we accumulate a certain amount of learning, a magic thing will happen.

Indeed, this way of thinking has influenced the way of teaching and learning for pretty much the entire history of civilization. The famous Chinese philosopher Mencius (372–289 BC; second only to Confucius, 551–479 BC) once said that "a master can only teach students rules and regulations and he cannot make them innovative." The innovative mind will emerge, or not, only after the students accumulate sufficient amounts of rules and regulations.

Sound familiar? The only difference is that Mencius's rules and regulations are today's specialty knowledge.

Certainly, spending more time learning and accumulating will help one to become creative and innovative, as in the case of Leonardo da Vinci (1452–1519), who had spent 14 years as an apprentice before becoming a great master. But extending the time for an engineering curriculum today is not a viable option, let alone not the wishes of students. "I would die in my forties if I do," lamented one student in answering if one can become a master of all trades, or a polymath, even with the knowledge that da Vinci, one of the greatest polymaths, had lived to his late sixties in his time.

So what is the solution to this problem? The answer, it turns out, lies in the wisdom of British philosopher Gilbert Ryle (1900–1976). As Ryle put it, learning how (the procedures) is not like learning that (the facts and truth). So other than spending all the time to learn *that*—the rules and regulations, or the specialty knowledge, one may spend some time to learn *how*—the procedures in which rules and regulations came about, or the specialty knowledge that was developed. As Ryle explained, knowing how to perform an act skillfully may be a matter of not only being able to reason practically, but also being able to put practical reasoning into action. It may further lead to the discovery of new facts and the development of new knowledge to replace the obsolete ones. After all, our knowledge of the world is expected to evolve, update, and renew, as evident by the saying that the greatest discovery of the nineteenth century is that equations of nature were linear, and the greatest discovery of the twentieth century is that they were not.

It is enlightening to know that our minds function differently in *learning that* and *learning how.* It makes us aware that learning only the rules and regulations, no matter how long it takes or how many rules and regulations a person accumulates, may never bring about the creative genie. Instead, learning how these rules and regulations, or specialty knowledge, are developed may provide the crucial link to becoming creative and innovative. Even for the food we eat, modern nutrition and health guidelines suggest that a full stomach may not be a good metric for guiding food consumption.

1.6 Connecting the Dots

Using today's words to describe *learning that* and *learning how*, we may refer to the common phrase *connecting the dots. Learning how* is like learning to connect the dots. Before connecting, you will need to collect them, *learning that*—the acquisition of information and known theories and principles (or rules and regulations in Mencius's words). Connecting the dots is the integrative process in which the acquired facts and rules are processed and integrated into interconnected knowledge, insight, and wisdom. Do not be satisfied by just collecting the dots; nothing much will happen if you do not connect them.

We all know what *connecting the dots* has done for Steve Jobs in inspiring him to create Apple Computers and other handheld i-devices. He did this even without a formal college education. So collect as many dots as possible, no matter where (or in what discipline) the dots lie or whether you are in college or out, and then follow through by connecting the dots you have collected. This surely will help you to become a master of integration and be able to generate creative new options and innovative solutions to today and tomorrow's problems.

1.7 Borrowing Zen's Way of Seeing the World with the Assistance of Computational Modeling

"Stay hungry and stay foolish!" To heed the parting advice that Steve Jobs left us after telling his story of *connecting the dots*, let us venture into a Zen Buddha's world for a moment. According to Daisetz Teitaro Suzuki (1870–1966), a Japanese Zen philosopher, Zen's way of knowing a flower should not be analytically reductive, in which one would pluck the flower, bring it to a laboratory, dissect it, and go through all the necessary analytical processes, because once the flower is plucked, it is no longer the flower one sees or intends to know. Instead, Zen's way is not to detach it from the totality of its surroundings, but to leave it where it is, let it be in its living state and environment, and *contemplate* it.

I know what you are thinking, but please remember I am not here to promote Zen philosophy or to address Zen's acceptance issue. I am borrowing a useful idea—the idea of interacting with our surroundings in a totality and nonreductive way, or in other words, in an integrative way. Fortunately for us, we can do this in a way far better than Zen's way of contemplating. In my belief, a computational modeling–based approach is well positioned to provide a nonreductive and nondestructive, yet analytical and investigative means to address real-world problems—problems of not only a mechanical nature, but also electrical, electrostatic, electrochemical, thermal, electromagnetic, chemical, biochemical, and biological natures, among others, under the governing laws of thermodynamics, biochemistry, biology, and physics, as well as the probabilistic rules of statistics. It will provide a much needed practical tool for us to interact with our surroundings.

1.8 Seeking Convergence beyond Engineering

Steve Jobs once said, "It is in Apple's DNA that technology alone is not enough—it is technology married with liberal arts, married with the humanities, that yields us the result that makes our heart sing."

Technology married with liberal arts and humanities!

In a 1989 article "The Civilized Engineer," Samuel Florman summarized his views with many historical, as well as anecdotal, accounts in arguing for the need to broaden the horizons of engineering education to include liberal arts and humanities content (so as to make engineers less "boring" and more humanistically integrated into the world they live in). According to Florman, back in the early 1860s General Sylvanus Thayer (1785–1872), known as the father of the U.S. Military Academy at West Point, endowed an engineering school at Dartmouth College where he advocated the training of engineers in not only engineering subjects, science, and mathematics, but also liberal arts. However, General Thayer's idea never gained much traction on a larger scale because the passing of the Morrill Act, the so-called "land grants," by the U.S. Congress in 1862 tilted the engineering education in America toward the training of the industrial classes. And it has pretty much stayed that way ever since, even though calls for adding more content of liberal arts and humanities to engineering education have never faded over the years.

If we keep doing what we have been doing in the past, it will be a daunting challenge for the engineering profession to remain relevant to a changing world. Lately, a converging sense is that future engineers must be creative, innovative, lifelong learners and effective communicators in technical and nontechnical forums and competitive in a global environment. Future engineers will have to wrestle with problems that are rooted in physical sciences, biological sciences, environmental sciences, arts, humanities, and social and behavioral sciences, among others, in addition to the engineering aspects, in the spirit of seeking convergence to facilitate transdisciplinary integration of all these aspects as called for by the National Research Council of the National Academies of Science, Engineering and Medicine.

What does this mean in a practical sense? To me, it means that we all need to develop an integrative mindset and keep collecting and connecting dots. To encourage this practice, we, as a society, need to stop defining and categorizing ourselves or others by the fields of study in 4 years of one's life, as labeled in the diploma or degree, and instead identify people by their track records, and sometimes even their motivations.

After all, engineering is about creating what has never been and turning the opportunities into means for the sustainable advancement of the human race and our civilized society. A wrongly defined problem, even solved correctly in a technical sense, may lead to some unintended consequences. Thus, to be able to define the problems rightly in a societal-relevant context, engineers should be not only technically competent but also fully conscious of the humanistic and economic context surrounding these technical challenges, because all engineering problems are technical challenges rooted in a socially, economically, environmentally, and humanistically intertwined world. General George Marshall once complained that he did not receive a good education at Virginia Military Institute because there was no training in history. He knew that to be a leader, one must have a sense of history, for history is the human story. The same can be said for an engineer: to be able to innovate, the engineer must have a sense of humanistic appreciation of our society, for innovation is not just a technical endeavor, but a human one, as exemplified by "Apple's DNA" in Steve Jobs's words.

This book is designed to introduce a unique approach to help the reader or student learn not only *that* but also *how* through the process of learning and mastering the use of an advanced computational tool to embark on a journey of integrative learning, questioning, hypothesis testing, problem solving, invention, design, prototyping, and testing, among others, for the generation of novel solutions and the cultivation of senses of limitless possibilities in engineering research and industrial R&D activities. In the long run, I hope this journey will help pave some groundwork toward restructuring engineering education by promoting transdisciplinary learning, integrative thinking and reasoning, and *learning how* besides *learning that*, as well as making some curricular room for incorporating more relevant content from liberal arts and humanities in the engineering curricula.

1.9 Exercises

1. Reflect upon your views toward compartmentalized versus transdisciplinary and reductive versus integrative learning.

2. What are your thoughts regarding the discussion on a jack of all trades, master of one trade, or master of none?
3. What are your thoughts regarding the discussion on technology foolishness and venturing out of our comfort zones?
4. Knowing the difference between *learning that* and *learning how*, what will you do differently in your study and learning?

Recommended Readings

1. Roger L. Martin. 2009. *The Opposable Mind: How Successful Leaders Win through Integrative Thinking.* Brighton, MA: Harvard Business School Press.
2. James G. March. 1971. The technology of foolishness. *Civil o Konomen (Copenhagen)*, 18, 4, 4–12.
3. Diane L. Coutu. 2006. Ideas as Art: A Conversation with James G. March. *Harvard Business Review*, October, 83–89.
4. Gilbert Ryle. 2002. *The Concept of Mind.* Chicago: University of Chicago Press.
5. Steve Jobs. 2005. Commencement address at Stanford University. http://news.stanford.edu/news/2005/june15/jobs-061505.html.
6. Roy Melvyn and Daisetz Teitaro Suzuki. 2012. *The Core Teachings of D. T. Suzuki.* Amazon Kindle Edition. Lulu.com.
7. National Academy of Engineering. 2005. Educating the Engineer of 2020. Adapting Engineering Education to the New Century. Washington, DC: National Academy of Engineering Press.
8. Samuel C. Florman. 1989. The civilized engineer. Issues in *Science and Technology*, 5, 4, 82–88.
9. National Academy of Engineering Press. 2014. *Convergence: Facilitating Transdisciplinary Integration of Life Sciences, Physical Sciences, Engineering, and Beyond.* Washington, DC: National Academy of Engineering Press.

Part II

Cracking Open the Blackbox of Computational Modeling

2

Engineering Problems and Partial Differential Equations

Most of the physical phenomena encountered in engineering problems, such as fluid dynamics, mechanics, materials, electricity, magnetism, electrochemistry, optics, photonics, plasmonics, heat flow, and mass transport, can be described by partial differential equations because these phenomena follow the laws of thermodynamics in terms of mass, momentum, and energy conservation. Solutions to these partial differential equations under certain initial and boundary conditions can shed in-depth and systemic insights into the underlying mechanisms governing these physical phenomena and provide valuable information toward the analysis of real-world problems, as well as the design of engineering solutions.

2.1 Brief Review of Differential Equations

A differential equation is a mathematical function that contains derivatives of its dependent variable or variables (which are sometimes termed as the unknown or unknowns) with respect to an independent variable or several independent variables. Very often, these independent variables represent spatial locations in a physical space and temporal variations with respect to time. For example, in a mechanical problem, dependent variables include displacements, deformations, stresses, and strains, while in a heat transfer or mass diffusion problem, dependent variables can be temperature, concentration, and heat or mass fluxes, among others. In all these problems, independent variables are often the spacial locations and time. Differential equations can be classified as ordinary or partial, linear or nonlinear, or time independent or time dependent, and by their order and dimension, among others.

2.1.1 Ordinary versus partial differential equations

When a differential equation has only one independent variable, it is called an ordinary differential equation (ODE), and when it has two or more independent variables, it is a partial differential equation (PDE). As a case in point, letting a and b be known constants, Equation 2.1 describes a relationship between a dependent variable u and its derivative with respect to an independent variable x. Since x is the only independent variable appearing, Equation 2.1 is an ODE. In Equation 2.2, however, the dependent variable u appears in second-order partial derivatives with respect to two independent variables, x and y; thus, Equation 2.2 is a PDE.

$$a\frac{du}{dx} - bu = 0 \tag{2.1}$$

$$a\frac{\partial^2 u}{\partial x^2} + b\frac{\partial^2 u}{\partial y^2} = f(x, y) \tag{2.2}$$

2.1.2 Order of differential equations

ODEs and PDEs are often classified by the order of their highest derivatives appearing in the equation. For example, in Equation 2.1, the highest order in which the dependent variable appears in a derivative form is first order (sometimes called first derivative, for short); thus, it is a first-order ODE. In Equation 2.2, second derivative is the highest order, so it is a second-order PDE.

2.1.3 Linear versus nonlinear differential equations

Differential equations can be linear or nonlinear depending on whether they contain a single factor or multiple factors of the dependent variable or its derivatives. For example, in Equation 2.3 the dependent variable u appears only in single-factor terms of itself and its first- and second-order derivatives; thus, it is a linear PDE. In Equation 2.4, however, the dependent variable u appears in a multifactor (e.g., square) term, although its second-order derivative terms appear only once; therefore, it is nonlinear.

$$a_{11}\frac{\partial^2 u}{\partial x^2} + a_{12}\frac{\partial^2 u}{\partial x \partial y} + a_{22}\frac{\partial^2 u}{\partial y^2} + a_1\frac{\partial u}{\partial x} + a_2\frac{\partial u}{\partial y} + a_0 u = f(x, y) \tag{2.3}$$

$$a(x, y, z)\frac{\partial^2 u}{\partial x^2} + b(x, y, z)\frac{\partial^2 u}{\partial y^2} + c(x, y, z)\frac{\partial^2 u}{\partial z^2} + e(x, y, z)u^2 = f(x, y, z) \tag{2.4}$$

2.1.4 Constant versus nonconstant coefficients

The terms appearing with the dependent variable and its derivatives in an ODE or a PDE are the coefficients of the ODE or PDE. When these coefficients do not vary with the independent variables, they are constant coefficients. In this case, they are often expressed in simple alphabets, as in Equations 2.1 and 2.2, or indexed alphabets, as in Equation 2.3. When they vary with the independent variables, they are nonconstant coefficients. For example, when a certain material property varies with physical positions within a structure, this material property is a nonconstant property. In this case, the coefficients have to be expressed as functions of the independent variables, as in Equation 2.4. Sometimes, when a coefficient is not a constant, certain high-order derivatives in a differential equation may need to be expressed in a sequential derivative form, as in Equation 2.5, in which $\kappa(x)$ is a coefficient varying with x:

$$-\frac{d}{dx}\left[\kappa(x)\frac{du}{dx}\right] = f(x) \tag{2.5}$$

2.1.5 Dimension of differential equations

All the differential equations discussed above are functions of only the spatial variables, namely, x only, x and y, or x, y, and z. With different spatial variables, they describe problems of different spatial dimensions. For example, Equation 2.1 is a one-dimensional (1D) ODE describing a physical phenomenon occurring only in the x dimension. On the other hand, Equations 2.2 and 2.3 describe physical phenomena occurring in the two-dimensional (2D) space of x and y, and Equation 2.4 represents a physical phenomenon occurring in the three-dimensional (3D) space of x, y, and z; therefore, Equations 2.2 and 2.3 are 2D PDEs and Equation 2.4 is a 3D PDE.

2.1.6 Time-dependent and -independent differential equations

The differential equations listed earlier are not functions of time. In other words, they are time independent, meaning that they describe stationary or steady-state physical phenomena. Stationary or steady-state differential equations often deal with problems in which either the dependent variable does not change with time at all, or the change is so small that its effect can be conveniently ignored. For a stationary problem, we can think of a moment right before a diver makes a jump at the tip of a diving board. At this moment, nothing moves and all is in a static equilibrium. Of course, the events occurring after this moment will be transient and time dependent. For a steady-state problem, we can relate to a situation where a heat sink is absorbing heat from a microprocessor on one side and dissipating it to the surrounding air on the other sides without causing any changes in the overall temperature profile in the heat sink. In this case, the heat exchange is regarded as being in a state of dynamic equilibrium, or steady state.

When the dependent variable changes with time, the differential equation will have to include relevant time derivative terms of the dependent variable, as in Equation 2.6.

$$a_0\frac{\partial^2 u}{\partial t^2} + a_1\frac{\partial u}{\partial t} + b_1\frac{\partial^2 u}{\partial x^2} + b_2\frac{\partial^2 u}{\partial x \partial y} + b_3\frac{\partial^2 u}{\partial y^2} + d_1\frac{\partial u}{\partial x} + d_2\frac{\partial u}{\partial y} + eu = f(t,x,y) \tag{2.6}$$

Time derivative terms include velocity, acceleration, and the rate of change in heat or mass, among others.

2.1.7 Initial and boundary conditions

Differential equations use simple mathematical expressions to capture the governing principles underlying the problems one intends to analyze. The term *differential* often means that the governing equation is applied to a representing unit volume of the physical structure over a unit period of time (if the problems are time dependent). This makes differential equations powerful: a simple equation, or a set of equations, can describe many different physical problems. This, however, imposes strict requirements when solving the differential equations in order to have the solutions reflect truthfully the actual physical problems under investigation. It is therefore important to define an appropriate physical domain in which the differential equation is applied and specify the necessary boundary conditions at certain boundaries (along with initial values if it is time dependent) to properly constrain the differential equation according to the actual physical situations of the problems.

Dependent variables in a differential equation may appear directly or in their derivative forms. In direct forms, they are called primary variables, and in derivative forms they are secondary variables. Similarly, boundary conditions can also be given as either values for the primary variables or values for the secondary variables. For example, in solving Equation 2.7,

$$\frac{\partial u(t,x)}{\partial t} - \kappa \frac{\partial^2 u(t,x)}{\partial x^2} = f(t,x) \tag{2.7}$$

when the boundary conditions are given as values for the primary variable u directly as

$$u(t,a) = \alpha(t), \quad u(t,b) = \beta(t)$$

they are essential boundary conditions, which are sometimes called *Dirichlet boundary conditions*, and when they are known as values for the secondary variables, such as derivatives of u as

$$\frac{\partial u(t,a)}{\partial x} = \gamma(t), \quad \frac{\partial u(t,b)}{\partial x} = \lambda(t)$$

they are natural boundary conditions, which are also known as *Neumann boundary conditions*. The reason we call them natural boundary conditions is that these conditions are always related to natural phenomena, such as mechanical forces or flux of matters. When the boundary conditions are given in a mixed form of Dirichlet and Neumann, they are termed *Robins boundary conditions*. Since Equation 2.7 is a time-dependent PDE, an initial value at $t = 0$ is also necessary for solving it:

$$u(0,x) = u^0(x)$$

Example 2.1

Classify the following differential equations according to their categories, including ODE or PDE, order, dimension, linearity, time dependency, and type of coefficient. Also, identify the dependent and independent variables.

a.
$$\frac{dx}{dt} + tx = 0$$

b.
$$\frac{\partial u}{\partial t} - \frac{\partial^2 u}{\partial x^2} = (1 + t)\sin(x)$$

c.
$$\frac{\partial w}{\partial t} + w\frac{\partial w}{\partial x} = 0$$

Answer

a. It is an ODE, first-order, linear, 0D (because x is the dependent variable and there is no independent dimensional variable), time-dependent equation, with nonconstant coefficients (t is the coefficient of x, which is not a constant). x is a dependent variable and t is the independent time variable.

b. It is a PDE, second-order, linear, 1D, time-dependent equation, with constant coefficient. u is a dependent variable and x is the independent dimensional variable.

c. It is a PDE, first-order, nonlinear (it has the product of w and $\frac{\partial w}{\partial x}$), 1D, time-dependent equation, with constant coefficient. w is a dependent variable, x is the independent dimensional variable, and t is the independent time variable.

2.2 Connecting PDEs to the Engineering World

Most engineering problems can be represented by differential equations. In this section, we review some common ODEs and PDEs and link them to the physics of many engineering problems. Before we do that, it will be helpful to review some of the differential notations and symbols.

2.2.1 Some differential notations

2.2.1.1 ∇ operator

∇ (pronounced "del") is a mathematical notation used to serve as a vector form differential operator. In a 3D spacial domain, it can be expressed as a vector in terms of three first derivatives:

$$\nabla = \frac{\partial}{\partial x}\vec{i} + \frac{\partial}{\partial y}\vec{j} + \frac{\partial}{\partial z}\vec{k} \tag{2.8}$$

where $\vec{i}, \vec{j}, \vec{k}$ are the standard unit vectors along the x, y, and z directions, respectively, in the Cartesian coordinate system.

As an operator, the ∇ symbol can be simply applied to a field variable, and as a vector, it can be multiplied, either in a dot product or in a cross product, with another vector. As a differential operator, ∇ follows the algebra rules of calculus. For example, when F and G are field variables and k is a constant, we have the following properties:

1. Sum rule: $\nabla(F+G) = \nabla F + \nabla G$
2. Difference rule: $\nabla(F-G) = \nabla F - \nabla G$
3. Constant multiple rule: $\nabla(kF) = k\nabla F$
4. Product rule: $\nabla(FG) = F\nabla G + G\nabla F$
5. Quotient rule: $\nabla\left(\frac{F}{G}\right) = \frac{G\nabla F - F\nabla G}{G^2}$

Clearly, these rules are familiar to us when we think of the ∇ operator as d/dx or $\partial/\partial x$.

2.2.1.2 Gradient of a field

When the ∇ operator is applied to a field quantity, $\Phi(x, y, z)$, the resulting expression is called the gradient of Φ, which is a vector:

$$\text{grad}\,\Phi = \nabla\Phi = \frac{\partial\Phi}{\partial x}\vec{i} + \frac{\partial\Phi}{\partial y}\vec{j} + \frac{\partial\Phi}{\partial z}\vec{k} \tag{2.9}$$

In a physical sense, the gradient of a field measures the variation of the field quantity with respect to its spacial variables. For example, when Φ is a 1D field, that is, $\Phi = \Phi(x)$, $\nabla\Phi$ simply measures the slope of this field with respect to the x axis, as illustrated in Figure 2.1. Since all variables in 1D are varying with x only, the unit vector, $\vec{i}$, is often omitted. In 2D and 3D

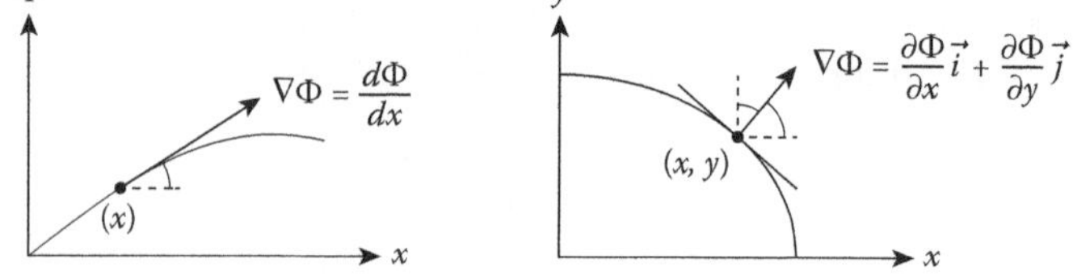

FIGURE 2.1
Gradient of a field in 1D and 2D spaces.

spaces, the gradient represents the magnitude and direction of the greatest change of the field quantity in space. For a 2D field, $\Phi = \Phi(x, y)$, $\nabla\Phi$ captures the steepness and direction of the greatest change in the field with respect to x and y, which can be represented by the vector normal to the tangent line of the field at (x, y), as illustrated in Figure 2.1. Similarly for a 3D field, $\Phi = \Phi(x, y, z)$, $\nabla\Phi$ measures the steepness and direction of the greatest change in the field with respect to x, y, and z by the vector normal to the tangent plane of the field at (x, y, z).

2.2.1.3 Dot product and divergence of a field

Next, we will look at the dot product of the ∇ vector with another vector. First, let us recall the definition of the dot product. As illustrated in Figure 2.2, the dot product of two vectors, $u = u_x\vec{i} + u_y\vec{j} + u_z\vec{k}$ and $v = v_x\vec{i} + v_y\vec{j} + v_z\vec{k}$, defines the length of the first vector (e.g., $|u|$) multiplying the projection length of the second vector on the first (e.g., $|v|\cos\theta$), where θ is the angle between the two vectors. By vector algebra and the law of cosines, the dot product of two vectors is no longer a vector but a scalar, and its magnitude can be expressed as (refer to Appendix B for more details)

$$u \cdot v = |u||v|\cos\theta = u_x v_x + u_y v_y + u_z v_z$$

The dot product of the ∇ vector with any vector field, $F = F_x(x, y, z)\vec{i} + F_y(x, y, z)\vec{j} + F_z(x, y, z)\vec{k}$, is called the divergence of F, which is no longer a vector but a scalar:

$$\nabla \cdot F = \operatorname{div} F = \frac{\partial F_x}{\partial x} + \frac{\partial F_y}{\partial y} + \frac{\partial F_z}{\partial z} \tag{2.10}$$

Physically, the divergence of a vector field (often a flow vector) measures the flux density of the vector field within a given region of space. Here, flux describes the amount of matter (mass, energy, current, etc.) entering or existing through a surface of unit area in a unit amount of time. Divergence is often used in the consideration of the conservation of matters when the principle of continuity applies. For example, by measuring the net flux of the matter passing through an enclosed surface surrounding the region of space, one can determine the change in the density of the matter. This statement can be

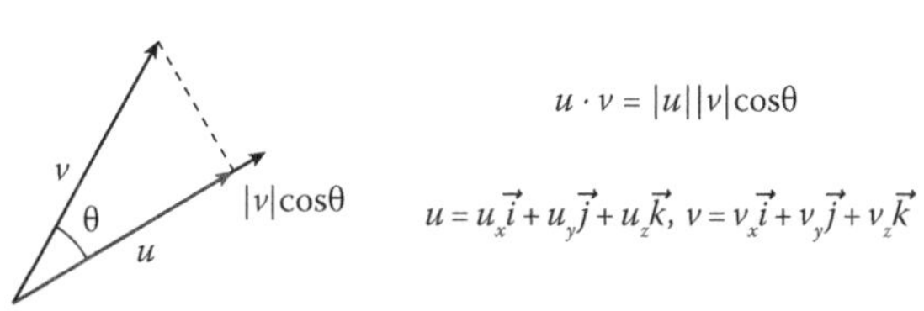

FIGURE 2.2
Dot product of two vectors.

expressed by the following equation, known as the divergence theorem:

$$\iint_A F \cdot n dA = \iiint_V \nabla \cdot F dV \tag{2.11}$$

The divergence theorem works in both 2D and 3D situations. As illustrated in Figure 2.3, in a 3D space it states that the amount of an expanding vector field F outflowing through the boundary surface (A) of a spherical space can be determined by integrating the divergence of the field (i.e., the flux density) over the enclosed volume (V). Similarly, in a 2D space, the amount of an expanding vector field F outflowing through the boundary (L) of an enclosed region can be determined by integrating the divergence of the field over the area (S) of the enclosed region.

2.2.1.4 Cross product and curl of a field

As illustrated in Figure 2.4, assuming that two vectors, $u = u_x\vec{i} + u_y\vec{j} + u_z\vec{k}$ and $v = v_x\vec{i} + v_y\vec{j} + v_z\vec{k}$, are not parallel to each and that they intersect at an angle θ, by definition, the cross product of these two vectors can be expressed

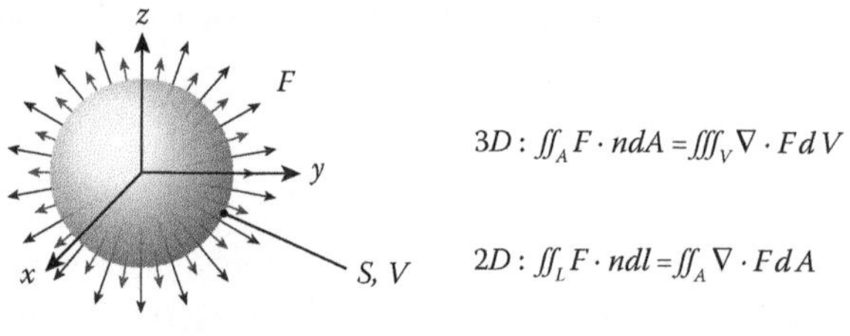

FIGURE 2.3
Illustration of the divergence theorem.

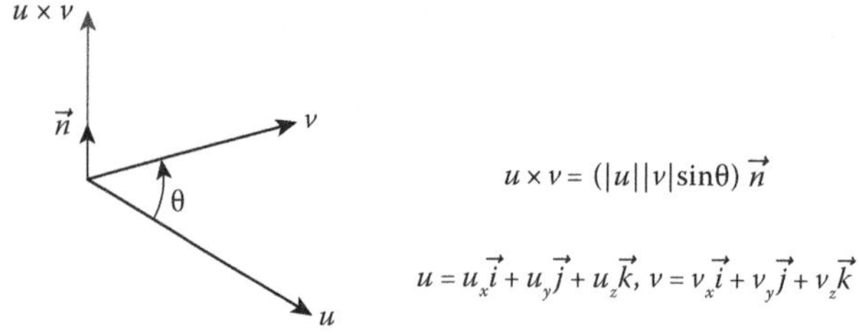

FIGURE 2.4
Cross product of two vectors.

as follows (see Appendix B for more details):

$$u \times v = (|u||v| \sin \theta)\, \vec{n} = \begin{bmatrix} \vec{i} & \vec{j} & \vec{k} \\ u_x & u_y & u_z \\ v_x & v_y & v_z \end{bmatrix}$$
$$= (u_y v_z - u_z v_y)\vec{i} - (u_x v_z - u_z v_x)\vec{j} + (u_x v_y - u_y v_x)\vec{k}$$

Unlike the dot product, the cross product is a vector, and its direction (with a unit vector $\vec{n}$) is determined by the right-hand rule: by curling your fingers along the angle (θ) from u to v, the direction your right thumb points is the direction of $\vec{n}$.

The cross product of the ∇ vector with the vector field F is called the curl of F, which is a vector:

$$\nabla \times F = \operatorname{curl} F = \begin{bmatrix} \vec{i} & \vec{j} & \vec{k} \\ \dfrac{\partial}{\partial x} & \dfrac{\partial}{\partial y} & \dfrac{\partial}{\partial z} \\ F_x & F_y & F_z \end{bmatrix}$$
$$= \left(\frac{\partial F_z}{\partial y} - \frac{\partial F_y}{\partial z}\right)\vec{i} + \left(\frac{\partial F_x}{\partial z} - \frac{\partial F_z}{\partial x}\right)\vec{j} + \left(\frac{\partial F_y}{\partial x} - \frac{\partial F_x}{\partial y}\right)\vec{k} \tag{2.12}$$

Physically, the curl vector measures the rate of circulation (or circulation density) of a rotating vector field with its direction determined by the right-hand rule: when the fingers curl along the direction of rotation, the thumb points in the direction of the curl vector (see Figure 2.5). The curl operation can be illustrated by Stokes' theorem, which states that the circulation of a rotating flow vector F along an enclosed path L in the direction counterclockwise with respect to the surface's unit normal vector (n) can be determined by the integral of the dot product of the curl of the rotating vector ($\nabla \times F$) with the unit vector (n) over the enclosed projection area S, as illustrated in Figure 2.5.

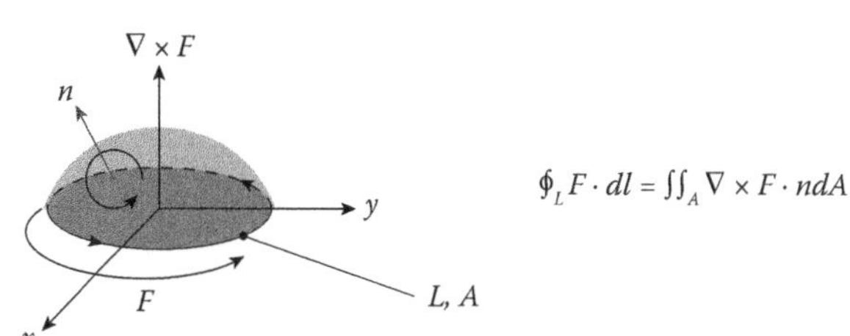

FIGURE 2.5
Illustration of Stokes' theorem.

2.2.1.5 Laplacian of a field

The dot product of the ∇ vector with the gradient of Φ (i.e., $\nabla\Phi$) is a scalar commonly known as the Laplacian of Φ:

$$\nabla \cdot \nabla\Phi = \nabla^2\Phi = \frac{\partial^2\Phi}{\partial x^2} + \frac{\partial^2\Phi}{\partial y^2} + \frac{\partial^2\Phi}{\partial z^2} \tag{2.13}$$

Here, the notation (∇^2) is called the Laplacian operator, representing the sum of three second-order derivatives:

$$\nabla^2 = \frac{\partial^2}{\partial x^2} + \frac{\partial^2}{\partial y^2} + \frac{\partial^2}{\partial z^2}$$

The Laplacian operator plays a very important role in differential equations describing many engineering problems. The Laplacian of a field allows us to quantitatively compare the field at a selected point with those at neighboring points. An intuitive way to understand this is to recall the way we find extremes (maximum and minimum) of a 1D function: first, we set the first-order derivative of the function to zero to find the locations of the extremes, and then to know whether an extreme point is a maximum or minimum, we evaluate the corresponding second-order derivative. If the second-order derivative is greater than zero, we have a minimum; if it is zero, we have a local constant field; and if it is less than zero, we have a maximum.

Similarly, with the Laplacian operator we can say the following:

1. When $\nabla^2 u > 0$ at a point (x, y, z), $u(x, y, z)$ will be smaller than the average of u at its neighboring points.
2. When $\nabla^2 u = 0$ at a point (x, y, z), $u(x, y, z)$ will be equal to the average of u at its neighboring points.
3. When $\nabla^2 u < 0$ at a point (x, y, z), $u(x, y, z)$ will be greater than the average of u at its neighboring points.

2.2.2 Common engineering problems and their governing PDEs

As pointed out earlier, most of the physical phenomena encountered in engineering problems can be described by PDEs because these problems obey the laws of physics and thermodynamics. Without going into any details, we now give a quick overview of some common PDEs and link them to the engineering problems they govern.

For many mechanical problems, such as structural movements or deformations under internal and external forces or loads, PDEs are commonly used to relate their dependent variables, often the displacements of the structure at a given point, to their spacial and temporal independent variables, as well as constraints like loads, tractions, and motions. Here, let us have a look at two 1D examples. The first, as listed in Equation 2.14, describes a 1D bar structure undergoing deformation or motions in response to a volume load $f(x,t)$, and the second, given in Equation 2.15, describes the vibration of a string:

$$\rho\frac{\partial^2 u}{\partial t^2} = k\frac{\partial^2 u}{\partial x^2} + f(x,t) \tag{2.14}$$

$$\rho\frac{\partial^2 u}{\partial t^2} = a^2\frac{\partial^2 u}{\partial x^2} \tag{2.15}$$

These two PDEs, although describing two different physical phenomena, share some common mathematical traits: they both have a second-order derivative term with respect to time, representing the acceleration (or force), and a second-order derivative term with respect to x, which is the Laplacian of u in 1D space. In other words, these PDEs can be interpreted to mean that the acceleration (or force) is proportional to the Laplacian ($\nabla^2 u$). Based on the knowledge we learned in Section 2.2.1, we know that when $\nabla^2 u > 0$ at a point (in the case of the vibrating string), the transverse displacement of this point will be less than the average of its neighboring points. In this situation, the point will move outward to catch up with the neighboring points by increasing the acceleration. The commonality in these two PDEs indicates that although we face two different mechanical problems, we actually deal with the same type of differential equations.

In the case of heat transfer, the dependent variable, temperature (T), obeys the following PDE in terms of its first-order time derivative, the Laplacian, and a volume heat source (Q):

$$\rho c\frac{\partial T}{\partial t} = \nabla\cdot(\kappa\nabla T) + Q \tag{2.16}$$

Equation 2.16 can be interpreted to mean that the change in temperature with respect to time is proportional to the Laplacian of temperature, $\nabla^2 T$. This means that the temperature at a point will increase if the temperature at that point is less than the average of its neighboring points ($\nabla^2 T > 0$), or vice versa.

In the case of mass transport by diffusion, the dependent variable, namely, the concentration (c) of a substance, obeys the following PDE in terms of its first-order time derivative and the Laplacian, as well as a rate volume reaction source (R):

$$\frac{\partial c}{\partial t} = \nabla\cdot(D\nabla c) + R \tag{2.17}$$

Similarly, since the change in concentration with respect to time is proportional to the Laplacian of concentration, $\nabla^2 c$, as shown in Equation 2.17, the concentration at a point will increase if the concentration at that point is less than the average of its neighboring points (i.e., $\nabla^2 c > 0$), or vice versa. Moreover, although we have in Equation 2.16 a heat transfer problem and in Equation 2.17 a diffusion problem, these two PDEs are identical mathematically. This is another example showing that although we face two engineering problems of different physics, we practically deal with the same partial differential equation.

For the propagation of acoustic (mechanical or sound) waves, the dependent variable u (representing the particle displacement in the case of a mechanical wave, or the pressure in the case of a sound wave) obeys the following PDE:

$$\frac{1}{c_s^2}\frac{\partial^2 u}{\partial t^2} = \nabla \cdot (\nabla u) \tag{2.18}$$

where c_s is the wave phase velocity. Mathematically, Equation 2.18 is of the same type of PDEs as Equations 2.14 and 2.15, in which the acceleration of particles (or sound) is proportional to the Laplacian of the particle displacement (or the pressure).

PDEs also play a major role in helping us deal with electrical and electromagnetic problems. For example, the phenomenon of electrostatics is governed by the following PDE:

$$\epsilon_0 \epsilon_r \nabla^2 V = -\rho \tag{2.19}$$

Here, ϵ_0 and ϵ_r are the permittivity of the vacuum and dielectric medium, respectively, V the electrical potential, and ρ the charge density. Again, we see the Laplacian term. Due to the nonzero term on the right-hand side, Equation 2.19 is often referred to as Poisson's equation. In this equation, potential V varies smoothly in a quadratic relationship with its spacial variables and V has a minimum (or maximum) when $\rho < 0$ (or $\rho > 0$).

To sum up, this section is not intended to give an exhaustive list of PDEs. Instead, it presents some common PDEs and discusses their meanings in relation to engineering problems from a differential equation–oriented view. From this exercise, we noted that the PDEs applied to different problems are sometimes of the same mathematical type. This fact suggests that although there are countless real-world problems, their governing differential equations are actually of limited numbers and types. It is therefore beneficial to examine these problems from a differential equation–oriented angle.

Solving PDEs analytically for complex problems, however, is very difficult and sometimes impossible. To make matters worse, as the saying goes, the greatest discovery of the nineteenth century is that equations of nature were linear, and the greatest discovery of the twentieth century is that they were not. This means that complex real-world problems are not only of a transdisciplinary nature but also sometimes governed by nonlinear PDEs. The good news is that the explosion in computational powers and capabilities makes solving multiphysics nonlinear PDEs not only possible but also relatively easier to do. Therefore, in this book we will learn to take advantage of a computational method to solve complex PDEs. The ability to solve real-world problems of a transdisciplinary nature, like bioengineering problems, in this way can help break the barriers among the traditional disciplines, provide a holistic way to gain better insights into the real problems, and present a practical way to seek new possibilities.

2.3 Brief Review of Matrix Algebra

A matrix is a rectangular array of elements, consisting of numbers, symbols, or other expressions, arranged in rows and columns. The number of rows and the number of columns define the dimension of a matrix. For example,

$$\{A\} = \begin{bmatrix} a_{11} & a_{12} & \cdots & a_{1n} \\ a_{21} & a_{22} & \cdots & a_{2n} \\ \vdots & \vdots & \ddots & \vdots \\ a_{m1} & a_{m2} & \cdots & a_{mn} \end{bmatrix}$$

is a $m \times n$ matrix having m rows and n columns. The elements of a matrix are often expressed as a_{ij}, in which i is the row index number $(i = 1, 2, \ldots, m)$ and j is the column index number $(j = 1, 2, \ldots, n)$.

2.3.1 Row and column vectors

A matrix of dimension $1 \times n$ is called a $1 \times n$ row vector, and a matrix of dimension $m \times 1$ is called a $m \times 1$ column vector. For example,

$$\{a\} = \begin{bmatrix} 2 & 9 & 5 \end{bmatrix}$$

is a 1×3 row vector and

$$\{b\} = \begin{Bmatrix} 3 \\ 7 \\ 15 \\ -8 \\ 4 \end{Bmatrix}$$

is a 5×1 column vector. Very often, we use square brackets for row vectors and curly brackets for column vectors.

2.3.2 Addition and subtraction

Matrix addition and subtraction can be performed when two or more matrices are of the same dimension, and they are calculated by the addition or subtraction of the corresponding elements. For example,

$$\begin{bmatrix} 5 & 9 \\ 2 & 8 \end{bmatrix} + \begin{bmatrix} 8 & 3 \\ 4 & 7 \end{bmatrix} = \begin{bmatrix} 13 & 12 \\ 6 & 15 \end{bmatrix}$$
$$\begin{bmatrix} 5 & 9 \\ 2 & 8 \end{bmatrix} - \begin{bmatrix} 8 & 3 \\ 4 & 7 \end{bmatrix} = \begin{bmatrix} -3 & 6 \\ -2 & 1 \end{bmatrix}$$

2.3.3 Multiplication by a scalar

When a matrix is multiplied by a scalar, all the elements in the matrix are multiplied by the scalar. For example,

$$10^3 \times \begin{bmatrix} 25 & 9 \\ 2 & 8 \end{bmatrix} = \begin{bmatrix} 25000 & 9000 \\ 2000 & 8000 \end{bmatrix}$$

This operation is often useful in factoring out a common multiplier, as in

$$\begin{bmatrix} 25000 & 9000 \\ 2000 & 8000 \end{bmatrix} = 10^3 \begin{bmatrix} 25 & 9 \\ 2 & 8 \end{bmatrix}$$

2.3.4 Matrix–matrix multiplication

Two matrices can be multiplied only when the column number of the first matrix equals the row number of the second matrix, and the resulting matrix will have its row number equaling that of the first matrix, and column number that of the second matrix.

$$[A]_{m\times n}[B]_{n\times p} = [C]_{m\times p}$$

where

$$c_{mp} = \sum_{k=1}^{n} a_{mk} b_{kn}$$

For example,

$$\begin{bmatrix} 2 & 8 & 9 & 6 \\ 5 & 4 & 7 & 3 \end{bmatrix}_{2\times 4} \times \begin{bmatrix} 1 & 4 & 6 \\ 2 & 6 & 9 \\ 3 & 8 & 10 \\ 7 & 8 & 5 \end{bmatrix}_{4\times 3} = \begin{bmatrix} 87 & 176 & 204 \\ 55 & 124 & 151 \end{bmatrix}_{2\times 3}$$

2.3.5 Transposition

The transpose of a matrix can be obtained by converting its rows into its columns. For example,

$$[A] = \begin{bmatrix} 2 & 8 & 9 & 6 \\ 5 & 4 & 7 & 3 \end{bmatrix}, \qquad [A]^T = \begin{bmatrix} 2 & 5 \\ 8 & 4 \\ 9 & 7 \\ 6 & 3 \end{bmatrix}$$

$$[B] = \begin{bmatrix} 1 & 4 & 6 \\ 2 & 6 & 9 \\ 3 & 8 & 10 \\ 7 & 8 & 5 \end{bmatrix}, \qquad [B]^T = \begin{bmatrix} 1 & 2 & 3 & 7 \\ 4 & 6 & 8 & 8 \\ 6 & 9 & 10 & 5 \end{bmatrix}$$

where the superscript T denotes the transpose operation.

2.3.6 Differentiation and integration

By definition, the elements of a matrix can be scalar constants, expressions, or functional expressions. For example,

$$[A] = \begin{bmatrix} 2x^2 & 8x + 9 \\ 5x - 4 & 9x^3 - 3x^2 \end{bmatrix}$$

In this case, the matrix may be differentiated and integrated. The derivative or integral of a matrix is obtained by taking the derivative, or integral, of each element as follows:

$$\frac{d}{dx}[A] = \begin{bmatrix} 4x & 8 \\ 5 & 27x^2 - 6x \end{bmatrix}$$

$$\int_0^x [A]dx = \begin{bmatrix} \dfrac{2x^3}{3} & 4x^2 + 9x \\ \dfrac{5x^2}{2} - 4x & \dfrac{9x^4}{4} - x^3 \end{bmatrix}$$

2.3.7 Square matrix

When the row number of a matrix equals its column number, the matrix is called a square matrix. For example,

$$[A] = \begin{bmatrix} 5 & 4 & 6 \\ 8 & 7 & 9 \\ 3 & 15 & 17 \end{bmatrix}$$

is a square matrix.

2.3.8 Diagonal matrix

When a square matrix has only nonzero elements along its principal diagonal, it is called a diagonal matrix. For example,

$$[M] = \begin{bmatrix} 5 & 0 & 0 & 0 \\ 0 & 4 & 0 & 0 \\ 0 & 0 & 7 & 0 \\ 0 & 0 & 0 & 9 \end{bmatrix}$$

2.3.9 Identity matrix

The identity matrix, sometimes called unit matrix, is a diagonal matrix with 1's along its principal diagonal. We often use $[I]$ for the identity matrix,

$$[I] = \begin{bmatrix} 1 & 0 & 0 & 0 \\ 0 & 1 & 0 & 0 \\ 0 & 0 & 1 & 0 \\ 0 & 0 & 0 & 1 \end{bmatrix}$$

2.3.10 Symmetric matrix

A symmetric matrix is a square matrix whose elements satisfy

$$a_{ij} = a_{ji}$$

By the definition of matrix transposition, a square matrix satisfies

$$[A] = [A]^T$$

For example,

$$[A] = \begin{bmatrix} 7 & -8 & 1 \\ -8 & 16 & -8 \\ 1 & -8 & 7 \end{bmatrix}$$

is a symmetric matrix.

2.3.11 Determinant

For a 2×2 square matrix $[A]$, its determinant $det[A]$ is calculated by the product of the elements along the principal diagonal minus the product of the elements along the secondary diagonal. For example,

$$[A] = \begin{bmatrix} a & b \\ c & d \end{bmatrix}$$

$$det[A] = ad - bc$$

For matrices of higher dimension, one can always reduce them, using the matrix partition method, to 2×2 matrices and then calculate their determinants. If the determinant of a matrix is 0, the matrix is called *singular*.

2.3.12 Matrix inversion

For a square and nonsingular matrix $[A]$, its inverse $[A]^{-1}$ is a matrix such that

$$[A][A]^{-1} = [I]$$

For a 2×2 matrix,

$$[A] = \begin{bmatrix} a & b \\ c & d \end{bmatrix}$$

$$[A]^{-1} = \frac{1}{det|A|} \begin{bmatrix} d & -b \\ -c & a \end{bmatrix} = \frac{1}{ad - bc} \begin{bmatrix} d & -b \\ -c & a \end{bmatrix}$$

2.3.13 Matrix partition

A matrix of large dimension can be partitioned into a matrix of submatrices of smaller dimension. For example,

$$[A] = \left[\begin{array}{ccc|ccc} a_{11} & a_{12} & a_{13} & a_{14} & a_{15} & a_{16} \\ a_{21} & a_{22} & a_{23} & a_{24} & a_{25} & a_{26} \\ \hline a_{31} & a_{32} & a_{33} & a_{34} & a_{35} & a_{36} \\ a_{41} & a_{42} & a_{43} & a_{44} & a_{45} & a_{46} \\ a_{51} & a_{52} & a_{53} & a_{54} & a_{55} & a_{56} \end{array}\right]$$

can be partitioned into

$$[A] = \begin{bmatrix} A_{11} & A_{12} \\ A_{21} & A_{22} \end{bmatrix}$$

where

$$[A_{11}] = \begin{bmatrix} a_{11} & a_{12} & a_{13} \\ a_{21} & a_{22} & a_{23} \end{bmatrix}, \quad [A_{12}] = \begin{bmatrix} a_{14} & a_{15} & a_{16} \\ a_{24} & a_{25} & a_{26} \end{bmatrix}$$

$$[A_{21}] = \begin{bmatrix} a_{31} & a_{32} & a_{33} \\ a_{41} & a_{42} & a_{43} \\ a_{51} & a_{52} & a_{53} \end{bmatrix}, \quad [A_{22}] = \begin{bmatrix} a_{34} & a_{35} & a_{36} \\ a_{44} & a_{45} & a_{46} \\ a_{54} & a_{55} & a_{56} \end{bmatrix}$$

The partitioned matrix follows the same algebra rules as listed above.

2.3.14 Matrix calculation using MATLAB

MATLAB® is a useful tool for performing matrix algebra calculations. For example, at a MATLAB prompt (>>), typing $\underline{A = [2\ \ 8; 4\ \ 9]}$ will define matrix $[A]$ as (note that the underline is used here to highlight the input text for MATLAB)

$$[A] = \begin{bmatrix} 2 & 8 \\ 4 & 9 \end{bmatrix}$$

Typing $\underline{A'}$ will produce its transpose,

$$[A]^T = \begin{bmatrix} 2 & 4 \\ 8 & 9 \end{bmatrix}$$

Typing $\underline{det(A)}$ will calculate its determinant,

$$det[A] = -14$$

And typing $\underline{A\hat{}\ -1}$ will produce its inverse,

$$[A]^{-1} = \frac{-1}{14}\begin{bmatrix} 9 & -8 \\ -4 & 2 \end{bmatrix} = \begin{bmatrix} -0.6429 & 0.5714 \\ 0.2857 & -0.1429 \end{bmatrix}$$

Similarly, typing $\underline{A = [5\ \ 9; 2\ \ 8]; B = [8\ \ 3; 4\ \ 7];}$ will define matrices $[A]$ and $[B]$ as

$$[A] = \begin{bmatrix} 5 & 9 \\ 2 & 8 \end{bmatrix} \quad \text{and} \quad [B] = \begin{bmatrix} 8 & 3 \\ 4 & 7 \end{bmatrix}$$

Typing $\underline{A + B}$ will produce their addition:

$$[A] + [B] = \begin{bmatrix} 13 & 12 \\ 6 & 15 \end{bmatrix}$$

Typing $\underline{A * B}$ will calculate their multiplication:

$$[A][B] = \begin{bmatrix} 76 & 78 \\ 48 & 62 \end{bmatrix}$$

MATLAB can also be used to find the solutions to matrix algebra equations. For example, to solve

$$\begin{bmatrix} 2 & 8 \\ 4 & 9 \end{bmatrix} \begin{Bmatrix} x_1 \\ x_2 \end{Bmatrix} = \begin{Bmatrix} 13 \\ 9 \end{Bmatrix}$$

one just types $\underline{A = [2\ \ 8; 4\ \ 9]; B = [13; 9];}$ at a MATLAB prompt such that the algebra equation above can be structured as

$$[A]\{X\} = \{B\}$$

Then by typing $\underline{X = A\hat{}\ -1 * B}$, one can find its solution,

$$\{X\} = \begin{Bmatrix} x_1 \\ x_2 \end{Bmatrix} = [A]^{-1}\{B\} = \begin{Bmatrix} -3.2143 \\ 2.4286 \end{Bmatrix}$$

The reader is encouraged to review the MATLAB manual for more matrix algebra operations.

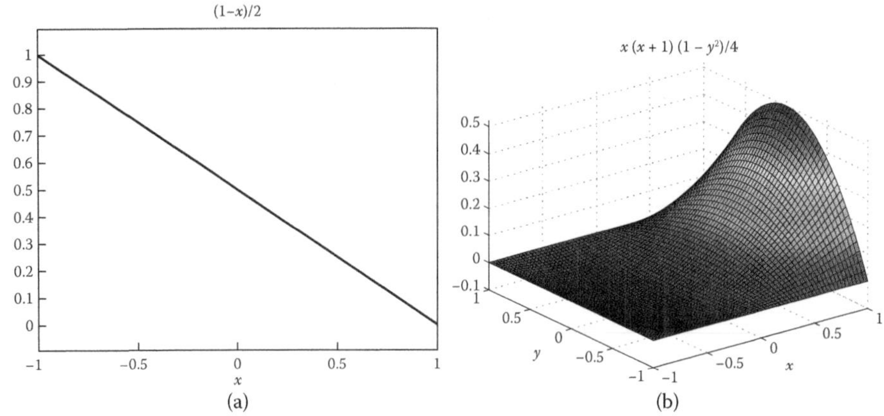

FIGURE 2.6
A 2D line plot and 3D surface plot made using MATLAB®.

2.3.15 Making plots using MATLAB

MATLAB can also be used to make easy 2D and 3D plots. For example, to make a 2D line plot of function $(1-x)/2$ for x from -1 to 1 with MATLAB, one first types figure to activate a figure box, and then types ezplot('(1 − x)/2',[−1,1]) to make the plot. The obtained plot is shown in Figure 2.6a.

To make a 3D surface plot of function $x(1+x)(1-y^2)/4$ for x from -1 to 1 and y from -1 to 1, one just types figure to activate a figure box, and then types ezsurf('x*(1 + x)*(1 − y^ 2)/4',[−1,1,−1,1]). For a 3D surface plot, one can use the Rotate 3D button to adjust the viewing angle before saving the plot in jpg or other file formats. The obtained plot is shown in Figure 2.6b.

2.4 Exercises

1. Classify the following differential equations according to their categories, such as ODE or PDE, order, dimension, linearity, time dependency, and type of coefficient. Also, identify the dependent and independent variables.

a.

$$\frac{d^2x}{dt^2} + 2\frac{dx}{dt} + 7tx = 0$$

b.

$$\frac{\partial u}{\partial t} - 5\frac{\partial^2 u}{\partial y^2} = (1+5t)\sin(y)$$

c.

$$\frac{\partial^3 w}{\partial x^3} + w\frac{\partial w}{\partial x} + 9w = 0$$

d.

$$\frac{d^2 x}{dt^2} - 2\frac{1}{t^2}x = 0$$

e.

$$\frac{\partial v}{\partial t} + \left(\frac{\partial v}{\partial x}\right)^2 + 8v = x + t^2 + 8xt$$

f.

$$\frac{\partial w}{\partial t} - \frac{\partial}{\partial x}\left[2w\frac{\partial^2 w}{\partial x^2}\right] - 8w = 0$$

2. Classify the following differential equations according to their categories, such as ODE or PDE, order, dimension, linearity, time dependency, and type of coefficient. Also, identify the dependent and independent variables.

a.

$$\frac{d^3\theta}{dt^3} + 5\theta + \sin(\theta) = 0$$

b.

$$\frac{\partial^2 u}{\partial x^2} - 2\frac{\partial u}{\partial x} + 15\frac{\partial u}{\partial y} = 1 + x + y$$

c.

$$\rho(x,y,z)\frac{\partial^2 u}{\partial t^2} + \alpha(x,y,z)\frac{\partial u}{\partial t} - T(x,y,z)\left\{\frac{\partial^2 u}{\partial x^2} + \frac{\partial^2 u}{\partial y^2} + \frac{\partial^2 u}{\partial z^2}\right\} = g(x,y,z)$$

d.

$$\frac{d^2 v}{dt^2} - 2\frac{dv}{dt} + t^2 v = 0$$

e.

$$\rho(x)c(x)\left(\frac{\partial y}{\partial t}\right)^3 - \frac{\partial}{\partial x}\left(\kappa(x)\frac{\partial y}{\partial x}\right) = 0$$

f.

$$\frac{d^2 x}{dt^2} + 2\frac{d^4 x}{dt^4} + 2015x^2 = \sin(\pi t)$$

3. Determine whether each of the following is a solution of the corresponding differential equation in Exercise 1:

a.
$$x(t) = te^t$$

b.
$$u(y,t) = t\sin(y)$$

c.
$$w(x) = x^3 + 5x$$

d.
$$x(t) = \frac{1}{t}$$

e.
$$v(x,t) = tx$$

f.
$$w(x,t) = x^2 t$$

4. Identify the size and type of the given matrices and denote whether each is a square, column, diagonal, row, identity, or symmetric matrix.

a.
$$\begin{bmatrix} 23 & 12 & 0 \\ 12 & 40 & 25 \\ 0 & 25 & 9 \end{bmatrix},$$

b.
$$\begin{Bmatrix} t \\ t^2 \\ t^3 \\ t^4 \end{Bmatrix},$$

c.
$$\begin{bmatrix} 1 & x & x^2 & x^3 \end{bmatrix},$$

d.
$$\begin{bmatrix} 6 & 3 \\ 5 & 7 \\ 4 & 1 \end{bmatrix},$$

e.
$$\begin{bmatrix} 1 & 0 & 0 & 0 \\ 0 & 1 & 0 & 0 \\ 0 & 0 & 1 & 0 \\ 0 & 0 & 0 & 1 \end{bmatrix},$$

f.

$$\begin{bmatrix} a_1 & 0 & 0 & 0 & 0 \\ 0 & a_2 & 0 & 0 & 0 \\ 0 & 0 & a_3 & 0 & 0 \\ 0 & 0 & 0 & a_4 & 0 \\ 0 & 0 & 0 & 0 & a_5 \end{bmatrix}$$

5. Given matrices

$$[A] = \begin{bmatrix} 7 & 3 & 2 \\ 9 & 0 & -8 \\ 5 & -7 & 4 \end{bmatrix}, \ [B] = \begin{bmatrix} 5 & 4 & -3 \\ 9 & 4 & 6 \\ 2 & 1 & -6 \end{bmatrix}, \text{ and } [C] = \begin{Bmatrix} 3 \\ -7 \\ 9 \end{Bmatrix}$$

perform the following operations:

a. $[A] + [B] = ?$
b. $5[A] = ?$
c. $[A][B] = ?$
d. $[B][A] = ?$
e. $[A]\{C\} = ?$
f. $[B]^2 = ?$
g. Show that $[I][A] = [A][I] = [A]$.

6. Given the matrices

$$[A] = \begin{bmatrix} 1 & 6 & 9 \\ 7 & 3 & 2 \\ 5 & -1 & 4 \end{bmatrix} \quad \text{and} \quad [B] = \begin{bmatrix} 0 & 8 & -3 \\ -5 & 9 & 3 \\ 2 & 5 & -9 \end{bmatrix}$$

perform the following operations:

a. $[A]^T = ?$ and $[B]^T = ?$
b. Verify that $([A] + [B])^T = [A]^T + [B]^T$
c. Verify that $([A][B])^T = [B]^T[A]^T$

7. Given the following matrices

$$[A] = \begin{bmatrix} 2 & 7 & -5 \\ 8 & 9 & 7 \\ 13 & -5 & 6 \end{bmatrix} \quad \text{and} \quad [B] = \begin{bmatrix} 3 & 8 & -2 \\ 5 & 13 & 0 \\ 14 & -7 & 6 \end{bmatrix}$$

calculate

a. Determinant of [A] and [B]
b. Determinant of $[A]^T$
c. Determinant of 7[A]

8. Given the following matrices

$$[A] = \begin{bmatrix} 0 & 7 & 0 \\ 4 & 3 & 5 \\ 9 & -4 & -7 \end{bmatrix}$$

calculate the determinant of [A] and of $[\text{A}]^T$.

9. Solve the following matrix equation by using the Gauss elimination method and MATLAB:

$$\begin{bmatrix} 2187500 & -937500 & 0 \\ -937500 & 2187500 & -1250000 \\ 0 & -1250000 & 1250000 \end{bmatrix} \begin{Bmatrix} u_2 \\ u_3 \\ u_4 \end{Bmatrix} = \begin{Bmatrix} 0 \\ 0 \\ 500 \end{Bmatrix}$$

10. Calculate the inverse of the following matrices:

$$[A] = \begin{bmatrix} 7 & 0 & 0 & 0 \\ 0 & 1 & 0 & 0 \\ 0 & 0 & 3 & 0 \\ 0 & 0 & 0 & 6 \end{bmatrix}, \; [B] = \begin{bmatrix} 1 & 1 & 1 \\ 3 & 7 & 2 \\ -1 & 3 & 4 \end{bmatrix}, \text{ and } [C] = \begin{bmatrix} k_{11} & k_{12} \\ k_{21} & k_{22} \end{bmatrix}$$

Recommended Readings

1. A. N. Tikhonov and A. A. Samarskii. 1963. *Equations of Mathematical Physics.* New York: Dover.
2. S. L. Sobolev. 1964. *Partial Differential Equations for Mathematical Physics.* New York: Dover.
3. Stanley J. Farlow. 1982. *Partial Differential Equations for Scientists and Engineers.* New York: Dover.
4. M. D. Mikhailov and M. N. Ozisik. 1984. *Unified Analysis and Solutions of Heat and Mass Diffusion.* New York: Dover.
5. Mark S. Gockenbach. 2011. *Partial Differential Equations, Analytical and Numerical Methods.* 2nd ed. Philadelphia: SIAM.
6. MATLAB manuals and tutorials.

3

Where Do Differential Equations Come From?

Differential equations are developed mathematically upon the fundamental theorem of calculus according to the laws of thermodynamics in terms of mass, force, momentum, and energy conservation, as well as other relevant laws and principles. In this chapter, we revisit some of the partial differential equations (PDEs) listed earlier. This time we do so from the very beginning to find out how a "differential unit" is selected and how the laws of physics and thermodynamics are applied. Through these exercises, we will know how differential equations are developed. To simplify matters, we will work on the development of several one-dimensional (1D) PDEs. When necessary, expanding 1D PDEs to multidimensional PDEs should be fairly straightforward.

3.1 PDE for a Hanging Bar

Let us first examine a hanging bar. As illustrated in Figure 3.1, a slender (its lateral dimension is much smaller than its longitudinal dimension) linear elastic structure is assumed to have a uniform cross section area of A and length of l, and it is subjected to downward pulling due to gravity. Because of its large length-to-width ratio, it mainly undergoes longitudinal (or axial) loading and deformation with negligible lateral deformation (e.g., narrowing due to the Poisson's ratio effect); we consider this to be a 1D mechanical bar structure. Note that Poisson's ratio, named after Simeon Denis Poisson (1781–1840), a French mathematician and physicist, describes the dimensional change in a transverse direction (e.g., narrowing) caused by the change in the longitudinal direction (e.g., elongation) in a fractional ratio.

To develop its governing PDE, we isolate an arbitrary infinitesimal section of the bar between x and $x + \Delta x$, and examine the equilibrium of this section in terms of force and motion. As shown in the free-body diagram of the isolated section, there are three forces acting on it: $F(x)$ at the upper edge, $F(x + \Delta x)$ at the lower edge, and a downward volume force (including gravity) f. According to Newton's second law of motion, named after Isaac Newton (1642–1726), $\Sigma F = ma$, where m is mass and a is acceleration, we have

$$\Sigma F = F(x + \Delta x) + A\Delta x f - F(x) = ma$$

Let u be the dependent variable representing the displacement of the bar at any given time t and location along the x direction; then the displacement at x can be expressed as $u(x,t)$, the displacement at $x+\Delta x$ as $u(x+\Delta x,t)$, and the acceleration as $a = \partial^2 u/\partial t^2$.

With $m = \rho A\Delta x$, where ρ is the mass density of the bar material, we express the above equation further as

$$F(x+\Delta x) - F(x) + A\Delta x f = \rho A\Delta x\frac{\partial^2 u}{\partial t^2}$$

Multiplying both sides of the equation by $1/\Delta x$, we have

$$\frac{F(x+\Delta x) - F(x)}{\Delta x} + Af = \rho A\frac{\partial^2 u}{\partial t^2}$$

By the fundamental theorem of calculus, we know $[F(x+\Delta x) - F(x)]/\Delta x = \partial F/\partial x$; thus, we arrive at the following differential equation:

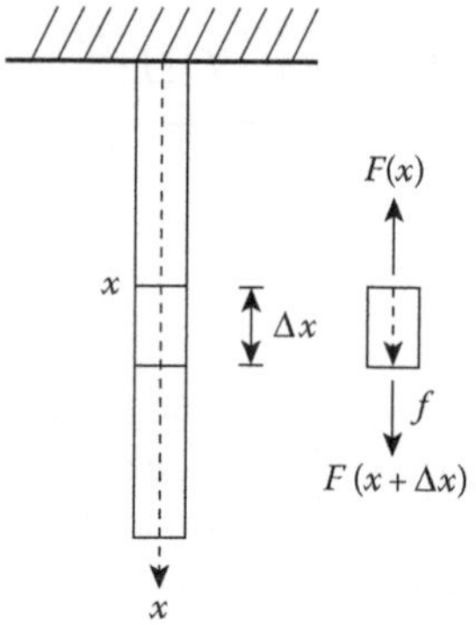

FIGURE 3.1
Hanging bar.

$$\frac{\partial F(x)}{\partial x} + Af = \rho A\frac{\partial^2 u}{\partial t^2} \tag{3.1}$$

We now introduce a term called strain (ϵ), which represents the relative change in length. By this definition, the strains at x can be expressed as

$$\epsilon(x,t) = \frac{u(x+\Delta x,t) - u(x,t)}{\Delta x} = \frac{\partial u}{\partial x}(x,t)$$

For this linear elastic bar structure, this strain can be related to force by applying Hooke's law, named after Robert Hooke (1635–1703), an English natural philosopher, architect, and polymath. Hooke's law states that the stress, $\sigma(x)$, in a structure is linearly proportional to its strain: $\sigma(x) = E\epsilon(x)$, where E is *Young's modulus*, named in honor of Thomas Young (1773–1829), an English polymath and physician, which is also known as the *modulus of elasticity*. Since stress is defined as force per unit area, multiplying the stress by the cross section area of the bar, we can calculate the corresponding force:

$$F(x) = A\sigma(x) = AE\epsilon(x) = AE\frac{\partial u}{\partial x}(x,t)$$

By substituting this force expression into Equation 3.1, eliminating A, and rearranging it, we have

$$\rho\frac{\partial^2 u}{\partial t^2}(x,t) = \frac{\partial}{\partial x}\left[E\frac{\partial u(x,t)}{\partial x}\right] + f \tag{3.2}$$

When E is a constant, it can be moved outside the differential operator; thus, we have

$$\rho \frac{\partial^2 u}{\partial t^2}(x,t) = E\frac{\partial^2 u}{\partial x^2}(x,t) + f$$

Equation 3.2 is the 1D PDE for a hanging bar, in which u is the displacement of the bar (m), ρ is the mass density of the bar material (kg/m^3), E is the Young's modulus (N/m^2), and f is the volume force (N/m^3). From the derivation steps, we see that this PDE is obtained by considering the force equilibrium of an arbitrary infinitesimal section of the bar, and by applying Hooke's law of elasticity and Newton's second law of motion, as well as the fundamental theorem of calculus. In comparing the obtained differential equation of a hanging bar with Equation 2.14, we can see that the coefficients ρ and k in Equation 2.14 are, respectively, the mass density and Young's modulus of the material of which the linear elastic bar is made. Since this is a mechanical problem, expanding it to a higher dimension is a relatively complicated process due to the vector fields, as well as Poisson's ratio effect. We discuss this issue in Chapter 8.

3.2 PDE for a Vibrating String

We now consider a thin string fixed at its two ends (A and B) vibrating in a two-dimensional (2D) space, as illustrated in Figure 3.2. To be regarded as a string, the structure is often considered to be (1) linear elastic and homogeneous, (2) very thin such that its gravitational force is negligible compared with the tension force applied to the string, (3) having vibrational displacement in only the transverse direction (i.e., the u direction), and (4) possessing no resistance to bending (therefore, it will only transfer tension force tangent to the string).

Figure 3.2 shows a free-body diagram of an arbitrary infinitesimal section (Δx) of the string at time t with tension forces $T(x,t)$ and $T(x+\Delta x,t)$ applied at its two ends. Let u be the transverse displacement of the string;

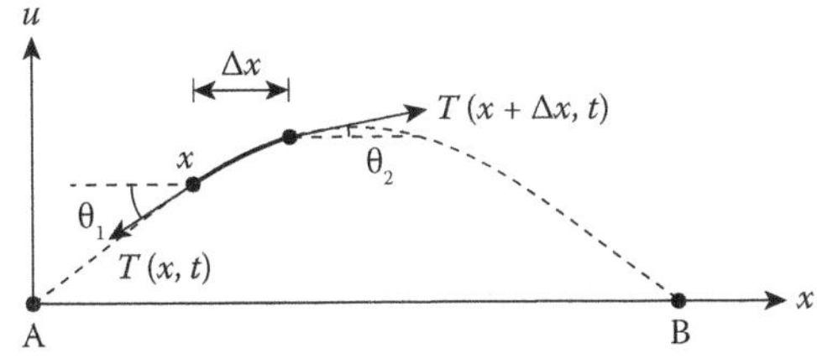

FIGURE 3.2
Vibrating string.

then the vibrational acceleration for this isolated string section is $a = \partial^2 u/\partial t^2$. Since the string only moves in the u direction, we can write the following two conditions at time t according to Newton's second law of motion for the equilibrium of the free body:

$$\Sigma F_x = 0: \quad T(x+\Delta x, t)\cos\theta_2 - T(x,t)\cos\theta_1 = 0$$

$$\Sigma F_u = ma: \quad T(x+\Delta x, t)\sin\theta_2 - T(x,t)\sin\theta_1 = \rho_l \Delta x \frac{\partial^2 u}{\partial t^2}(x,t)$$

where ρ_l is linear density (i.e., mass per unit length) for the string. Suppose that the string is vibrating with a very small amplitude (imagine a string on a string instrument); then the two angles, θ_1 and θ_2, ought to be extremely small as well. Therefore, by relationships of trigonometry we express

$$\cos\theta_1 \approx \cos\theta_2 \approx 1$$

$$\sin\theta_1 = \frac{\frac{\partial u}{\partial x}(x,t)}{\sqrt{1+(\frac{\partial u}{\partial x})^2}} \approx \frac{\partial u}{\partial x}(x,t), \quad \sin\theta_2 = \frac{\frac{\partial u}{\partial x}(x+\Delta x,t)}{\sqrt{1+(\frac{\partial u}{\partial x})^2}} \approx \frac{\partial u}{\partial x}(x+\Delta x,t)$$

Plugging the first set of expressions into the x direction equilibrium equation, we find that $T(x+\Delta x, t) = T(x,t)$. This means that the tension force does not vary with x; thus, it is a constant (T). And substituting the second set of expressions into the u direction equilibrium equation, we arrive at

$$T\left[\frac{\partial u}{\partial x}(x+\Delta x,t) - \frac{\partial u}{\partial x}(x,t)\right]\frac{1}{\Delta x} = \rho_l \frac{\partial^2 u}{\partial t^2}(x,t)$$

With $\frac{1}{\Delta x}\left[\frac{\partial u}{\partial x}(x+\Delta x,t) - \frac{\partial u}{\partial x}(x,t)\right] = \frac{\partial^2 u}{\partial x^2}(x,t)$, we can write

$$\rho_l \frac{\partial^2 u}{\partial t^2}(x,t) = T\frac{\partial^2 u}{\partial x^2}(x,t) \tag{3.3}$$

Equation 3.3 is the PDE for a vibrating string, in which u is the transverse vibrational displacement (m), ρ_l is the mass per unit length of the string material (kg/m), and T is the tension force in the string (N). Again, this PDE is obtained by considering the force equilibrium of an arbitrary infinitesimal section of the string and Newton's second law of motion. Comparing Equation 3.3 with Equation 2.15, it is clear that a^2 in Equation 2.15 is actually the string tension force T.

3.3 PDE for Heat Transfer

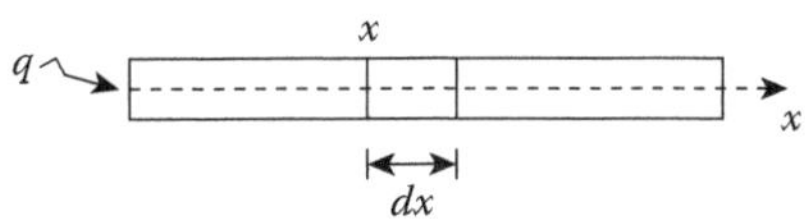

FIGURE 3.3
Heat transfer in a rod.

Next, we examine a heat transfer problem. As illustrated in Figure 3.3, a long and thin rod structure with a uniform cross section area is subjected to a heat flux at its left end, causing temperature to change in the rod. Because the rod is thin and long, we assume that the dependent variable temperature (T) varies only in the longitudinal direction (i.e., the x direction) and with time t. To develop a differential equation for this heat transfer problem, we first isolate an arbitrary infinitesimal section between x and $x + \Delta x$ and examine the state of its energy equilibrium.

According to the definition of heat energy, a rise in temperature with respect to a reference temperature T_0, $\Delta T = T - T_0$, will cause a change in its heat energy by $(A\rho c)\Delta x(T - T_0)$, where A is the cross section area of the bar, and ρ and c are, respectively, the mass density and specific heat of the rod material.

Then the rate of heat (energy) change can be expressed by taking its time derivative as $(A\rho c)\Delta x\partial T/\partial t$. By energy conservation, this rate of heat change is the result of the heat being generated from an internal volume heat source Q per unit time and the net heat flux entering (at x) and exiting (at $x + \Delta x$) this isolated section. Here, the term *flux* describes the amount of substance (e.g., mass, energy, or current) per unit area. According to Fourier's law of heat conduction, named after Jean–Baptiste Joseph Fourier (1768–1830), a French mathematician and physicist, the heat flux (q) entering a cross section is linearly related to the negative temperature gradient: $q = -\kappa\partial T/\partial x$, where κ is the thermal conductivity of the bar. So, the heat fluxes entering the small isolated section at x and exiting at $x + \Delta x$ can be expressed as $Aq(x, t)$ and $Aq(x + \Delta x, t)$, respectively. Putting all these together, we have

$$(A\rho c)\Delta x\frac{\partial T}{\partial t}(x,t) = A\Delta xQ + A[q(x,t) - q(x + \Delta x, t)]$$

Multiplying both sides of this equation by $1/A\Delta x$ and rearranging it, we have

$$\rho c\frac{\partial T}{\partial t}(x,t) = Q - \frac{1}{\Delta x}[q(x + \Delta x, t) - q(x,t)]$$

By equating $\frac{1}{\Delta x}[q(x + \Delta x, t) - q(x,t)]$ to $\partial q/\partial x$, we express

$$\rho c\frac{\partial T}{\partial t}(x,t) = Q - \frac{\partial q}{\partial x}(x,t) \tag{3.4}$$

and substituting q with $-\kappa\partial T/\partial x$, we arrive at

$$\rho c\frac{\partial T}{\partial t}(x,t) = \frac{\partial}{\partial x}\left[\kappa\frac{\partial T}{\partial x}(x,t)\right] + Q \tag{3.5}$$

Equation 3.5 is the PDE for heat transfer (it is often called the heat equation). In this equation, T is the temperature (K), ρ is the mass density (kg/m^3), c is the specific heat (J/[kg · K]), κ is the thermal conductivity (W/[K · m]), and Q is the volume heat source (W/m^3). Once again, this equation is obtained in a similar manner as the previous two cases in which the heat energy equilibrium of an arbitrary infinitesimal section of the rod is considered by applying Fourier's law of heat transfer.

Since this is a scalar field problem, we can easily expand this 1D heat equation to a higher dimension. Referring to Equation 3.4, we can write

$$\rho c\frac{\partial T}{\partial t}(x,y,z,t) = Q - \frac{\partial q_x}{\partial x}(x,y,z,t) - \frac{\partial q_y}{\partial y}(x,y,z,t) - \frac{\partial q_z}{\partial z}(x,y,z,t)$$

By assuming a thermally isotropic material, we have $q_x = -\kappa\partial T/\partial x$, $q_y = -\kappa\partial T/\partial y$, and $q_z = -\kappa\partial T/\partial z$; therefore, we write

$$\rho c\frac{\partial T}{\partial t} = \frac{\partial}{\partial x}\left[\kappa\frac{\partial T}{\partial x}\right] + \frac{\partial}{\partial y}\left[\kappa\frac{\partial T}{\partial y}\right] + \frac{\partial}{\partial z}\left[\kappa\frac{\partial T}{\partial z}\right] + Q$$

By the definition of divergence (see Equation 2.10) in Section 2.2.1.3, we simplify this equation to

$$\rho c\frac{\partial T}{\partial t} = \nabla\cdot(\kappa\nabla T) + Q$$

This equation is exactly the same as Equation 2.16. However, when the material is not thermally isotropic, we may not treat the thermal conductivity (κ) as a constant. For instance, for a thermally orthotropic material, we may express $q_x = -\kappa_x\partial T/\partial x$, $q_y = -\kappa_y\partial T/\partial y$, and $q_z = -\kappa_z\partial T/\partial z$; thus, the PDE is written as

$$\rho c\frac{\partial T}{\partial t} = \frac{\partial}{\partial x}\left[\kappa_x\frac{\partial T}{\partial x}\right] + \frac{\partial}{\partial y}\left[\kappa_y\frac{\partial T}{\partial y}\right] + \frac{\partial}{\partial z}\left[\kappa_z\frac{\partial T}{\partial z}\right] + Q$$

3.4 PDE for Mass Diffusion

In this section, we examine a problem of mass transport by diffusion. As shown in Figure 3.4, a given substance is being transported along a channel having a uniform cross section area. Because the channel is long and thin, the concentration of the substance (c) can be considered to vary only in the longitudinal direction (i.e., the x direction) and with time t.

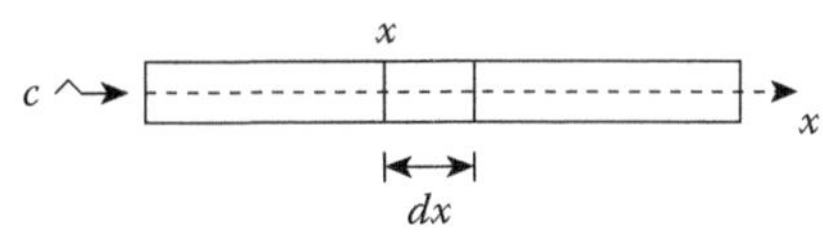

FIGURE 3.4
Diffusion through a channel.

We now examine the state of mass balance in an arbitrary infinitesimal section of the channel between x and $x + \Delta x$. At time t, the amount of mass of the substance in this isolated section can be expressed as $\Delta x A c(x,t)$; then the rate of change in mass can be determined by taking its time derivative as $\Delta x A \partial c/\partial t$. According to Fick's first law of diffusion, named after Adolf Eugen Fick (1829–1901), a German physician and physiologist, the rate of mass diffusion (r) across a sectional area is linearly related to the negative concentration gradient: $r = -D\partial c/\partial x$, where D is the diffusion coefficient. So, the mass flux entering the isolated section at x and exiting at $x + \Delta x$ can be expressed as $Ar(x,t)$ and $Ar(x + \Delta x, t)$, respectively. By mass conservation, the rate of change in mass is the result of substance being generated internally by a volume reaction source (R) per unit time and the net mass flux entering and exiting the isolated section:

$$\Delta x A \frac{\partial c}{\partial t}(x,t) = \Delta x A R + A[r(x,t) - r(x + \Delta x, t)]$$

Multiplying both sides of this equation by $1/A\Delta x$ and rearranging it, we have

$$\frac{\partial c}{\partial t}(x,t) = R - \frac{1}{\Delta x}[r(x + \Delta x, t) - r(x,t)]$$

By equating $\frac{1}{\Delta x}[r(x + \Delta x, t) - r(x,t)]$ to $\partial r/\partial x$ and substituting r with $-D\partial c/\partial x$, we arrive at

$$\frac{\partial c}{\partial t}(x,t) = \frac{\partial}{\partial x}\left[D\frac{\partial c}{\partial x}(x,t)\right] + R \tag{3.6}$$

Equation 3.6 is the PDE for mass diffusion (it is often called the diffusion equation), in which c is the concentration of the diffusive substance (kg/m^3), D is the diffusion coefficient (m^2/s), and R is the rate volume reaction source (kg/[m$^3 \cdot$ s]). Clearly, this PDE is obtained in the same manner as in other cases in which the mass conservation of the diffusive substance within an arbitrary infinitesimal section of the channel is considered by applying Fick's first law of diffusion.

Similarly as in the case of heat transfer, this 1D scalar field mass diffusion equation can be expanded to a higher dimension as follows when the diffusive medium is homogeneous:

$$\frac{\partial c}{\partial t} = \nabla \cdot (D\nabla c) + R$$

which is exactly the same as Equation 2.17.

3.5 PDE for Beam Structures

In problems of solid mechanics, when a slender structure is mainly used for sustaining axial loading and deformation, we call it a bar (like the hanging bar). However, in reality almost all slender mechanical structures bear some flexure loading and deformation in addition to the axial ones. The reason we consider certain structures as bars is that in these cases, the axial type of loading and deformation dominates the flexure type. When the flexure loading and deformation become significant, we refer to these slender structures as beams. That is, with beams we mainly deal with transverse loading and flexure deformation. For this reason, although a beam is a slender structure, we consider it a 3D structure, or a 2D one if we limit the transverse loading and deformation to a single plane.

Figure 3.5 shows a cantilever beam subjected to a transversely line-distributed load $f(x)$, a bending moment M_0, and a shear force V_0. Imagine that under such a loading condition, the beam bends downward with a deflection curve of $u(x)$, as marked by a dashed line in the figure, with a bending radius of r. This deflection will cause rotation of any cross section (except at the fixed end) about an axis normal to the page (let it be the z axis).

It is often assumed that cross sections perpendicular to the axis of the beam (the x axis) will remain plane and perpendicular to the axis after deformation. This means that the two cross sections on both sides of the free-body diagram are considered planes perpendicular to the rotated axis (the dashed line). Referring to the free-body diagram, which is in equilibrium under two bending moments (M and $M + dM$), two shear forces (V and $V + dV$), and a distributed force, $f(x)$, we can write (note that the moment equilibrium is taken at a point on the right side of the free body; hence, the shear force

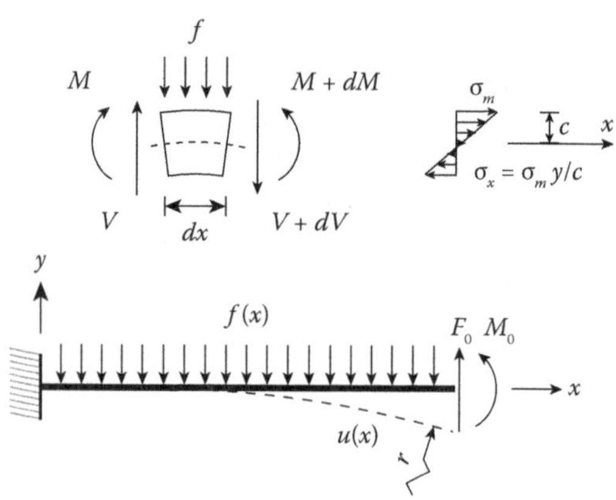

FIGURE 3.5
Beam deflection under transverse loading.

$V + dV$ does not contribute to it)

$$\sum F_y = 0\text{: } V - f dx - (V + dV) = 0$$
$$\sum M_z = 0\text{: } V dx - (M + dM) + M = 0$$

Thus, we have

$$f = -\frac{dV}{dx} \text{ and } V = \frac{dM}{dx}$$

which yields

$$f = -\frac{d^2M}{dx^2} \tag{3.7}$$

Because all forces and moments experienced by the beam are vectors, it is necessary to set some sign conventions for distinguishing their directions.

1. For distributed forces, a downward force (in the same direction as the gravity) is positive and upward one is negative.
2. For transverse point forces (or shear forces), one that causes clockwise shearing motion is positive, and one causing counterclockwise shearing motion is negative.
3. For bending moments, one that causes upside concavity is positive, and vice versa.

Based on these conventions, the forces and moments shown in the figure are all positive. This means that any forces or moments that have the same directions as those shown in the figure will be entered in positive values, and those with opposite directions will be entered in negative values.

Within a cross section, by assuming a linear elastic material property we can express the normal stress as $\sigma_x = \sigma_m y/c$, where σ_m is the maximum stress value within the cross section, c is the distance between the upper edge of the beam (where the maximum stress occurs) and the neutral axis (where $\sigma_x = 0$), and y is the vertical coordinate.

From force and moment equilibrium, again, we have

$$\sum F_x = 0\text{:} \quad \iint \sigma_x dA = 0 = \iint \frac{\sigma_m}{c} y dA = \frac{\sigma_m}{c} \iint y dA = 0 \tag{3.8}$$
$$\sum M_z = 0\text{:} \quad M = \iint \sigma_x y dA = \iint \frac{\sigma_m}{c} y^2 dA = \frac{\sigma_m}{c} \iint y^2 dA \tag{3.9}$$

Since the integral in Equation 3.8 represents the product of the distance from the centroid of the cross section to the neutral axis and the area of the cross section, the fact that Equation 3.8 equals zero indicates that the neutral axis actually goes through the centroid. The integral in Equation 3.9 defines the second moment of inertia of the cross section area of the beam, which we often denote, using I, as

$$I = \iint y^2 dA$$

By Hooke's law of linear elasticity, we can relate the maximum stress σ_m to the maximum strain ϵ_m by Young's modulus E as

$$\sigma_m = E\epsilon_m$$

Since strain measures relative changes in length, it can be expressed as the ratio of change in length over the whole length. In this case, the change in length on the upper edge of the beam is proportional to the radius of rotation with respect to the neutral axis (c) and the whole length is proportional to the radius of the bent beam (r); thus, we write

$$\epsilon_m = \frac{c}{r}$$

Putting them all together, we have

$$M = \frac{\sigma_m}{c} I = EI\frac{1}{r}$$

where the inverse of the beam bending radius, namely, the bending curvature, $1/r$, can be determined from the deflection curve of the beam, $u(x)$, as

$$\frac{1}{r} = \frac{\frac{d^2u}{dx^2}}{\sqrt{\left(1 + \left(\frac{du}{dx}\right)^2\right)^3}} \approx \frac{d^2u}{dx^2}$$

Therefore, we have

$$M = EI\frac{d^2u}{dx^2}$$

By the relationship between M and f obtained in Equation 3.7, we express the following:

$$\frac{d^2}{dx^2}\left(EI\frac{d^2u}{dx^2}\right) + f = 0 \tag{3.10}$$

Equation 3.10 is the PDE for a beam structure. Unlike any other PDEs discussed in previous sections, this PDE is a fourth-order equation. In this equation, u represents the deflection of the beam (m), E is the Young's modulus (N/m^2), I is the second moment of inertia of the beam cross section area (m^4), and f is the line-distributed force (N/m). In a product form, EI is called the flexure rigidity (Nm^2), measuring the capability of the beam to resist bending.

3.6 Commonality in PDEs for Different Problems

It is now clear that differential equations are developed mathematically upon the fundamental theorem of calculus according to the laws of thermodynamics in terms of mass, force, momentum, and energy conservation, as well as other relevant laws and principles of physics, such as Hooke's law of elasticity, Newton's second law of motion, Fourier's law of heat transfer, and Fick's law of diffusion. From the PDEs given in Equations 3.2, 3.3, 3.5, and 3.6, we can see that PDEs sometimes are of the same mathematical type even though they govern problems of different physics, thus suggesting that for countless real-world problems we may only need to deal with limited types of governing differential equations. Moreover, most of these PDEs contain the Laplacian of the corresponding field of interest, except for the beam problem where the PDE contains a double Laplacian.

Of the PDEs given in Equations 3.2, 3.5, and 3.6, if we are only concerned with stationary or steady-state conditions (note the vibrating string is always a time-dependent problem), we can ignore the time-related terms in all these PDEs. Thus, these PDEs will reduce to, respectively,

$$\frac{\partial}{\partial x}\left(E\frac{\partial u}{\partial x}\right) + f = 0, \quad \nabla\cdot(\kappa\nabla T) + Q = 0, \quad \nabla\cdot(D\nabla c) + R = 0$$

These differential equations are mathematically identical, except that the first equation is valid only for mechanical and structural problems that can be simplified to 1D problems.

3.7 Exercises

1. Summarize the commonality in the procedures used in the development of the PDEs discussed in this chapter.
2. In view of the fact that the heat equation and diffusion equation are mathematically identical, what are your thoughts regarding the ways in which we learn and solve problems?
3. Identify a PDE that is not discussed in this chapter and show detailed steps for the development of the PDE. Make sure you provide sufficient details in order for others to understand.
4. Considering the discussion on *learning that* and *learning how* in Chapter 1, examine how have you put your *learning how* to work by showing the steps you developed for the problem above to an engineering friend to see if he or she can follow and understand. Have you provided the needed information so that your friend can understand the underlying logic and reasoning?

Recommended Readings

1. Stanley J. Farlow. 1982. *Partial Differential Equations for Scientists and Engineers.* New York: Dover.
2. M. D. Mikhailov and M. N. Ozisik. 1984. *Unified Analysis and Solutions of Heat and Mass Diffusion.* New York: Dover.
3. Mark S. Gockenbach. 2011. *Partial Differential Equations, Analytical and Numerical Methods.* 2nd ed. Philadelphia: SIAM.

4

Approximate Solutions to Differential Equations

Analytically, there are many ways to solve differential equations. These methods are often discussed in detail in textbooks on ordinary differential equations (ODEs) or partial differential equations (PDEs). Here, we do not concern ourselves with these analytical methods because solving PDEs analytically for complex problems will be very difficult and sometimes impossible. Instead, we focus on using numerical methods to find approximate solutions to differential equations by taking advantage of today's computational powers and numerical capabilities.

4.1 Approximate Solutions

First, let us obtain some basic knowledge about what approximate solutions to differential equations are like and how they are found. We begin with a differential equation having a second-order derivative (the Laplacian) as

$$-\frac{d}{dx}\left(x\frac{du}{dx}\right)+2u=0;\ 0<x<1;\ u(0)=1,\ x\frac{du}{dx}\bigg|_{x=1}=0 \tag{4.1}$$

For classifications, this is a second-order, one-dimensional (1D), linear, and time-independent ODE in which the dependent variable u varies with the independent variable x. The 1D physical domain for this ODE spans from $x = 0$ to $x = 1$ along the x axis. It is constrained by two boundary conditions; one is an essential *Dirichlet* type, and the other is a natural *Neumann* type.

Intuitively, the solution to this ODE ought to be a function of x, which we wish to approximate with a polynomial function. In general, such a polynomial function needs to contain the lowest-order terms, including the zeroth- and first-degree terms and up to the highest terms admissible.

$$\tilde{u}(x) = a_0 + a_1x + a_2x^2 + a_3x^3 + \cdots$$

Now our task is to find the coefficients for this polynomial function such that it satisfies the ODE and the boundary conditions given in Equation 4.1. In doing so, one might realize that it is easier to work with an alternative form of a polynomial function:

$$\tilde{u}(x) = \phi_0 + c_1\phi_1 + c_2\phi_2 + \cdots \tag{4.2}$$

where c_1 and c_2 are constants to be determined, and ϕ_0, ϕ_1, and ϕ_2 are preselected polynomial functions that satisfy the boundary conditions. In this alternative form, the same requirements apply: each selected polynomial function needs to contain the lowest-order terms, including the zeroth- and first-degree terms and up to the highest terms admissible.

Of these preselected polynomials, ϕ_0 is a zeroth-degree term, or a constant (a special case of polynomial). Aside from this zeroth-degree term, a sufficient number of polynomial functions must be selected such that the corresponding coefficients can be determined. For example, for a polynomial function of $\tilde{u}(x) = \phi_0 + c_1\phi_1 + c_2\phi_2$, to determine the values of constants, c_1 and c_2, we need to select two distinct polynomials besides ϕ_0.

Here, let us go through an exercise to select three polynomial functions, ϕ_0, ϕ_1, and ϕ_2, such that $\tilde{u}(x) = \phi_0 + c_1\phi_1 + c_2\phi_2$ satisfies the constraints of $u(0) = 1$ and $x\left.\frac{du}{dx}\right|_{x=1} = 0$.

For the zeroth-degree term, let $\phi_0 = a$, where a is an arbitrary constant. By applying the first boundary condition, we have $\phi_0 = a = 1$. With $\phi_0 = 1$, the other two functions, ϕ_1 and ϕ_2, need to meet the conditions of $\phi_i(0) = 0$ and $x\left.\frac{d\phi_i}{dx}\right|_{x=1} = 0$. Intuitively, a polynomial meeting these conditions should have a general form of $x^n - nx$, for an integer $n \geq 2$. So, going from the lowest number upwards, we take $n = 2$ and $n = 3$. Therefore, we have

$$\phi_0 = 1, \quad \phi_1 = x^2 - 2x, \quad \phi_2 = x^3 - 3x$$

With these selected polynomials, we express the approximate solution as

$$\tilde{u}(x) = 1 + c_1(x^2 - 2x) + c_2(x^3 - 3x) \tag{4.3}$$

All we need to do next is to determine the two coefficients, c_1 and c_2, by plugging Equation 4.3 into the ODE given in Equation 4.1. In doing so, we obtain the following:

$$\begin{aligned} -\frac{d}{dx}\left(x\frac{d\tilde{u}}{dx}\right) + 2\tilde{u} &= -\frac{d\tilde{u}}{dx} - x\frac{d^2\tilde{u}}{dx^2} + 2\tilde{u} \\ &= 2c_2x^3 + (2c_1 - 9c_2)x^2 - (8c_1 + 6c_2)x + (3c_2 + 2c_1 + 2) = 0 \end{aligned}$$

For c_1 and c_2 to satisfy this equation at all x within the domain $0 < x < 1$, we must have

$$c_2 = 0, \quad 2c_1 - 9c_2 = 0, \quad 8c_1 + 6c_2 = 0, \quad 3c_2 + 2c_1 + 2 = 0$$

It is obvious that no c_1 and c_2 can be found to satisfy all four conditions simultaneously. This means that the approximate solution (i.e., Equation 4.3) will not satisfy the ODE given in Equation 4.1.

4.2 Approximate Solutions by Weighted Integral

The fact that we cannot find proper coefficients c_1 and c_2 to make the approximate solution (Equation 4.3) satisfy the ODE given in Equation 4.1 means

$$-\frac{d}{dx}\left(x\frac{d\tilde{u}}{dx}\right) + 2\tilde{u} \neq 0$$

In other words, by seeking an approximate solution, we introduce an error, which we will call residual and express in R as follows:

$$R = -\frac{d}{dx}\left(x\frac{d\tilde{u}}{dx}\right) + 2\tilde{u}$$

Now instead of seeking $R = 0$, we introduce a weight function $w(x)$ and set the weighted integral of the residual to zero as follows:

$$\int_0^1 w(x)R\,dx = 0 \tag{4.4}$$

With the approximate solution given in Equation 4.3, we determine

$$R = 2c_2x^3 + (2c_1 - 9c_2)x^2 - (8c_1 + 6c_2)x + (3c_2 + 2c_1 + 2)$$

Since there are two unknown coefficients, we need two weight functions. For the weight functions, we again turn to something we are very familiar with, that is, polynomials. Since there are no more boundary conditions to satisfy, we just select single-term polynomials of the zeroth- and first-degree as

$$w_1 = 1 \quad \text{and} \quad w_2 = x$$

With these two weight functions, we construct the following two weighted integrals of the residual and use them to determine the values of c_1 and c_2:

$$\int_0^1 1 \cdot R\,dx = 0 \quad \text{and} \quad \int_0^1 x \cdot R\,dx = 0$$

By substituting the R expression into these two integrals, we have

$$\int_0^1 [2c_2x^3 + (2c_1 - 9c_2)x^2 - (8c_1 + 6c_2)x + (3c_2 + 2c_1 + 2)]dx$$
$$= \frac{1}{2}c_2 + \frac{1}{3}(2c_1 - 9c_2) - \frac{1}{2}(8c_1 + 6c_2) + (3c_2 + 2c_1 + 2)$$
$$= 2 - \frac{4}{3}c_1 - \frac{5}{2}c_2 = 0$$
$$\int_0^1 x[2c_2x^3 + (2c_1 - 9c_2)x^2 - (8c_1 + 6c_2)x + (3c_2 + 2c_1 + 2)]dx$$
$$= \frac{2}{5}c_2 + \frac{1}{4}(2c_1 - 9c_2) - \frac{1}{3}(8c_1 + 6c_2) + \frac{1}{2}(3c_2 + 2c_1 + 2)$$
$$= 1 - \frac{7}{6}c_1 - \frac{47}{20}c_2 = 0$$

Solving these two algebraic equations simultaneously, we obtain

$$c_1 = \frac{132}{13} \quad \text{and} \quad c_2 = -\frac{60}{13}$$

So by allowing a residual and forcing the weighted integral of the residual zero, we now find an approximate solution,

$$\tilde{u}(x) = 1 + \frac{132}{13}(x^2 - 2x) - \frac{60}{13}(x^3 - 3x)$$

to the ODE defined in Equation 4.1.

4.3 How Good Are Approximate Solutions?

Knowing that the method of weighted integral of residual helps find approximate solutions to differential equations, one cannot stop wondering how good such approximate solutions are. The answer is: it depends. Sometimes, the solution can be very good when appropriate polynomials and weight functions are selected. Since a closed-form solution to the ODE given in Equation 4.1 is hard to find, we cannot make a direct comparison between the approximate and the analytical solutions in the previous case. Thus, we now take a look at a simpler ODE equation.

Example 4.1

Find the exact and approximate solutions to the ODE given in Equation 4.5, in which the dependent variable u varies with the independent variable x in a 1D domain between $x = 0$ and $x = 1$. This ODE is constrained by two Dirichlet-type boundary conditions.

$$\frac{d^2u}{dx^2} - 500x^2 - 25 = 0; \quad 0 < x < 1; \quad u(0) = 0, \quad u(1) = 0 \tag{4.5}$$

Answer
By direct integration along with the constraints of the given boundary conditions, we find a closed-form analytical expression as the exact solution to this ODE:

$$u = \frac{125}{3}x^4 + \frac{25}{2}x^2 - \frac{325}{6}x \tag{4.6}$$

Next, we use the weighted integral method to find approximated solutions and compare them with this analytical solution. Referring to Equation 4.2, we consider two cases for the approximate solutions: in the first case, we consider one polynomial term and one weight function, $\tilde{u}(x) = \phi_0 + c_1\phi_1$ and w_1, and in the second case, two polynomial terms and two weight functions, $\tilde{u}(x) = \phi_0 + c_1\phi_1 + c_2\phi_2, w_1$, and w_2.

For the first case, we need to determine ϕ_0 and ϕ_1. For the first term, $\phi_0 = 0$ meets the given boundary conditions. For the second term, to satisfy the boundary conditions $u(0) = 0$ and $u(1) = 0$, a polynomial should have a general form of $x^m(x-1)^n$, for integers $m, n \geq 1$. So we take the lowest-order case of $m = n = 1$. Therefore, we have

$$\phi_0 = 0, \quad \phi_1 = x^2 - x$$

Then we have

$$\tilde{u}(x) = c_1(x^2 - x)$$

with which we find the residual as

$$R = -500x^2 + 2c_1 - 25$$

For the weight function, without introducing more new polynomials, this time we just use the selected ϕ_1 for it, namely, $w = \phi_1 = x^2 - x$. Constructing a weighted integral with the selected polynomial function and the weight function, we obtain

$$\int_0^1 wRdx = \int_0^1 (x^2 - x)[-500x^2 + 2c_1 - 25]dx = \frac{175}{6} - \frac{1}{3}c_1 = 0$$

which yields $c_1 = 175/2$. Thus, the approximate solution for this first case is

$$\tilde{u}(x) = \frac{175}{2}(x^2 - x) \tag{4.7}$$

For the second case, we need to select one more polynomial function, namely, ϕ_2, in addition to ϕ_0 and ϕ_1. For this, we go to the next case in the general form of $x^m(x-1)^n$, that is, $m = 2, n = 1$. Thus, we have

$$\phi_0 = 0, \quad \phi_1 = x^2 - x, \quad \phi_2 = x^3 - x^2$$

Then the approximate solution can be expressed as

$$\tilde{u}(x) = c_1(x^2 - x) + c_2(x^3 - x^2)$$

with which we express the residual as

$$R = 2c_1 - 2c_2 + 6c_2x - 500x^2 - 25$$

For weight functions, we need two in this case because we have two unknown coefficients. Again, for convenience sake we select $w_1 = \phi_1 = x^2 - x$ and $w_2 = \phi_2 = x^3 - x^2$. Now by constructing two weighted integrals using the selected polynomials and weight functions, we arrive at

$$\int_0^1 (x^2 - x)[2c_1 - 2c_2 + 6c_2x - 500x^2 - 25]dx = \frac{175}{6} - \frac{1}{3}c_1 - \frac{1}{6}c_2 = 0$$

$$\int_0^1 (x^3 - x^2)[2c_1 - 2c_2 + 6c_2x - 500x^2 - 25]dx = \frac{75}{4} - \frac{1}{6}c_1 - \frac{2}{15}c_2 = 0$$

Solving these two algebra equations simultaneously, we find

$$c_1 = \frac{275}{6} \quad \text{and} \quad c_2 = \frac{250}{3}$$

The approximate solution for this second case is therefore

$$\tilde{u}(x) = \frac{275}{6}(x^2 - x) + \frac{250}{3}(x^3 - x^2) \tag{4.8}$$

Knowing the closed-form analytical solution (Equation 4.6) and the one-term and two-term approximate solutions (Equations 4.7 and 4.8), we now make some comparisons based on these results. As shown in Figure 4.1, the one-term approximate solution, although following the general pattern of the analytical solution and satisfying the two boundary conditions, differs significantly from the analytical solution. The two-term approximate solution, however, aside from satisfying the boundary conditions, agrees fairly well with the analytical solution.

This example demonstrates that the polynomial-based approximate solutions can sometimes produce results that closely match the analytical solution when proper polynomial terms are selected. In fact, if we go one step further by selecting a fourth-degree polynomial function, then the approximate solution will be exactly the same as the analytical one. The reader is encouraged to show this as an exercise.

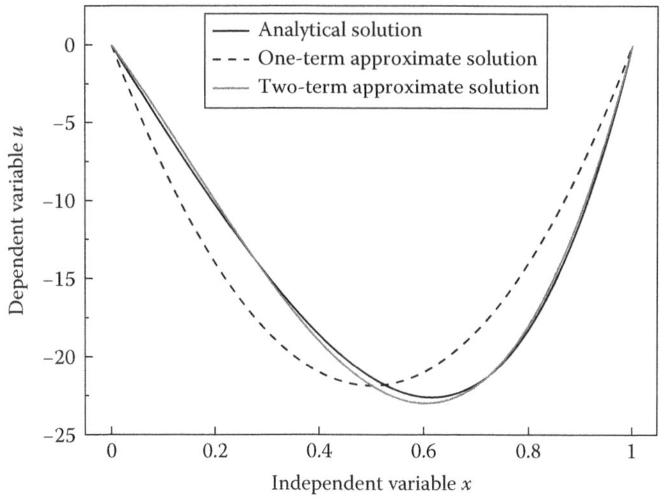

FIGURE 4.1
Comparison of approximate solutions with analytical solution.

4.4 Influence of Weight Functions

In Section 4.3, we learned that the weighted integral of residual method allows us to find approximate solutions to ODEs and PDEs because of its use of certain weight functions. In the examples discussed earlier, we have seen two different ways of selecting the weight functions. In the first, we select the polynomial base terms such as 1, x, x^2, ..., as the weight functions, and in the second, we use the interpolation functions as the weight functions. When the weight functions are the same as the interpolation functions, the weighted integral–based approximation method is called the Galerkin method, honoring its creator, Boris Galerkin (1871–1945), a Russian mathematician and engineer. When the weight functions are different from the interpolation functions, they are of some modified versions of the Galerkin method. For instance, the one using the polynomial base terms is called the Petrov–Galerkin (P–G) method.

Example 4.2

Revisit Example 4.1 by examining and comparing several two-term approximate solutions based on the Galerkin and P–G methods.

Answer
We begin with the following interpolation functions:

$$\tilde{u}(x) = \phi_0 + c_1\phi_1 + c_2\phi_2 \quad \text{with} \quad \phi_0 = 0,\ \phi_1 = x^2 - x,\ \phi_2 = x^3 - x^2$$

With these functions, we have

$$R = 2c_1 - 2c_2 + 6c_2x - 500x^2 - 25$$

Next, we select different weight functions to evaluate the following two weighted integrals in order to determine the two constants, c_1 and c_2:

$$\int_0^1 w_1[2c_1 - 2c_2 + 6c_2x - 500x^2 - 25]dx = 0$$

$$\int_0^1 w_2[2c_1 - 2c_2 + 6c_2x - 500x^2 - 25]dx = 0$$

For the Galerkin method, we select

$$w_1 = \phi_1 = x^2 - x \quad \text{and} \quad w_2 = \phi_2 = x^3 - x^2$$

and for the P–G method, we consider the following four cases:

1. $w_1 = 1$ and $w_2 = x$ 2. $w_1 = x$ and $w_2 = x^2$
3. $w_1 = x$ and $w_2 = x^3$ 4. $w_1 = x^2$ and $w_2 = x^3$

Figure 4.2 shows the obtained results. Of these cases considered, the Galerkin method appears to provide the best approximate solution. The second and third cases of the P–G method also provide reasonably good approximation. But the first and fourth cases are way off the mark: the curve for the first P–G case is below the analytical curve, and the curve for the fourth P–G case is above the analytical curve. So this example shows that to produce a two-term approximate solution,

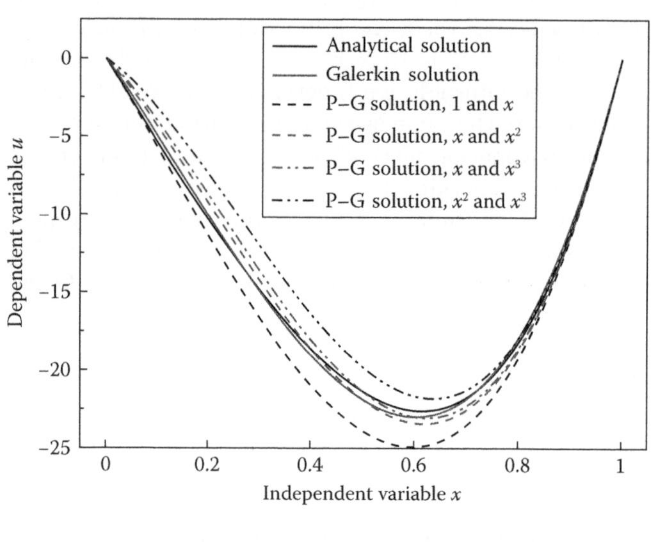

FIGURE 4.2
Comparison of different approximate solutions.

the Galerkin method gives the best result. Aside from this comparison, another benefit of using the Galerkin method is that we only need to select one set of polynomial functions to be used as the interpolation functions and weight functions.

4.5 Exercises

1. Use the weighted integral approximation method discussed in this chapter to solve the following ODE:

$$\frac{d^2y}{dx^2} - 50x^3 + 15x - 10 = 0; \;\; 0 \leq x \leq 1; \;\; y(0) = 0, \; y(1) = 0$$

   Be sure to show all the steps you take and plot your approximated solutions together with the exact solution, which you will need to find.

   a. Use a one-term polynomial function (ϕ_1, w_1).
   b. Use a two-term polynomial function $(\phi_1, \phi_2, w_1, w_2)$.
   c. Use a three-term polynomial function $(\phi_1, \phi_2, \phi_3, w_1, w_2, w_3)$.

2. Use the weighted integral approximation method along with a three-term polynomial function to solve the following ODE:

$$\frac{d^2y}{dx^2} - 2015x^2 + 7x + 4 = 0; \;\; 0 \leq x \leq 1; \;\; y(0) = 0, \; y(1) = 0$$

   Plot your approximated solutions together with the exact solution, which you will need to find.

3. Use the weighted integral approximation method along with a two-term polynomial function to solve the following ODEs and plot your approximated solution together with the exact solution, which you will need to find.

   a.
$$\frac{d^2y}{dx^2} - 147x^2 + 10 = 0; \;\; 0 \leq x \leq 1; \;\; y(0) = 0, \; y(1) = 0$$

   b.
$$\frac{d^2y}{dx^2} + 55x^3 + 11 = 0; \;\; 0 \leq x \leq 1; \;\; y(0) = 0, \; y(1) = 0$$

   c.
$$\frac{d^2y}{dx^2} + 63x^2 - 189x + 21 = 0; \;\; 0 \leq x \leq 1; \;\; y(0) = 0, \; y(1) = 0$$

d.

$$\frac{d^2y}{dx^2} + 127x^3 - 97x + 51 = 0; \;\; 0 \leq x \leq 1; \;\; y(0) = 0, \; y(1) = 0$$

4. Use the weighted integral approximation method along with a three-term polynomial function $(\phi_1, \phi_2, \phi_3, w_1, w_2, w_3)$ to solve the ODE discussed in Section 4.3, and compare your approximated solution with the exact solution given in Equation 4.6 in a plot.
5. Use the weighted integral method to find a two-term polynomial approximate solution to the following ODE with the given boundary conditions,

$$-7\frac{d}{dx}\left(x\frac{du}{dx}\right) + 5u = 0; \; 0 < x < 1; \; u(0) = 1, \; x\frac{du}{dx}\bigg|_{x=1} = 0$$

for the following two cases:

a. Use x and x^2 as the weight functions.
b. Use the two selected polynomial functions as the weight functions.

Plot both solutions in a single graph and compare the results.

6. Use the weighted integral method to find a three-term polynomial approximate solution to the following ODE with the given boundary conditions,

$$9\frac{d}{dx}\left(x\frac{du}{dx}\right) + 25u = 0; \; 0 < x < 1; \; u(0) = 1, \; x\frac{du}{dx}\bigg|_{x=1} = 0$$

for the following two cases:

a. Use x, x^2, and x^3 as the weight functions.
b. Use the three selected polynomial functions as the weight functions.

Plot both solutions in a single graph and compare the results.

7. Use the weighted integral method to find two-term polynomial approximate solutions to the following ODE with the given boundary conditions,

$$\frac{d^2y}{dx^2} + 23x^3 - 15x^2 - 21x + 7 = 0; \;\; 0 \leq x \leq 1; \;\; y(0) = 0, \; y(1) = 0$$

for the following four cases:

a. Use x and x^2 as the weight functions.
b. Use x and x^3 as the weight functions.

c. Use x^2 and x^3 as the weight functions.

d. Use the two selected polynomial functions as the weight functions.

Plot all solutions in a single graph and compare the results with the analytical solution, which you will need to find yourself.

Recommended Readings

1. J. N. Reddy. 1993. *An Introduction to the Finite Element Method.* 2nd ed. Boston: McGraw-Hill.
2. Nan-Ho Kim and Bhavani V. Sankar. 2009. *Introduction to Finite Element Analysis and Design.* Hoboken, NJ: John Wiley & Sons.

5

Discretization of Physical Domains

Knowing that polynomial-based approximate solutions can sometimes provide very satisfying solutions to differential equations, one may wonder if such an approximate-solution-finding procedure based on polynomial functions can be handled by a computer program. Finite element method (FEM), which is also known as finite element analysis (FEA), is exactly one such computerized numerical procedure for finding approximate solutions to a wide range of scientific and engineering problems. Although the term *finite element* was coined by Ray W. Clough in 1960, the concept of using framework method and polynomial interpolations was first introduced by Alexander Hrennikoff and Richard Courant in the 1940s for solving structural engineering problems. Since 1960, the field of finite elements has witnessed many significant leaps, moving from solving problems of solid mechanics, fluid flow, heat transfer, and nonlinear and large deformations, to dealing with issues like mass transport, electricity and electronics, chemical reactions, and electrochemistry. Lately, it is moving to tackle problems of multiphysics and multiscale natures, thanks to the rapid advances in computer sciences and engineering and to the drastic explosion of computational powers and capabilities.

5.1 Dividing Physical Domains into Small Elements

In direct translation, *finite element* means small pieces of a structure with finite sizes. That is, in FEM we break physical constructs (e.g., mechanical structures, or sometimes just the spacial volumes, like those inside a heating or cooling duct) into small pieces. The physical space occupied by these constructs is often referred to as *domain.* These small pieces are called the *elements* of a domain. In other words, an element is a geometric unit of a physical domain. The word *finite* is used to distinguish these small elements from those infinitesimal elements we referred to during the development of differential equations. Depending on the spacial dimensions of a physical domain, these finite elements can take various shapes and sizes of different dimensions. In general, for one-dimensional (1D) structures elements are line segments, for two-dimensional (2D) structures elements can be triangles or quadrilaterals, and for three-dimensional (3D) structures elements can be tetrahedrons, hexahedrons, and so on.

For example, the slender structures we assumed during the development of differential equations for a hanging bar and heat transfer, as well as mass diffusion, can be divided into segments of 1D elements as shown in Figure 5.1.

When a structure is thin in one dimension compared with the other two dimensions, we can regard it as a 2D structure. Strain gages commonly used for mechanical and biomechanical measurements are one such example. In this case, the physical domain of the strain gage can be regarded as a 2D domain, which is often divided into 2D elements like triangles and quadrilaterals. Figure 5.2 shows a 2D model strain gage in which domains of both the metallic foil (in blue) and the backing film are divided into quadrilateral elements for the upper leg of the foil gage and triangular elements for the rest part of the foil gage and the backing film. It is common that the elements are not of the same size or shape.

The physical space occupied by a 3D structure is regarded as a 3D domain, especially when the structure is not of the truss type. A 3D domain is often divided into 3D elements like tetrahedrons or hexahedrons, among others. Figure 5.3 shows a 3D denture model in which the 3D spacial domain of the denture is divided into numerous small tetrahedral elements. Similarly as in 2D situations, although all the elements are of the tetrahedral type, they may differ in sizes and shapes. It is obvious that in regions having smaller and finer geometric features, the elements tend to be smaller as well. We will learn more about this at a later time.

These general element division rules apply to most of the situations except for a few occasions, such as when the structures are of the truss type. A truss structure is one in which its components are made of multiple slender members

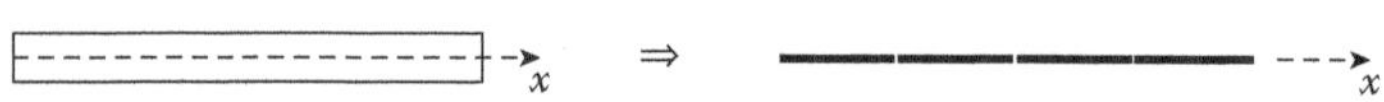

FIGURE 5.1
Division of a 1D domain into small line elements.

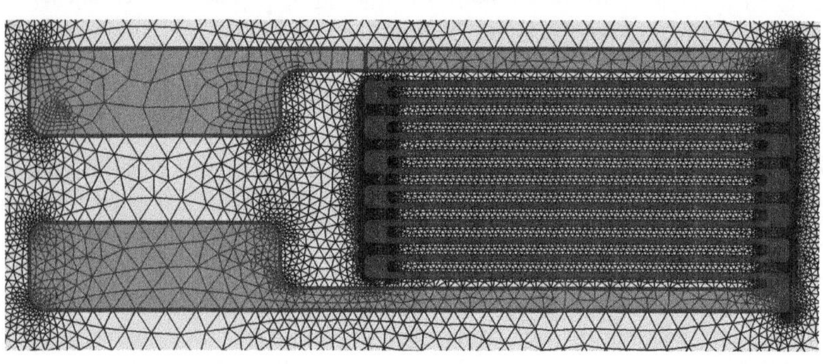

FIGURE 5.2
Division of a 2D domain into quadrilateral and triangular elements.

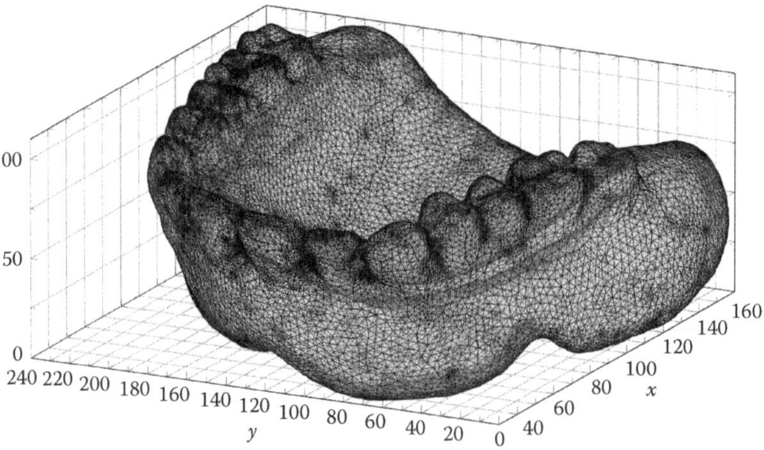

FIGURE 5.3
Division of a 3D domain into small tetrahedral elements.

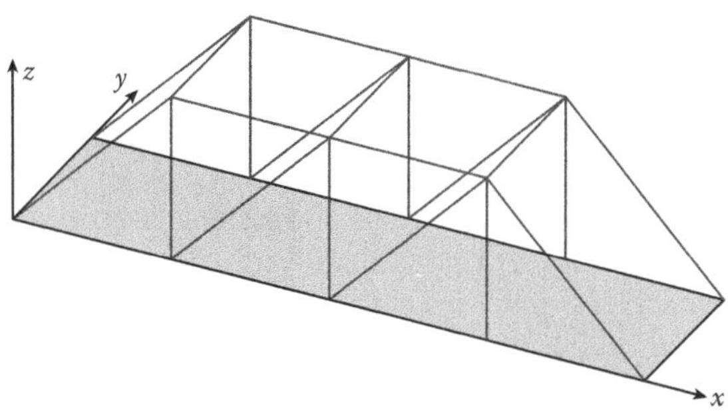

FIGURE 5.4
Truss bridge made of long and thin members.

connected into a frame-like structure. As illustrated in Figure 5.4, an everyday example for a 3D truss structure is a truss bridge or a suspension bridge. For this type of structure, we are more concerned about the wire-frame structure and its members and less about the space enveloped by the 3D structure. Therefore, whether they are 2D or 3D truss structures, we always divide these truss frames into 1D elements.

5.2 Nodal Connectivity and Degrees of Freedom

Although a domain in FEM is always divided into small elements of finite sizes, these elements are not individually separated pieces. Instead, they are linked to their neighboring elements through connecting points, known as *nodes.* Through these connecting nodes, elements are connected together to form a network of elements to represent the entire domain. In FEM, this network of elements is called *mesh.* The examples given in Figures 5.2 and 5.3 show the corresponding mesh in each case. When referring to a mesh, we often use the term *mesh density* to describe the number of elements in the mesh. A high mesh density means more elements (and consequently smaller elements) are in the mesh, and a low mesh density means fewer elements (and consequently larger elements) are in the mesh.

Nodes are very important in FEM. Aside from providing connections between neighboring elements, nodes are where the geometric information of the physical domain is passed to the elements through the coordinates of nodes. As illustrated in Figure 5.5, the 1D domain on the left-hand side is divided into four elements, (1) through (4), and these elements are linked together by three nodes (2 through 4). Sometimes we refer to these connecting nodes as common nodes to distinguish them from the end nodes (e.g., nodes 1 and 5). In each element, the coordinates of these nodes define the physical shape, position, orientation, and length of the element. Similarly, for domains of higher dimensions, nodes are not only where elements are connected, but also where the position and shape of the elements are defined. As illustrated in Figure 5.5, three and four nodes of known coordinates are needed to mark the locations, shapes, and sizes of triangular and quadrilateral elements, respectively.

Additionally, nodes are also where the admissible variations of a field quantity (e.g., displacement, temperature, or concentration) are specified and their values are determined. Here, the number and type of admissible variations at any node are termed nodal *degrees of freedom* (DOF). Nodal DOF are often specified according to the underlying physical problems. When an unknown field quantity belongs to a scalar field problem, the DOF of each node will be determined solely by the number and type of dependent variables regardless of the dimension of the problems. For example, in a heat transfer problem, since temperature (a scalar field quantity) is the only dependent variable, the admissible variation of a node will be the temperature; thus, the nodal DOF = 1 no matter whether the problem is in 1D, 2D, or 3D spaces. For this

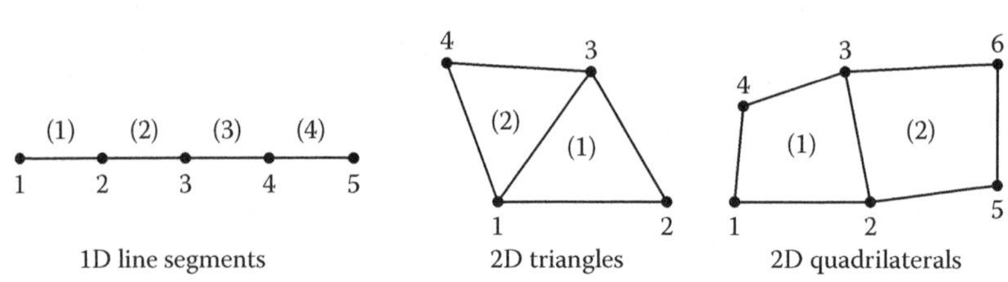

FIGURE 5.5
Nodes as connecting points of elements.

reason, scalar field problems are sometimes called single-variable problems. However, when the unknown field quantity belongs to a vector field problem (e.g., a solid mechanics problem), the nodal DOF will be determined by the number of dependent variables as well as the number of dimensions. For instance, in a 3D mechanical problem, a node may move along (in translation) an axis and rotate about the same axis (say the x axis). Thus, there will be two admissible variables (DOF $= 2$) in each axis. Extending this to all three axes, the admissible DOF for each node becomes six (DOF $= 6$), representing three translational movements and three rotational movements. When the rotation movements are ignored, the nodal DOF is reduced to three translational movements only. Accordingly, if the problem is simplified to 2D, the admissible movements in the third dimension can be ignored. In this case, the corresponding nodal DOF $= 4$, representing two translational and two rotational movements. If only the translational movements are considered, the DOF reduces to 2.

5.3 Linking Nodal DOF to Polynomial Functions

One of the purposes of dividing a physical domain into small finite elements is to develop a polynomial-finding routine that can be handled by a computer program. So the question we ask now is, how are elements linked to polynomial functions? It is done through information dealt with at nodes. A node in FEM is associated with two things. The first is its physical location, which is specified by a set of coordinates (think of this as its address in a physical domain), and the second is the nodal DOF in the form of dependent variables it represents (think of this as its boundary condition). In this section, we discuss how the nodal information is linked to polynomial functions, or in other words, how we can find polynomial functions that satisfy the boundary conditions at the nodes.

For the sake of convenience, we limit our discussion to a scalar field quantity or a vector field quantity in a single dimension. This means that we will have single degree of freedom (DOF $= 1$) for each node, and this single DOF at each node will represent directly the field quantity of interest, such as displacement, temperature, or concentration. This limitation, however, will not affect the generality of the discussion because we always use the same set of polynomial functions to approximate the field quantities in other dimensions.

5.3.1 1D elements

We begin with 1D elements with nodal DOF representing the field quantity. Figure 5.6 shows a 1D element consisting of two nodes with their coordinates given at $x_1 = 0$ and $x_2 = l$, respectively. From these coordinates we know that the element has a length of l. Since each node has DOF $= 1$, we know that

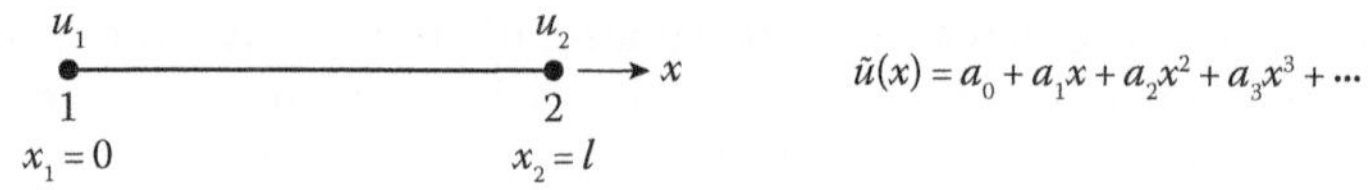

FIGURE 5.6
A 2-node 1D element.

the elementary DOF for this 2-node element is 2. Let $u(x)$ be the single field quantity to be solved over this 1D element; we express the two elementary DOF as u_1 and u_2 for node 1 and node 2, respectively.

Recalling that approximate solutions to partial differential equations (PDEs) can be expressed in polynomial functions, we refer to the general polynomial function given in Figure 5.6 to find an expression to approximate the unknown field quantity $u(x)$ over the entire element. Knowing the coordinates and nodal DOF for the two nodes, we express the following boundary conditions in terms of the two known DOF for the given 1D 2-node element:

$$\begin{aligned} x = x_1 = 0, \quad u(x) = u_1 \\ x = x_2 = l, \quad u(x) = u_2 \end{aligned} \tag{5.1}$$

These two conditions allow us to select a polynomial function with two constants. Thus, by starting from the lowest-degree terms, we take

$$\tilde{u}(x) = a_0 + a_1 x$$

By applying the two nodal boundary conditions given in Equation 5.1 to this polynomial function, we obtain

$$\tilde{u}(0) = a_0 = u_1 \quad \text{and} \quad \tilde{u}(l) = a_0 + a_1 l = u_2$$

hence,

$$a_0 = u_1 \quad \text{and} \quad a_1 = \frac{u_2 - u_1}{l}$$

Then through substitution to the two-term polynomial function, we express

$$\tilde{u}(x) = u_1 + \frac{u_2 - u_1}{l} x$$

With some rearrangements, we have

$$\tilde{u}(x) = \frac{l - x}{l} u_1 + \frac{x}{l} u_2 \tag{5.2}$$

Equation 5.2 is a linear polynomial function that satisfies the boundary conditions at the two nodes. This fact means that for a 1D 2-node element we can write a linear polynomial function in terms of its nodal coordinates and nodal DOF as an approximate expression for the field quantity. This 1D

2-node element is therefore a linear element. Since this equation approximates the field quantity over the entire element, it is often called the interpolation function for the field quantity.

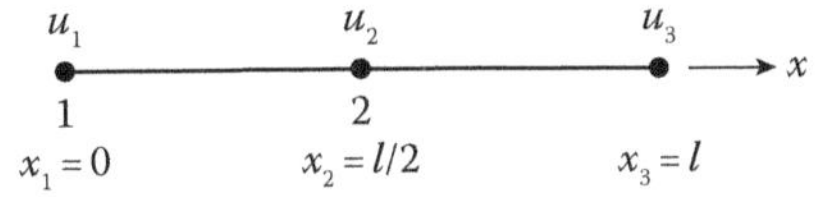

FIGURE 5.7
A 3-node 1D element.

Similarly, for the 1D 3-node element shown in Figure 5.7, with elementary DOF = 3, represented by u_1, u_2, and u_3 for nodes 1 through 3, respectively, we have the following three boundary conditions:

$$x = x_1 = 0, \quad u(x) = u_1$$
$$x = x_2 = l/2, \quad u(x) = u_2$$
$$x = x_3 = l, \quad u(x) = u_3$$

Based on these three conditions, we select a three-term polynomial function to interpolate the field quantity:

$$\tilde{u}(x) = a_0 + a_1 x + a_2 x^2$$

Through a similar exercise, we find the three constants:

$$a_0 = u_1, \; a_1 = \frac{-3u_1 + 4u_2 - u_3}{l}, \; a_2 = \frac{2(u_1 - 2u_2 + u_3)}{l^2}$$

By plugging them into the three-term polynomial function we have

$$\tilde{u}(x) = \frac{l^2 - 3lx + 2x^2}{l^2} u_1 + \frac{4lx - 4x^2}{l^2} u_2 + \frac{-lx + 2x^2}{l^2} u_3 \tag{5.3}$$

Equation 5.3 is a quadratic polynomial function that satisfies the boundary conditions at the three nodes. This means that using a 1D 3-node element we can write a quadratic polynomial function in terms of the nodal coordinates and nodal DOF as the interpolation function for the field quantity over the entire element. This 1D 3-node element is therefore a quadratic element.

As these two examples demonstrate, the number of nodes in a 1D element dictates the number of constants we can have for the polynomial interpolation function as an approximate representation of the field quantity of interest. This in turn determines the order of the interpolation function. More specifically, a 2-node element produces a linear interpolation function, and a 3-node element a quadratic interpolation function. We often regard this as the *order of element discretization*. For example, for 1D elements, we have linear elements (2-node elements), quadratic elements (3-node elements), cubic elements (4-node elements), and quartic elements (5-node elements).

5.3.2 2D elements

We now expand our discussion to 2D situations. With 2D elements, all nodal DOF are restricted to vary within a 2D plane and no out-of-plane DOF are admissible. Again, we will consider single DOF per node to represent the 2D field quantity of either a scalar field or a vector field, $u(x, y)$.

So for the triangular element shown in Figure 5.8, we have elementary DOF $= 3$. We express the three nodal DOF as u_1, u_2, and u_3 at nodes 1, 2, and 3, respectively. With the geometry of the element defined by its nodal coordinates, we write the following boundary conditions as the three nodes:

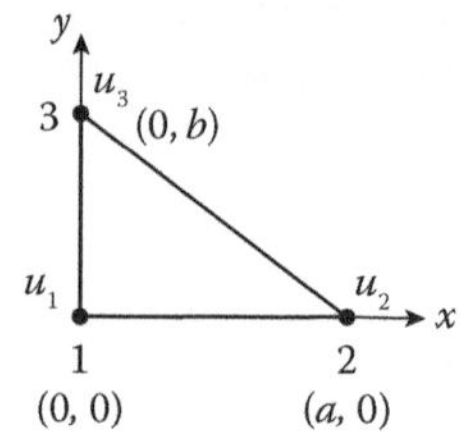

FIGURE 5.8
A 2D triangular element.

$$
\begin{aligned}
x = 0, y = 0, &\quad u(x, y) = u_1 \\
x = a, y = 0, &\quad u(x, y) = u_2 \\
x = 0, y = b, &\quad u(x, y) = u_3
\end{aligned}
$$

Knowing these three conditions, we select a three-term 2D polynomial function to interpolation the field quantity:

$$\tilde{u}(x, y) = b_0 + b_1 x + b_2 y$$

After substitution along with some algebraic exercises, we find the three constants as

$$b_0 = u_1, \quad b_1 = \frac{u_2 - u_1}{a}, \quad \text{and } b_2 = \frac{u_3 - u_1}{b}$$

and then the interpolation function as

$$\tilde{u}(x, y) = \left(1 - \frac{x}{a} - \frac{y}{b}\right) u_1 + \frac{x}{a} u_2 + \frac{y}{b} u_3 \tag{5.4}$$

Equation 5.4 is a 2D linear polynomial function that satisfies the boundary conditions. This result points to the fact that with a 3-node triangular element, we can express a linear 2D polynomial function in terms of the nodal coordinates and nodal DOF as an interpolation function for the field quantity over the element.

Figure 5.9 shows a 2D rectangular (a particular case of quadrilateral elements) element. Again, by considering single DOF per node, we have elementary DOF $= 4$. For the 2D field quantity, $u(x, y)$, to be solved over this 2D rectangular element, we express the four elementary DOF as u_1, u_2, u_3, and u_4 at nodes 1 through 4, respectively, and select a four-term 2D polynomial function (without the square terms) to interpolate the field quantity:

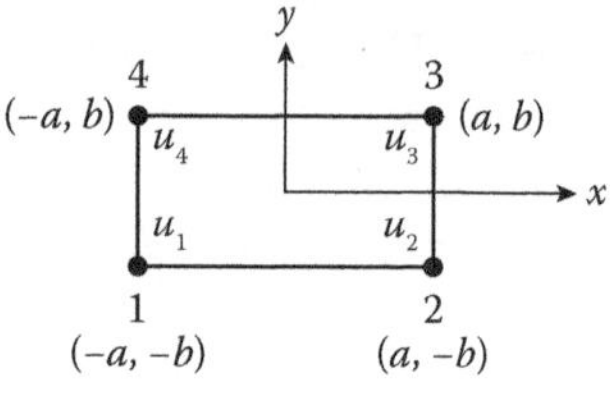

FIGURE 5.9
A 2D rectangular element.

$$\tilde{u}(x, y) = b_0 + b_1 x + b_2 y + b_3 xy$$

With the geometric information of the element given, we write the following four boundary conditions at the nodes:

$$
\begin{aligned}
x = -a,\ y = -b,\ \ u(x,y) &= u_1 \\
x = a,\ y = -b,\ \ u(x,y) &= u_2 \\
x = a,\ y = b,\ \ u(x,y) &= u_3 \\
x = -a,\ y = b,\ \ u(x,y) &= u_4
\end{aligned}
$$

After substitution along with some algebraic exercises, we find the four constants as

$$
\begin{aligned}
b_0 &= \frac{u_1 + u_2 + u_3 + u_4}{4}, \quad b_1 = \frac{-u_1 + u_2 + u_3 - u_4}{4a} \\
b_2 &= \frac{-u_1 - u_2 + u_3 + u_4}{4b}, \quad b_3 = \frac{u_1 - u_2 + u_3 - u_4}{4ab}
\end{aligned}
$$

By plugging these constants into the interpolation function with some rearrangements, we arrive at

$$
\begin{aligned}
\tilde{u}(x,y) = {} & \frac{(a-x)(b-y)}{4ab}u_1 + \frac{(a+x)(b-y)}{4ab}u_2 \\
& + \frac{(a+x)(b+y)}{4ab}u_3 + \frac{(a-x)(b+y)}{4ab}u_4
\end{aligned} \tag{5.5}
$$

Equation 5.5 is a 2D quadratic polynomial function that satisfies the boundary conditions. This result states that for a 4-node rectangular element, we can express a 2D quadratic polynomial function (without the square terms) in terms of the nodal coordinates and nodal DOF as an interpolation function for the field quantity over the entire element.

5.4 Choice of Polynomial Terms

From the above discussions, we note that although different polynomial functions are associated with different elements, the choice for the terms of a polynomial function is not arbitrary. For the 1D cases, the 2-node element is linked to a two-term linear polynomial function of x, and the 3-node element to a three-term quadratic polynomial function of x. For the 2D cases, the 3-node triangular element is associated with a three-term linear polynomial function of x and y, and the 4-node rectangular element with a four-term quadratic polynomial function of x and y without the square terms. Based on these facts, we can make the following observations: (1) the number of terms in all these polynomial functions equals the number of elementary DOF and (2) the polynomial functions all contain terms of the lowest degree (e.g., zeroth- and first-degree terms) up to the highest degree permissible.

Since the use of polynomial functions is for interpolating a field quantity (i.e., a dependent variable of PDEs), the selected function has to meet the requirements of a field quantity in a general sense. The two general requirements for a field quantity are

1. It must have the lowest-degree terms, including the zeroth- and first-degree terms such that the field quantity can capture a constant and linear condition in a stationary, steady-state, or rigid-body motion situation.
2. It must be balanced with respect to all the independent variables (e.g., x, y, z) without favoring any individual variable. In other words, the function should remain characteristically unchanged when any two independent variables swap places.

5.4.1 Pascal triangle

In 2D space, the selection of proper terms for polynomial functions is made easy when we refer to the 2D Pascal triangle shown in Table 5.1. In this 2D Pascal triangle, the base terms of polynomials are listed in rows by the degree of the terms. The zeroth-degree term is at the pinnacle of the triangle, and it is followed by the two first-degree terms, then three second-degree terms, and so on. Polynomial functions having all the terms of the same degree, as well as all the terms of lower degrees down to the zeroth degree, are called complete polynomials. For example, a polynomial having the $1, x,$ and y terms is a complete one, and so is the one with the $1, x, y, x^2, xy,$ and y^2 terms. Obviously, a complete polynomial is also a balanced one. However, completeness is not a requirement for the selection of polynomial functions for field quantity interpolation.

To see how the Pascal triangle is utilized, let us revisit the cases discussed earlier. For the 1D elements, since x is the only variable, we ignore the y term. This of course leaves us with a series of x terms in an ascending degree along the left side of the Pascal triangle. For the 2-node case, with elementary

TABLE 5.1
Pascal triangle for the selection of polynomial terms in 2D

Polynomial base terms									Order of terms
				1					0th degree (constant)
			x		y				1st degree (linear)
		x^2		xy		y^2			2nd degree (quadratic)
	x^3		x^2y		xy^2		y^3		3rd degree (cubic)
x^4		x^3y		x^2y^2		xy^3		y^4	4th degree (quartic)

DOF = 2, we select 1 and x as the base terms to make the two-term polynomial function

$$\tilde{u}(x) = a_0 + a_1 x$$

For the 3-node case, with its elementary DOF = 3, we select 1, x, and x^2 as the base terms to make the three-term polynomial function

$$\tilde{u}(x) = a_0 + a_1 x + a_2 x^2$$

For the 2D elements, we need both the x and y terms. For the 3-node triangular case, with elementary DOF = 3, we select 1, x, and y as the base terms to make the three-term polynomial function

$$\tilde{u}(x, y) = b_0 + b_1 x + b_2 y$$

So the interpolation function for a 2D triangular element is a complete polynomial.

For the 4-node rectangular case, with elementary DOF = 4, we need to select four base terms. Starting from the zeroth-degree term upward, we pick the first three base terms, 1, x, and y, straightforwardly. The difficulty comes when deciding which one of the three second-degree terms, namely, x^2, xy, or y^2, we should pick. Clearly, by referring to the second requirement for the polynomial functions, it becomes obvious that of these three terms, only the xy term meets the field balance requirement for x and y. Otherwise, the selected function will favor either x or y. Therefore, we select

$$\tilde{u}(x, y) = b_0 + b_1 x + b_2 y + b_3 xy$$

for the 4-node rectangular case. Although this polynomial is not a complete one, as it does not have all the second-degree terms, it is nevertheless a balanced polynomial function.

5.4.2 Pascal pyramid and 3D elements

This polynomial term selection scheme can be extended to 3D situations. By considering three independent variables x, y, and z, we can construct a Pascal pyramid as illustrated in Figure 5.10. As in the 2D Pascal triangle, the base terms in the Pascal pyramid are arranged in layers by the degree of the terms. The zeroth-degree term is at the pinnacle of the pyramid, and it is followed by the three first-degree terms, then the six second-degree terms, and so on.

For using the Pascal pyramid, let us take a look at the two 3D elements shown in Figure 5.10. For the 4-node tetrahedral element, with elementary DOF = 4, we can select a four-term polynomial function as the interpolation function for the field quantity. Referring to the Pascal pyramid, it is fairly straightforward that we select four terms as 1, x, y, and z. Thus, we have the

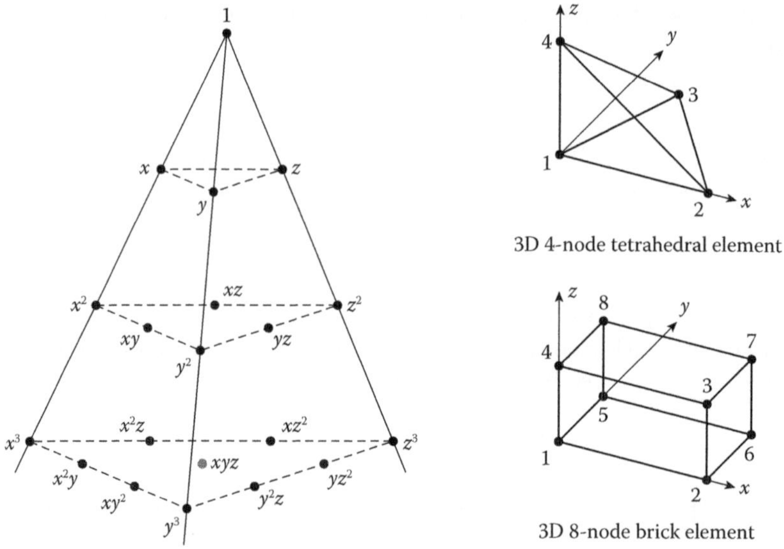

FIGURE 5.10
Pascal pyramid and 3D elements.

four-term 3D polynomial function

$$\tilde{u}(x, y) = c_0 + c_1x + c_2y + c_3z$$

for the 4-node tetrahedral element. Since it has all the zeroth- and first-degree terms, the interpolation function for the 4-node tetrahedral element is a complete polynomial; thus, it is a balanced one.

For the 8-node hexahedral element, with elementary DOF $= 8$, we can select an eight-term polynomial function to interpolate the field quantity. By the Pascal pyramid, we pick the first four terms as 1, x, y, and z. For the rest, we move down to the layers of higher-degree terms. In the second-degree layer, we have six terms, of which three are square terms (x^2, y^2, and z^2) and three are product terms, xy, yz, and xz. Since we cannot pick all six terms, our choice is reduced to three, in order to meet the balance requirement for polynomial selection. So the question now is, should we choose the three square terms or the three product terms? To answer this question, we need to see the difference between a square term and a product term. Although both terms are of second degree, a product term consists of two single-factor (i.e., linear) variables, while a square term is one variable in double factors (i.e., quadratic). Therefore, according to the first requirement for the lowest-degree terms, the product terms are preferred over the square terms. So we select three more terms as xy, yz, and xz. This still leaves us with one more term to go. Since we cannot select any one of the remaining three square terms, we move to the next layer, where 10 cubic terms are available. For picking one term out of these 10 cubic terms to satisfy the field balance requirement, we quickly narrow the choice to the xyz term. With these eight terms, we write the eight-term polynomial function as

$$\tilde{u}(x, y) = c_0 + c_1x + c_2y + c_3z + c_4xy + c_5yz + c_6xz + c_7xyz$$

for the 8-node hexahedral element. Obviously, this interpolation function is not a complete polynomial but a balanced one.

5.5 Shape Functions

In Section 5.4, we learned that a given element can be linked to a polynomial function based on the information on its nodal DOF and nodal coordinates. In a close inspection of these polynomial expressions (see Equations 5.2 through 5.5), we notice that these equations can be written in a generalized form in terms of the nodal DOF, u_m, and their corresponding polynomial functions, N_m, for $m = 1, \ldots, n_e$, as

$$\tilde{u} = N_1u_1 + N_2u_2 + \cdots = \sum_{m=1}^{n_e} N_m u_m \tag{5.6}$$

where n_e represents the number of elementary DOF. In expressing the approximate field quantity in this generalized form, we can now relate the polynomial functions, N_m, $(m = 1, \ldots, n_e)$ to the actual elements they represent in a physically meaningful way.

For the 1D 2-node element $(n_e = 2)$, by matching the terms in Equation 5.2 with those in Equation 5.6, we can write

$$N_1(x) = \frac{l - x}{l} \quad \text{and} \quad N_2(x) = \frac{x}{l}$$

By plotting these two polynomial functions in position with the element, as shown in Figure 5.11, we can see that both $N_1(x)$ and $N_2(x)$ vary linearly with x, and they exhibit the following behavior:

$$\begin{aligned} &N_1(x) = 1 \text{ and } N_2(x) = 0 \ \text{ at node 1} \\ &N_1(x) = 0 \text{ and } N_2(x) = 1 \ \text{ at node 2} \\ &N_1(x) + N_2(x) = 1 \quad \text{throughout the element} \end{aligned} \tag{5.7}$$

Clearly, $N_1(x)$ and $N_2(x)$ are also polynomial interpolation functions. They depict the variation of the field quantity, normalized by the corresponding admissible nodal DOF (u_1 or u_2), over the entire element. More specifically, $N_1(x)$ describes the shape of the normalized interpolation function for the first fundamental nodal DOF under the constraints of $u_1 = 1$ and $u_2 = 0$, while

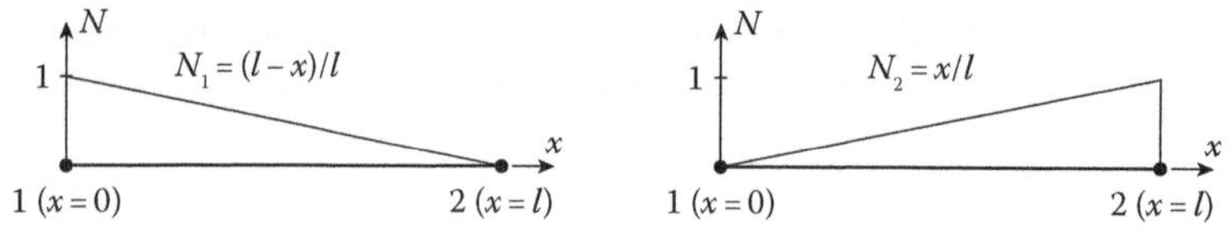

FIGURE 5.11
Shape functions for 2-node 1D elements.

$N_2(x)$ describes the shape of the normalized interpolation function for the second fundamental nodal DOF under the constraints of $u_1 = 0$ and $u_2 = 1$. For this reason, we call these normalized interpolation functions shape functions. In other words, shape functions are polynomial base functions (normalized polynomial functions) corresponding to each of the admissible DOF allowed individually for interpolating the field quantities.

The observations listed in Equation 5.7 can be generalized as

1. $N_m(x_m) = 1$, and $N_m(x_i) = 0$ when $i \neq$ m
2. $\sum_{m=1}^{n_e} N_m = 1$, where n_e is the number of nodes in each

These conditions, in turn, ensure that the resulting field interpolation function given by Equation 5.6 meets the polynomial selection requirements.

Knowing the physical meanings of $N_1(x)$ and $N_2(x)$, Equation 5.6 can be interpreted as saying that a field quantity can be approximated over the entire element by an interpolation function expressed in the sum of the products of the associated nodal DOF and the shape function for each every node. For example, for the 1D 2-node element we have $\tilde{u}(x, y) = \sum_{m=1}^{2} N_m u_m = N_1 u_1 + N_2 u_2$.

We call these polynomials shape functions for a good reason. Imagine the element as a thin flexible wire; we fasten the wire at the nodal points with small rings (note that this type of fastening only restricts translational movements and not rotations). We first remove the ring at node 1 and move the node by 1 to represent the unity amount for the field quantity at node 1. The function describing the shape of the wire at this moment is the first shape function. Next, we put node 1 back to its original position, remove the ring at node 2, and move the node by unity amount (1). The function representing the shape of the wire this time is the second shape function. The benefit of expressing the approximate field quantity in this form is that the shape functions of any element can be determined when the nodal DOF and coordinates are known, as demonstrated in the following examples.

Example 5.1

Find the shape functions for the 2-node element.

Answer
In this example, we also review some basic knowledge of matrix algebra. Abiding by the polynomial selection requirements, for the 2-node element (with elementary DOF = 2) we write the following interpolation function as an approximate expression for the field quantity:

$$\tilde{u}(x) = a_0 + a_1 x$$

Substituting the nodal DOF and coordinates, we have

$$u_1 = a_0 + a_1 x_1 \quad \text{and} \quad u_2 = a_0 + a_1 x_2$$

Expressing these relationships in matrix forms, we arrive at

$$\tilde{u}(x) = \begin{bmatrix} 1 & x \end{bmatrix} \begin{Bmatrix} a_0 \\ a_1 \end{Bmatrix} \quad \text{and} \quad \begin{Bmatrix} u_1 \\ u_2 \end{Bmatrix} = \begin{bmatrix} 1 & x_1 \\ 1 & x_2 \end{bmatrix} \begin{Bmatrix} a_0 \\ a_1 \end{Bmatrix}$$

Let

$$p = \begin{bmatrix} 1 & x \end{bmatrix} \quad \text{and} \quad M = \begin{bmatrix} 1 & x_1 \\ 1 & x_2 \end{bmatrix}$$

we can write

$$\begin{Bmatrix} a_0 \\ a_1 \end{Bmatrix} = M^{-1} \begin{Bmatrix} u_1 \\ u_2 \end{Bmatrix} \text{ and } \tilde{u}(x) = p \begin{Bmatrix} a_0 \\ a_1 \end{Bmatrix} = pM^{-1} \begin{Bmatrix} u_1 \\ u_2 \end{Bmatrix} = N \begin{Bmatrix} u_1 \\ u_2 \end{Bmatrix}$$

where M^{-1} is the inverse matrix of M, and $N = pM^{-1}$. By substituting the nodal coordinates given in Figure 5.6, namely, $x_1 = 0$ and $x_2 = l$, we have

$$N = pM^{-1} = \begin{bmatrix} 1 & x \end{bmatrix} \begin{bmatrix} 1 & 0 \\ 1 & l \end{bmatrix}^{-1} = \frac{\begin{bmatrix} 1 & x \end{bmatrix}}{l} \begin{bmatrix} l & 0 \\ -1 & 1 \end{bmatrix} = \frac{1}{l} \begin{bmatrix} l - x & x \end{bmatrix}$$

By separating the two individual shape functions, we have

$$N_1 = \frac{l - x}{l} \quad \text{and} \quad N_2 = \frac{x}{l} \tag{5.8}$$

Example 5.2

Find the shape functions for the 1D 3-node element.

Answer
According to the polynomial selection requirements, we write the following interpolation function for the field quantity in a 1D 3-node element

having elementary DOF = 3:

$$\tilde{u}(x) = a_0 + a_1 x + a_2 x^2$$

with $p = \begin{bmatrix} 1 & x & x^2 \end{bmatrix}$. Substituting the nodal information, we have

$$\begin{Bmatrix} u_1 \\ u_2 \\ u_3 \end{Bmatrix} = \begin{bmatrix} 1 & x_1 & x_1^2 \\ 1 & x_2 & x_2^2 \\ 1 & x_3 & x_3^2 \end{bmatrix} \begin{Bmatrix} a_0 \\ a_1 \\ a_2 \end{Bmatrix} \quad \text{and} \quad M = \begin{bmatrix} 1 & x_1 & x_1^2 \\ 1 & x_2 & x_2^2 \\ 1 & x_3 & x_3^2 \end{bmatrix}$$

By plugging in the nodal coordinates listed in Figure 5.7, namely, $x_1 = 0$, $x_2 = l/2$, and $x_3 = l$, we obtain

$$N = pM^{-1} = \begin{bmatrix} 1 & x & x^2 \end{bmatrix} \begin{bmatrix} 1 & 0 & 0 \\ 1 & l/2 & (l/2)^2 \\ 1 & l & l^2 \end{bmatrix}^{-1} = \frac{\begin{bmatrix} 1 & x & x^2 \end{bmatrix}}{l^2} \begin{bmatrix} l^2 & 0 & 0 \\ -3l & 4l & -l \\ 2 & -4 & 2 \end{bmatrix}$$

which yields

$$N = \frac{1}{l^2} \begin{bmatrix} l^2 - 3lx + 2x^2 & 4lx - 4x^2 & -lx + 2x^2 \end{bmatrix}$$

By separating the individual shape functions, we obtain the following three quadratic functions as the shape functions:

$$N_1 = \frac{l^2 - 3lx + 2x^2}{l^2}, \quad N_2 = \frac{4lx - 4x^2}{l^2}, \quad N_3 = \frac{-lx + 2x^2}{l^2} \tag{5.9}$$

Figure 5.12 shows the plots of these three quadratic shape functions. Again, we can see that $N_i = 1$ when $x = x_i$, $N_i = 0$ when $x = x_j$, and $\sum N_i = 1$.

These shapes can also be intuitively explained by imagining the 3-node element as a thin flexible wire fastened with three small rings at nodes 1 through 3. First, we remove the ring at node 1 and move the node by 1. The shape the wire takes at this moment is the first shape. Next, we start from the original position, remove the ring at node 2, and move the node by 1. The shape the wire takes at this moment is the second shape. Finally, we repeat the process and remove the ring at node 3, and move the node by 1. The shape the wire takes now is the third shape. Moreover, it can be shown that $N_m(x_m) = 1$ and

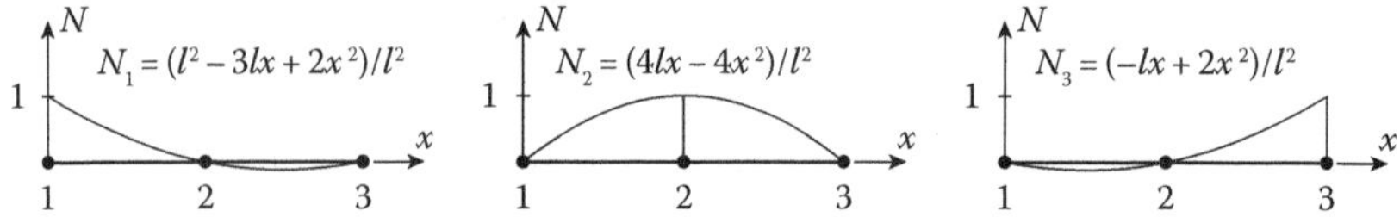

FIGURE 5.12
Shape functions for 3-node 1D elements.

$N_m(x_i) = 0$ when $i \neq m$, and $\sum_{m=1}^{n_e} N_m = 1$ for $m = 1, \ldots, 3$. The reader is encouraged to show these relationships as an exercise.

Example 5.3

Find the shape functions for the 3-node triangular element shown in Figure 5.8.

Answer

According to the polynomial selection requirements, we write the following interpolation function for the field quantity in a 3-node triangle element with elementary DOF = 3:

$$\tilde{u}(x) = b_0 + b_1 x + b_2 y \quad \text{with} \quad p = \begin{bmatrix} 1 & x & y \end{bmatrix} \quad \text{and} \quad M = \begin{bmatrix} 1 & x_1 & y_1 \\ 1 & x_2 & y_2 \\ 1 & x_3 & y_3 \end{bmatrix}$$

With the nodal coordinates given in Figure 5.8, namely, $x_1 = y_1 = 0$, $x_2 = a, y_2 = 0$, and $x_3 = 0, y_3 = b$, we express the shape functions as

$$N = pM^{-1} = \begin{bmatrix} 1 & x & y \end{bmatrix} \begin{bmatrix} 1 & 0 & 0 \\ 1 & a & 0 \\ 1 & 0 & b \end{bmatrix}^{-1} = \begin{bmatrix} 1 & x & y \end{bmatrix} \begin{bmatrix} 1 & 0 & 0 \\ -1/a & 1/a & 0 \\ -1/b & 0 & 1/b \end{bmatrix}$$

which yields

$$N = \begin{bmatrix} \left(1 - \frac{x}{a} - \frac{y}{b}\right) & \frac{x}{a} & \frac{y}{b} \end{bmatrix}$$

Separating them out, we have the following three linear shape functions:

$$N_1 = 1 - \frac{x}{a} - \frac{y}{b}, \quad N_2 = \frac{x}{a}, \quad N_3 = \frac{y}{b} \tag{5.10}$$

Figure 5.13 shows the surface plots of these three linear shape functions, with each showing a function of a tilted flat plane (linear function). The reader is encouraged to show that $N_m(x_i, y_i) = 1$ when $i = m$, and $N_m(x_i, y_i) = 0$ when $i \neq m$, and $\sum_{m=1}^{n_e} N_m = 1$ for $m = 1, \ldots, 3$. These shapes can also be intuitively explained by imagining the following: fasten a thin flexible sheet with small rings at node 1, node 2, and node 3, and then remove one ring at a time and move the released node by a unity amount (1). Each time, the resulting shape of the thin flexible sheet describes the corresponding shape function.

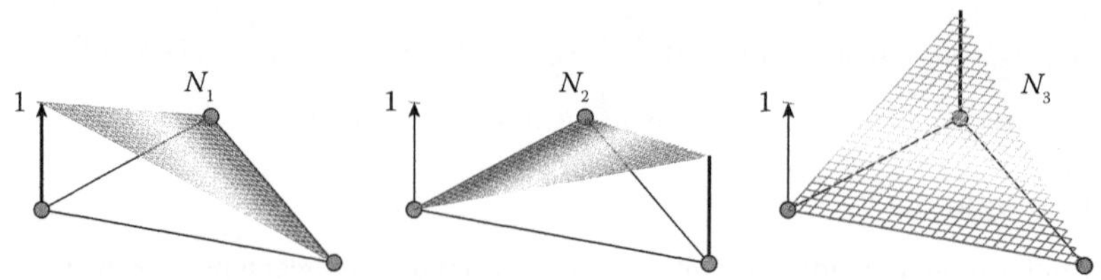

FIGURE 5.13
Shape functions for 3-node triangular elements.

Example 5.4

Find the shape functions for the 4-node rectangular element shown in Figure 5.9.

Answer
By the polynomial selection requirements, we write the following interpolation function for the field quantity in a 4-node rectangular element with elementary DOF = 4:

$$\tilde{u}(x) = b_0 + b_1 x + b_2 y + b_3 xy$$

In the same way as in previous examples, we express

$$p = \begin{bmatrix} 1 & x & y & xy \end{bmatrix}, \quad M = \begin{bmatrix} 1 & x_1 & y_1 & x_1y_1 \\ 1 & x_2 & y_2 & x_2y_2 \\ 1 & x_3 & y_3 & x_3y_3 \\ 1 & x_4 & y_4 & x_4y_4 \end{bmatrix}$$

With the nodal coordinates given in Figure 5.9, namely, $x_1 = -a$, $y_1 = -b$; $x_2 = a, y_2 = -b$; $x_3 = a, y_3 = b$; and $x_4 = -a, y_4 = b$, we calculate the shape functions using $N = pM^{-1}$:

$$N = pM^{-1} = p \begin{bmatrix} 1 & -a & -b & ab \\ 1 & a & -b & -ab \\ 1 & a & b & ab \\ 1 & -a & b & -ab \end{bmatrix}^{-1} = \frac{\begin{bmatrix} 1 & x & y & xy \end{bmatrix}}{4ab} \begin{bmatrix} ab & ab & ab & ab \\ -b & b & b & -b \\ -a & -a & a & a \\ 1 & -1 & 1 & -1 \end{bmatrix}$$

By multiplying the terms out and rearranging them, we obtain the following:

$$N = \begin{bmatrix} \dfrac{(a-x)(b-y)}{4ab} & \dfrac{(a+x)(b-y)}{4ab} & \dfrac{(a+x)(b+y)}{4ab} & \dfrac{(a-x)(b+y)}{4ab} \end{bmatrix}$$

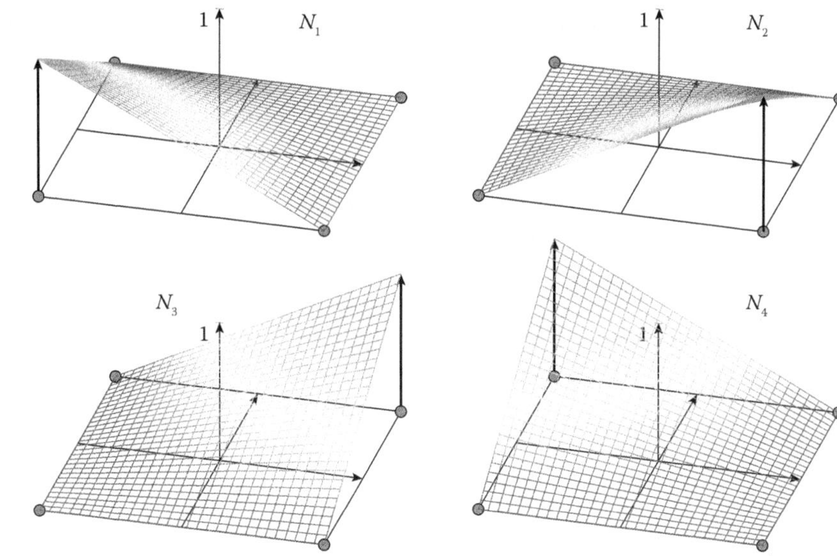

FIGURE 5.14
Shape functions for 4-node rectangular elements.

By separating the four terms, we arrive at the following four quadratic shape functions:

$$\begin{aligned} N_1 &= \frac{(a-x)(b-y)}{4ab}, \quad N_2 = \frac{(a+x)(b-y)}{4ab} \\ N_3 &= \frac{(a+x)(b+y)}{4ab}, \quad N_4 = \frac{(a-x)(b+y)}{4ab} \end{aligned} \tag{5.11}$$

Figure 5.14 shows the surface plots of these four shape functions, each showing a slightly curved quadratic surface. That these surfaces are curved can be intuitively pictured based on the fact that the moved node cannot be in the same plane formed by the three unmoved nodes. Again, the reader is encouraged to show that $N_m(x_i, y_i) = 1$ when $i = m$, and $N_m(x_i, y_i) = 0$ when $i \neq m$, and $\sum_{m=1}^{n_e} N_m = 1$ for $m = 1, \ldots, 4$. These shapes can also be explained intuitively: (1) fasten a thin flexible sheet with small rings at nodes 1 through 4, (2) remove one ring at a time, and (3) move the released node by a unity amount (1). Each time, the resulting shape of the thin flexible sheet gives the corresponding nodal shape function.

5.6 Lagrange Interpolation Formulas

The intuitive way of imagining the shape functions can actually be expressed by mathematical equations based on the Lagrange interpolation formula. In its original form, Lagrange interpolation uses a polynomial function to construct a smooth curve passing through a set of points. By passing through these points, the Lagrange interpolation formula reproduces the values of the ordinates of all the points.

5.6.1 Lagrange formula for 1D elements

We begin by considering 1D situations. For k points in 2D Cartesian coordinates with their abscissas and ordinates given as x_m and y_m, respectively, for $m = 1, \ldots, k$, the Lagrange interpolation formula produces a smooth polynomial curve of $(k-1)$th degree to pass through all these k points using the following expression:

$$y(x) = \sum_{m=1}^{k} y_m \prod_{i=1(i\neq m)}^{k} \frac{x - x_i}{x_m - x_i} = \sum_{m=1}^{k} y_m L_m(x) \tag{5.12}$$

in which

$$\begin{aligned} L_m(x) &= \prod_{i=1(i\neq m)}^{k} \frac{x - x_i}{x_m - x_i} \\ &= \frac{(x - x_1)\cdots(x - x_{m-1})(x - x_{m+1})\cdots(x - x_k)}{(x_m - x_1)\cdots(x_m - x_{m-1})(x_m - x_{m+1})\cdots(x_m - x_k)} \end{aligned}$$

for $m = 1, \ldots, k$, are called the base functions of the Lagrange interpolation formula. Note that when calculating each $L_m(x)$, to ensure $i \neq m$, the term with an index of $i = m$ is skipped.

To illustrate the usage of this formula, let us look at an example. As shown in Figure 5.15, to produce a smooth interpolation curve passing through the five given points (filled circles), a fourth-degree polynomial curve, $y(x)$, can be written based on the Lagrange interpolation formula (Equation 5.12) in terms of the known values for the abscissas (x_m) and ordinates (y_m) of these points.

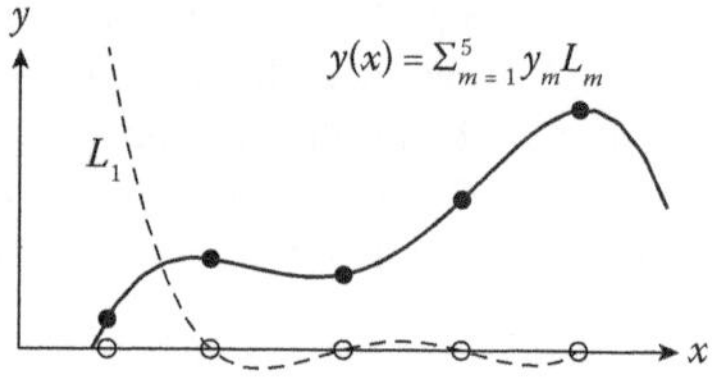

FIGURE 5.15
Lagrange interpolation curves.

These base functions, $L_m(x)$ ($m = 1, \ldots, k$), are also interpolation functions. The only difference is that with these base functions, the points being interpolated are the projection points of the original ones on the x axis, as marked by the hollow circles. As we can see from the $L_m(x)$ formula, the numerator part ensures that the functions are zero at $x = x_1, x_2, \ldots, x_k$ except at $x = x_m$, and the denominator part guarantees that the functions are unity at $x = x_m$. In other words, these $L_m(x)$ functions pass through all the projection points except the mth point, where $L_m(x_m) = 1$.

Based on the definition, we know they are actually shape functions. Therefore, we express

$$N_m(x) = L_m(x) = \prod_{i=1(i \neq m)}^{n_e} \frac{x - x_i}{x_m - x_i} \tag{5.13}$$

as the mth shape function, for $m = 1, \ldots, n_e$, of an element with n_e nodes. So in a 1D situation, the Lagrange formula is a product of polynomial functions of a single independent variable; thus, we refer to it as a single-variable product. As an example, Figure 5.15 shows the curve for the $m = 1$ case, where the L_1 function is plotted in a dashed line. Imagine this dashed line as a rigid but flexible wire fastened with small rings at all five project points; we first remove the ring at the left end, and then move that end by unity amount ($y = 1$). The resulting shape of the wire will overlap with the dashed curve.

To represent shape functions, these polynomial functions, $L_m(x)$, have to meet certain conditions (such that the interpolation functions meet the polynomial selection requirements). The reader is encouraged to show that $N_m(x_m) = 1$ and $N_m(x_i) = 0$ when $i \neq m$, and that $\sum_{m=1}^{n_e} N_m = 1$. Next, we will go through some examples to see how this formula is utilized.

Example 5.1a

Repeat Example 5.1 to find the shape functions using the Lagrange formula.

Answer

For the 1D 2-node element, $n_e = 2$:

$$m = 1{:}\quad N_1 = \prod_{i=1(i \neq 1)}^{2} \frac{x - x_i}{x_1 - x_i} = \frac{x - x_2}{x_1 - x_2}$$

$$m = 2{:}\quad N_2 = \prod_{i=1(i \neq 2)}^{2} \frac{x - x_i}{x_2 - x_i} = \frac{x - x_1}{x_2 - x_1}$$

With the nodal coordinates given in Figure 5.6, namely, $x_1 = 0$ and $x_2 = l$, we obtain the same shape functions as in Equation 5.8, as follows:

$$N_1 = \frac{l - x}{l} \quad \text{and} \quad N_2 = \frac{x}{l}$$

Example 5.1b

Repeat Example 5.2 to find the shape functions using the Lagrange formula.

Answer

For the 1D 3-node element, $n_e = 3$:

$$m = 1:\ N_1 = \prod_{i=1(i\neq 1)}^{3} \frac{x - x_i}{x_1 - x_i} = \frac{(x - x_2)(x - x_3)}{(x_1 - x_2)(x_1 - x_3)}$$

$$m = 2:\ N_2 = \prod_{i=1(i\neq 2)}^{3} \frac{x - x_i}{x_2 - x_i} = \frac{(x - x_1)(x - x_3)}{(x_2 - x_1)(x_2 - x_3)}$$

$$m = 3:\ N_3 = \prod_{i=1(i\neq 3)}^{3} \frac{x - x_i}{x_3 - x_i} = \frac{(x - x_1)(x - x_2)}{(x_3 - x_1)(x_3 - x_2)}$$

With the nodal coordinates of $x_1 = 0$, $x_2 = l/2$, and $x_3 = l$ (see Figure 5.7), we arrive at the same shape functions as in Equation 5.9:

$$N_1 = \frac{l^2 - 3lx + 2x^2}{l^2}, \quad N_2 = \frac{4lx - 4x^2}{l^2}, \quad N_3 = \frac{-lx + 2x^2}{l^2}$$

5.6.2 Lagrange formula for 2D quadrilateral elements

In a 2D situation, the Lagrange interpolation formula can be obtained by extending the 1D formula (Equation 5.13) to include a second product of the second independent variable. For example, with x and y as the two independent variables, we express the 2D formula as the product of the x-variable product and the y-variable product:

$$L_{m_x,m_y}(x, y) = \prod_{i=1(i\neq m_x)}^{n_x} \frac{x - x_i}{x_{m_x} - x_i} \prod_{j=1(j\neq m_y)}^{n_y} \frac{y - y_j}{y_{m_y} - y_j}$$

where m_x and m_y are nodal coordinate indexes: $m_x = 1, \ldots, n_x$ and $m_y = 1, \ldots, n_y$, n_x, and n_y are the number of nodes in the element along the x and y directions, respectively.

By this way of expansion, the number of nodes in 2D elements will be $n = n_x \times n_y$. Since the values of n_x and n_y dictate the degree of polynomial functions in each dimension, due to the field balance requirement, elements with $n_x \neq n_y$ are rarely used. When $n_x = n_y$, the elementary DOF is a square digit, such as the 4-node and 9-node quadrilateral elements.

This means that we can only use this formula to obtain shape functions for 2D elements having the number of nodes in a square digit (e.g., 4, 9, 16, ...). A case in point, although 2D triangular elements are Lagrange elements, because they do not possess such a nodal arrangement, we cannot use this formula to write their shape functions. For triangular elements, a different form of Lagrange interpolation formula is needed, which we discuss in Section 5.6.4.

Example 5.1c

Repeat Example 5.4 to find the shape functions using the Lagrange formula.

Answer
For the 2D 4-node rectangular element, we have $n_x = n_y = 2$. As illustrated in Figure 5.16, the nodal coordinate indexes can be assigned in the following manner: node 1 with $m_x = 1, m_y = 1$; node 2 with $m_x = 2, m_y = 1$; node 3 with $m_x = 2, m_y = 2$; and node 4 with $m_x = 1, m_y = 2$. Thus, we write

$$N_1 = L_{1,1}(x,y) = \prod_{i=1(i\neq 1)}^{2} \frac{x - x_i}{x_1 - x_i} \prod_{j=1(j\neq 1)}^{2} \frac{y - y_j}{y_1 - y_j} = \frac{x - x_2}{x_1 - x_2}\frac{y - y_2}{y_1 - y_2}$$

$$N_2 = L_{2,1}(x,y) = \prod_{i=1(i\neq 2)}^{2} \frac{x - x_i}{x_2 - x_i} \prod_{j=1(j\neq 1)}^{2} \frac{y - y_j}{y_1 - y_j} = \frac{x - x_1}{x_2 - x_1}\frac{y - y_2}{y_1 - y_2}$$

$$N_3 = L_{2,2}(x,y) = \prod_{i=1(i\neq 2)}^{2} \frac{x - x_i}{x_2 - x_i} \prod_{j=1(j\neq 2)}^{2} \frac{y - y_j}{y_2 - y_j} = \frac{x - x_1}{x_2 - x_1}\frac{y - y_1}{y_2 - y_1}$$

$$N_4 = L_{1,2}(x,y) = \prod_{i=1(i\neq 1)}^{2} \frac{x - x_i}{x_1 - x_i} \prod_{j=1(j\neq 2)}^{2} \frac{y - y_j}{y_2 - y_j} = \frac{x - x_2}{x_1 - x_2}\frac{y - y_1}{y_2 - y_1}$$

With the nodal coordinates of $x_1 = -a, x_2 = a, y_1 = -b$, and $y_2 = b$, we obtain the same shape functions as those given in Equation 5.11 and sketched in Figure 5.14:

$$N_1 = \frac{(a-x)(b-y)}{4ab}, \qquad N_2 = \frac{(a+x)(b-y)}{4ab}$$
$$N_3 = \frac{(a+x)(b+y)}{4ab}, \qquad N_4 = \frac{(a-x)(b+y)}{4ab}$$

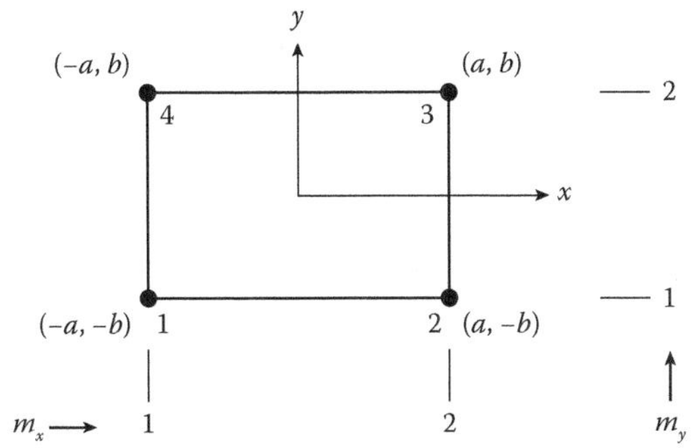

FIGURE 5.16
Coordinate indexes used for a 2D 4-node rectangle element.

Similarly, this formula can be applied to a 9-node rectangular element with four midside nodes and an interior center node, in which $n_x = n_y = 3$. As illustrated in Figure 5.17, its nodal coordinate indexes can be written as

$$m_x = m_y = 1 \text{ for node 1}, \quad m_x = 3, m_y = 1 \text{ for node 2}$$
$$m_x = m_y = 3 \text{ for node 3}, \quad m_x = 1, m_y = 3 \text{ for node 4}$$
$$m_x = 2, m_y = 1 \text{ for node 5}, \quad m_x = 3, m_y = 2 \text{ for node 6}$$
$$m_x = 2, m_y = 3 \text{ for node 7}, \quad m_x = 1, m_y = 2 \text{ for node 8}$$
$$m_x = m_y = 2 \text{ for node 9}$$

With $x_1 = -a, x_2 = 0, x_3 = a, y_1 = -b, y_2 = 0$, and $y_3 = b$, we apply the Lagrange formula to obtain the selected shape functions as follows:

$$N_1 = L_{1,1}(x,y) = \prod_{i=1(i\neq 1)}^{3} \frac{x - x_i}{x_1 - x_i} \prod_{j=1(j\neq 1)}^{3} \frac{y - y_j}{y_1 - y_j}$$
$$= \frac{x - x_2}{x_1 - x_2}\frac{x - x_3}{x_1 - x_3}\frac{y - y_2}{y_1 - y_2}\frac{y - y_3}{y_1 - y_3} = \frac{xy(a-x)(b-y)}{4a^2b^2}$$
$$N_3 = L_{3,3}(x,y) = \prod_{i=1(i\neq 3)}^{3} \frac{x - x_i}{x_3 - x_i} \prod_{j=1(j\neq 3)}^{3} \frac{y - y_j}{y_3 - y_j}$$
$$= \frac{x - x_1}{x_3 - x_1}\frac{x - x_2}{x_3 - x_2}\frac{y - y_1}{y_3 - y_1}\frac{y - y_2}{y_3 - y_2} = \frac{xy(a+x)(b+y)}{4a^2b^2}$$
$$N_6 = L_{3,2}(x,y) = \prod_{i=1(i\neq 3)}^{3} \frac{x - x_i}{x_3 - x_i} \prod_{j=1(j\neq 2)}^{3} \frac{y - y_j}{y_2 - y_j}$$
$$= \frac{x - x_1}{x_3 - x_1}\frac{x - x_2}{x_3 - x_2}\frac{y - y_1}{y_2 - y_1}\frac{y - y_3}{y_2 - y_3} = \frac{x(a+x)(b^2-y^2)}{4a^2b^2}$$

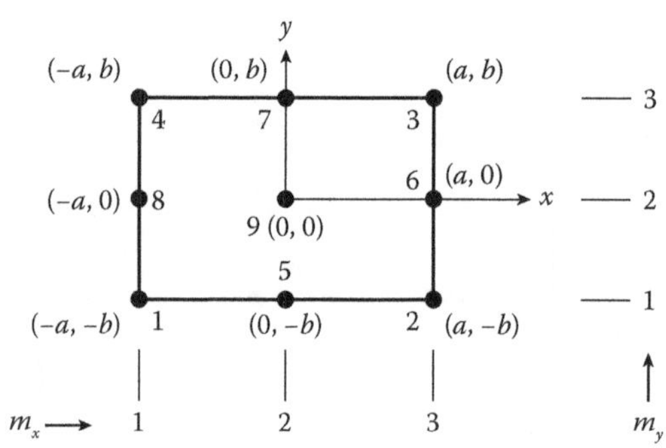

FIGURE 5.17
Coordinate indexes used for a 2D 9-node rectangle element.

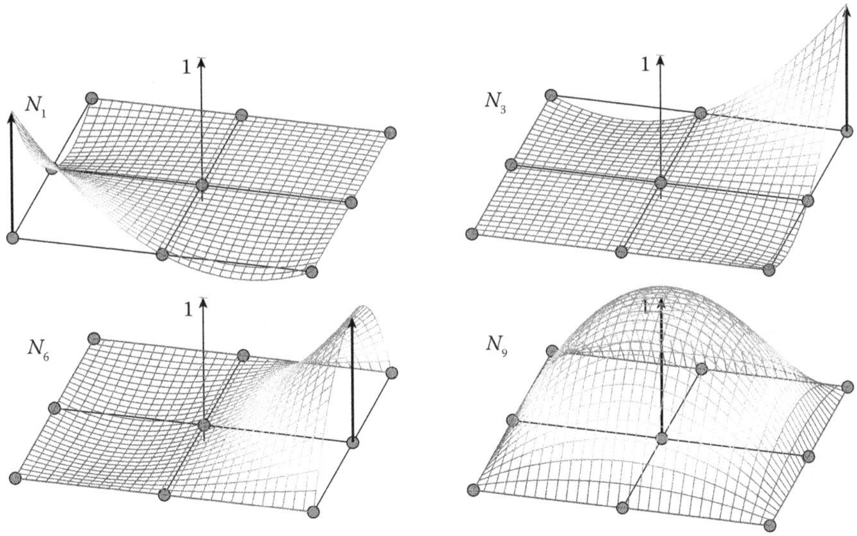

FIGURE 5.18
Selected shape functions for 9-node rectangular elements.

$$N_9 = L_{2,2}(x,y) = \prod_{i=1(i\neq 2)}^{3} \frac{x-x_i}{x_2-x_i} \prod_{j=1(j\neq 2)}^{3} \frac{y-y_j}{y_2-y_j}$$
$$= \frac{x-x_1}{x_2-x_1}\frac{x-x_3}{x_2-x_3}\frac{y-y_1}{y_2-y_1}\frac{y-y_3}{y_2-y_3} = \frac{(a^2-x^2)(b^2-y^2)}{4a^2b^2}$$

The reader is encouraged to find the rest of the shape functions for the 9-node rectangular element.

Figure 5.18 shows the surface plots of these four shapes functions, N_1, N_3, N_6, and N_9, for the 9-node rectangular element. Because this element is a Lagrange element, comparing with the shape functions of a 4-node rectangular element (see Figure 5.14), these plots clearly show that these nodes act like additional ring fasteners to constrain the element.

5.6.3 Shape functions for serendipity elements

As we can see in the above example, having interior nodes makes finding the shape functions for rectangular elements straightforward because we can use the Lagrange formula. Since interior nodes do not connect with neighboring elements, they will complicate the numerical calculations.

It is thus desirable to omit these interior nodes. Quadrilateral elements without any interior nodes are often referred to as serendipity elements. For example, omitting the interior node of a 9-node rectangular element results in an 8-node rectangular serendipity element, as shown in Figure 5.19.

Similarly, omitting all the interior nodes in a 16-node rectangular element will lead to a 12-node serendipity element.

For serendipity elements, since we cannot use the Lagrange formula to find the shape functions directly, we need to use another method for it. A common way to do this is to omit N_9 and use it to adjust the remaining eight shape functions. Here, we use the matrix method to find the eight shape functions. Considering one DOF per node with the elementary DOF = 8, we express the nodal DOF as u_1, u_2, u_3, u_4, u_5, u_6, u_7, and u_8. Then, we select the following polynomial function with eight constants as an approximate interpolation function:

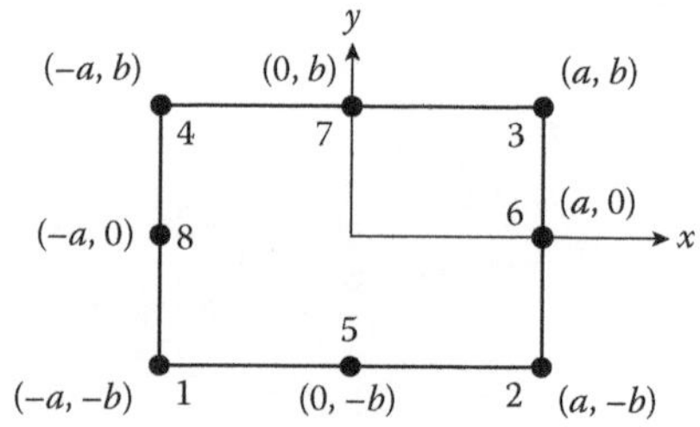

FIGURE 5.19
An 8-node serendipity element.

$$\tilde{u}(x) = b_0 + b_1 x + b_2 y + b_3 x^2 + b_4 xy + b_5 y^2 + b_6 x^2 y + b_7 xy^2 \tag{5.14}$$

With this interpolation function, we express its corresponding polynomial vector:

$$p = \begin{bmatrix} 1 & x & y & x^2 & xy & y^2 & x^2y & xy^2 \end{bmatrix}$$

and then construct the $[M]$ matrix:

$$M = \begin{bmatrix} 1 & x_1 & y_1 & x_1^2 & x_1y_1 & y_1^2 & x_1^2y_1 & x_1y_1^2 \\ 1 & x_2 & y_2 & x_2^2 & x_2y_2 & y_2^2 & x_2^2y_2 & x_2y_2^2 \\ 1 & x_3 & y_3 & x_3^2 & x_3y_3 & y_3^2 & x_3^2y_3 & x_3y_3^2 \\ 1 & x_4 & y_4 & x_4^2 & x_4y_4 & y_4^2 & x_4^2y_4 & x_4y_4^2 \\ 1 & x_5 & y_5 & x_5^2 & x_5y_5 & y_5^2 & x_5^2y_5 & x_5y_5^2 \\ 1 & x_6 & y_6 & x_6^2 & x_6y_6 & y_6^2 & x_6^2y_6 & x_6y_6^2 \\ 1 & x_7 & y_7 & x_7^2 & x_7y_7 & y_7^2 & x_7^2y_7 & x_7y_7^2 \\ 1 & x_8 & y_8 & x_8^2 & x_8y_8 & y_8^2 & x_8^2y_8 & x_8y_8^2 \end{bmatrix}$$

Referring to Figure 5.19, we have the following nodal coordinates:

$$x = -a, y = -b, \quad u(x,y) = u_1 \qquad x = a, y = -b, \quad u(x,y) = u_2$$

$$x = a, y = b, \quad u(x,y) = u_3 \qquad x = -a, y = b, \quad u(x,y) = u_4$$

$$x = 0, y = -b, \quad u(x,y) = u_5 \qquad x = a, y = 0, \quad u(x,y) = u_6$$

$$x = 0, y = b, \quad u(x,y) = u_7 \qquad x = -a, y = 0, \quad u(x,y) = u_8$$

Substituting these relationships into the $[M]$ matrix, we obtain

$$M = \begin{bmatrix} 1 & -a & -b & a^2 & ab & b^2 & -a^2b & -ab^2 \\ 1 & a & -b & a^2 & -ab & b^2 & -a^2b & ab^2 \\ 1 & a & b & a^2 & ab & b^2 & a^2b & ab^2 \\ 1 & -a & b & a^2 & -ab & b^2 & a^2b & -ab^2 \\ 1 & 0 & -b & 0 & 0 & b^2 & 0 & 0 \\ 1 & a & 0 & a^2 & 0 & 0 & 0 & 0 \\ 1 & 0 & b & 0 & 0 & b^2 & 0 & 0 \\ 1 & -a & 0 & a^2 & 0 & 0 & 0 & 0 \end{bmatrix}$$

Taking its inverse, we have

$$M^{-1} = \frac{1}{4a^2b^2} \begin{bmatrix} -a^2b^2 & -a^2b^2 & -a^2b^2 & -a^2b^2 & 2a^2b^2 & 2a^2b^2 & 2a^2b^2 & 2a^2b^2 \\ 0 & 0 & 0 & 0 & 0 & 2ab^2 & 0 & -2ab^2 \\ 0 & 0 & 0 & 0 & -2a^2b & 0 & 2a^2b & 0 \\ b^2 & b^2 & b^2 & b^2 & -2b^2 & 0 & -2b^2 & 0 \\ 4ab & -ab & ab & -ab & 0 & 0 & 0 & 0 \\ a^2 & a^2 & a^2 & a^2 & 0 & -2a^2 & 0 & -2a^2 \\ -b & -b & b & b & 2b & 0 & -2b & 0 \\ -a & a & a & -a & 0 & -2a & 0 & 2a \end{bmatrix}$$

Using the formula $N = pM^{-1}$, we obtain the shape functions for the 8-node serendipity rectangular element:

$$N^T = \begin{bmatrix} N_1 \\ N_2 \\ N_3 \\ N_4 \\ N_5 \\ N_6 \\ N_7 \\ N_8 \end{bmatrix} = \frac{1}{4a^2b^2} \begin{bmatrix} -(a-x)(b-y)(ay+bx+ab) \\ -(a+x)(b-y)(ay-bx+ab) \\ (a+x)(b+y)(ay+bx-ab) \\ (a-x)(b+y)(ay-bx-ab) \\ 2b(a^2-x^2)(b-y) \\ 2a(a+x)(b^2-y^2) \\ 2b(a^2-x^2)(b+y) \\ 2a(a-x)(b^2-y^2) \end{bmatrix}$$

Figure 5.20 shows the surface plots of the eight shape functions for the 8-node serendipity element. Comparing with those shown in Figure 5.18, especially the corresponding ones (say, N_6), we can see that omitting the center interior node not only releases the constraint at the center location but also alters the rest of the shape functions. In a similar way, we can find the shape functions for other serendipity elements.

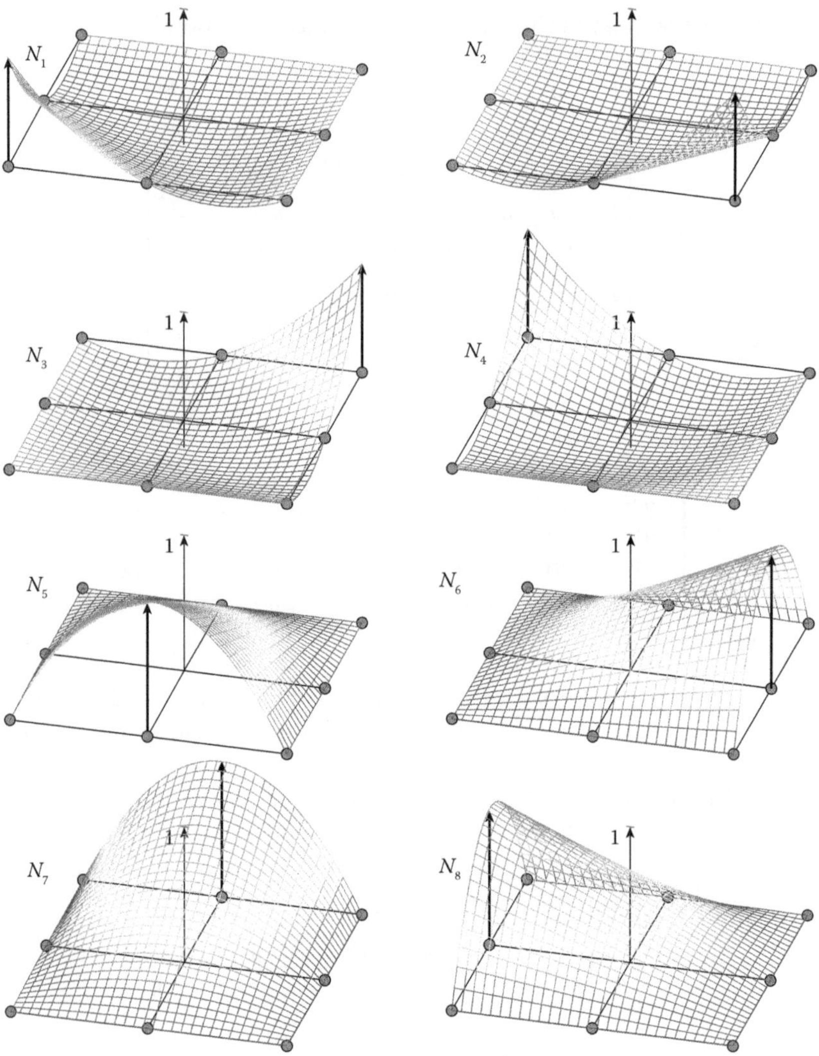

FIGURE 5.20
Shape functions for the 8-node serendipity element.

5.6.4 Lagrange formulas for 2D triangular elements

5.6.4.1 Area coordinates for triangles

We now discuss the development of the Lagrange interpolation formula for 2D triangular elements. To do that, we need to first define an area coordinate system for triangles. Figure 5.21 shows a triangle defined by vertices 1, 2, and 3 with their coordinates given. Point $O(x, y)$ is an arbitrary interior point that

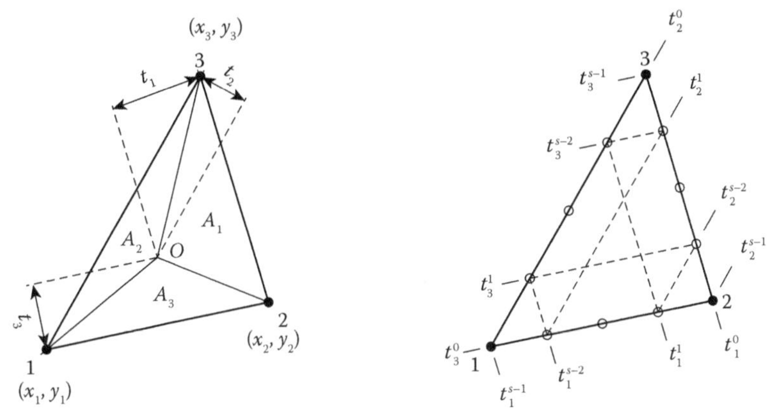

FIGURE 5.21
Area coordinates for triangular elements.

divides the triangle into three subtriangles. Let A_0, A_1, A_2, and A_3, respectively, be the areas of the original triangle and the three subtriangles; we define three area coordinates, t_1, t_2, and t_3, one with respect to each vertex, as follows:

$$t_1 = \frac{A_1}{A_0},\ t_2 = \frac{A_2}{A_0},\ t_3 = \frac{A_3}{A_0} \tag{5.15}$$

Clearly, several observations can be made about these three area coordinates: (1) they vary with x and y as point O moves around within the triangle; (2) $t_1 = 1$ at vertex 1, $t_2 = 1$ at vertex 2, and $t_3 = 1$ at vertex 3; and (3) $t_1 + t_2 + t_3 = 1$.

Physically, each of these area coordinates measures the distance from point O to a base normalized by the height of the triangle measured from the same base. For example, t_1 measures the normalized distance from the base opposite of node 1 to a line parallel to the same base passing through point O. Thus, when point O coincides with vertex 1, $t_1 = 1$. Similarly, t_2 and t_3 measure the normalized distance from their respective bases to the corresponding parallel lines passing through point O, and when point O coincides with vertex 2, $t_2 = 1$, and when it coincides with vertex 3, $t_3 = 1$. The fact that $t_1 + t_2 + t_3 = 1$ indicates that these area coordinates are not independent of each other.

Since the area of a triangle can be calculated by the determinant of a matrix formed in terms of the Cartesian coordinates of its three vertices, we express the following:

$$A_0 = \frac{1}{2}\det\begin{bmatrix} 1 & x_1 & y_1 \\ 1 & x_2 & y_2 \\ 1 & x_3 & y_3 \end{bmatrix},\quad A_1 = \frac{1}{2}\det\begin{bmatrix} 1 & x & y \\ 1 & x_2 & y_2 \\ 1 & x_3 & y_3 \end{bmatrix}$$

$$A_2 = \frac{1}{2}\det\begin{bmatrix}1 & x_1 & y_1\\1 & x & y\\1 & x_3 & y_3\end{bmatrix},\quad A_3 = \frac{1}{2}\det\begin{bmatrix}1 & x_1 & y_1\\1 & x_2 & y_2\\1 & x & y\end{bmatrix}$$

For example, for the triangle shown in Figure 5.8, we have

$$A_0 = \frac{1}{2}\det\begin{bmatrix}1 & 0 & 0\\1 & a & 0\\1 & 0 & b\end{bmatrix} = \frac{ab}{2},\quad A_1 = \frac{1}{2}\det\begin{bmatrix}1 & x & y\\1 & a & 0\\1 & 0 & b\end{bmatrix} = \frac{ab-bx-ay}{2}$$

$$A_2 = \frac{1}{2}\det\begin{bmatrix}1 & 0 & 0\\1 & x & y\\1 & 0 & b\end{bmatrix} = \frac{bx}{2},\quad A_3 = \frac{1}{2}\det\begin{bmatrix}1 & 0 & 0\\1 & a & 0\\1 & x & y\end{bmatrix} = \frac{ay}{2}$$

Therefore, we have the three area coordinates for this particular case as

$$t_1 = 1 - \frac{x}{a} - \frac{y}{b},\quad t_2 = \frac{x}{a},\quad t_3 = \frac{y}{b} \tag{5.16}$$

Referring to Equation 5.10, we know that these are actually the three shape functions of the 3-node triangular element. This means that the three area coordinates of a triangle not only describe the location of the interior point O but also represent the three shape functions of a 3-node triangular element.

Now, let us consider a general case in which a triangular element has s nodes on each side as shown in Figure 5.21. With the area coordinate system, we use t_i^p to mark the locations of these nodes, where the superscript p represents the location index ($p = 0, \ldots, s-1$) of the nodes, and the subscript i the index of the associated vertex node, $i = 1, 2, 3$. For example, the nodes on the base opposite of node 1 (i.e., alongside 2–3) all have an area coordinate of t_1^0, the nodes on the next parallel line have an area coordinate of t_1^1, and so on. The last node in this counting order (which is node 1) has an area coordinate of t_1^{s-1}. Similarly, $t_2^0, t_2^1, \ldots, t_2^{s-1}$ mark the coordinates of nodes on the base and the respective parallel lines opposite of node 2, and $t_3^0, t_3^1, \ldots, t_3^{s-1}$ the coordinates of nodes on the base and parallel lines opposite of node 3. Note that with a superscript, t_i^p no longer represents the coordinate of an arbitrary point but that of a node (also, keep in mind that a superscript here denotes indexes and not exponents or power terms).

When these nodes are evenly spaced, we can calculate the actual values of their coordinates using the following formula:

$$t_i^p = \frac{p}{s-1} \tag{5.17}$$

for $i = 1$, 2, and $p = 0, 1, \ldots, s-1$. For instance, in a triangular element with two nodes on each side ($s = 2$), we have $t_i^0 = 0$ and $t_i^1 = 1$, and in a triangular element with three nodes on each side ($s = 3$), we have $t_i^0 = 0$, $t_i^1 = 1/2$, and $t_i^2 = 1$.

5.6.4.2 Lagrange formulas for 2D triangular elements

With the above information, we now write the Lagrange formulas for triangular elements with s evenly spaced nodes in each of the three area coordinates. We first assign a set of area coordinates, (t_i, t_j, t_k), with respect to the three vertices of a triangle (i, j, and k), to an arbitrary interior point, and then mark the locations of the nodes with $(t_i^{p_i}, t_j^{p_j}, t_k^{p_k})$, in which p_i, p_j, and p_k are location indexes with $p_i, p_j, p_k = 0, 1, \ldots, s-1$. Because the three area coordinates are not independent of each other, these nodal location indexes are also not independent ($p_i + p_j + p_k = s - 1$). With these assignments, we write the following multiproduct formula containing a t_i-variable product, a t_j-variable product and a t_k-variable product, as

$$L_{p_i,p_j,p_k} = \prod_{m=0}^{p_i-1(p_i\neq 0)} \frac{t_i - t_i^m}{t_i^{p_i} - t_i^m} \prod_{m=0}^{p_j-1(p_j\neq 0)} \frac{t_j - t_j^m}{t_j^{p_j} - t_j^m} \prod_{m=0}^{p_k-1(p_k\neq 0)} \frac{t_k - t_k^m}{t_k^{p_k} - t_k^m} \tag{5.18}$$

Like the other Lagrange interpolation formulas we have seen before, the numerator parts of this formula make L_{p_i,p_j,p_k} zero at all nodes except at $(t_i^{p_i}, t_j^{p_j}, t_k^{p_k})$, and the denominator parts ensure that L_{p_i,p_j,p_k} is unity when the arbitrary point (t_i, t_j, t_k) coincides with $(t_i^{p_i}, t_j^{p_j}, t_k^{p_k})$. In using Equation 5.18 to write the shape functions, when any individual location index, namely, p_i, p_j, or p_k, is zero, the corresponding t_i, t_j, or t_k product term is to be omitted.

As we know, in a triangular element, the location of a node can be generally categorized into three groups: (1) at a vertex, (2) on a side, and (3) at an interior location. In the first group, nodes have one nonzero area coordinate; in the second group, nodes have two nonzero area coordinates; and in the third group, none of the area coordinates are zero. Thus, this general formula can be used directly to obtain the shape functions for interior nodes.

For nodes at vertices, since they are associated with only one nonzero area coordinate, we can express their coordinates as $(t_i^{p_i}, 0, 0)$ for $i = 1$, 2, and 3. Thus, by omitting the t_j and t_k product terms in Equation 5.18 and letting $p_i = s - 1$ (note that a vertex node has an index of $s - 1$), we have the following single-variable product formula for the three vertex nodes ($i = 1$, 2, and 3):

$$L_{i,s} = \prod_{m=0}^{s-2} \frac{t_i - t_i^m}{t_i^{s-1} - t_i^m} = \frac{t_i - t_i^0}{t_i^{s-1} - t_i^0} \frac{t_i - t_i^1}{t_i^{s-1} - t_i^1} \cdots \frac{t_i - t_i^{s-2}}{t_i^{s-1} - t_i^{s-2}} \tag{5.19}$$

Clearly, $L_{i,s}$ is unity when $t_i = t_i^{s-1}$, and zero at $t_i = t_i^0, t_i^1, \ldots, t_i^{s-2}$.

Similarly, for the nodes on a side, say the side of $i - j$ ($i, j = 1$, 2, 3), we express their coordinates as $(t_i^{p_i}, t_j^{p_j}, 0)$. Then by omitting the k product term in Equation 5.18, we have the following two-product formula consisting of the

t_i-variable and t_j-variable products for the side nodes:

$$L_{p_i,p_j} = \prod_{m=0}^{p_i-1(p_i\neq 0)} \frac{t_i - t_i^m}{t_i^{p_i} - t_i^m} \prod_{m=0}^{p_j-1(p_j\neq 0)} \frac{t_j - t_j^m}{t_j^{p_j} - t_j^m} \tag{5.20}$$

Again, this formula ensures that L_{p_i,p_j} is unity when the arbitrary point coincides with $(t_i^{p_i}, t_j^{p_j}, 0)$ and zero when it takes the locations of the rest of the nodes. Now let us see how these formulas are applied through some examples.

Example 5.5

Find the shape functions for the 3-node, 6-node, and 10-node triangular elements shown in Figure 5.22 using the Lagrange interpolation formulas for triangle elements.

Answer

In the 3-node triangular element, there are only three vertex nodes, 1, 2, and 3. With $s = 2$, we calculate the following nodal coordinates using Equation 5.17:

$$t_1^0 = t_2^0 = t_3^0 = 0,\ t_1^1 = t_2^1 = t_3^1 = 1$$

By Equation 5.19, since $s - 1 = 1$ and $s - 2 = 0$, we only have one term (i.e., the term of $m = 0$) in the product. Thus, we calculate the shape functions for the three vertex nodes as

$$N_1 = L_{\substack{i=1\\s=2}} = \prod_{m=0}^{0} \frac{t_1 - t_1^m}{t_1^1 - t_1^m} = \frac{t_1 - t_1^0}{t_1^1 - t_1^0} = \frac{t_1 - 0}{1 - 0} = t_1$$

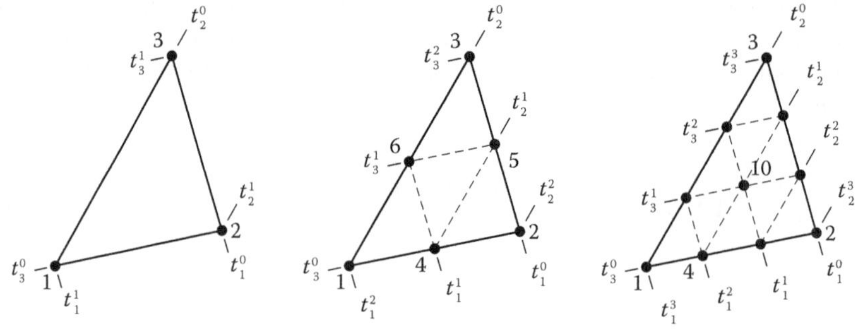

FIGURE 5.22
Three-node, 6-node, and 10-node triangle elements in area coordinates.

$$N_2 = L_{\substack{i=2\\s=2}} = \prod_{m=0}^{0} \frac{t_2 - t_2^m}{t_2^1 - t_2^m} = \frac{t_2 - t_2^0}{t_2^1 - t_2^0} = \frac{t_2 - 0}{1 - 0} = t_2$$

$$N_3 = L_{\substack{i=3\\s=2}} = \prod_{m=0}^{0} \frac{t_3 - t_3^m}{t_3^1 - t_3^m} = \frac{t_3 - t_3^0}{t_3^1 - t_3^0} = \frac{t_3 - 0}{1 - 0} = t_3$$

where t_1, t_2, and t_3 are the area coordinates defined in Equation 5.15. These results confirm that the three area coordinates are shape functions.

For the 6-node triangular element with three nodes on each side, $s = 3$, we have the following nodal coordinates based on Equation 5.17: $t_1^0 = t_2^0 = t_3^0 = 0$, $t_1^1 = t_2^1 = t_3^1 = 1/2$, and $t_1^2 = t_2^2 = t_3^2 = 1$.

With $s - 1 = 2$ and $s - 2 = 1$, by Equation 5.19 we have two terms $(m = 0, 1)$ in the product. Thus, we express the following as the shape functions for the three vertex nodes:

$$N_1 = L_{\substack{i=1\\s=3}} = \prod_{m=0}^{1} \frac{t_1 - t_1^m}{t_1^2 - t_1^m} = \frac{t_1 - t_1^0}{t_1^2 - t_1^0} \frac{t_1 - t_1^1}{t_1^2 - t_1^1} = t_1(2t_1 - 1)$$

$$N_2 = L_{\substack{i=2\\s=3}} = \prod_{m=0}^{1} \frac{t_2 - t_2^m}{t_2^2 - t_2^m} = \frac{t_2 - t_2^0}{t_2^2 - t_2^0} \frac{t_2 - t_2^1}{t_2^2 - t_2^1} = t_2(2t_2 - 1)$$

$$N_3 = L_{\substack{i=3\\s=3}} = \prod_{m=0}^{1} \frac{t_3 - t_3^m}{t_3^2 - t_3^m} = \frac{t_3 - t_3^0}{t_3^2 - t_3^0} \frac{t_3 - t_3^1}{t_3^2 - t_3^1} = t_3(2t_3 - 1)$$

For a side node, say, node 4 along the side of 1–2, it has vertex indexes of $i = 1$ and $j = 2$ and area coordinates of $(t_1^1, t_2^1, 0)$, along with the corresponding location indexes $p_i = 1$ and $p_j = 1$. By Equation 5.20, we have one term $(m = 0)$ in each of the i and j product terms:

$$N_4 = L_{\substack{p_i=1,p_j=1\\i=1,j=2}} = \prod_{m=0}^{0} \frac{t_1 - t_1^m}{t_1^1 - t_1^m} \prod_{m=0}^{0} \frac{t_2 - t_2^m}{t_2^1 - t_2^m} = \frac{t_1 - t_1^0}{t_1^1 - t_1^0} \frac{t_2 - t_2^0}{t_2^1 - t_2^0} = 4t_1t_2$$

Similarly, we have

$$N_5 = 4t_2t_3, \quad N_6 = 4t_1t_3$$

Figure 5.23 shows the surface plots of the shape functions for the 6-node triangular element. They are quite different from those for the 3-node element shown in Figure 5.13 due to the additional nodal constraints. However, since this 6-node element is a Lagrange element, these shapes can be intuitively imagined by considering the element as a thin flexible sheet fastened with small rings at nodes 1 through 6.

Finally, for the 10-node triangular element with four nodes on each side, $s = 4$, we have the following area coordinates:

$$t_1^0 = t_2^0 = t_3^0 = 0, \; t_1^1 = t_2^1 = t_3^1 = 1/3, \; t_1^2 = t_2^2 = t_3^2 = 2/3, \; t_1^3 = t_2^3 = t_3^3 = 1$$

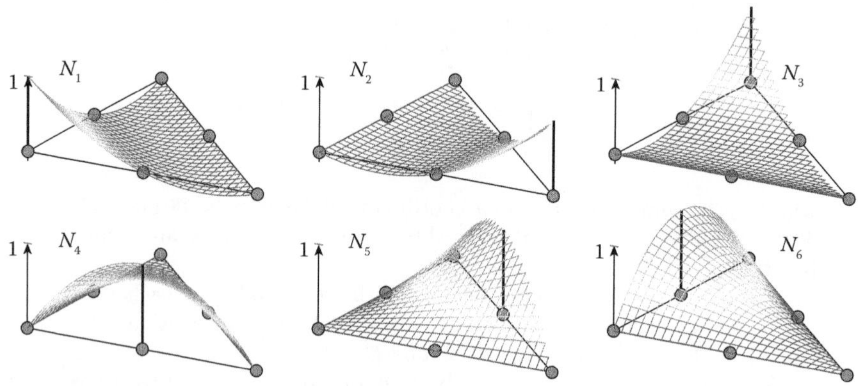

FIGURE 5.23
Shape functions for 6-node triangular elements.

With $s-1=3, s-2=2$, by Equation 5.19 we have three terms ($m = 0,1,2$) in the product of the shape function for vertex node 1:

$$N_1 = L_{\substack{i=1\\s=4}} = \prod_{m=0}^{2} \frac{t_1 - t_1^m}{t_1^3 - t_1^m} = \frac{t_1 - t_1^0}{t_1^3 - t_1^0}\frac{t_1 - t_1^1}{t_1^3 - t_1^1}\frac{t_1 - t_1^2}{t_1^3 - t_1^2} = \frac{1}{2}t_1(3t_1 - 1)(3t_1 - 2)$$

For side nodes, let us again take node 4, which has vertex indexes of $i = 1$ and $j = 2$ and area coordinates of $(t_1^2, t_2^1, 0)$ along with location indexes $p_i = 2$ and $p_j = 1$. Thus, by using Equation 5.20, we have two terms ($m = 0,1$) in the i product and one term ($m = 0$) in the j product:

$$\begin{aligned} N_4 = L_{\substack{p_i=2,p_j=1\\i=1,j=2}} &= \prod_{m=0}^{1} \frac{t_1 - t_1^m}{t_1^2 - t_1^m} \prod_{m=0}^{0} \frac{t_2 - t_2^m}{t_2^1 - t_2^m} \\ &= \frac{t_1 - t_1^0}{t_1^2 - t_1^0}\frac{t_1 - t_1^1}{t_1^2 - t_1^1}\frac{t_2 - t_2^0}{t_2^1 - t_2^0} = \frac{9}{2}t_1 t_2(3t_1 - 1) \end{aligned}$$

For interior nodes, we only have one node, that is node 10 in this case. Node 10 has its area coordinates at (t_1^1, t_2^1, t_3^1) with the corresponding vertex indexes of $i = 1, j = 2$, and $k = 3$ and location indexes of $p_i = 1, p_j = 1$, and $p_k = 1$. Thus, by Equation 5.18 we have one term ($m = 0$) in each of the i, j, and k product terms:

$$\begin{aligned} N_{10} = L_{\substack{p_i=1,p_j=1,p_k=1\\i=1,j=2,k=3}} &= \prod_{m=0}^{0} \frac{t_1 - t_1^m}{t_1^1 - t_1^m} \prod_{m=0}^{0} \frac{t_2 - t_2^m}{t_2^1 - t_2^m} \prod_{m=0}^{0} \frac{t_3 - t_3^m}{t_3^1 - t_3^m} \\ &= \frac{t_1 - t_1^0}{t_1^1 - t_1^0}\frac{t_2 - t_2^0}{t_2^1 - t_2^0}\frac{t_3 - t_3^0}{t_3^1 - t_3^0} = 27t_1 t_2 t_3 \end{aligned}$$

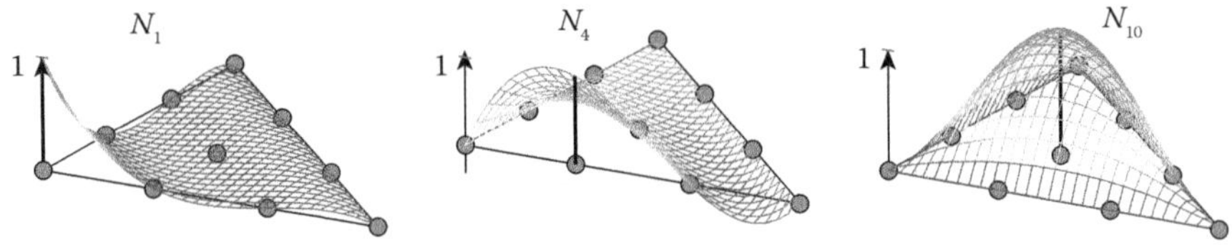

FIGURE 5.24
Selected shape functions for 10-node triangular elements.

The reader is encouraged to find the rest of the shape functions as an exercise. Figure 5.24 shows the surface plots for these three shape functions. Again, because this 10-node element is a Lagrange element, comparing with those shown in Figures 5.13 and 5.23, these shape functions are quite different because the additional nodes act like additional ring fasteners to constrain the element.

5.6.5 Lagrange formula for 3D hexahedral elements

In a similar way, the 1D Lagrange interpolation formula given in Equation 5.13 can also be extended to a 3D situation with x, y, and z as the independent variables:

$$L_{m_x,m_y,m_z} = \prod_{i=1(i\neq m_x)}^{n_x} \frac{x-x_i}{x_{m_x}-x_i} \prod_{j=1(j\neq m_y)}^{n_y} \frac{y-y_j}{y_{m_y}-y_j} \prod_{k=1(k\neq m_z)}^{n_z} \frac{z-z_k}{z_{m_z}-z_k}$$

for $m_x = 1, \ldots, n_x$; $m_y = 1, \ldots, n_y$; and $m_z = 1, \ldots, n_z$, where n_x, n_y, and n_z are the number of nodes in the element along the x, y, and z directions, respectively. Again, by this way of expansion, the number of nodes in 3D elements will be $n = n_x \times n_y \times n_z$. That is, only 3D elements having this kind of nodal arrangement can use this formula to obtain their shape functions. Similarly, due to the field balance requirement, elements with $n_x \neq n_y \neq n_z$ are rarely used. When $n_x = n_y = n_z$, the elementary DOF is a cubic digit, such as the 8-node and 27-node hexahedral elements.

Example 5.6

Find the shape functions for a 3D 8-node hexahedral element shown in Figure 5.25 using the Lagrange formula.

Answer
Since the 8-node hexahedral element has two nodes along each edge, $n_x = n_y = n_z = 2$, we assign the nodal indexes, i, j, and k, as follows:

Node 1: $i = 1, j = 1, k = 1$
Node 2: $i = 2, j = 1, k = 1$
Node 3: $i = 2, j = 2, k = 1$

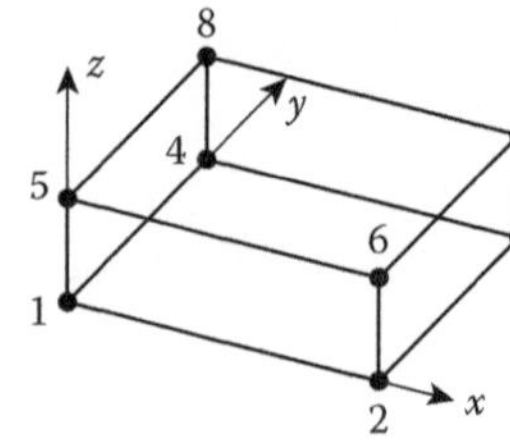

FIGURE 5.25
An 8-node hexahedral element.

Node 4: $i = 1, j = 2, k = 1$
Node 5: $i = 1, j = 1, k = 2$
Node 6: $i = 2, j = 1, k = 2$
Node 7: $i = 2, j = 2, k = 2$
Node 8: $i = 1, j = 2, k = 2$

Then, based on the 3D Lagrange formula, we express the following:

$$N_1 = L_{1,1,1} = \prod_{i=1(i\neq 1)}^{2} \frac{x - x_i}{x_1 - x_i} \prod_{j=1(j\neq 1)}^{2} \frac{y - y_j}{y_1 - y_j} \prod_{k=1(k\neq 1)}^{2} \frac{z - z_k}{z_1 - z_k}$$

$$N_2 = L_{2,1,1} = \prod_{i=1(i\neq 2)}^{2} \frac{x - x_i}{x_2 - x_i} \prod_{j=1(j\neq 1)}^{2} \frac{y - y_j}{y_1 - y_j} \prod_{k=1(k\neq 1)}^{2} \frac{z - z_k}{z_1 - z_k}$$

$$N_3 = L_{2,2,1} = \prod_{i=1(i\neq 2)}^{2} \frac{x - x_i}{x_2 - x_i} \prod_{j=1(j\neq 2)}^{2} \frac{y - y_j}{y_2 - y_j} \prod_{k=1(k\neq 1)}^{2} \frac{z - z_k}{z_1 - z_k}$$

$$N_4 = L_{1,2,1} = \prod_{i=1(i\neq 1)}^{2} \frac{x - x_i}{x_1 - x_i} \prod_{j=1(j\neq 2)}^{2} \frac{y - y_j}{y_2 - y_j} \prod_{k=1(k\neq 1)}^{2} \frac{z - z_k}{z_1 - z_k}$$

$$N_5 = L_{1,1,2} = \prod_{i=1(i\neq 1)}^{2} \frac{x - x_i}{x_1 - x_i} \prod_{j=1(j\neq 1)}^{2} \frac{y - y_j}{y_1 - y_j} \prod_{k=1(k\neq 2)}^{2} \frac{z - z_k}{z_2 - z_k}$$

$$N_6 = L_{2,1,2} = \prod_{i=1(i\neq 2)}^{2} \frac{x - x_i}{x_2 - x_i} \prod_{j=1(j\neq 1)}^{2} \frac{y - y_j}{y_1 - y_j} \prod_{k=1(k\neq 2)}^{2} \frac{z - z_k}{z_2 - z_k}$$

$$N_7 = L_{2,2,2} = \prod_{i=1(i\neq 2)}^{2} \frac{x - x_i}{x_2 - x_i} \prod_{j=1(j\neq 2)}^{2} \frac{y - y_j}{y_2 - y_j} \prod_{k=1(k\neq 2)}^{2} \frac{z - z_k}{z_2 - z_k}$$

$$N_8 = L_{1,2,2} = \prod_{i=1(i\neq 1)}^{2} \frac{x - x_i}{x_1 - x_i} \prod_{j=1(j\neq 2)}^{2} \frac{y - y_j}{y_2 - y_j} \prod_{k=1(k\neq 2)}^{2} \frac{z - z_k}{z_2 - z_k}$$

Since all the product terms have only one term, we can easily write them out:

$$N_1 = \frac{x - x_2}{x_1 - x_2} \frac{y - y_2}{y_1 - y_2} \frac{z - z_2}{z_1 - z_2}, \quad N_2 = \frac{x - x_1}{x_2 - x_1} \frac{y - y_2}{y_1 - y_2} \frac{z - z_2}{z_1 - z_2}$$

$$N_3 = \frac{x-x_1}{x_2-x_1}\frac{y-y_1}{y_2-y_1}\frac{z-z_2}{z_1-z_2}, \quad N_4 = \frac{x-x_2}{x_1-x_2}\frac{y-y_1}{y_2-y_1}\frac{z-z_2}{z_1-z_2}$$
$$N_5 = \frac{x-x_2}{x_1-x_2}\frac{y-y_2}{y_1-y_2}\frac{z-z_1}{z_2-z_1}, \quad N_6 = \frac{x-x_1}{x_2-x_1}\frac{y-y_2}{y_1-y_2}\frac{z-z_1}{z_2-z_1}$$
$$N_7 = \frac{x-x_1}{x_2-x_1}\frac{y-y_1}{y_2-y_1}\frac{z-z_1}{z_2-z_1}, \quad N_8 = \frac{x-x_2}{x_1-x_2}\frac{y-y_1}{y_2-y_1}\frac{z-z_1}{z_2-z_1}$$

Assuming the hexahedral element has a right-angle hexahedral shape, then by letting $x_1 = y_1 = z_1 = 0, x_2 = a, y_2 = b$, and $z_2 = c$, we can associate the nodes with the following coordinates:

Node 1 at (0, 0, 0) Node 2 at (a, 0, 0)
Node 3 at (a, b, 0) Node 4 at (0, b, 0)
Node 5 at (0, 0, c) Node 6 at (a, 0, c)
Node 7 at (a, b, c) Node 8 at (0, b, c)

Plugging these coordinate values into the shape function expressions, we obtain the following eight shape functions for the 3D 8-node hexahedral element:

$$\begin{aligned} N_1 &= \frac{(a-x)(b-y)(c-z)}{abc}, \quad N_2 = \frac{x(b-y)(c-z)}{abc}, \quad N_3 = \frac{xy(c-z)}{abc} \\ N_4 &= \frac{(a-x)y(c-z)}{abc}, \quad N_5 = \frac{(a-x)(b-y)z}{abc}, \quad N_6 = \frac{x(b-y)z}{abc} \\ N_7 &= \frac{xyz}{abc}, \quad N_8 = \frac{(a-x)yz}{abc} \end{aligned} \tag{5.21}$$

5.6.6 Lagrange formulas for 3D tetrahedral elements

5.6.6.1 Volume coordinates for tetrahedrons

Since 3D tetrahedral elements do not possess the nodal arrangement required for using the 3D Lagrange interpolation formula for the hexahedrons discussed in the last section, we cannot use it to write the shape functions for tetrahedral elements. However, because a tetrahedron to a hexahedron in 3D is like a triangle to a rectangle in 2D, using a similar approach, we can define a set of volume coordinates and use them to write the Lagrange interpolation formula for tetrahedral elements.

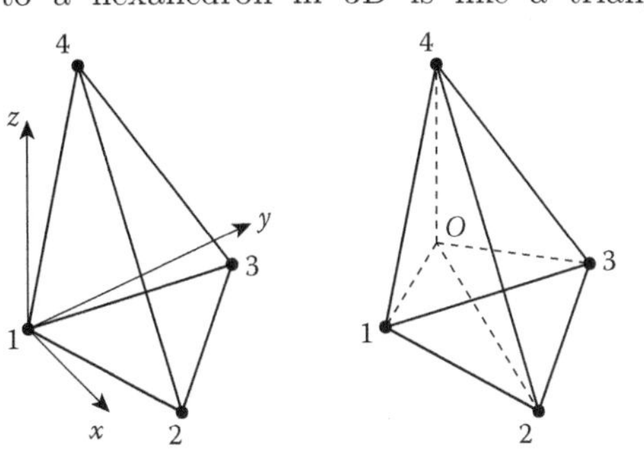

FIGURE 5.26
Four-node tetrahedral elements.

As shown in Figure 5.26, for the tetrahedron defined by vertices 1 through 4, let point $O(x, y, z)$ be an arbitrary interior point that divides the tetrahedron into four subtetrahedrons; then we define four volume coordinates, one with respect to each vertex, $t_1, t_2, t_3,$

and t_4, as follows:

$$t_1 = \frac{V_1}{V_0},\ t_2 = \frac{V_2}{V_0},\ t_3 = \frac{V_3}{V_0},\ t_4 = \frac{V_4}{V_0} \tag{5.22}$$

where V_0 is the volume of the original tetrahedron, V_1 is the volume of the subtetrahedron formed by point O and the surface opposite of vertex 1, and V_2, V_3, and V_4 the volumes of the remaining three subtetrahedrons formed by point O and the surfaces opposite of vertices 2, 3, and 4, respectively. Similarly, as with the area coordinates for triangles, these volume coordinates vary with x, y, and z as point $O(x, y, z)$ moves around within the tetrahedron. Moreover, $t_1 = 1$ at vertex 1, $t_2 = 1$ at vertex 2, $t_3 = 1$ at vertex 3, $t_4 = 1$ at vertex 4, and $t_1 + t_2 + t_3 + t_4 = 1$. Therefore, these four volume coordinates actually represent the four shape functions of a 4-node tetrahedral element.

Since the volume of a tetrahedron can be calculated by the determinant of a matrix formed in terms of the Cartesian coordinates of its four vertices, we express the following:

$$V_0 = \frac{1}{6}\det\begin{bmatrix} 1 & x_1 & y_1 & z_1 \\ 1 & x_2 & y_2 & z_2 \\ 1 & x_3 & y_3 & z_3 \\ 1 & x_4 & y_4 & z_4 \end{bmatrix}$$

$$A_1 = \frac{1}{6}\det\begin{bmatrix} 1 & x & y & z \\ 1 & x_2 & y_2 & z_2 \\ 1 & x_3 & y_3 & z_3 \\ 1 & x_4 & y_4 & z_4 \end{bmatrix}, \quad A_2 = \frac{1}{6}\det\begin{bmatrix} 1 & x_1 & y_1 & z_1 \\ 1 & x & y & z \\ 1 & x_3 & y_3 & z_3 \\ 1 & x_4 & y_4 & z_4 \end{bmatrix}$$

$$A_3 = \frac{1}{6}\det\begin{bmatrix} 1 & x_1 & y_1 & z_1 \\ 1 & x_2 & y_2 & z_2 \\ 1 & x & y & z \\ 1 & x_4 & y_4 & z_4 \end{bmatrix}, \quad A_4 = \frac{1}{6}\det\begin{bmatrix} 1 & x_1 & y_1 & z_1 \\ 1 & x_2 & y_2 & z_2 \\ 1 & x_3 & y_3 & z_3 \\ 1 & x & y & z \end{bmatrix}$$

With these relationships, the four volume coordinates of any tetrahedron can be calculated by using Equation 5.22.

Like the area coordinates, these volume coordinates measure the distance from point O to a surface normalized by the height of the tetrahedron measured from the same surface. For example, t_1 measures the normalized distance from the surface opposite of vertex 1 to a plane parallel to the surface passing through point O. Thus, when point O coincides with vertex 1, $t_1 = 1$. Similarly, t_2, t_3, and t_4 measure the normalized distance from their respective surfaces to any parallel planes passing through point O, and when point O coincides with vertices 2, 3, and 4, $t_2 = 1, t_3 = 1$, and $t_4 = 1$, respectively.

With these volume coordinates, we again use t_i^p to mark the locations of nodes in a tetrahedral element with s nodes along each edge, where the superscript p represents the location index ($p = 0, \ldots, s-1$) of the nodes, and the subscript i the index of the associated vertex node, $i = 1, 2, 3, 4$. Keep in mind that a superscript here does not represent a power degree, and that with a superscript, t_i^p no longer represents the coordinate of an arbitrary point but that of a node. When these nodes are evenly spaced, the formula given in Equation 5.17 can be used to calculate the actual values of the nodal volume coordinates.

5.6.6.2 Lagrange formulas for 3D tetrahedral elements

To write the Lagrange formula for tetrahedral elements with s evenly spaced nodes along each edge, we first assign a set of volume coordinates (t_i, t_j, t_k, t_l), with respect to the four vertices of the tetrahedron $(i, j, k$, and $l)$, to an arbitrary interior point, and then mark the locations of the nodes with $(t_i^{p_i}, t_j^{p_j}, t_k^{p_k}, t_l^{p_l})$, in which p_i, p_j, p_k, and p_l are location indexes with $p_i, p_j, p_k, p_l = 0, 1, \ldots, s-1$ and $p_i + p_j + p_k + p_l = s-1$. With these assignments, we write the following multiproduct formula consisting of the t_i-variable product, t_j-variable product, t_k-variable product, and t_l-variable product for tetrahedral elements:

$$\begin{aligned} L_{p_i,p_j,p_k,p_l} = & \prod_{m=0}^{p_i-1(p_i\neq 0)} \frac{t_i - t_i^m}{t_i^{p_i} - t_i^m} \prod_{m=0}^{p_j-1(p_j\neq 0)} \frac{t_j - t_j^m}{t_j^{p_j} - t_j^m} \\ & \times \prod_{m=0}^{p_k-1(p_k\neq 0)} \frac{t_k - t_k^m}{t_k^{p_k} - t_k^m} \prod_{m=0}^{p_l-1(p_l\neq 0)} \frac{t_l - t_l^m}{t_l^{p_l} - t_l^m} \end{aligned} \tag{5.23}$$

In using Equation 5.23 to write the shape functions, when any individual location index, namely, p_i, p_j, p_k, or p_l, is zero, the corresponding t_i, t_j, t_k, or t_l product term is to be omitted.

For nodes at vertices, since they are associated with only one nonzero volume coordinate, we can express their coordinates as $(t_i^{p_i}, 0, 0, 0)$ for $i = 1$, 2, 3, and 4. Thus, by omitting the t_j, t_k, and t_l product terms in Equation 5.23 and letting $p_i = s-1$, we have the following single-variable-product formula for the four vertex nodes ($i = 1$, 2, 3, and 4):

$$L_{i,s} = \prod_{m=0}^{s-2} \frac{t_i - t_i^m}{t_i^{s-1} - t_i^m} \tag{5.24}$$

Similarly, for the nodes on a surface, say the surface of $i - j - k$ $(i, j, k = 1$, 2, 3, 4), we express their coordinates as $(t_i^{p_i}, t_j^{p_j}, t_k^{p_k}, 0)$. Then by omitting the t_l product term in Equation 5.23, we have the following three-product formula for the surface nodes:

$$L_{p_i,p_j,p_k} = \prod_{m=0}^{p_i-1(p_i\neq 0)} \frac{t_i - t_i^m}{t_i^{p_i} - t_i^m} \prod_{m=0}^{p_j-1(p_j\neq 0)} \frac{t_j - t_j^m}{t_j^{p_j} - t_j^m} \prod_{m=0}^{p_k-1(p_k\neq 0)} \frac{t_k - t_k^m}{t_k^{p_k} - t_k^m} \tag{5.25}$$

Note that Equation 5.25 is technically equivalent to Equation 5.18, with the only difference being that t_i $(i = 1, 2, \ldots)$ is calculated using Equation 5.22

for tetrahedral elements and using Equation 5.15 for triangular elements. This means that when a node falls onto a surface, the Lagrange formula for a tetrahedral element can be further simplified depending on whether the node is on a side edge or in an interior location of the triangular surface (see Section 5.6.4 for more details).

Example 5.7

Find the shape functions for the 4-node and 10-node tetrahedral elements shown in Figure 5.27 using the Lagrange interpolation formula for tetrahedrons.

Answer

For the 4-node tetrahedral element, with $s = 2$, according to Equation 5.17, we have $t_i^0 = 0$ and $t_i^1 = 1$, for $i = 1, \ldots, 4$.

Referring to Equation 5.24, we have only one term, that is, the term of $m = 0$, in the product; thus, we express

$$N_1 = L_{\substack{i=1\\s=2}} = \prod_{m=0}^{0} \frac{t_1 - t_1^m}{t_1^1 - t_1^m} = \frac{t_1 - t_1^0}{t_1^1 - t_1^0} = t_1$$

$$N_2 = L_{\substack{i=2\\s=2}} = \prod_{m=0}^{0} \frac{t_2 - t_2^m}{t_2^1 - t_2^m} = \frac{t_2 - t_2^0}{t_2^1 - t_2^0} = t_2$$

$$N_3 = L_{\substack{i=3\\s=2}} = \prod_{m=0}^{0} \frac{t_3 - t_3^m}{t_3^1 - t_3^m} = \frac{t_3 - t_3^0}{t_3^1 - t_3^0} = t_3$$

$$N_4 = L_{\substack{i=4\\s=2}} = \prod_{m=0}^{0} \frac{t_4 - t_4^m}{t_4^1 - t_4^m} = \frac{t_4 - t_4^0}{t_4^1 - t_4^0} = t_4$$

These results confirm that the four volume coordinates are indeed shape functions of a 4-node tetrahedral element. For the 4-node tetrahedral

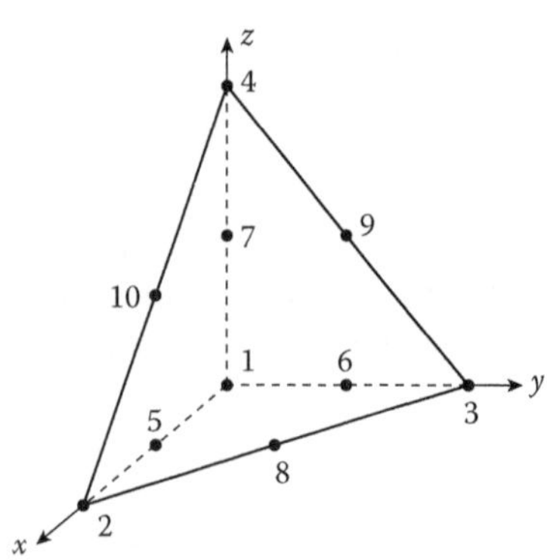

Node 1: (0, 0, 0) Node 6: (0, b/2, 0)
Node 2: (a, 0, 0) Node 7: (0, 0, c/2)
Node 3: (0, b, 0) Node 8: (a/2, b/2, 0)
Node 4: (0, 0, c) Node 9: (0, b/2, c/2)
Node 5: (a/2 ,0, 0) Node 10: (a/2, 0, c/2)

FIGURE 5.27
Tetrahedral element with either 4 nodes or 10 nodes.

element shown in Figure 5.27, we have its vertex coordinates at $(0,0,0),(a,0,0),(0,b,0)$, and $(0,0,c)$ for nodes 1 through 4, respectively. By using Equation 5.22 along with the matrix formulas for calculating volumes, we obtain the following:

$$N_1 = t_1 = 1 - \frac{x}{a} - \frac{y}{b} - \frac{z}{c}, \quad N_2 = t_2 = \frac{x}{a}, \quad N_3 = t_3 = \frac{y}{b}, \quad N_4 = t_4 = \frac{z}{c} \tag{5.26}$$

For the 10-node tetrahedral element, with $s = 3$, we have $t_i^0 = 0$, $t_i^1 = 1/2$, and $t_i^2 = 1$, for $i = 1, \ldots, 4$. For the vertex nodes, referring to Equation 5.24, we express

$$N_1 = L_{\substack{i=1\\s=3}} = \prod_{m=0}^{1} \frac{t_1 - t_1^m}{t_1^1 - t_1^m} = \frac{t_1 - t_1^0}{t_1^1 - t_1^0}\frac{t_1 - t_1^1}{t_1^1 - t_1^1} = t_1(2t_1 - 1)$$

$$N_2 = L_{\substack{i=2\\s=3}} = \prod_{m=0}^{1} \frac{t_2 - t_2^m}{t_2^1 - t_2^m} = \frac{t_2 - t_2^0}{t_2^1 - t_2^0}\frac{t_2 - t_2^1}{t_2^1 - t_2^1} = t_2(2t_2 - 1)$$

$$N_3 = L_{\substack{i=3\\s=3}} = \prod_{m=0}^{1} \frac{t_3 - t_3^m}{t_3^1 - t_3^m} = \frac{t_3 - t_3^0}{t_3^1 - t_3^0}\frac{t_3 - t_3^1}{t_3^1 - t_3^1} = t_3(2t_3 - 1)$$

$$N_4 = L_{\substack{i=4\\s=3}} = \prod_{m=0}^{1} \frac{t_4 - t_4^m}{t_4^1 - t_4^m} = \frac{t_4 - t_4^0}{t_4^1 - t_4^0}\frac{t_4 - t_4^1}{t_4^1 - t_4^1} = t_4(2t_4 - 1)$$

For the rest of the nodes, since all of them are on side edges, their volume coordinates can be expressed as $(t_i^{p_i}, t_j^{p_j}, 0, 0)$ for $i, j = 1, \ldots, 4$. Because of this, the k and l product terms in Equation 5.23 can be omitted; thus, we can directly use Equation 5.20, of course with the volume coordinates rather than the area coordinates. Moreover, since node 5 is between vertices 1 and 2, it has vertex indexes of $i = 1$ and $j = 2$ and location indexes of $p_i = 1$ and $p_j = 1$. Then, we have

$$N_5 = L_{\substack{p_i=1,p_j=1\\i=1,j=2}} = \prod_{m=0}^{0} \frac{t_1 - t_1^m}{t_1^1 - t_1^m} \prod_{m=0}^{0} \frac{t_2 - t_2^m}{t_2^1 - t_2^m} = \frac{t_1 - t_1^0}{t_1^1 - t_1^0}\frac{t_2 - t_2^0}{t_2^1 - t_2^0} = 4t_1t_2$$

In a similar manner, we find

$$N_6 = L_{\substack{p_i=1,p_j=1\\i=1,j=3}} = 4t_1t_3$$

$$N_7 = L_{\substack{p_i=1,p_j=1\\i=1,j=4}} = 4t_1t_4$$

$$N_8 = L_{\substack{p_i=1,p_j=1\\i=2,j=3}} = 4t_2t_3$$

$$N_9 = L_{\substack{p_i=1,p_j=1\\i=3,j=4}} = 4t_3t_4$$

$$N_{10} = L_{\substack{p_i=1,p_j=1\\i=2,j=4}} = 4t_2t_4$$

where t_1, t_2, t_3, and t_4 are given in Equation 5.26.

5.7 Hermite Interpolation

The elements we have discussed to this point are of the Lagrange type, in which the nodal DOF represent directly the field quantity of interest. The shape functions associated with these elements are interpolations functions of the Lagrange type. Although the field interpolation based on the Lagrange interpolation is continuous at the nodes between neighboring elements, there is no guarantee that any derivatives of the field quantity will be continuous as well. This could bring serious problems when we deal with certain structures. Take the case of the 3D bridge truss sketched in Figure 5.4 as an example; if we use 1D Lagrange elements for bridge truss discretization, we basically assume that relevant members are connected together by pins, which means that all the members can freely rotate at all the joints. This of course is not the case. In real life, as we know, these members are welded together to form joints in these truss bridges. So we need a new type of element for situations like this. The elements we need should capture the continuity not only at the level of the field quantity, but also at the derivative levels of the field quantity. Obviously, the Lagrange interpolation functions will not be able to provide the appropriate shape functions for such elements. For this reason, we turn to Hermite interpolation.

5.7.1 Hermite interpolation formulas

Like Lagrange interpolation, Hermite interpolation provides a smooth curve passing through a given number points. But their similarities end there. Instead of using only the ordinate information, the Hermite interpolation uses both the ordinate and slope information to produce a smooth interpolation curve that provides continuity to a higher order.

Let us first discuss how the Hermite interpolation works. For a set of k points in a 2D Cartesian coordinate system with their abscissas and ordinates given as x_m and y_m (for $m = 1, \ldots, k$), respectively, a Hermite interpolation curve is a polynomial function that not only passes through these k points but also has the slope of the curve at these points controlled at y'_m (for $m = 1, \ldots, k$). To describe this statement in mathematical expressions, we first construct a kth-degree Lagrange polynomial function having zeros at $x = x_m$ for $m = 1, \ldots, k$:

$$L(x) = \prod_{m=1}^{k} (x - x_m)$$

With this function, we express the Hermite interpolation formula as

$$y(x) = \sum_{m=1}^{k} \left[y_m h_m^{(1)}(x) + y'_m h_m^{(2)}(x) \right] \tag{5.27}$$

where

$$h_m^{(1)}(x) = \left[1 - \frac{L''(x_m)}{L'(x_m)}(x - x_m)\right] \lambda_m^2(x) \quad \text{and} \quad h_m^{(2)}(x) = (x - x_m)\lambda_m^2(x)$$

are the base functions for the Hermite interpolation formula, $L'(x)$ and $L''(x)$ are the first and second derivatives of $L(x)$, respectively, and

$$\lambda_m(x) = \frac{L(x)}{L'(x_m)(x - x_m)}$$

Figure 5.28 shows an example where a Hermite interpolation curve passes two points with controllable tangents at both points: the curve has a slope of zero (i.e., 0° angle) at the left point and a slope of 1 (or 45° angle) at the right point. As we learned earlier, the Lagrange interpolated curve passing these two points would be a straight line. Clearly, the Hermite formula provides a higher-degree polynomial function than the Lagrange formula to ensure the continuity of the interpolated curve to the first-derivative level or higher.

The two sets of base functions in the Hermite interpolation formula, namely, $h_m^{(1)}(x)$ and $h_m^{(2)}$ for $m = 1, \ldots, k$, are also interpolation functions. Judging from the interpolation formula and the curve shown in Figure 5.28, we can see that they provide polynomial interpolation functions depicting the variation of the field quantity normalized by the respective admissible nodal DOF (u_1, u_1', u_2, or u_2') over the element. So they are actually shape functions.

Therefore, we express the following for $m = 1, \ldots, n_e$,

$$N_{2m-1}(x) = h_m^{(1)}(x) \quad \text{and} \quad N_{2m}(x) = h_m^{(2)}(x) \tag{5.28}$$

as the $2n_e$ shape functions for an element with n_e nodes with nodal DOF of u and u'.

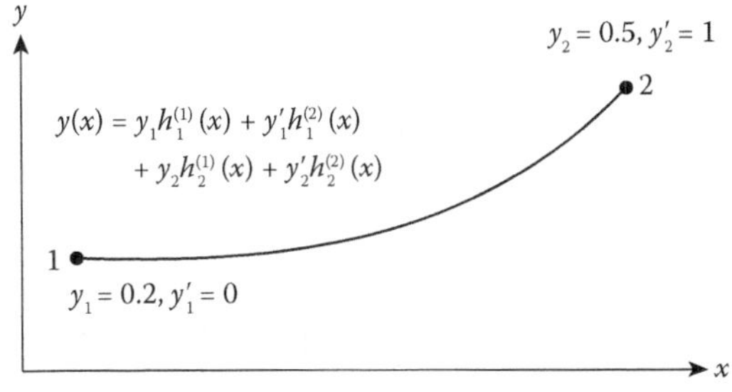

FIGURE 5.28
Hermite interpolation.

As shape functions, these base functions satisfy the following conditions:

$$\sum_{m=1}^{n_e} h_m^{(1)}(x) = 1 \quad \text{and} \quad \sum_{m=1}^{n_e} \left[x_m h_m^{(1)}(x) + h_m^{(2)}(x)\right] = x$$

$$h_m^{(1)}(x_m) = 1 \quad \text{and} \quad h_m^{(1)}(x_j) = 0, j \neq m$$

$$h_m^{'(2)}(x_m) = 1 \quad \text{and} \quad h_m^{'(2)}(x_j) = 0, j \neq m$$

5.7.2 Shape functions for beam elements

As we discussed in Section 3.5, in mechanical terms, a bar structure is mainly used for supporting axial loading, while a beam is mainly used for supporting transverse loading and sustaining flexure deformations. In other words, when axial loading and deformations dominate, we consider a slender mechanical structure as a bar, but when the transverse loading and flexure deformations dominate, we treat it as a beam.

This difference calls for the consideration of different modes of deformations for these slender structures. For example, the tension wires in an Ilizarov ring frame external fixation device, illustrated in Figure 5.29, are such slender members used to provide tensions (axial loading) to strengthen the ring frame and at the same time offer flexure resistance for the bone segments to limit their vertical movements. For these wires, their transverse deflection and the associated rotation (often measured as the slope of the deflection) are of great concern.

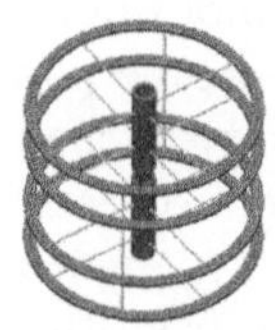

FIGURE 5.29
Ilizarov fixation device.

To capture the mechanical behavior of a beam structure, a special type of element is needed to provide control of nodal admissible variations in not only the transverse deflection but also the rotation caused by the bending moments in the beam structures. This means that these elements will have DOF to represent the transverse deflection (expressed as u) and the slope of the deflection (expressed as the first derivative of deflection u').

For the 2-node beam element illustrated in Figure 5.30, to simplify matters, we assume that the deflection and rotation of the beam occur within the x-y plane. Doing this will not affect the expansion of our discussion to other planes because we will use the same set of shape functions for deflections and rotations there. Thus, we only need to consider two admissible DOF for each node; one is the transverse deflection $u(x)$ and the other the slope $u'(x)$ caused by the deflection of the beam. Thus, the elementary DOF for a 2-node beam

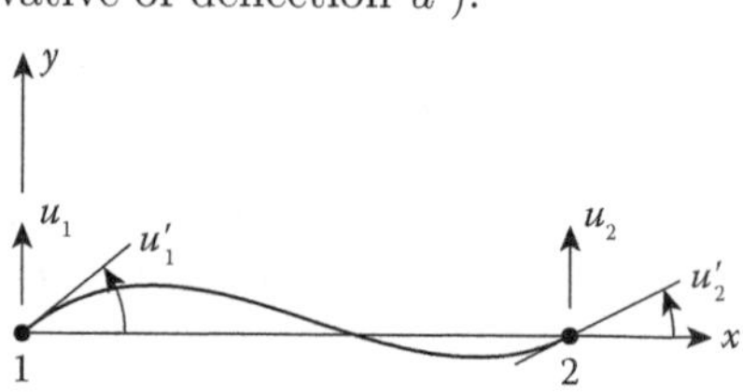

FIGURE 5.30
A 2-node beam element.

element is 4, and they are u_1, u'_1, u_2, and u'_2. Next, we use the Hermite interpolation formula to find the shape functions for such a beam element.

Example 5.8

Find the shape functions for a 2-node beam element using the Hermite interpolation formula.

Answer
For a 2-node beam element, we have $n = 2$, and assuming $x_1 = 0$ and $x_2 = l$, we express

$$L(x) = \prod_{m=1}^{n}(x - x_m) = (x - x_1)(x - x_2) = x^2 - lx$$

Taking the first and second derivatives of $L(x)$, we have

$$L'(x) = 2x - l, \quad L''(x) = 2$$

With substitution of the nodal coordinates, we have

$$L'(x_1) = -l, \quad L'(x_2) = l, \quad L''(x_1) = 2, \quad L''(x_2) = 2$$

Knowing these expressions, we can evaluate $\lambda_m(x)$ for $m = 1$ and 2

$$\begin{aligned}\lambda_1(x) &= \frac{L(x)}{L'(x_1)(x - x_1)} = \frac{x^2 - lx}{-l(x)} = \frac{l - x}{l}\\ \lambda_2(x) &= \frac{L(x)}{L'(x_2)(x - x_2)} = \frac{x^2 - lx}{l(x - l)} = \frac{x}{l}\end{aligned}$$

With these relationships, we calculate $h_m^{(1)}(x)$ and $h_m^{(2)}(x)$ for $m = 1$ and 2

$$\begin{aligned}h_1^{(1)}(x) &= \left[1 - \frac{L''(x_1)}{L'(x_1)}(x - x_1)\right]\lambda_1^2(x) = \left[1 - \frac{2}{(-l)}(x)\right]\frac{(l - x)^2}{l^2} = 1 - \frac{3x^2}{l^2} + \frac{2x^3}{l^3}\\ h_1^{(2)}(x) &= (x - x_1)\lambda_1^2(x) = (x)\frac{(1 - x)^2}{l^2} = x - \frac{2x^2}{l} + \frac{x^3}{l^2}\\ h_2^{(1)}(x) &= \left[1 - \frac{L''(x_2)}{L'(x_2)}(x - x_2)\right]\lambda_2^2(x) = \left[1 - \frac{2}{(l)}(x - l)\right]\frac{x^2}{l^2} = \frac{3x^2}{l^2} - \frac{2x^3}{l^3}\\ h_2^{(2)}(x) &= (x - x_2)\lambda_2^2(x) = (x - l)\frac{x^2}{l^2} = -\frac{x^2}{l} + \frac{x^3}{l^2}\end{aligned}$$

Therefore, according to Equation 5.28 we have

$$\begin{aligned}N_1 &= 1 - \frac{3x^2}{l^2} + \frac{2x^3}{l^3}, \quad & N_2 &= x - \frac{2x^2}{l} + \frac{x^3}{l^2}\\ N_3 &= \frac{3x^2}{l^2} - \frac{2x^3}{l^3}, \quad & N_4 &= -\frac{x^2}{l} + \frac{x^3}{l^2}\end{aligned} \tag{5.29}$$

Figure 5.31 shows the sketches of these four shape functions in position with the element.

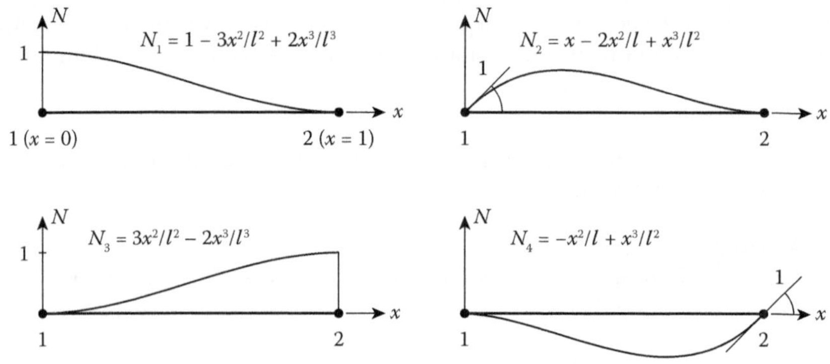

FIGURE 5.31
Shape functions for 2-node beam elements.

The reader is encouraged to show the following for $j, m = 1$ and 2:

$$\sum_{m=1}^{2} N_{2m-1}(x) = 1 \quad \text{and} \quad \sum_{m=1}^{2} [x_m N_{2m-1}(x) + N_{2m}(x)] = x$$

$$N_{2m-1}(x_m) = 1 \quad \text{and} \quad N_{2m-1}(x_j) = 0, j \neq m$$

$$N'_{2m}(x_m) = 1 \quad \text{and} \quad N'_{2m}(x_j) = 0, j \neq m$$

Example 5.8b

Repeat Example 5.8 using the matrix method.

Answer
We rework this example by using the matrix method to demonstrate that the matrix method can be applied to both the Lagrange elements and the Hermite elements. Since both the translational and rotational movements are considered, we have 2 DOF per node; thus, for a 2-node beam element, the elementary DOF = 4. Then we can select a 1D polynomial function with four constants to express the approximate field quantity:

$$\tilde{u}(x) = a_0 + a_1 x + a_2 x^2 + a_3 x^3$$

which, in a matrix form, can be written as

$$\tilde{u}(x) = p \begin{Bmatrix} a_0 \\ a_1 \\ a_2 \\ a_3 \end{Bmatrix}, \quad \text{where} \quad p = \begin{bmatrix} 1 & x & x^2 & x^3 \end{bmatrix} \tag{5.30}$$

The slope of the field is calculated by taking the first derivative of $\tilde{u}(x)$ as

$$\tilde{u}'(x) = a_1 x + 2a_2 x + 3a_3 x^2$$

With the nodal information, we express

$$\begin{Bmatrix} u_1 \\ u_1' \\ u_2 \\ u_2' \end{Bmatrix} = \begin{bmatrix} 1 & x_1 & x_1^2 & x_1^3 \\ 0 & 1 & 2x_1 & 3x_1^2 \\ 1 & x_2 & x_2^2 & x_2^3 \\ 0 & 1 & 2x_2 & 3x_2^2 \end{bmatrix} \begin{Bmatrix} a_0 \\ a_1 \\ a_2 \\ a_3 \end{Bmatrix}$$

$$\text{let } M = \begin{bmatrix} 1 & x_1 & x_1^2 & x_1^3 \\ 0 & 1 & 2x_1 & 3x_1^2 \\ 1 & x_2 & x_2^2 & x_2^3 \\ 0 & 1 & 2x_2 & 3x_2^2 \end{bmatrix}; \text{ we have } \begin{Bmatrix} a_0 \\ a_1 \\ a_2 \\ a_3 \end{Bmatrix} = M^{-1} \begin{Bmatrix} u_1 \\ u_1' \\ u_2 \\ u_2' \end{Bmatrix} \tag{5.31}$$

Recall the field quantity expression in terms of nodal DOF:

$$\tilde{u}(x) = N_1 u_1 + N_2 u_1' + N_3 u_2 + N_4 u_2'$$

With this expression along with Equations 5.30 and 5.31, we can write

$$\tilde{u}(x) = N \begin{Bmatrix} u_1 \\ u_1' \\ u_2 \\ u_2' \end{Bmatrix} = p \begin{Bmatrix} a_0 \\ a_1 \\ a_2 \\ a_3 \end{Bmatrix} = pM^{-1} \begin{Bmatrix} u_1 \\ u_1' \\ u_2 \\ u_2' \end{Bmatrix}$$

By substituting the values of the nodal coordinates, namely, $x_1 = 0$ and $x_2 = l$, we obtain

$$N = pM^{-1} = \begin{bmatrix} 1 & x & x^2 & x^3 \end{bmatrix} \begin{bmatrix} 1 & 0 & 0 & 0 \\ 0 & 1 & 0 & 0 \\ 1 & l & l^2 & l^3 \\ 0 & 1 & 2l & 3l^2 \end{bmatrix}^{-1}$$

$$= \begin{bmatrix} 1 & x & x^2 & x^3 \end{bmatrix} \begin{bmatrix} 1 & 0 & 0 & 0 \\ 0 & 1 & 0 & 0 \\ -3/l^2 & -2/l & 3/l^2 & -1/l \\ 2/l^3 & l/l^2 & -2/l^3 & 1/l^2 \end{bmatrix}$$

which yields

$$N = \begin{bmatrix} 1 - \dfrac{3x^2}{l^2} + \dfrac{2x^3}{l^3} & x - \dfrac{2x^2}{l} + \dfrac{x^3}{l^2} & \dfrac{3x^2}{l^2} - \dfrac{2x^3}{l^3} & -\dfrac{x^2}{l} + \dfrac{x^3}{l^2} \end{bmatrix}$$

By separating them out, we obtain the following four individual cubic shape functions:

$$N_1 = 1 - \frac{3x^2}{l^2} + \frac{2x^3}{l^3},\ N_2 = x - \frac{2x^2}{l} + \frac{x^3}{l^2},\ N_3 = \frac{3x^2}{l^2} - \frac{2x^3}{l^3},\ N_4 = -\frac{x^2}{l} + \frac{x^3}{l^2}$$

Obviously, these four shape functions are exactly the same as those obtained by using the Hermite interpolation formula (see Equation 5.29).

Equipped with the knowledge of the shape functions of beam elements, we now take another look at the discussions on the distinction between a bar structure and a beam structure and ask when one should use bar elements or beam elements to discretize them. In fact, bar elements are applicable to slender structures that are not necessarily only going through axial deformation under axial loads. As long as we can ignore the rotational DOF in a slender structure (hence a Lagrange type of elements will suffice to capture its DOF), we can use bar elements to discretize it. For example, for the vibrating string problem we discussed in Chapter 3, the main displacement of the string is actually the lateral transverse one and not the axial one. Since we neglect its rotational constraints or DOF, there is no need for a Hermite type of elements for discretization; therefore, the string vibration problem can be modeled with bar elements (in many software packages, bar elements are also called truss elements). A detailed discussion on modeling a vibrating string is presented in Chapter 14.

5.7.3 Plate and shell elements

As we pointed out earlier, although both are 1D structures, a bar structure is mainly used for sustaining axial loads and deformations, while a beam structure is used for transverse loads and deformations. In a similar extension, there are 2D structures that are mainly used for sustaining out-of-plane loads and deformations. Since the 2D elements we have discussed in previous sections are all for sustaining in-plane loads and deformations, we need different elements to capture the out-of-plane deformations in these 2D structures.

In FEM, we use two types of 2D elements for these structures; one type is the plate elements and the other is the shell elements (also known as membrane elements). The difference between a plate element and a shell (or membrane) element is in the thickness of the structure. When the structure is extremely thin such that the mechanical variation across the thickness is negligible, we consider it as a shell, like an eggshell (or a membrane, like an inflated balloon). Otherwise, we consider it as a plate, although its thickness is small relative to its other two dimensions. The out-of-plane deformations these 2D structures undergo often include transverse deflection, which in turn will lead to rotations of the structure with respect to its midplane. Because of this, plate and shell elements are of the Hermite type. By extending the Hermite interpolation formula to 2D, we can find the shape functions for these plate and shell types of elements.

5.8 Interpolation of Field Quantities in a Matrix Form

From the discussions in the previous sections, we know that a field quantity can be approximated by a polynomial interpolation function over the domain of a given element, and that this single polynomial interpolation function can be replaced by multiple subinterpolation functions, known as the shape functions. Moreover, the number of shape functions associated with an element equals the number of the elementary DOF, and the equations for the shape functions can be determined directly by using either the matrix method or an interpolation formula, for example, the Lagrange or Hermite formulas, depending on the continuity requirements for the elements.

Equipped with this knowledge, we now revisit the general expression given in Equation 5.6, that is,

$$\tilde{u} = \sum_{m=1}^{n_e} N_m u_m$$

This equation states that a field quantity can be interpolated mathematically in terms of the elementary DOF and their corresponding shape functions. For example, for a 1D 3-node element, $\tilde{u}(x) = N_1(x)u_1 + N_2(x)u_2 + N_3(x)u_3$; for a 2-node beam element, $\tilde{u}(x) = N_1(x)u_1 + N_2(x)u_1' + N_3(x)u_2 + N_4(x)u_2'$; and for an 8-node hexahedral element, $\tilde{u}(x, y, z) = N_1(x, y, z)u_1 + N_2(x, y, z)u_2 + N_3(x, y, z)u_3 + N_4(x, y, z)u_4 + N_5(x, y, z)u_5 + N_6(x, y, z)u_6 + N_7(x, y, z)u_7 + N_8(x, y, z)u_8$. Clearly, this type of expression can be expanded to any elements with any number of elementary DOF.

These expressions are often condensed to matrix forms. For instance, the equation for the 1D 3-node element can be expressed as

$$\tilde{u}(x) = \begin{bmatrix} N_1(x) & N_2(x) & N_3(x) \end{bmatrix} \begin{Bmatrix} u_1 \\ u_2 \\ u_3 \end{Bmatrix}$$

The equation for the 2-node beam element can be expressed as

$$\tilde{u}(x) = \begin{bmatrix} N_1(x) & N_2(x) & N_3(x) & N_4(x) \end{bmatrix} \begin{Bmatrix} u_1 \\ u_1' \\ u_2 \\ u_2' \end{Bmatrix}$$

The equation for the 2D 4-node rectangular element can be expressed as

$$\tilde{u}(x, y) = \begin{bmatrix} N_1(x, y) & N_2(x, y) & N_3(x, y) & N_4(x, y) \end{bmatrix} \begin{Bmatrix} u_1 \\ u_2 \\ u_3 \\ u_4 \end{Bmatrix}$$

And the equation for the 3D 8-node hexahedral element can be rewritten as

$$\tilde{u}(x, y, z) = \begin{bmatrix} N_1 & N_2 & N_3 & N_4 & N_5 & N_6 & N_7 & N_8 \end{bmatrix} \begin{Bmatrix} u_1 \\ u_2 \\ u_3 \\ u_4 \\ u_5 \\ u_6 \\ u_7 \\ u_8 \end{Bmatrix}$$

Seeing these new expressions, we can write a compact general expression for all these cases as

$$\tilde{u} = \sum_{m=1}^{n_e} N_m u_m = [N]\{d_0\} \tag{5.32}$$

where $[N]$ is called the elementary shape function matrix and $\{d_0\}$ is the elementary DOF vector.

For scalar field problems (which sometimes are also referred to as single-variable problems) and 1D vector field problems, an element with elementary DOF $= n_e$ will have a $n_e \times 1$ vector for $\{d_0\}$ containing the individual elementary DOF in its rows and a $1 \times n_e$ matrix for $[N]$ containing the shape functions in its columns. Thus, their single-variable field quantity can be approximated as

$$\tilde{u} = [N]\{d_0\} = \begin{bmatrix} N_1 & N_2 & \cdots & N_{n_e} \end{bmatrix} \begin{Bmatrix} u_1 \\ u_2 \\ \vdots \\ u_{n_e} \end{Bmatrix} \tag{5.33}$$

For 2D vector field problems, the field quantity is a 2×1 vector as $\{d\} = \{u_x\ u_y\}^T$, but we use the same set of shape functions to interpolate them:

$$\tilde{u}_x = \sum_{m=1}^{n_e} N_m u_{mx}, \quad \tilde{u}_y = \sum_{m=1}^{n_e} N_m u_{my}$$

Thus, we have the following expression, with a $2n_e \times 1$ $\{d_0\}$ vector and a $2 \times 2n_e$ $[N]$ matrix for an element with elementary DOF $= n_e$:

$$\{d\} = \begin{Bmatrix} \tilde{u}_x \\ \tilde{u}_y \end{Bmatrix} = \begin{bmatrix} N_1 & 0 & N_2 & 0 & \cdots & N_{n_e} & 0 \\ 0 & N_1 & 0 & N_2 & \cdots & 0 & N_{n_e} \end{bmatrix} \begin{Bmatrix} u_{1x} \\ u_{1y} \\ u_{2x} \\ u_{2y} \\ \vdots \\ u_{n_e x} \\ u_{n_e y} \end{Bmatrix} = [N]\{d_0\} \tag{5.34}$$

Similarly, for 3D vector field problems, their 3×1 field quantity vector, $\{d\} = \{u_x \; u_y \; u_z\}^T$, is approximated as

$$\{d\} = \begin{Bmatrix} \tilde{u}_x \\ \tilde{u}_y \\ \tilde{u}_z \end{Bmatrix}$$

$$= \begin{bmatrix} N_1 & 0 & 0 & N_2 & 0 & 0 & \cdots & N_{n_e} & 0 & 0 \\ 0 & N_1 & 0 & 0 & N_2 & 0 & \cdots & 0 & N_{n_e} & 0 \\ 0 & 0 & N_1 & 0 & 0 & N_2 & \cdots & 0 & 0 & N_{n_e} \end{bmatrix} \begin{Bmatrix} u_{1x} \\ u_{1y} \\ u_{1z} \\ u_{2x} \\ u_{2y} \\ u_{2z} \\ \vdots \\ u_{n_e x} \\ u_{n_e y} \\ u_{n_e z} \end{Bmatrix}$$

$$= [N] \{d_0\} \tag{5.35}$$

This equation shows that for 3D vector field problems, an element with elementary DOF $= n_e$ has a $3n_e \times 1$ $\{d_0\}$ vector and a $3 \times 3n_e$ $[N]$ matrix.

5.9 Exercises

1. Describe the following terms:

   a. Finite element
   b. Elements
   c. Nodes
   d. Domain
   e. Mesh
   f. Mesh density
   g. Shape functions
   h. Requirements for the selection of polynomial terms
   i. Order of element discretization

2. What are nodes in FEM for? What information is dealt with at nodes?

3. How is a vector problem different from a scalar problem in terms of DOF?

4. What are the requirements for choosing polynomial terms to form interpolation functions? What can one do to simplify the selection process?
5. What types of polynomial functions are regarded as balanced functions and what as complete? Which condition is a required one?
6. How would you describe the connections between the types of elements and the types and orders of polynomial functions?
7. What are serendipity elements, and are there any benefits of using them?
8. Use the matrix method discussed in Section 5.5 to find the shape functions for the following elements. Sketch the shape functions you found in either 2D or 3D plots. Also, show that all the shape functions meet the following two requirements:

   a. $N_m(x_m) = 1$ and $N_m(x_i) = 0$ when $i \neq m$

   b. $\sum_{m=1}^{n_e} N_m = 1$, where n_e is the number of nodes in each element

      i. A 1D 2-node element with $l = 3$ shown in Figure 5.32
      ii. A 1D 3-node element with $l = 4$ shown in Figure 5.32
      iii. A 2D 3-node triangle element shown in Figure 5.33
      iv. A 2D 4-node rectangle element with $a = 2$ and $b = 1$ shown in Figure 5.33

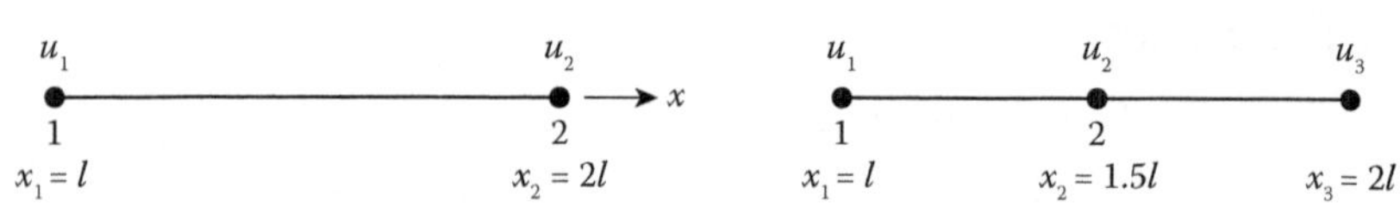

FIGURE 5.32
One-dimensional 2-node and 3-node elements.

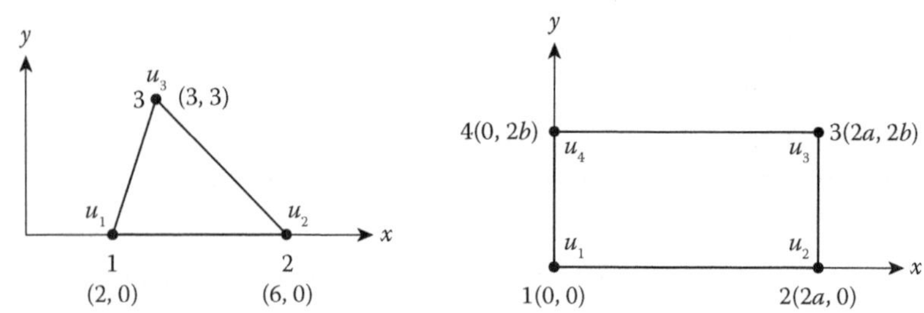

FIGURE 5.33
Two-dimensional 3-node triangle and 4-node rectangle elements.

9. Use the Lagrange interpolation formulas discussed in Section 5.6 to find the shape functions for the following elements. Sketch the shape functions you found and compare the results of Exercises 8a, 9a, and 9c, and Exercises 8b, 9b, and 9d. What can you conclude from the comparison?

    a. A 1D 2-node element with $l = 3$ shown in Figure 5.34
    b. A 1D 3-node element with $l = 4$ shown in Figure 5.34
    c. A 1D 2-node element with $l = 3$ shown in Figure 5.35
    d. A 1D 3-node element with $l = 4$ shown in Figure 5.35

10. Use the Lagrange interpolation formulas to find the shape functions for the following elements. Sketch the shape functions you found.

    a. The same 4-node 2D rectangle element in Exercise 8b(iv)
    b. A 2D 9-node rectangle element shown on the left in Figure 5.36 with the following coordinate locations: $1(2, 2)$, $2(6, 2)$, $3(6, 5)$, $4(2, 5)$, $5(4, 2)$, $6(6, 3.5)$, $7(4, 5)$, $8(2, 3.5)$, and $9(4, 3.5)$
    c. The same element given in (b), but with its location moved, having node 1 coincide with the origin of the coordinate system, as shown on the right in Figure 5.36.

11. What are the advantages for using the area coordinate and volume coordinate systems in developing the Lagrange interpolation formulas for 2D triangle elements and 3D tetrahedral elements, respectively?

12. Use the Lagrange interpolation formulas for triangle elements to show

$$N_5 = 4t_2t_3 \quad \text{and} \quad N_6 = 4t_1t_3$$

for the 6-node element given in Example 5.5.

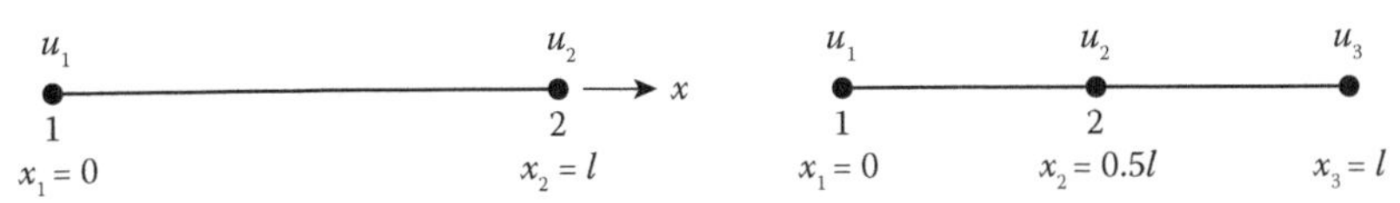

FIGURE 5.34
One-dimensional 2-node and 3-node elements.

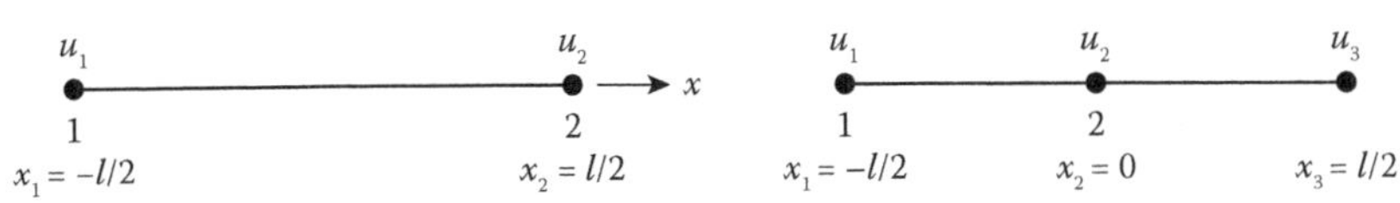

FIGURE 5.35
One-dimensional 2-node and 3-node elements.

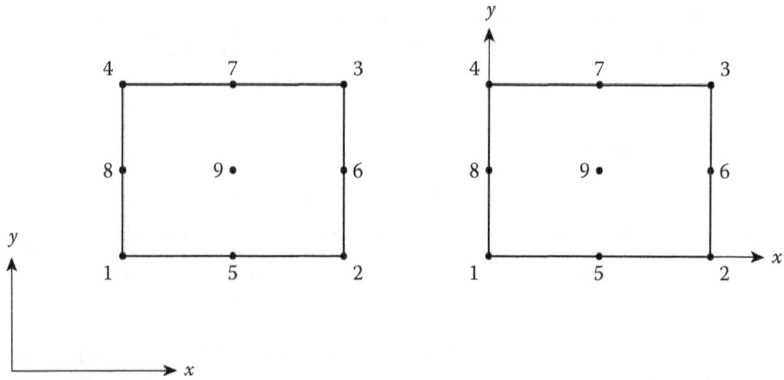

FIGURE 5.36
A 9-node 2D rectangle element.

13. Use the Lagrange interpolation formulas for triangle elements to show

$$
\begin{aligned}
N_2 &= t_2(3t_2 - 1)(3t_2 - 2)/2 \\
N_3 &= t_3(3t_3 - 1)(3t_3 - 2)/2 \\
N_5 &= 9t_1t_2(3t_2 - 1)/2 \\
N_6 &= 9t_2t_3(3t_2 - 1)/2 \\
N_7 &= 9t_2t_3(3t_3 - 1)/2 \\
N_8 &= 9t_1t_3(3t_3 - 1)/2 \\
N_9 &= 9t_1t_3(3t_1 - 1)/2
\end{aligned}
$$

for the 10-node element given in Example 5.5.

14. Use the Lagrange interpolation formulas for tetrahedral elements to show the details for verifying the results given for shape functions N_6 through N_{10} for the 10-node tetrahedral element discussed in Example 5.7, namely,

$$N_6 = 4t_1t_3, \quad N_7 = 4t_1t_4, \quad N_8 = 4t_2t_3, \quad N_9 = 4t_3t_4, \quad N_{10} = 4t_2t_4$$

15. Referring to the four shape functions obtained for the beam element in Example 5.8, show the following relationships for $j, m = 1$ and 2:

$$\sum_{m=1}^{2} N_{2m-1}(x) = 1 \quad \text{and} \quad \sum_{m=1}^{2} [x_m N_{2m-1}(x) + N_{2m}(x)] = x$$

$$N_{2m-1}(x_m) = 1 \ \text{ and } \ N_{2m-1}(x_j) = 0, j \neq m$$

$$N_{2m}^{'}(x_m) = 1 \ \text{ and } \ N_{2m}^{'}(x_j) = 0, j \neq m$$

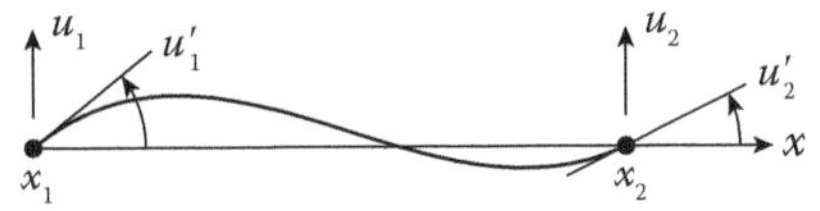

FIGURE 5.37
A 2-node beam element.

16. What are the main differences between the elements developed using the Lagrange interpolation and Hermite interpolation methods?
17. Use the Hermite interpolation formulas to find the shape functions for a 2-node beam element shown in Figure 5.37 with $x_1 = l$ and $x_2 = 2l$.
18. Why are different elements, such as bar elements, beam elements, 2D elements, and 3D elements, needed in FEM?

Recommended Readings

1. J. N. Reddy. 1993. *An Introduction to the Finite Element Method.* 2nd ed. Boston: McGraw-Hill.
2. Robert D. Cook, David S. Malkus, Michael E. Plesha, and Robert J. Witt. 2002. *Concepts and Applications of Finite Element Analysis.* 4th ed. Hoboken, NJ: John Wiley & Sons.
3. Tirupathi R. Chandrupatla and Ashok D. Belegundu. 2002. *Introduction to Finite Elements in Engineering.* 3rd ed. Upper Saddle River, NJ: Prentice Hall.
4. Jacob Fish and Ted Belytschko. 2007. *A First Course in Finite Elements.* Hoboken, NJ: John Wiley & Sons.

Recommended Readings

6

Solving Differential Equations Computationally

Discretization of a physical domain into finite elements is for linking nodal degrees of freedom (DOF) to polynomial interpolation functions such that an approximate solution to the original problem can be found. Let us not get lost in this pursuit. Recall that in answering the question "Where do differential equations come from?" we have learned not only that they are developed mathematically upon the fundamental theorem of calculus according to the laws of thermodynamics in terms of mass, force, momentum, and energy conservation, as well as other relevant laws and principles, such as Hooke's law of elasticity, Newton's second law of motion, Fourier's law of heat transfer, and Fick's law of diffusion, but also that partial differential equations (PDEs) governing different engineering problems are sometimes of the same mathematical type. This suggests that although there are countless real-world problems, there are limited number of types of differential equations.

In developing various differential equations, we have seen firsthand that PDEs for different problems indeed share many commonalities, especially that most of them contain the second derivative or the Laplacian of a field quantity of interest. Also, of the PDEs given in Equations 3.2, 3.5, and 3.6 that govern mechanical, heat transfer, and mass transport problems, respectively, if we ignore the time effect, all these PDEs reduce to a mathematically identical form, as can be seen from the following three PDEs:

$$\frac{\partial}{\partial x}\left[E\frac{\partial u}{\partial x}\right]+f=0,\quad \frac{\partial}{\partial x}\left[\kappa\frac{\partial T}{\partial x}\right]+Q=0,\quad \frac{\partial}{\partial x}\left[D\frac{\partial c}{\partial x}\right]+R=0$$

Thus, in this chapter, we learn how to solve PDEs of a common mathematical type for different engineering problems defined over slender structures or domains. To facilitate this, we express them in the following common form, with u standing for u, T, or c; k for E, κ, or D; and g for f, Q, or R, as:

$$\frac{\partial}{\partial x}\left[k\frac{\partial u(x)}{\partial x}\right]+g=0$$

6.1 Differential Equations in Strong and Weak Forms

In this chapter, we limit our discussion to slender structures or domains. Assuming that such a slender structure or domain has a uniform cross section area of A and a length of l, we express the common form differential equation as

$$\frac{d}{dx}\left[k\frac{du(x)}{dx}\right]+g=0 \tag{6.1}$$

for $0 \leq x \leq l$. Using an approximate solution $\tilde{u}$, we calculate a residual as

$$R=\frac{d}{dx}\left[k\frac{d\tilde{u}(x)}{dx}\right]+g$$

Let $w(x)$ be a set of weight functions (which are sometimes also called test functions); we construct the following weighted integral of residual over the entire three-dimensional (3D) domain first and then reduce it to one-dimensional (1D) as

$$\begin{aligned}\iiint_V w(x)\left[\frac{d}{dx}\left[k\frac{d\tilde{u}(x)}{dx}\right]+g\right]dV &= \int_0^l w(x)\left[\frac{d}{dx}\left[k\frac{d\tilde{u}(x)}{dx}\right]+g\right]Adx \\ &= \int_0^l w(x)\frac{d}{dx}\left[k\frac{d\tilde{u}(x)}{dx}\right]Adx \\ &\quad + \int_0^l w(x)gAdx = 0\end{aligned} \tag{6.2}$$

By the product rule of differentiation, we know

$$\frac{d}{dx}\left[w(x)k\frac{d\tilde{u}(x)}{dx}\right]=w(x)\frac{d}{dx}\left[k\frac{d\tilde{u}(x)}{dx}\right]+\frac{dw(x)}{dx}k\frac{d\tilde{u}(x)}{dx}$$

Substituting this relationship into Equation 6.2, we have

$$\int_0^l \frac{d}{dx}\left[w(x)k\frac{d\tilde{u}(x)}{dx}\right]Adx-\int_0^l \frac{dw(x)}{dx}k\frac{d\tilde{u}(x)}{dx}Adx+\int_0^l w(x)gAdx=0$$

Integrating the first term and rearranging it, we arrive at

$$\int_0^l \frac{dw(x)}{dx}k\frac{d\tilde{u}(x)}{dx}Adx=\int_0^l w(x)gAdx+\left[w(x)Ak\frac{d\tilde{u}(x)}{dx}\right]_0^l \tag{6.3}$$

Equation 6.3 is called the weak-form differential equation of Equation 6.1 because it has the reduced (or weakened) continuity requirement for the field quantity u from second derivative to first derivative. In this sense, PDEs in their original forms, like Equation 6.1, are called strong-form PDEs. In the weak-form equation, the reduced requirement for the field continuity is made possible by the use of weight functions through the method of weighted integral of the residual. Note that the order of reduction in the continuity requirement could be 1 or higher depending on the original strong-form PDEs. For example, the weak-form PDE for beams discussed in Section 6.7.1 is reduced by an order of 2 in the continuity requirement compared with its strong-form PDE.

The two terms on the right-hand side of the equation are related to the physical constraints. For example, the first term describes the influence of a volume quantity, and the second term, $Akd\tilde{u}(x)/dx$, represents a point load in mechanical problems, a heat flux in thermal problems, and a mass flux in transport problems.

6.2 FEM Formulation Using the Galerkin Method

As we learned in Section 4.4, the Galerkin method provides not only better approximate results but also the benefit of using the interpolation functions as the weight functions. Thus, by using the shape functions of an element (with the elementary DOF = n_e) as the weight functions (or test functions), we have

$$w_m = N_m \text{ for } m = 1, \ldots, n_e$$

Substituting this set of relationships into Equation 6.3, we obtain

$$\int_0^l \frac{dN_m}{dx} k \frac{d\tilde{u}(x)}{dx} A dx = \int_0^l N_m g A dx + \left[N_m A k \frac{d\tilde{u}(x)}{dx} \right]_0^l$$

for $m = 1, \ldots, n_e$. According to Equation 5.32, the approximate field quantity can be written in terms of the shape functions and nodal DOF in a matrix form; thus, we have

$$\tilde{u}(x) = \sum_{m=1}^{n_e} N_m u_m = [N]\{d_0\}$$

Plugging this expression into the term on the left side of the equation above and rearranging it, we arrive at

$$\int_0^l \frac{dN_m}{dx} k \frac{d([N]\{d_0\})}{dx} A dx = \int_0^l N_m g A dx + \left[N_m A k \frac{d\tilde{u}}{dx}(x) \right]_0^l$$

Since only the shape function matrix, $[N]$, varies with x and the nodal DOF vector, $\{d_0\}$, does not, we rearrange it as

$$\int_0^l \frac{dN_m}{dx} k \left[\frac{dN}{dx} \right] A dx \{d_0\} = \int_0^l N_m g A dx + \left[N_m A k \frac{d\tilde{u}}{dx}(x) \right]_0^l$$

for $m = 1, \ldots, n_e$. By summing all these n_e equations together,

$$\int_0^l \frac{dN_1}{dx} k \left[\frac{dN}{dx}\right] A dx \{d_0\} = \int_0^l N_1 g A dx + \left[N_1 A k \frac{d\tilde{u}}{dx}(x)\right]_0^l$$

$$+$$

$$\int_0^l \frac{dN_2}{dx} k \left[\frac{dN}{dx}\right] A dx \{d_0\} = \int_0^l N_2 g A dx + \left[N_2 A k \frac{d\tilde{u}}{dx}(x)\right]_0^l$$

$$\cdots$$

$$+$$

$$\int_0^l \frac{dN_{n_e}}{dx} k \left[\frac{dN}{dx}\right] A dx \{d_0\} = \int_0^l N_{n_e} g A dx + \left[N_{n_e} A k \frac{d\tilde{u}}{dx}(x)\right]_0^l$$

we obtain the finite element method (FEM) formulation for the differential equation given in Equation 6.1:

$$\int_0^l \left[\frac{dN}{dx}\right]^T k \left[\frac{dN}{dx}\right] A dx \{d_0\} = \int_0^l [N]^T g A dx + \left[[N]^T A k \frac{d\tilde{u}}{dx}(x)\right]_0^l \quad (6.4)$$

6.2.1 Elementary $[K_e]$ matrix

The coefficient associated with the elementary DOF vector, $\{d_0\}$, on the left-hand side of Equation 6.4 is called the elementary $[K_e]$ matrix, that is,

$$[K_e] = A \int_0^l \left[\frac{dN}{dx}\right]^T k \left[\frac{dN}{dx}\right] dx \quad (6.5)$$

Note that the $[K_e]$ matrix has different meanings for different engineering problems. For example, when k stands for Young's modulus E in a mechanical problem, $[K_e]$ is called the stiffness matrix, and when k represents thermal conductivity κ in a heat transfer problem, $[K_e]$ becomes the conductance matrix.

Because it is calculated as the product of a matrix and its transpose, the $[K_e]$ matrix possesses the following three properties:

1. It is a square matrix ($n_e \times n_e$ for an element with elementary DOF $= n_e$).
2. It is symmetric about the principal diagonal.
3. All the diagonal terms are positive.

Now let us go through some examples to see how the $[K_e]$ matrix is determined.

Example 6.1

Find the elementary $[K_e]$ matrix for a 2-node bar element with two nodes at $x = 0$ and $x = l$, respectively, and a constant k value.

Answer

From Equation 5.8, we write the 1×2 elementary shape function matrix for the 2-node bar element as

$$[N] = \begin{bmatrix} N_1 & N_2 \end{bmatrix} = \begin{bmatrix} \frac{l-x}{l} & \frac{x}{l} \end{bmatrix}$$

Then, taking the first derivative of the $[N]$ matrix with respect to x, we have

$$\left[\frac{dN}{dx}\right] = \begin{bmatrix} \frac{dN_1}{dx} & \frac{dN_2}{dx} \end{bmatrix} = \frac{1}{l}\begin{bmatrix} -1 & 1 \end{bmatrix}$$

Substituting it into Equation 6.5, we obtain

$$[K_e] = \frac{kA}{l^2}\int_0^l \begin{bmatrix} -1 \\ 1 \end{bmatrix} \begin{bmatrix} -1 & 1 \end{bmatrix} dx$$

Multiplying out the two matrices and taking the integral, we obtain the following elementary $[K_e]$ matrix for a 2-node bar element:

$$[K_e] = \frac{kA}{l^2}\int_0^l \begin{bmatrix} 1 & -1 \\ -1 & 1 \end{bmatrix} dx = \frac{kA}{l}\begin{bmatrix} 1 & -1 \\ -1 & 1 \end{bmatrix} \tag{6.6}$$

Obviously, this matrix is a 2×2 square matrix, is symmetric about the principal diagonal, and has positive diagonal terms, thus possessing the three properties discussed earlier. The reader is encouraged to show that this result is applicable to any 2-node bar element, no matter where it is located.

Example 6.2

Find the elementary $[K_e]$ matrix for the 3-node bar element with three nodes at $x = 0, x = l/2$, and $x = l$, respectively, with a constant k value.

Answer

For the 3-node bar element, from the shape functions given in Equation 5.9, we express the 1×3 elementary shape function matrix as

$$[N] = \begin{bmatrix} N_1 & N_2 & N_3 \end{bmatrix}$$

with its three individual shape functions being

$$N_1 = \frac{l^2 - 3lx + 2x^2}{l^2}, \quad N_2 = \frac{4lx - 4x^2}{l^2}, \quad \text{and } N_3 = \frac{-lx + 2x^2}{l^2}$$

By taking the first derivative of the $[N]$ matrix, we have

$$\left[\frac{dN}{dx}\right] = \begin{bmatrix} \frac{dN_1}{dx} & \frac{dN_2}{dx} & \frac{dN_3}{dx} \end{bmatrix} = \frac{1}{l^2}\begin{bmatrix} -3l + 4x & 4l - 8x & -l + 4x \end{bmatrix}$$

Then, substituting it into Equation 6.5, multiplying out the two matrices, and taking the integral, we obtain the elementary $[K_e]$ matrix for the 3-node bar element:

$$
\begin{aligned}
[K_e] &= \frac{kA}{l^4}\int_0^l \begin{bmatrix} -3l+4x \\ 4l-8x \\ -l+4x \end{bmatrix} \begin{bmatrix} -3l+4x & 4l-8x & -l+4x \end{bmatrix} dx \\
&= \frac{kA}{l^4}\int_0^l \begin{bmatrix} 9l^2-24lx+16x^2 & -12l^2+40lx-32x^2 & 3l^2-16lx+16x^2 \\ -12l^2+40lx-32x^2 & 16l^2-64lx+64x^2 & -4l^2+24lx-32x^2 \\ 3l^2-16lx+16x^2 & -4l^2+24lx-32x^2 & l^2-8lx+16x^2 \end{bmatrix} dx \\
&= \frac{kA}{l^4}\begin{bmatrix} 9l^2x-12lx^2+\frac{16x^3}{3} & -12l^2x+20lx^2-\frac{32x^3}{3} & 3l^2x-8lx^2+\frac{16x^3}{3} \\ -12l^2x+20lx^2-\frac{32x^3}{3} & 16l^2x-32lx^2+\frac{64x^3}{3} & -4l^2x+12lx^2-\frac{32x^3}{3} \\ 3l^2x-8lx^2+\frac{16x^3}{3} & -4l^2x+12lx^2-\frac{32x^3}{3} & l^2x-4lx^2+\frac{16x^3}{3} \end{bmatrix}_0^l \\
&= \frac{kA}{3l}\begin{bmatrix} 27-36+16 & -36+60-32 & 9-24+16 \\ -36+60-32 & 48-96+64 & -12+36-32 \\ 9-24+16 & -12+36-32 & 3-12+16 \end{bmatrix} \\
&= \frac{kA}{3l}\begin{bmatrix} 7 & -8 & 1 \\ -8 & 16 & -8 \\ 1 & -8 & 7 \end{bmatrix}
\end{aligned}
$$

Again, the result is a 3×3 square matrix, and it is symmetric about the principal diagonal with positive diagonal terms. The reader is encouraged to show that this result is applicable to any 3-node bar element with even spacing between nodes, no matter where it is located.

6.2.2 Volumetric and point loads or constraints

Knowing the meaning of the term on the left-hand side of Equation 6.4, let us now move to the right-hand side. The first term on the right resolves the volumetric quantity (if any), for example, a volume force, a volume heat source, or a volume reaction source, into equivalent nodal quantities, and the second term distributes a point constraint, for example, a point load, a heat flux, or a mass flux, to the nodes of the element. Let us go through some examples to see how these expressions are used to resolve the nodal equivalences.

Example 6.3

For the 2-node and 3-node 1D bar elements shown in Figure 6.1, find the nodal equivalent loads of a volumetrically distributed load g and a point load P (note that g and P can be mechanical loads, heat fluxes and sources, or mass fluxes and sources).

Answer

We first examine the volumetrically distributed load. For the nodal equivalences of a volumetrically distributed load g, we use the first integral expression on the right-hand side of Equation 6.4, namely,

$$\int_0^l [N]^T gA dx$$

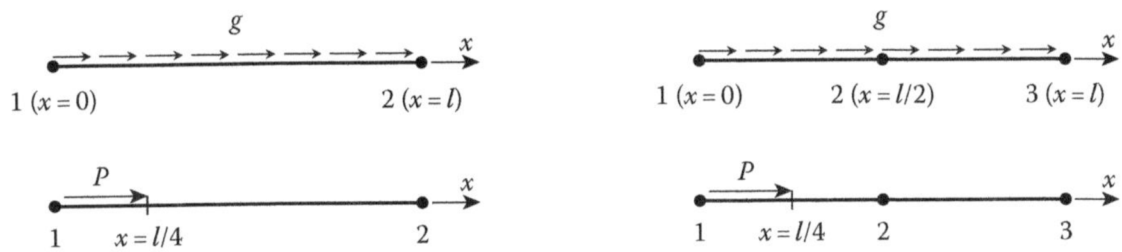

FIGURE 6.1
Two-node and 3-node 1D elements.

For the 2-node element, by plugging in its shape function matrix, we have

$$\int_0^l \begin{Bmatrix} \dfrac{l-x}{l} \\ \dfrac{x}{l} \end{Bmatrix} gA dx = \frac{gAl}{2} \begin{Bmatrix} 1 \\ 1 \end{Bmatrix}$$

The result is a 2×1 vector containing the two nodal equivalent loads of a volumetrically distributed load in a 2-node bar element. Clearly, because the two shape functions are linear equations, each node takes one-half of the total volume load exerting on the element (i.e., g times the volume).

For the 3-node bar element, using its shape function matrix we have

$$\int_0^l \begin{Bmatrix} \dfrac{l^2 - 3lx + 2x^2}{l^2} \\ \dfrac{4lx - 4x^2}{l^2} \\ \dfrac{-lx + 2x^2}{l^2} \end{Bmatrix} gA dx = \frac{gAl}{6} \begin{Bmatrix} 1 \\ 4 \\ 1 \end{Bmatrix}$$

For this 3-node bar element, we have a 3×1 vector containing the three nodal equivalent loads of a volumetrically distributed load. Unlike in the 2-node case, the nodal equivalence of a volumetrically distributed load in a 3-node bar element is not evenly divided among the nodes. The two end nodes get one-sixth of the total volume load and the midnode two-thirds of the total volume load.

Next, we examine the nodal distribution of a point load or constraint. As mentioned earlier, the term $Akd\tilde{u}(x)/dx$ represents a point load in mechanical problems, a heat flux in thermal problems, a mass flux in transport problems, and so on. If we express it in a unified term P, that is, $P = Akd\tilde{u}(x)/dx$, then the second term on the right-hand side of Equation 6.4 can be written as

$$\left[[N]^T Ak \frac{d\tilde{u}}{dx}(x) \right]_0^l = \left[[N]^T P \right]_0^l$$

For the 2-node element, by plugging in its shape function matrix along with a constant P at $x = \frac{l}{4}$, we have

$$\left[[N]^T P\right]_0^l = \left\{ \begin{array}{c} \frac{l-x}{l} \\ \frac{x}{l} \end{array} \right\}_{x=\frac{l}{4}} \times P = \left\{ \begin{array}{c} 3 \\ 1 \end{array} \right\} \frac{P}{4}$$

Similarly, for the 3-node element, by substituting its shape function matrix along with a constant P at $x = \frac{l}{4}$, we obtain

$$\left[[N]^T P\right]_0^l = \left\{ \begin{array}{c} \frac{l^2 - 3lx + 2x^2}{l^2} \\ \frac{4lx - 4x^2}{l^2} \\ \frac{-lx + 2x^2}{l^2} \end{array} \right\}_{x=\frac{l}{4}} \times P = \left\{ \begin{array}{c} 3 \\ 6 \\ -1 \end{array} \right\} \frac{P}{8}$$

The results show that the point load P is distributed to the corresponding nodes according to a formula determined by the shape functions evaluated at the location of the point constraints. The resulting nodal load is a 2×1 vector for the 2-node element and a 3×1 vector for the 3-node element. Based on the characteristics of shape functions, it is clear that when a point load is on a node, this particular node will bear all the load and the other nodes get none.

6.3 Single-Element Structure

To put the above discussions together, let us take a look at a slender mechanical structure with Young's modulus E, uniform cross section area A, and length l, as shown in Figure 6.2. Assume that the structure is subjected to a volumetrically distributed force f over the entire structure and a point load P at the right end and is fixed at its left end.

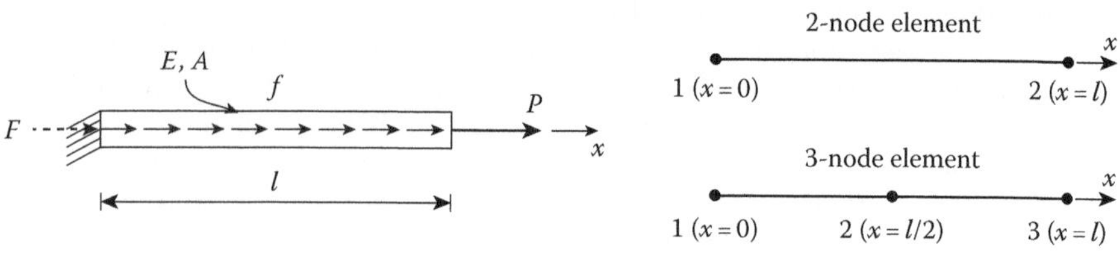

FIGURE 6.2
Bar structure and 1D bar elements.

Since this slender structure is under axial loads and deformations, by ignoring the Poisson ratio effect, we can treat it as a bar structure that is governed by the differential Equations 6.1 and 6.4. Thus, we can use 1D bar elements for its domain discretization.

First, we consider a 2-node bar element with $\{d_0\} = [u_1\ u_2]^T$. The $[K_e]$ matrix and the nodal equivalences of the distributed load can be found by referring to Examples 6.1 and 6.3. For the point loads, in a free-body mode, the left constraint is replaced by an unknown reaction force F acting on node 1; thus, we have two point loads. The one at node 1 will be assigned totally to node 1, and the one at node 2 to node 2. Therefore, putting them all into Equation 6.4 along with $k = E$, we arrive at

$$\frac{EA}{l}\begin{bmatrix} 1 & -1 \\ -1 & 1 \end{bmatrix}\begin{Bmatrix} u_1 \\ u_2 \end{Bmatrix} = \frac{fAl}{2}\begin{Bmatrix} 1 \\ 1 \end{Bmatrix} + \begin{Bmatrix} F \\ P \end{Bmatrix}$$

Next, we consider a 3-node bar element with $\{d_0\} = [u_1\ u_2\ u_3]^T$. By Equation 6.4 along with $k = E$ and the results from Examples 6.2 and 6.3, we obtain

$$\frac{EA}{3l}\begin{bmatrix} 7 & -8 & 1 \\ -8 & 16 & -8 \\ 1 & -8 & 7 \end{bmatrix}\begin{Bmatrix} u_1 \\ u_2 \\ u_3 \end{Bmatrix} = \frac{fAl}{6}\begin{Bmatrix} 1 \\ 4 \\ 1 \end{Bmatrix} + \begin{Bmatrix} F \\ 0 \\ P \end{Bmatrix}$$

It is now clear that Equation 6.4 is actually a matrix form algebraic equation. In a general form, we can express these matrix algebraic equations as

$$[K_e]\{d_0\} = \{P_e\} \tag{6.7}$$

where $\{P_e\}$ is the nodal load vector. This fact indicates that a FEM formulation procedure has not only reduced a PDE or ordinary differential equation (ODE) from its strong form (e.g., Equation 6.1) to a weak form, but also linearized the weak-form PDE or ODE into an algebraic matrix equation in the form of Equation 6.7.

6.4 From Elementary to Global through Assembly

In calculating the weighted integral of residual to find the approximate solution to differential equation 6.1, we assumed that the physical domain consists of only one element; thus, the integration over the entire domain is reduced to one element (see Equation 6.2). However, when the physical domain consists of m elements, this expression needs to be rewritten as

$$\iiint_V w(x)\left[\frac{d}{dx}\left[k_i\frac{d\tilde{u}(x)}{dx}\right]+g\right]dV = \sum_{i=1}^{m}\int_0^{l_i} w(x)\left[\frac{d}{dx}\left[k_i\frac{d\tilde{u}(x)}{dx}\right]+g\right]A_i dx$$
$$= 0$$

This in turn leads to a modified version of Equation 6.4 as

$$\sum_{i=1}^{m}\int_0^{l_i}\left[\frac{dN}{dx}\right]^T k_i\left[\frac{dN}{dx}\right]A_i dx\{d_0^{(i)}\} = \sum_{i=1}^{m}\int_0^{l_i}[N]^T gA_i dx + \sum_{i=1}^{m}\left[[N]^T A_i k_i\frac{d\tilde{u}}{dx}(x)\right]_0^{l_i} \tag{6.8}$$

where l_i is the length, A_i the cross section area, k_i the physics-related property, and $\{d_0^{(i)}\}$ is the DOF vector of the ith element ($i = 1, \ldots, m$).

Referring to Equation 6.7, we can further express it in a matrix form:

$$\sum_{i=1}^{m}[K_e^{(i)}]\{d_0^{(i)}\} = \sum_{i=1}^{m}\{P_e^{(i)}\} \tag{6.9}$$

This equation states that for a domain that is discretized into m elements, its governing matrix algebraic equation can be obtained by summing all individual elementary matrix equations together. As we learned in previous sections, the term on the right-hand side of Equation 6.9 is a vector containing the equivalent nodal loads resulting from volumetrically distributed quantities or point quantities. When the discretized structure has n nodes with 1 DOF for each node, the load vector should be a $n \times 1$ vector, with its rows filled with the corresponding nodal equivalent loads, or zeros if the nodes are not associated with any loads. Thus, we can express it in a global load vector as

$$\{P\} = \sum_{i=1}^{m}\{P_e^{(i)}\} = \{p_1\ p_2\ \ldots\ p_{n-1}\ p_n\}^T$$

On the other hand, the structural DOF vector consists of all the nodal DOF (note that elementary DOF vectors are subsets of the structural DOF vector), making it also a $n \times 1$ vector. Since the structural DOF vector is common to all elements, we thus express it as a global DOF vector:

$$\{D\} = \{u_1\ u_2\ \ldots\ u_{n-1}\ u_n\}^T$$

With these two global vectors, we rewrite Equation 6.9 as

$$\left(\sum_{i=1}^{m}[K_e^{(i)}]\right)\{D\} = \{P\} \tag{6.10}$$

6.4.1 Global $[K]$ matrix

Recall that $[K_e]$ is a square matrix with n_e rows and n_e columns, where n_e is the elementary DOF and $n_e < n$. Since $\{D\}$ is a $n \times 1$ vector, to make Equation 6.10 work, we need to expand each of the $[K_e]$ matrices from $n_e \times n_e$ to $n \times n$ by filling the expanded terms with zeros.

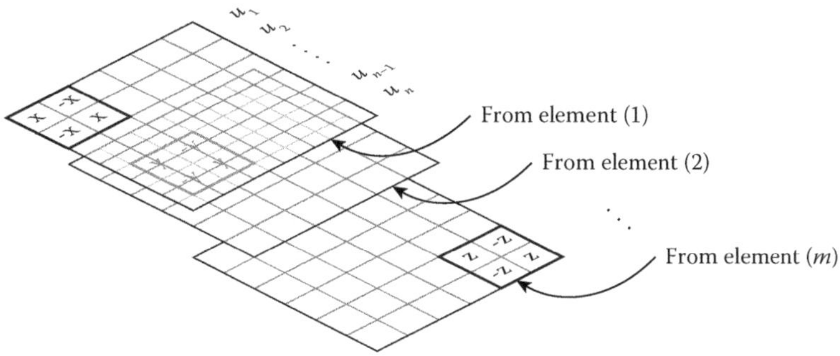

FIGURE 6.3
Assembly of elementary matrices into global matrix.

Figure 6.3 shows such an expansion scheme. Each expanded elementary matrix is now a $n \times n$ square matrix, in which the original terms are placed in proper rows and columns corresponding to the positions of the respective elementary DOF in the global DOF vector. The blank spaces in these expanded matrices will be filled with zeros. The summation of all these m expanded elementary $[K_e]$ matrices is often referred to as the assembly of the global $[K]$ matrix, namely,

$$[K] = \sum_{i=1}^{m} [K_e^{(i)}]$$

The global $[K]$ matrix possesses the same properties of as elementary $[K_e]$ matrix; namely, it is a square matrix, is symmetric about the principal diagonal, and has positive diagonal terms. Moreover, like the elementary $[K_e]$ matrix, the global $[K]$ matrix also represents different physical parameters in different problems, including the stiffness matrix and the conductance matrix. With the global $[K]$ matrix and DOF and load vectors, Equation 6.10 can be expressed in a general algebraic matrix equation:

$$[K]\{D\} = \{P\} \tag{6.11}$$

6.5 Bar Elements for 1D Problems

In this section, we use two examples, a mechanical (or vector) problem and a heat (or scalar) problem, to get better understanding of how global matrix equations are developed and solved by imposing proper boundary conditions.

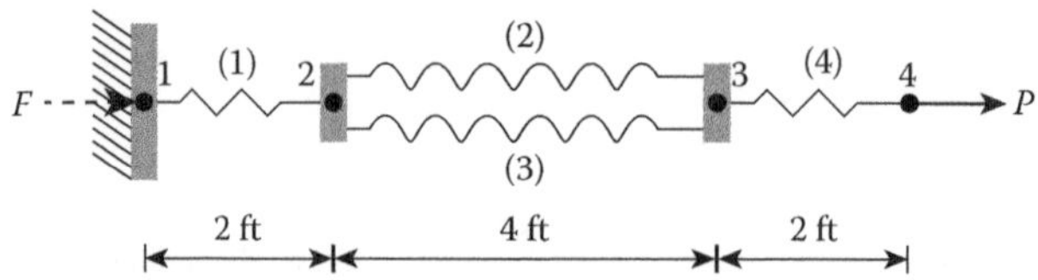

FIGURE 6.4
Spring loading structure.

Example 6.4

The spring loading structure shown in Figure 6.4 is made of four members. The structure has a fixed constraint on the left and a point load $P = 500$ lb on the right. The two side members have a length of $l_1 = l_4 = 2$ ft and a cross section area of $A_1 = A_4 = 1$ in.^{2}, and the two middle members have a length of $l_2 = l_3 = 4$ ft and a cross section area of $A_2 = A_3 = 0.75$ in.^{2}. All members are made of steel with Young's modulus $E = 30 \times 10^6$ lb/in.^{2}. Use the matrix equation to find the displacements at four joints 1 through 4.

Answer
Since these members mainly sustain axial forces and deformations, they are governed by the PDE given in Equation 6.1. Thus, the structure can be discretized by bar elements. As illustrated in the figure, the spring structure is discretized into four 2-node elements, (1) through (4), connected by nodes 1 through 4. For the four 2-node bar elements, each has elementary DOF = 2; thus, by using Equation 6.6 with $k = E$, we obtain the following 2×2 elementary stiffness matrices:

$$[K_e^{(1)}] = [K_e^{(4)}] = 1250000 \begin{bmatrix} 1 & -1 \\ -1 & 1 \end{bmatrix} \text{ (lb/in.)}$$

$$[K_e^{(2)}] = [K_e^{(3)}] = 468750 \begin{bmatrix} 1 & -1 \\ -1 & 1 \end{bmatrix} \text{ (lb/in.)}$$

For this structure, its global nodal DOF vector can be expressed as $\{D\} = [u_1\ u_2\ u_3\ u_4]^T$. In reference to this vector, we expand each elementary stiffness matrix from 2×2 to 4×4 with the original terms highlighted:

$$[K_e^{(1)}] = \begin{bmatrix} 1250000 & -1250000 & 0 & 0 \\ -1250000 & 1250000 & 0 & 0 \\ 0 & 0 & 0 & 0 \\ 0 & 0 & 0 & 0 \end{bmatrix},$$

$$[K_e^{(2)}] = \begin{bmatrix} 0 & 0 & 0 & 0 \\ 0 & 468750 & -468750 & 0 \\ 0 & -468750 & 468750 & 0 \\ 0 & 0 & 0 & 0 \end{bmatrix}$$

$$[K_e^{(3)}] = \begin{bmatrix} 0 & 0 & 0 & 0 \\ 0 & 468750 & -468750 & 0 \\ 0 & -468750 & 468750 & 0 \\ 0 & 0 & 0 & 0 \end{bmatrix},$$

$$[K_e^{(4)}] = \begin{bmatrix} 0 & 0 & 0 & 0 \\ 0 & 0 & 0 & 0 \\ 0 & 0 & 1250000 & -1250000 \\ 0 & 0 & -1250000 & 1250000 \end{bmatrix}$$

By summing these expanded matrices, we obtain the global $[K]$ matrix:

$$[K] = \begin{bmatrix} 1250000 & -1250000 & 0 & 0 \\ -1250000 & 2187500 & -937500 & 0 \\ 0 & -937500 & 2187500 & -1250000 \\ 0 & 0 & -1250000 & 1250000 \end{bmatrix} \text{(lb/in.)}$$

The structure is not subjected to any volumetric loads, but it has a point load applied at node 4. Moreover, in a free-body mode, the left constraint is replaced by an unknown reaction force F acting on node 1. Therefore, we determine the global load vector as

$$\{P\} = \begin{Bmatrix} F \\ 0 \\ 0 \\ 500 \end{Bmatrix} \text{(lb)}$$

Thus, by $[K]\{D\} = \{P\}$ (Equation 6.11) we have

$$\begin{bmatrix} 1250000 & -1250000 & 0 & 0 \\ -1250000 & 2187500 & -937500 & 0 \\ 0 & -937500 & 2187500 & -1250000 \\ 0 & 0 & -1250000 & 1250000 \end{bmatrix} \begin{Bmatrix} u_1 \\ u_2 \\ u_3 \\ u_4 \end{Bmatrix} = \begin{Bmatrix} F \\ 0 \\ 0 \\ 500 \end{Bmatrix} \text{(lb)} \qquad (6.12)$$

Because this equation is developed based on the equilibrium of a free body, it is not constrained. To solve this equation, we need to impose some boundary conditions to constrain it. For the problem given, since the left end is fixed, we have $u_1 = 0$. This suggests that we have one less unknown to solve in the matrix equation. Thus, by partitioning the matrix equation, we can reduce it to simpler equations. For example, the following matrix equation,

$$\left[\begin{array}{c|c} A & B \\ \hline G & H \end{array}\right] \begin{Bmatrix} U_1 \\ U_2 \end{Bmatrix} = \begin{Bmatrix} F_1 \\ F_2 \end{Bmatrix}$$

can be partitioned into two submatrix equations as

$$[A]\{U_1\} + [B]\{U_2\} = \{F_1\} \quad \text{and} \quad [G]\{U_1\} + [H]\{U_2\} = \{F_2\}$$

When $\{U_1\}$ is known, the second equation can be used to find $\{U_2\}$. Subsequently, the first equation, along with $\{U_2\}$, can be used to find $[F_1]$

in the following manner:

$$\begin{aligned}[H]\{U_2\} &= \{F_2\} - [G]\{U_1\} \\ \{F_1\} &= [A]\{U_1\} + [B]\{U_2\}\end{aligned} \tag{6.13}$$

In particular, when $U_1 = 0$, the first equation in Equation 6.13 becomes

$$[H]\{U_2\} = \{F_2\}$$

if the row and column of the matrix equation associated with U_1 before partitioning are striked out.

Using this matrix partition concept, we partition Equation 6.12 as follows with the corresponding $[H], \{U_2\}$, and $\{F_2\}$ highlighted:

$$\begin{bmatrix} 1250000 & -1250000 & 0 & 0 \\ -1250000 & 2187500 & -937500 & 0 \\ 0 & -937500 & 2187500 & -1250000 \\ 0 & 0 & -1250000 & 1250000 \end{bmatrix} \begin{Bmatrix} 0 \\ u_2 \\ u_3 \\ u_4 \end{Bmatrix} = \begin{Bmatrix} F \\ 0 \\ 0 \\ 500 \end{Bmatrix} \text{ (lb)}$$

Since $u_1 = 0$ (or $U_1 = 0$ in Equation 6.13), the above equation is simplified further by striking out the row and column corresponding to the constraint $u_1 = 0$, that is, the first row and first column of the matrix equation, to a constrained matrix equation in the form of $[H]\{U_2\} = \{F_2\}$:

$$\begin{bmatrix} 2187500 & -937500 & 0 \\ -937500 & 2187500 & -1250000 \\ 0 & -1250000 & 1250000 \end{bmatrix} \begin{Bmatrix} u_2 \\ u_3 \\ u_4 \end{Bmatrix} = \begin{Bmatrix} 0 \\ 0 \\ 500 \end{Bmatrix} \text{ (lb)}$$

By solving it, we find

$$\begin{Bmatrix} u_2 \\ u_3 \\ u_4 \end{Bmatrix} = \begin{bmatrix} 2187500 & -937500 & 0 \\ -937500 & 2187500 & -1250000 \\ 0 & -1250000 & 1250000 \end{bmatrix}^{-1} \begin{Bmatrix} 0 \\ 0 \\ 500 \end{Bmatrix} = 10^{-3} \begin{Bmatrix} 0.40 \\ 0.93 \\ 1.33 \end{Bmatrix} \text{ (in.)}$$

Together with $u_1 = 0$, we obtain the global DOF vector:

$$\{D\} = \begin{Bmatrix} u_1 \\ u_2 \\ u_3 \\ u_4 \end{Bmatrix} = 10^{-3} \begin{Bmatrix} 0 \\ 0.40 \\ 0.93 \\ 1.33 \end{Bmatrix} \text{ (in.)}$$

The unknown reaction force can be determined by using the second expression in Equation 6.13:

$$\begin{aligned}\{F\} &= [A]\{U_1\} + [B]\{U_2\} = 1250000 \times u_1 - 1250000 \times u_2 + 0 \times u_3 + 0 \times u_4 \\ &= -1250000 \times 0.4 \times 10^{-3} = -500 \text{ (lb)}\end{aligned}$$

In a nutshell, the above procedure can be summarized as

1. Structural discretization using proper elements
2. Calculation of all the elementary $[K_e]$ matrices
3. Assembly of the global $[K]$ matrix, DOF vector, and load vector and establishment of a global matrix equation
4. Partitioning of the matrix equation according to boundary conditions
5. Solution finding for the unknown DOF and other associated physical parameters

Example 6.5

For the heat conduction rod shown in Figure 6.5, determine the temperature distribution along the bar. The rod has a uniform diameter (d) of 10 cm and length (l) of 80 cm with a thermal conductivity (κ) of 380 W/[m·K]. The left end of the bar is subjected to a heat source (Q_s) of 2500 W/m^2, the right end held at a constant temperature (T_0) at 100°C, and the side insulated.

Answer

Based on the problem description, heat conduction in this slender rod structure will be mainly along the longitudinal direction. Moreover, because this problem is governed by the PDE given in Equation 6.1, the structure can be discretized by using bar elements. For this problem, we will use two 2-node bar elements for domain discretization, as illustrated in the figure. For the two 2-node bar elements, each with elementary DOF = 2, we use Equation 6.6 with $k = \kappa = 380$ W/[m·K], $l_1 = l_2 = 0.4$ m, and $A = \pi d^2/4, d = 0.1$ m to obtain the following 2×2 elementary stiffness matrices:

$$[K_e^{(1)}] = [K_e^{(2)}] = 7.46 \begin{bmatrix} 1 & -1 \\ -1 & 1 \end{bmatrix} \quad \text{(W/K)}$$

Since the whole rod structure has three nodes, its global nodal DOF vector can be expressed as $\{D\} = \{T_1\ T_2\ T_3\}^T$. Using this global DOF

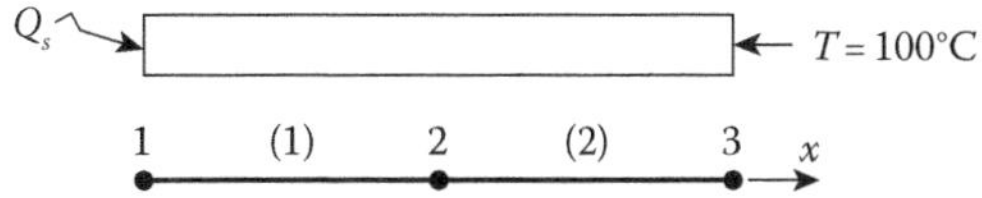

FIGURE 6.5
Heat conduction in a rod.

vector as a reference, we expand each elementary stiffness matrix from 2×2 to 3×3:

$$[K_e^{(1)}] = \begin{bmatrix} 7.46 & -7.46 & 0 \\ -7.46 & 7.46 & 0 \\ 0 & 0 & 0 \end{bmatrix}, \quad [K_e^{(2)}] = \begin{bmatrix} 0 & 0 & 0 \\ 0 & 7.46 & -7.46 \\ 0 & -7.46 & 7.46 \end{bmatrix}$$

By summing these expanded matrices, we obtain the global $[K]$ matrix:

$$[K] = \begin{bmatrix} 7.46 & -7.46 & 0 \\ -7.46 & 14.92 & -7.46 \\ 0 & -7.46 & 7.46 \end{bmatrix} \text{ (W/K)}$$

The structure is not subject to any volumetric heat source, but it has a heat flux applied at node 1, along with an unknown heat flux q_3 at node 3. Thus, we write the global load vector as

$$\{P\} = \begin{Bmatrix} 2500 \\ 0 \\ q_3 \end{Bmatrix} \frac{\pi d^2}{4} = \begin{Bmatrix} 19.63 \\ 0 \\ q_3 \times 7.85 \times 10^{-3} \end{Bmatrix} \text{ (W)}$$

Thus, by $[K]\{D\} = \{P\}$ (Equation 6.11) we have

$$\left[\begin{array}{cc|c} 7.46 & -7.46 & 0 \\ -7.46 & 14.92 & -7.46 \\ \hline 0 & -7.46 & 7.46 \end{array}\right] \begin{Bmatrix} T_1 \\ T_2 \\ T_3 \end{Bmatrix} = \begin{Bmatrix} 19.63 \\ 0 \\ \hline q_3 \times 7.85 \times 10^{-3} \end{Bmatrix} \text{ (W)}$$

For the problem given, since the right end is at a constant temperature, we have $T_3 = 100°\text{C} = 373$ K. So by using the partition method, we write

$$\begin{bmatrix} 7.46 & -7.46 \\ -7.46 & 14.92 \end{bmatrix} \begin{Bmatrix} T_1 \\ T_2 \end{Bmatrix} + \begin{Bmatrix} 0 \\ -7.46 \end{Bmatrix} T_3 = \begin{Bmatrix} 19.63 \\ 0 \end{Bmatrix} \text{ (W)}$$

By substituting the known boundary condition, that is, $T_3 = 373$ K, we obtain the following constrained matrix equation:

$$\begin{bmatrix} 7.46 & -7.46 \\ -7.46 & 14.92 \end{bmatrix} \begin{Bmatrix} T_1 \\ T_2 \end{Bmatrix} = \begin{Bmatrix} 19.63 \\ 2783.1 \end{Bmatrix} \text{ (W)}$$

Solving it, we have

$$\begin{Bmatrix} T_1 \\ T_2 \end{Bmatrix} = \begin{Bmatrix} 378.26 \\ 375.63 \end{Bmatrix} \text{ (K)}$$

Together with the known boundary condition, we have

$$\begin{Bmatrix} T_1 \\ T_2 \\ T_3 \end{Bmatrix} = \begin{Bmatrix} 378.26 \\ 375.63 \\ 373.00 \end{Bmatrix} \text{ (K)}$$

By using Equation 5.32, we obtain the following temperature distribution along the conduction rod:

$$\tilde{T} = \sum_{m=1}^{2} N_m T_m = \left(1 - \frac{x}{0.4}\right) T_1 + \frac{x}{0.4} T_2 = 378.26 - 6.58x \text{ (K)}$$

or

$$\tilde{T} = \sum_{m=1}^{2} N_m T_m = \left(1 - \frac{x - 0.4}{0.4}\right) T_2 + \frac{x - 0.4}{0.4} T_3 = 378.26 - 6.58x \text{ (K)}$$

Clearly, a procedure similar to the one used in Example 6.4 is used here for solving this problem.

6.6 Bar Elements for 2D and 3D Truss Structures

6.6.1 2D truss structures

As we learned earlier, slender mechanical structures supporting axial loading and sustaining axial deformations can be discretized as bar elements. Although a bar element can only support axial loading, the orientation of the bar structure does not need to be parallel to an axis.

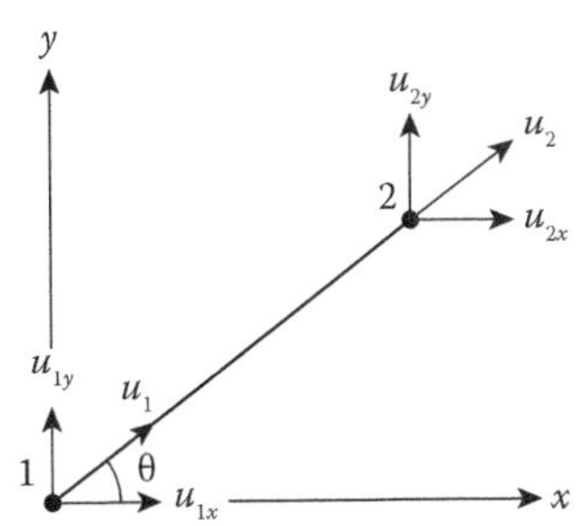

FIGURE 6.6
Bar in 2D space.

Let us consider a bar structure in two-dimensional (2D) Cartesian coordinates, x and y. As shown in Figure 6.6, a 2-node bar element is oriented in an arbitrary angle (θ) with respect to the x axis. The element has an elementary DOF vector of $\{u_1 \quad u_2\}^T$, defining the admissible DOF of the two nodes in the axial (or more precisely, the longitudinal) direction of the bar structure.

In this 2D space, these nodal DOF, u_1 and u_2, can be expressed in terms of their Cartesian components, namely, u_{1x}, u_{1y}, u_{2x}, and u_{2y}, respectively. Referring to the figure along with trigonometry relationships, we express

$$\begin{aligned} u_1 &= u_{1x} \cos\theta + u_{1y} \sin\theta \\ u_2 &= u_{2x} \cos\theta + u_{2y} \sin\theta \end{aligned}$$

In a matrix form, these two equations can be written as

$$\begin{Bmatrix} u_1 \\ u_2 \end{Bmatrix} = \begin{bmatrix} \cos\theta & \sin\theta & 0 & 0 \\ 0 & 0 & \cos\theta & \sin\theta \end{bmatrix} \begin{Bmatrix} u_{1x} \\ u_{1y} \\ u_{2x} \\ u_{2y} \end{Bmatrix} \tag{6.14}$$

This means that in a vector field problem, when a bar element is oriented in 2D space, its nodal DOF becomes 2, making the elementary DOF = 4 for a 2-node bar element. From Equation 6.7, we have

$$[K_e]\begin{Bmatrix} u_1 \\ u_2 \end{Bmatrix} = \begin{Bmatrix} P_1 \\ P_2 \end{Bmatrix}$$

or

$$[K_e]\begin{bmatrix} \cos\theta & \sin\theta & 0 & 0 \\ 0 & 0 & \cos\theta & \sin\theta \end{bmatrix}\begin{Bmatrix} u_{1x} \\ u_{1y} \\ u_{2x} \\ u_{2y} \end{Bmatrix} = \begin{Bmatrix} P_1 \\ P_2 \end{Bmatrix} \quad (6.15)$$

Let

$$[R2] = \begin{bmatrix} \cos\theta & \sin\theta & 0 & 0 \\ 0 & 0 & \cos\theta & \sin\theta \end{bmatrix}$$

Multiplying both sides of Equation 6.15 by $[R2]^T$, we obtain

$$[R2]^T[K_e][R2]\begin{Bmatrix} u_{1x} \\ u_{1y} \\ u_{2x} \\ u_{2y} \end{Bmatrix} = [R2]^T\begin{Bmatrix} P_1 \\ P_2 \end{Bmatrix} = \begin{Bmatrix} P_{1x} \\ P_{1y} \\ P_{2x} \\ P_{2y} \end{Bmatrix}$$

This equation is actually the 2D equivalent of Equation 6.7, that is, the 2D expanded matrix equation for bar elements,

$$[K_{e2}]\{d_0\} = \{P_{e2}\}$$

where

$$[K_{e2}] = [R2]^T[K_e][R2]$$
$$\{P_{e2}\} = [R2]^T\{P_e\}$$

For a 1D 2-node bar element, by Equation 6.6, we have

$$[K_{e2}] = \frac{kA}{l}\begin{bmatrix} \cos\theta & 0 \\ \sin\theta & 0 \\ 0 & \cos\theta \\ 0 & \sin\theta \end{bmatrix}\begin{bmatrix} 1 & -1 \\ -1 & 1 \end{bmatrix}\begin{bmatrix} \cos\theta & \sin\theta & 0 & 0 \\ 0 & 0 & \cos\theta & \sin\theta \end{bmatrix}$$

which yields

$$[K_{e2}] = \frac{kA}{l}\begin{bmatrix} \cos^2\theta & \cos\theta\sin\theta & -\cos^2\theta & -\cos\theta\sin\theta \\ \cos\theta\sin\theta & \sin^2\theta & -\cos\theta\sin\theta & -\sin^2\theta \\ -\cos^2\theta & -\cos\theta\sin\theta & \cos^2\theta & \cos\theta\sin\theta \\ -\cos\theta\sin\theta & -\sin^2\theta & \cos\theta\sin\theta & \sin^2\theta \end{bmatrix} \quad (6.16)$$

So for an arbitrary oriented bar element in 2D space, Equation 6.16 is used to determine the elementary $[K_{e2}]$ matrix with known values of k, A, l, and θ.

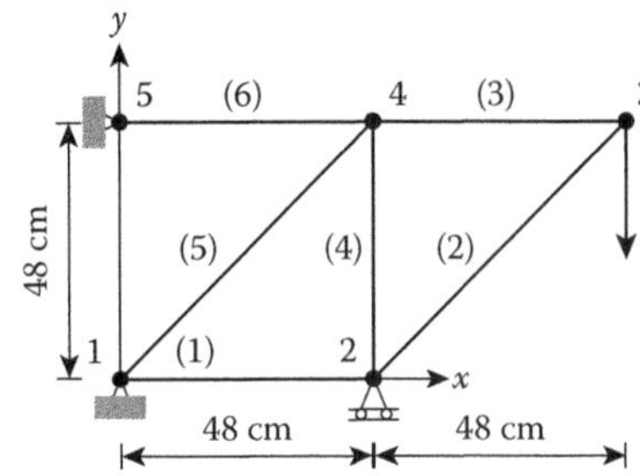

FIGURE 6.7
A 2D truss structure.

Example 6.6

For the 2D truss structure shown in Figure 6.7 consisting of six members and subjected to a vertical downward load $P = 700$ N at the upper right corner, determine the displacements at the joints and the stress and force in each member. All the members are made of steel material with Young's modulus 210 MPa with a cross section area of 80 cm^2. The lengths of the members are shown in the figure.

Answer
Since these members mainly sustain axial forces and deformations, they are governed by the PDE given in Equation 6.1. Thus, the structure is discretized by six 2-node bar elements (1) through (6), connected by nodes 1 through 5, as shown in the figure. For these linear bar elements in 2D, each has elementary DOF = 4. Knowing $k = E = 210 \times 10^6$ N/m^2, $A = 0.008$ m^2, $l_1 = l_3 = l_4 = l_6 = 0.48$ m, $l_2 = l_5 = 0.48\sqrt{2}$ m, $\theta_{(1)} = \theta_{(3)} = \theta_{(6)} = 0, \theta_{(2)} = \theta_{(5)} = 45°$, and $\theta_{(4)} = 90°$, by using Equation 6.16, we obtain the following elementary $[K_{e2}]$ matrices:

$$[K_e^{(1)}] = [K_{e2}^{(3)}] = [K_{e2}^{(6)}] = 3.5 \times 10^6 \begin{bmatrix} 1 & 0 & -1 & 0 \\ 0 & 0 & 0 & 0 \\ -1 & 0 & 1 & 0 \\ 0 & 0 & 0 & 0 \end{bmatrix} \text{ (N/m)}$$

$$[K_e^{(2)}] = [K_{e2}^{(5)}] = 1.2 \times 10^6 \begin{bmatrix} 1 & 1 & -1 & -1 \\ 1 & 1 & -1 & -1 \\ -1 & -1 & 1 & 1 \\ -1 & -1 & 1 & 1 \end{bmatrix},$$

$$[K_{e2}^{(4)}] = 3.5 \times 10^6 \begin{bmatrix} 0 & 0 & 0 & 0 \\ 0 & 1 & 0 & -1 \\ 0 & 0 & 0 & 0 \\ 0 & -1 & 0 & 1 \end{bmatrix}$$

Since the entire structure has five nodes, its global nodal DOF vector can be expressed as $\{D\} = \{u_{1x}\ u_{1y}\ u_{2x}\ u_{2y}\ u_{3x}\ u_{3y}\ u_{4x}\ u_{4y}\ u_{5x}\ u_{5y}\}^T$.

Using this as a reference, we expand each elementary stiffness matrix from 4×4 to 10×10 (note that the original terms are highlighted in each expanded matrix):

$$[K_{e2}^{(1)}] = 3.5 \times 10^6 \begin{bmatrix} 1 & 0 & -1 & 0 & 0 & 0 & 0 & 0 & 0 & 0 \\ 0 & 0 & 0 & 0 & 0 & 0 & 0 & 0 & 0 & 0 \\ -1 & 0 & 1 & 0 & 0 & 0 & 0 & 0 & 0 & 0 \\ 0 & 0 & 0 & 0 & 0 & 0 & 0 & 0 & 0 & 0 \\ 0 & 0 & 0 & 0 & 0 & 0 & 0 & 0 & 0 & 0 \\ 0 & 0 & 0 & 0 & 0 & 0 & 0 & 0 & 0 & 0 \\ 0 & 0 & 0 & 0 & 0 & 0 & 0 & 0 & 0 & 0 \\ 0 & 0 & 0 & 0 & 0 & 0 & 0 & 0 & 0 & 0 \\ 0 & 0 & 0 & 0 & 0 & 0 & 0 & 0 & 0 & 0 \\ 0 & 0 & 0 & 0 & 0 & 0 & 0 & 0 & 0 & 0 \end{bmatrix} \text{(N/m)}$$

$$[K_{e2}^{(2)}] = 1.2 \times 10^6 \begin{bmatrix} 0 & 0 & 0 & 0 & 0 & 0 & 0 & 0 & 0 & 0 \\ 0 & 0 & 0 & 0 & 0 & 0 & 0 & 0 & 0 & 0 \\ 0 & 0 & 1 & 1 & -1 & -1 & 0 & 0 & 0 & 0 \\ 0 & 0 & 1 & 1 & -1 & -1 & 0 & 0 & 0 & 0 \\ 0 & 0 & -1 & -1 & 1 & 1 & 0 & 0 & 0 & 0 \\ 0 & 0 & -1 & -1 & 1 & 1 & 0 & 0 & 0 & 0 \\ 0 & 0 & 0 & 0 & 0 & 0 & 0 & 0 & 0 & 0 \\ 0 & 0 & 0 & 0 & 0 & 0 & 0 & 0 & 0 & 0 \\ 0 & 0 & 0 & 0 & 0 & 0 & 0 & 0 & 0 & 0 \\ 0 & 0 & 0 & 0 & 0 & 0 & 0 & 0 & 0 & 0 \end{bmatrix} \text{(N/m)}$$

$$[K_{e2}^{(3)}] = 3.5 \times 10^6 \begin{bmatrix} 0 & 0 & 0 & 0 & 0 & 0 & 0 & 0 & 0 & 0 \\ 0 & 0 & 0 & 0 & 0 & 0 & 0 & 0 & 0 & 0 \\ 0 & 0 & 0 & 0 & 0 & 0 & 0 & 0 & 0 & 0 \\ 0 & 0 & 0 & 0 & 0 & 0 & 0 & 0 & 0 & 0 \\ 0 & 0 & 0 & 0 & 1 & 0 & -1 & 0 & 0 & 0 \\ 0 & 0 & 0 & 0 & 0 & 0 & 0 & 0 & 0 & 0 \\ 0 & 0 & 0 & 0 & -1 & 0 & 1 & 0 & 0 & 0 \\ 0 & 0 & 0 & 0 & 0 & 0 & 0 & 0 & 0 & 0 \\ 0 & 0 & 0 & 0 & 0 & 0 & 0 & 0 & 0 & 0 \\ 0 & 0 & 0 & 0 & 0 & 0 & 0 & 0 & 0 & 0 \end{bmatrix} \text{(N/m)}$$

$$[K_{e2}^{(4)}] = 3.5 \times 10^6 \begin{bmatrix} 0 & 0 & 0 & 0 & 0 & 0 & 0 & 0 & 0 & 0 \\ 0 & 0 & 0 & 0 & 0 & 0 & 0 & 0 & 0 & 0 \\ 0 & 0 & 0 & 0 & 0 & 0 & 0 & 0 & 0 & 0 \\ 0 & 0 & 0 & 1 & 0 & 0 & 0 & -1 & 0 & 0 \\ 0 & 0 & 0 & 0 & 0 & 0 & 0 & 0 & 0 & 0 \\ 0 & 0 & 0 & 0 & 0 & 0 & 0 & 0 & 0 & 0 \\ 0 & 0 & 0 & 0 & 0 & 0 & 0 & 0 & 0 & 0 \\ 0 & 0 & 0 & -1 & 0 & 0 & 0 & 1 & 0 & 0 \\ 0 & 0 & 0 & 0 & 0 & 0 & 0 & 0 & 0 & 0 \\ 0 & 0 & 0 & 0 & 0 & 0 & 0 & 0 & 0 & 0 \end{bmatrix} \text{(N/m)}$$

$$[K_{e2}^{(5)}] = 1.2 \times 10^6 \begin{bmatrix} 1 & 1 & 0 & 0 & 0 & 0 & -1 & -1 & 0 & 0 \\ 1 & 1 & 0 & 0 & 0 & 0 & -1 & -1 & 0 & 0 \\ 0 & 0 & 0 & 0 & 0 & 0 & 0 & 0 & 0 & 0 \\ 0 & 0 & 0 & 0 & 0 & 0 & 0 & 0 & 0 & 0 \\ 0 & 0 & 0 & 0 & 0 & 0 & 0 & 0 & 0 & 0 \\ 0 & 0 & 0 & 0 & 0 & 0 & 0 & 0 & 0 & 0 \\ -1 & -1 & 0 & 0 & 0 & 0 & 1 & 1 & 0 & 0 \\ -1 & -1 & 0 & 0 & 0 & 0 & 1 & 1 & 0 & 0 \\ 0 & 0 & 0 & 0 & 0 & 0 & 0 & 0 & 0 & 0 \\ 0 & 0 & 0 & 0 & 0 & 0 & 0 & 0 & 0 & 0 \end{bmatrix} \text{(N/m)}$$

$$[K_{e2}^{(6)}] = 3.5 \times 10^6 \begin{bmatrix} 0 & 0 & 0 & 0 & 0 & 0 & 0 & 0 & 0 & 0 \\ 0 & 0 & 0 & 0 & 0 & 0 & 0 & 0 & 0 & 0 \\ 0 & 0 & 0 & 0 & 0 & 0 & 0 & 0 & 0 & 0 \\ 0 & 0 & 0 & 0 & 0 & 0 & 0 & 0 & 0 & 0 \\ 0 & 0 & 0 & 0 & 0 & 0 & 0 & 0 & 0 & 0 \\ 0 & 0 & 0 & 0 & 0 & 0 & 0 & 0 & 0 & 0 \\ 0 & 0 & 0 & 0 & 0 & 0 & 1 & 0 & -1 & 0 \\ 0 & 0 & 0 & 0 & 0 & 0 & 0 & 0 & 0 & 0 \\ 0 & 0 & 0 & 0 & 0 & 0 & -1 & 0 & 1 & 0 \\ 0 & 0 & 0 & 0 & 0 & 0 & 0 & 0 & 0 & 0 \end{bmatrix} \text{(N/m)}$$

Summing them all together, we have

$$[K] = 10^6 \begin{bmatrix} 4.7 & 1.2 & -3.5 & 0 & 0 & 0 & -1.2 & -1.2 & 0 & 0 \\ 1.2 & 1.2 & 0 & 0 & 0 & 0 & -1.2 & -1.2 & 0 & 0 \\ -3.5 & 0 & 4.7 & 1.2 & -1.2 & -1.2 & 0 & 0 & 0 & 0 \\ 0 & 0 & 1.2 & 4.7 & -1.2 & -1.2 & 0 & -3.5 & 0 & 0 \\ 0 & 0 & -1.2 & -1.2 & 4.7 & 1.2 & -3.5 & 0 & 0 & 0 \\ 0 & 0 & -1.2 & -1.2 & 1.2 & 1.2 & 0 & 0 & 0 & 0 \\ -1.2 & -1.2 & 0 & 0 & -3.5 & 0 & 8.2 & 1.2 & -3.5 & 0 \\ -1.2 & -1.2 & 0 & -3.5 & 0 & 0 & 1.2 & 4.7 & 0 & 0 \\ 0 & 0 & 0 & 0 & 0 & 0 & -3.5 & 0 & 3.5 & 0 \\ 0 & 0 & 0 & 0 & 0 & 0 & 0 & 0 & 0 & 0 \end{bmatrix} \text{(N/m)}$$

The global load vector can be determined with the consideration of the point load P and reaction forces $F_{1x}, F_{1y}, F_{2y}, F_{5x}$, and F_{5y} at nodes 1, 2, and 5. Because all these point loads and forces are at nodes, we can simply write

$$\{P\} = \left\{F_{1x} \quad F_{1y} \quad 0 \quad F_{2y} \quad 0 \quad -700 \quad 0 \quad 0 \quad F_{5x} \quad F_{5y}\right\}^T \text{ (N)}$$

Thus, by $[K]\{D\} = \{P\}$ (Equation 6.11) we have

$$10^6 \begin{bmatrix} 4.7 & 1.2 & -3.5 & 0 & 0 & 0 & -1.2 & -1.2 & 0 & 0 \\ 1.2 & 1.2 & 0 & 0 & 0 & 0 & -1.2 & -1.2 & 0 & 0 \\ -3.5 & 0 & 4.7 & 1.2 & -1.2 & -1.2 & 0 & 0 & 0 & 0 \\ 0 & 0 & 1.2 & 4.7 & -1.2 & -1.2 & 0 & -3.5 & 0 & 0 \\ 0 & 0 & -1.2 & -1.2 & 4.7 & 1.2 & -3.5 & 0 & 0 & 0 \\ 0 & 0 & -1.2 & -1.2 & 1.2 & 1.2 & 0 & 0 & 0 & 0 \\ -1.2 & -1.2 & 0 & 0 & -3.5 & 0 & 8.2 & 1.2 & -3.5 & 0 \\ -1.2 & -1.2 & 0 & -3.5 & 0 & 0 & 1.2 & 4.7 & 0 & 0 \\ 0 & 0 & 0 & 0 & 0 & 0 & -3.5 & 0 & 3.5 & 0 \\ 0 & 0 & 0 & 0 & 0 & 0 & 0 & 0 & 0 & 0 \end{bmatrix} \begin{Bmatrix} u_{1x} \\ u_{1y} \\ u_{2x} \\ u_{2y} \\ u_{3x} \\ u_{3y} \\ u_{4x} \\ u_{4y} \\ u_{5x} \\ u_{5y} \end{Bmatrix} = \begin{Bmatrix} F_{1x} \\ F_{1y} \\ 0 \\ F_{2y} \\ 0 \\ -700 \\ 0 \\ 0 \\ F_{5x} \\ F_{5y} \end{Bmatrix}$$

With the boundary conditions, $u_{1x} = u_{1y} = u_{2y} = u_{5x} = u_{5y} = 0$, referring to Equation 6.13, we can simplify this matrix equation by striking out the relevant rows and columns and reducing it to the following constrained matrix equation:

$$10^6 \begin{bmatrix} 4.7 & -1.2 & -1.2 & 0 & 0 \\ -1.2 & 4.7 & 1.2 & -3.5 & 0 \\ -1.2 & 1.2 & 1.2 & 0 & 0 \\ 0 & -3.5 & 0 & 8.2 & 1.2 \\ 0 & 0 & 0 & 1.2 & 4.7 \end{bmatrix} \begin{Bmatrix} u_{2x} \\ u_{3x} \\ u_{3y} \\ u_{4x} \\ u_{4y} \end{Bmatrix} = \begin{Bmatrix} 0 \\ 0 \\ -700 \\ 0 \\ 0 \end{Bmatrix} \text{ (N)}$$

After solving it, we have

$$\begin{Bmatrix} u_{2x} \\ u_{3x} \\ u_{3y} \\ u_{4x} \\ u_{4y} \end{Bmatrix} = 10^{-3} \begin{Bmatrix} -0.20 \\ 0.36 \\ -1.12 \\ 0.16 \\ -0.04 \end{Bmatrix} \text{ (m)}$$

Together with $u_{1x} = u_{1y} = u_{2y} = u_{5x} = u_{5y} = 0$, we obtain the global DOF vector:

$$\{D\} = 10^{-3} \begin{Bmatrix} 0 \\ 0 \\ -0.20 \\ 0 \\ 0.36 \\ -1.12 \\ 0.16 \\ -0.04 \\ 0 \\ 0 \end{Bmatrix} \text{ (m)}$$

Recall that the global load vector $\{P\}$ consists of known applied nodal forces and unknown reaction forces; thus, we can express it as the sum of the two as follows:

$$\{P\} = \{F\} + \{R\}$$

where $\{F\}$ represents the known applied force vector and $\{R\}$ the unknown reaction force vector. Knowing the global $[K], \{D\}$, the reaction force vector can be found by using $[K]\{D\} = \{P\} = \{F\} + \{R\}$:

$$[K]\{D\} = \begin{Bmatrix} F_{1x} \\ F_{1y} \\ 0 \\ F_{2y} \\ 0 \\ 0 \\ 0 \\ 0 \\ F_{5x} \\ F_{5y} \end{Bmatrix} + \begin{Bmatrix} 0 \\ 0 \\ 0 \\ 0 \\ 0 \\ -700 \\ 0 \\ 0 \\ 0 \\ 0 \end{Bmatrix}, \text{ so } \{R\} = \begin{Bmatrix} F_{1x} \\ F_{1y} \\ 0 \\ F_{2y} \\ 0 \\ 0 \\ 0 \\ 0 \\ F_{5x} \\ F_{5y} \end{Bmatrix} = \begin{Bmatrix} 555.02 \\ -144.98 \\ 0 \\ 844.98 \\ 0 \\ 0 \\ 0 \\ 0 \\ -555.02 \\ 0 \end{Bmatrix} \text{ (N)}$$

From the obtained global DOF vector $\{D\}$, we can write the sub-DOF vector for each element. For example, for element (2), we have

$$\begin{Bmatrix} u_{2x} \\ u_{2y} \\ u_{3x} \\ u_{3y} \end{Bmatrix} = 10^{-3} \begin{Bmatrix} -0.20 \\ 0 \\ 0.36 \\ -1.12 \end{Bmatrix}$$

By using Equation 6.14, we can determine the local axial displacements in element (2) as follows:

$$\begin{Bmatrix} u_{2(axial)} \\ u_{3(axial)} \end{Bmatrix} = \begin{bmatrix} \cos 45 & \sin 45 & 0 & 0 \\ 0 & 0 & \cos 45 & \sin 45 \end{bmatrix} \begin{Bmatrix} u_{2x} \\ u_{2y} \\ u_{3x} \\ u_{3y} \end{Bmatrix} = 10^{-3} \begin{Bmatrix} -0.14 \\ -0.54 \end{Bmatrix}$$

Referring to Equation 5.33 along with the shape function matrix for a 2-node bar element, that is,

$$[N] = \frac{1}{l} \begin{bmatrix} l - x & x \end{bmatrix}$$

we write

$$u = [N] \begin{Bmatrix} u_{2(axial)} \\ u_{3(axial)} \end{Bmatrix}$$

According to Hooke's law and the definition for stress (see Section 3.1), we have

$$\sigma = E\frac{\partial u}{\partial x}, \quad F = A\sigma$$

then we calculate the stress in element (2) as follows:

$$\sigma_2 = E\frac{\partial u}{\partial x} = E\frac{\partial [N]}{\partial x} \begin{Bmatrix} u_{2(axial)} \\ u_{3(axial)} \end{Bmatrix} = \frac{E}{l}\left[u_{3(axial)} - u_{2(axial)}\right] = -1.24 \times 10^5$$

Following the same steps, we obtain the following global stress and force vectors with their elements representing the stress and force, respectively, in each element:

$$\{\sigma\} = 1 \times 10^5 \begin{Bmatrix} -0.87 \\ -1.24 \\ 0.87 \\ -0.18 \\ 0.25 \\ 0.69 \end{Bmatrix} \text{(N/m}^2\text{)} \quad \text{and} \quad \{f\} = \begin{Bmatrix} -700.00 \\ -989.94 \\ 700.00 \\ -144.98 \\ 205.02 \\ 555.02 \end{Bmatrix} \text{(N)}$$

6.6.2 3D truss structures

When a bar structure is in 3D space as illustrated in Figure 6.8, its orientation can be marked by a set of angles, θ_x, θ_y, and θ_z, formed between the

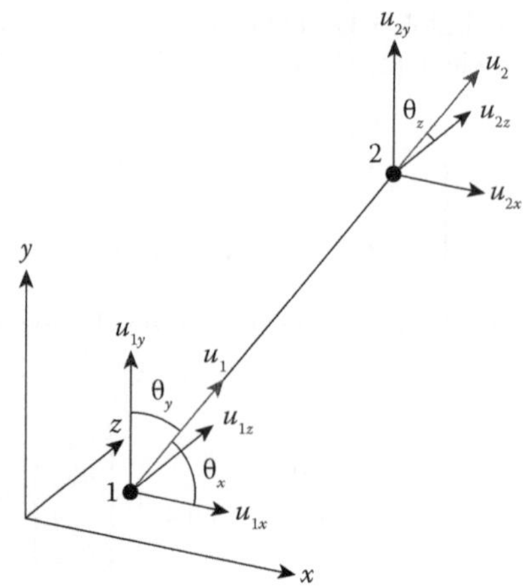

FIGURE 6.8
Bar in 3D space.

longitudinal line of the bar and Cartesian axes, x, y, and z, respectively, as

$$\begin{aligned}\cos\theta_x &= \frac{x_i - x_j}{\sqrt{(x_i - x_j)^2 + (y_i - y_j)^2 + (z_i - z_j)^2}}\\ \cos\theta_y &= \frac{y_i - y_j}{\sqrt{(x_i - x_j)^2 + (y_i - y_j)^2 + (z_i - z_j)^2}}\\ \cos\theta_z &= \frac{z_i - z_j}{\sqrt{(x_i - x_j)^2 + (y_i - y_j)^2 + (z_i - z_j)^2}}\end{aligned} \tag{6.17}$$

In this 3D space, the elementary DOF vector of a 2-node bar element, $\{u_1 \;\; u_2\}^T$, can be expressed in terms of its Cartesian components, namely, $u_{1x}, u_{1y}, u_{1z}, u_{2x}, u_{2y}$, and u_{2z} using the basic relationships in trigonometry:

$$\begin{aligned}u_1 &= u_{1x}\cos\theta_x + u_{1y}\cos\theta_y + u_{1z}\cos\theta_z\\ u_2 &= u_{2x}\cos\theta_x + u_{2y}\cos\theta_y + u_{2z}\cos\theta_z\end{aligned}$$

In a matrix form, these two equations can be written as

$$\begin{Bmatrix} u_1 \\ u_2 \end{Bmatrix} = \begin{bmatrix} \cos\theta_x & \cos\theta_y & \cos\theta_z & 0 & 0 & 0 \\ 0 & 0 & 0 & \cos\theta_x & \cos\theta_y & \cos\theta_z \end{bmatrix} \begin{Bmatrix} u_{1x} \\ u_{1y} \\ u_{1z} \\ u_{2x} \\ u_{2y} \\ u_{2z} \end{Bmatrix}$$

This indicates that for a mechanical bar structure in 3D, its nodal DOF expands from 1 to 3, making the elementary DOF = 6 for a 2-node bar element. Applying this expression to Equation 6.7, we have

$$[K_e]\begin{bmatrix} \cos\theta_x & \cos\theta_y & \cos\theta_z & 0 & 0 & 0 \\ 0 & 0 & 0 & \cos\theta_x & \cos\theta_y & \cos\theta_z \end{bmatrix}\begin{Bmatrix} u_{1x} \\ u_{1y} \\ u_{1z} \\ u_{2x} \\ u_{2y} \\ u_{2z} \end{Bmatrix} = \begin{Bmatrix} P_1 \\ P_2 \end{Bmatrix} \tag{6.18}$$

Let

$$[R3] = \begin{bmatrix} \cos\theta_x & \cos\theta_y & \cos\theta_z & 0 & 0 & 0 \\ 0 & 0 & 0 & \cos\theta_x & \cos\theta_y & \cos\theta_z \end{bmatrix}$$

Multiplying both sides of Equation 6.18 by $[R3]^T$, we obtain

$$[R3]^T[K_e][R3]\begin{Bmatrix} u_{1x} \\ u_{1y} \\ u_{1z} \\ u_{2x} \\ u_{2y} \\ u_{2z} \end{Bmatrix} = [R3]^T\begin{Bmatrix} P_1 \\ P_2 \end{Bmatrix} = \begin{Bmatrix} P_{1x} \\ P_{1y} \\ P_{1z} \\ P_{2x} \\ P_{2y} \\ P_{2z} \end{Bmatrix}$$

This equation is the 3D equivalent of Equation 6.7, that is, the 3D expanded matrix equation for bar elements

$$[K_{e3}]\{d_0\} = \{P_{e3}\}$$

where

$$[K_{e3}] = [R3]^T[K_e][R3]$$
$$\{P_{e3}\} = [R3]^T\{P_e\}$$

With the elementary $[K_e]$ matrix for a 1D 2-node bar element, we have

$$[K_{e3}] = \frac{kA}{l}\begin{bmatrix} \cos\theta_x & 0 \\ \cos\theta_y & 0 \\ \cos\theta_z & 0 \\ 0 & \cos\theta_x \\ 0 & \cos\theta_y \\ 0 & \cos\theta_z \end{bmatrix}\begin{bmatrix} 1 & -1 \\ -1 & 1 \end{bmatrix}$$
$$\times\begin{bmatrix} \cos\theta_x & \cos\theta_y & \cos\theta_z & 0 & 0 & 0 \\ 0 & 0 & 0 & \cos\theta_x & \cos\theta_y & \cos\theta_z \end{bmatrix}$$

Letting $c_x = \cos\theta_x, c_y = \cos\theta_y$, and $c_z = \cos\theta_z$, we simplify the above equation to

$$[K_{e3}] = \frac{kA}{l}\begin{bmatrix} c_x^2 & c_xc_y & c_xc_z & -c_x^2 & -c_xc_y & -c_xc_z \\ c_xc_y & c_y^2 & c_yc_z & -c_xc_y & -c_y^2 & -c_yc_z \\ c_xc_z & c_yc_z & c_z^2 & -c_xc_z & -c_yc_z & -c_z^2 \\ -c_x^2 & -c_xc_y & -c_xc_z & c_x^2 & c_xc_y & c_xc_z \\ -c_xc_y & -c_y^2 & -c_yc_z & c_xc_y & c_y^2 & c_yc_z \\ -c_xc_z & -c_yc_z & -c_z^2 & c_xc_z & c_yc_z & c_z^2 \end{bmatrix} \quad (6.19)$$

For an arbitrary oriented bar element in 3D space, Equation 6.19 is used to determine the elementary $[K_{e2}]$ matrix with known values of $k, A, l, \theta_x, \theta_y$, and θ_z.

Example 6.7

For the 3D truss structure shown in Figure 6.9, determine the displacements and the joint and reaction forces at the anchors.

The structure consists of three members, made of a material with a Young's modulus of 70 Msi with a cross section area of 1 in.^{2}, linked together at joint 4 with fixed constraints at joints 1 through 3 and a vertical load $P = 10000$ lb at joint 4. The coordinates of the joints are known as $1(0,0,0)$, $2(0,-12,12)$, $3(0,12,12)$ and $4(12,0,12)$ measured in inches.

Answer

For the given bar, by using Equation 6.17, we calculate the following:

$$\cos\theta_x = 0.707,\ \cos\theta_y = 0,\ \cos\theta_z = 0.707 \qquad \text{forelement (1)}$$
$$\cos\theta_x = 0.707,\ \cos\theta_y = 0.707,\ \cos\theta_z = 0 \qquad \text{forelement (2)}$$
$$\cos\theta_x = 0.707,\ \cos\theta_y = -0.707,\ \cos\theta_z = 0 \qquad \text{forelement (3)}$$

Since all the members are subjecting axial loads and deformations, we can use bar elements for structural discretization. Thus, by using

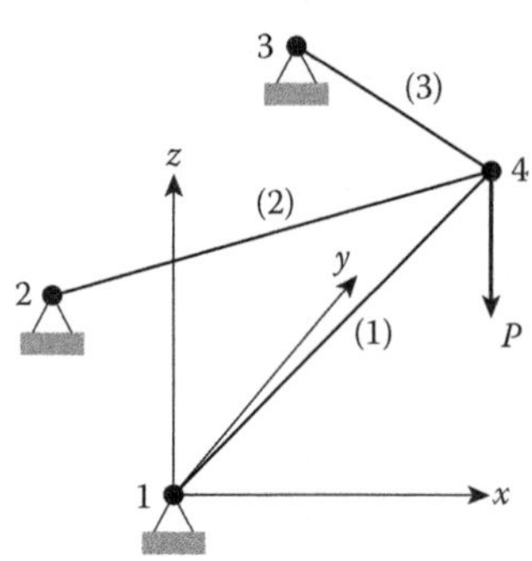

FIGURE 6.9
A 3D truss structure.

Equation 6.19, we calculate the following elementary $[K_{e3}]$ matrices:

$$[K_{e3}^{(1)}] = 1 \times 10^6 \begin{bmatrix} 2.0624 & 0 & 2.0624 & -2.0624 & 0 & -2.0624 \\ 0 & 0 & 0 & 0 & 0 & 0 \\ 2.0624 & 0 & 2.0624 & -2.0624 & 0 & -2.0624 \\ -2.0624 & 0 & -2.0624 & 2.0624 & 0 & 2.0624 \\ 0 & 0 & 0 & 0 & 0 & 0 \\ -2.0624 & 0 & -2.0624 & 2.0624 & 0 & 2.0624 \end{bmatrix} \text{(lb/in.)}$$

$$[K_{e3}^{(2)}] = 1 \times 10^6 \begin{bmatrix} 2.0624 & 2.0624 & 0 & -2.0624 & -2.0624 & 0 \\ 2.0624 & 2.0624 & 0 & -2.0624 & -2.0624 & 0 \\ 0 & 0 & 0 & 0 & 0 & 0 \\ -2.0624 & -2.0624 & 0 & 2.0624 & 2.0624 & 0 \\ -2.0624 & -2.0624 & 0 & 2.0624 & 2.0624 & 0 \\ 0 & 0 & 0 & 0 & 0 & 0 \end{bmatrix} \text{(lb/in.)}$$

$$[K_{e3}^{(3)}] = 1 \times 10^6 \begin{bmatrix} 2.0624 & -2.0624 & 0 & -2.0624 & 2.0624 & 0 \\ -2.0624 & 2.0624 & 0 & 2.0624 & -2.0624 & 0 \\ 0 & 0 & 0 & 0 & 0 & 0 \\ -2.0624 & 2.0624 & 0 & 2.0624 & -2.0624 & 0 \\ 2.0624 & -2.0624 & 0 & -2.0624 & 2.0624 & 0 \\ 0 & 0 & 0 & 0 & 0 & 0 \end{bmatrix} \text{(lb/in.)}$$

For this structure, the global DOF vector is

$$\{D\} = \{u_{1x}\, u_{1y}\ u_{1z}\ u_{2x}\ u_{2y}\ u_{2z}\ u_{3x}\ u_{3y}\ u_{3z}\ u_{4x}\ u_{4y}\ u_{4z}\}^T \text{ (in.)}$$

thus, using this vector as a reference, we expand the elementary $[K_{e3}]$ matrices as follows:

$$[K_{e3}^{(1)}] = 1 \times 10^6 \begin{bmatrix} 2.0624 & 0 & 2.0624 & 0 & 0 & 0 & 0 & 0 & 0 & -2.0624 & 0 & -2.0624 \\ 0 & 0 & 0 & 0 & 0 & 0 & 0 & 0 & 0 & 0 & 0 & 0 \\ 2.0624 & 0 & 2.0624 & 0 & 0 & 0 & 0 & 0 & 0 & -2.0624 & 0 & -2.0624 \\ 0 & 0 & 0 & 0 & 0 & 0 & 0 & 0 & 0 & 0 & 0 & 0 \\ 0 & 0 & 0 & 0 & 0 & 0 & 0 & 0 & 0 & 0 & 0 & 0 \\ 0 & 0 & 0 & 0 & 0 & 0 & 0 & 0 & 0 & 0 & 0 & 0 \\ 0 & 0 & 0 & 0 & 0 & 0 & 0 & 0 & 0 & 0 & 0 & 0 \\ 0 & 0 & 0 & 0 & 0 & 0 & 0 & 0 & 0 & 0 & 0 & 0 \\ 0 & 0 & 0 & 0 & 0 & 0 & 0 & 0 & 0 & 0 & 0 & 0 \\ -2.0624 & 0 & -2.0624 & 0 & 0 & 0 & 0 & 0 & 0 & 2.0624 & 0 & 2.0624 \\ 0 & 0 & 0 & 0 & 0 & 0 & 0 & 0 & 0 & 0 & 0 & 0 \\ -2.0624 & 0 & -2.0624 & 0 & 0 & 0 & 0 & 0 & 0 & 2.0624 & 0 & 2.0624 \end{bmatrix}$$

$$[K_{e3}^{(2)}] = 1 \times 10^6 \begin{bmatrix} 0 & 0 & 0 & 0 & 0 & 0 & 0 & 0 & 0 & 0 & 0 & 0 \\ 0 & 0 & 0 & 0 & 0 & 0 & 0 & 0 & 0 & 0 & 0 & 0 \\ 0 & 0 & 0 & 0 & 0 & 0 & 0 & 0 & 0 & 0 & 0 & 0 \\ 0 & 0 & 0 & 2.0624 & 2.0624 & 0 & 0 & 0 & 0 & -2.0624 & -2.0624 & 0 \\ 0 & 0 & 0 & 2.0624 & 2.0624 & 0 & 0 & 0 & 0 & -2.0624 & -2.0624 & 0 \\ 0 & 0 & 0 & 0 & 0 & 0 & 0 & 0 & 0 & 0 & 0 & 0 \\ 0 & 0 & 0 & 0 & 0 & 0 & 0 & 0 & 0 & 0 & 0 & 0 \\ 0 & 0 & 0 & 0 & 0 & 0 & 0 & 0 & 0 & 0 & 0 & 0 \\ 0 & 0 & 0 & 0 & 0 & 0 & 0 & 0 & 0 & 0 & 0 & 0 \\ 0 & 0 & 0 & -2.0624 & -2.0624 & 0 & 0 & 0 & 0 & 2.0624 & 2.0624 & 0 \\ 0 & 0 & 0 & -2.0624 & -2.0624 & 0 & 0 & 0 & 0 & 2.0624 & 2.0624 & 0 \\ 0 & 0 & 0 & 0 & 0 & 0 & 0 & 0 & 0 & 0 & 0 & 0 \end{bmatrix}$$

$$[K_{e3}^{(3)}] = 1 \times 10^6 \begin{bmatrix} 0 & 0 & 0 & 0 & 0 & 0 & 0 & 0 & 0 & 0 & 0 & 0 \\ 0 & 0 & 0 & 0 & 0 & 0 & 0 & 0 & 0 & 0 & 0 & 0 \\ 0 & 0 & 0 & 0 & 0 & 0 & 0 & 0 & 0 & 0 & 0 & 0 \\ 0 & 0 & 0 & 0 & 0 & 0 & 0 & 0 & 0 & 0 & 0 & 0 \\ 0 & 0 & 0 & 0 & 0 & 0 & 0 & 0 & 0 & 0 & 0 & 0 \\ 0 & 0 & 0 & 0 & 0 & 0 & 0 & 0 & 0 & 0 & 0 & 0 \\ 0 & 0 & 0 & 0 & 0 & 0 & 2.0624 & -2.0624 & 0 & -2.0624 & 2.0624 & 0 \\ 0 & 0 & 0 & 0 & 0 & 0 & -2.0624 & 2.0624 & 0 & 2.0624 & -2.0624 & 0 \\ 0 & 0 & 0 & 0 & 0 & 0 & 0 & 0 & 0 & 0 & 0 & 0 \\ 0 & 0 & 0 & 0 & 0 & 0 & -2.0624 & 2.0624 & 0 & 2.0624 & -2.0624 & 0 \\ 0 & 0 & 0 & 0 & 0 & 0 & 2.0624 & -2.0624 & 0 & -2.0624 & 2.0624 & 0 \\ 0 & 0 & 0 & 0 & 0 & 0 & 0 & 0 & 0 & 0 & 0 & 0 \end{bmatrix}$$

By summing them together, we obtain the global $[K]$ matrix:

$$[K] = 1 \times 10^6 \begin{bmatrix} 2.06 & 0 & 2.06 & 0 & 0 & 0 & 0 & 0 & 0 & -2.06 & 0 & -2.06 \\ 0 & 0 & 0 & 0 & 0 & 0 & 0 & 0 & 0 & 0 & 0 & 0 \\ 2.06 & 0 & 2.06 & 0 & 0 & 0 & 0 & 0 & 0 & -2.06 & 0 & -2.06 \\ 0 & 0 & 0 & 2.06 & 2.06 & 0 & 0 & 0 & 0 & -2.06 & -2.06 & 0 \\ 0 & 0 & 0 & 2.06 & 2.06 & 0 & 0 & 0 & 0 & -2.06 & -2.06 & 0 \\ 0 & 0 & 0 & 0 & 0 & 0 & 0 & 0 & 0 & 0 & 0 & 0 \\ 0 & 0 & 0 & 0 & 0 & 0 & 2.06 & -2.06 & 0 & -2.06 & 2.06 & 0 \\ 0 & 0 & 0 & 0 & 0 & 0 & -2.06 & 2.06 & 0 & 2.06 & -2.06 & 0 \\ 0 & 0 & 0 & 0 & 0 & 0 & 0 & 0 & 0 & 0 & 0 & 0 \\ -2.06 & 0 & -2.0 & -2.06 & -2.06 & 0 & -2.06 & 2.06 & 0 & 6.19 & 0 & 2.06 \\ 0 & 0 & 0 & -2.0 & -2.06 & 0 & 2.06 & -2.06 & 0 & 0 & 4.12 & 0 \\ -2.06 & 0 & -2.06 & 0 & 0 & 0 & 0 & 0 & 0 & 2.06 & 0 & 2.06 \end{bmatrix}$$

The global load vector for this 3D structure can be determined with the consideration of the point load P and reaction forces at nodes 1, 2, and 3. Because all these point loads and forces are at nodes, we can simply write

$$\{P\} = \{F_{1x} \quad F_{1y} \quad F_{1z} \quad F_{2x} \quad F_{2y} \quad F_{2z} \quad F_{3x} \quad F_{3y} \quad F_{3z} \quad 0 \quad 0 \quad -10000\}^T \text{ (lb)}$$

Thus, by $[K]\{D\} = \{P\}$, along with the boundary conditions, $u_{1x} = u_{1y} = u_{1z} = u_{2x} = u_{2y} = u_{2z} = u_{3x} = u_{3y} = u_{3z} = 0$, we obtain the following constrained matrix equation after applying the partition method (see Equation 6.13):

$$1 \times 10^6 \begin{bmatrix} 6.19 & 0 & 2.06 \\ 0 & 4.12 & 0 \\ 2.06 & 0 & 2.06 \end{bmatrix} \begin{Bmatrix} u_{4x} \\ u_{4y} \\ u_{4z} \end{Bmatrix} = \begin{Bmatrix} 0 \\ 0 \\ -10000 \end{Bmatrix} \text{ (lb)}$$

By solving it, we obtain

$$\begin{Bmatrix} u_{4x} \\ u_{4y} \\ u_{4z} \end{Bmatrix} = \begin{Bmatrix} 0.0024 \\ 0 \\ -0.0073 \end{Bmatrix} \text{ (in.)}$$

Putting it together with the known boundary conditions, we have the global DOF vector:

$$\{D\} = \begin{Bmatrix} 0 \\ 0 \\ 0 \\ 0 \\ 0 \\ 0 \\ 0 \\ 0 \\ 0 \\ 0.0024 \\ 0 \\ -0.0073 \end{Bmatrix} \text{(in.)}$$

The global reaction force vector can be determined as

$$\{R\} = \begin{Bmatrix} F_{1x} \\ F_{1y} \\ F_{1z} \\ F_{2x} \\ F_{2y} \\ F_{2z} \\ F_{3x} \\ F_{3y} \\ F_{3z} \\ 0 \\ 0 \\ 0 \end{Bmatrix} = [K]\{D\} - \begin{Bmatrix} 0 \\ 0 \\ 0 \\ 0 \\ 0 \\ 0 \\ 0 \\ 0 \\ 0 \\ 0 \\ 0 \\ -10000 \end{Bmatrix} = \begin{Bmatrix} 10000 \\ 0 \\ 10000 \\ -5000 \\ -5000 \\ 0 \\ -5000 \\ 5000 \\ 0 \\ 0 \\ 0 \\ 0 \end{Bmatrix} \text{(lb)}$$

6.7 FEM Formulation for Beams

To complete the discussion of FEM for slender structures and domains, we look at beam structures in this section, although beams are not governed by the differential equation given in Equation 6.1. However, as we shall see in the following section, the procedures we use to develop the weak-form PDE and FEM formulation are the same as those discussed in Sections 6.1 and 6.2.

6.7.1 Weak-form PDE for beams

As we learned in Section 3.5, the governing differential equation for beams is

$$\frac{d^2}{dx^2}\left(EI\frac{d^2u}{dx^2}\right) + f = 0$$

For this fourth-order PDE, we first develop its weak-form expression. By the method of weighted integral of residual, let $w(x)$ be a set of weight functions; then we express

$$\int_0^l w\left[\frac{d^2}{dx^2}\left(EI\frac{d^2\tilde{u}}{dx^2}\right)+f\right]dx=0 \tag{6.20}$$

According to the product rule of differentiation, we can write

$$\frac{d}{dx}\left[w\frac{d}{dx}\left(EI\frac{d^2\tilde{u}}{dx^2}\right)\right]=\frac{dw}{dx}\frac{d}{dx}\left(EI\frac{d^2\tilde{u}}{dx^2}\right)+w\frac{d^2}{dx^2}\left(EI\frac{d^2\tilde{u}}{dx^2}\right)$$

and

$$\frac{d}{dx}\left[\frac{dw}{dx}EI\frac{d^2\tilde{u}}{dx^2}\right]=\frac{d^2w}{dx^2}EI\frac{d^2\tilde{u}}{dx^2}+\frac{dw}{dx}\frac{d}{dx}\left(EI\frac{d^2\tilde{u}}{dx^2}\right)$$

Putting these two relationships together, we have

$$w\frac{d^2}{dx^2}\left(EI\frac{d^2\tilde{u}}{dx^2}\right)=\frac{d}{dx}\left[w\frac{d}{dx}\left(EI\frac{d^2\tilde{u}}{dx^2}\right)\right]-\frac{d}{dx}\left[\frac{dw}{dx}EI\frac{d^2\tilde{u}}{dx^2}\right]+\frac{d^2w}{dx^2}EI\frac{d^2\tilde{u}}{dx^2}$$

Substituting this relationship into Equation 6.20, we have

$$\int_0^l\left[\frac{d^2w}{dx^2}EI\frac{d^2\tilde{u}}{dx^2}\right]dx+\int_0^l wf\,dx+\left[w\frac{d}{dx}\left(EI\frac{d^2\tilde{u}}{dx^2}\right)\right]_0^l-\left[\frac{dw}{dx}EI\frac{d^2\tilde{u}}{dx^2}\right]_0^l=0$$

Recall that (see Section 3.5)

$$M=EI\frac{d^2\tilde{u}}{dx^2}\quad\text{and}\quad V=\frac{dM}{dx}=\frac{d}{dx}\left(EI\frac{d^2\tilde{u}}{dx^2}\right)$$

we obtain the following weak-form PDE for beams

$$\int_0^l\left[\frac{d^2w}{dx^2}EI\frac{d^2\tilde{u}}{dx^2}\right]dx=-\int_0^l wf\,dx-[wV]_0^l+\left[\frac{dw}{dx}M\right]_0^l \tag{6.21}$$

Note that in using this equation, one needs to obey the sign conventions discussed in Section 3.5.

6.7.2 FEM formulation

By applying the Galerkin method to Equation 6.21, along with Equation 5.32, we have

$$w_m=N_m\text{ and }\tilde{u}=\sum_{m=1}^{n_e}N_mu_m=[N]\{d_0\}$$

where $[N]$ is the shape function matrix for a beam element with elementary DOF $= n_e$. Substituting these expressions into Equation 6.21, we have

$$\int_0^l \left[\frac{d^2 N_m}{dx^2} EI \frac{d^2[N]\{d_0\}}{dx^2}\right] dx = -\int_0^l N_m f dx - [N_m V]_0^l + \left[\frac{dN_m}{dx} M\right]_0^l$$

for $m = 1, \ldots, n_e$. Since only the shape function matrix, $[N]$, is a function of x and the nodal DOF vector, $\{d_0\}$, is not, we simplify this equation to

$$\int_0^l \frac{d^2 N_m}{dx^2} EI \left[\frac{d^2 N}{dx^2}\right] dx\{d_0\} = -\int_0^l N_m f dx - [N_m V]_0^l + \left[\frac{dN_m}{dx} M\right]_0^l$$

for $m = 1, \ldots, n_e$.

By summing all these n_e equations together, as we did in Section 6.2, we obtain the following FEM formulation for a beam element:

$$\int_0^l \left[\frac{d^2 N}{dx^2}\right]^T EI \left[\frac{d^2 N}{dx^2}\right] dx\{d_0\} = -\int_0^l [N]^T f dx - [N]^T|_0^l + \left[\frac{dN}{dx}\right]^T M|_0^l \tag{6.22}$$

The first integral gives the elementary $[K_e]$ matrix (i.e., the stiffness matrix) for a beam element:

$$[K_e] = \int_0^l \left[\frac{d^2 N}{dx^2}\right]^T EI \left[\frac{d^2 N}{dx^2}\right] dx \tag{6.23}$$

Example 6.8

Find the elementary $[K_e]$ matrix for the 2-node beam element shown in Figure 6.10 having a flexure rigidity of EI, where E is Young's modulus and I is the second moment of inertia of the cross section of the beam.

Answer

For the 2-node beam element, by using the Hermite interpolation formula (see Equation 5.28 and follow the steps in Example 5.8 in Section 5.7.2), with $x_1 = l, x_2 = 2l$, we obtain the four shape

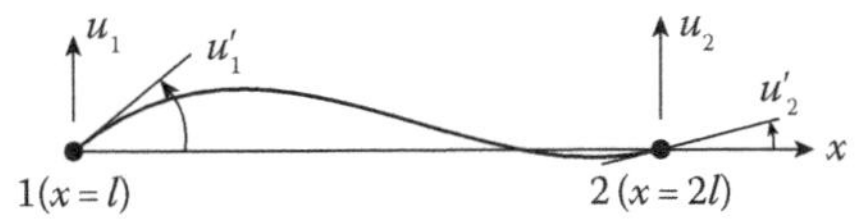

FIGURE 6.10
A 2-node beam element.

functions as follows:

$$N_1 = \frac{(2x-l)(x-2l)^2}{l^3}, \quad N_2 = \frac{(x-l)(x-2l)^2}{l^2}$$
$$N_3 = \frac{(x-l)^2(5l-2x)}{l^3}, \quad N_4 = \frac{(x-l)^2(x-2l)}{l^2}$$

With these shape functions, we write the following shape function matrix:

$$[N] = \left[\frac{(2x-l)(x-2l)^2}{l^3} \quad \frac{(x-l)(x-2l)^2}{l^2} \quad \frac{(x-l)^2(5l-2x)}{l^3} \quad \frac{(x-l)^2(x-2l)}{l^2}\right]$$

Then, we calculate

$$\left[\frac{d^2N}{dx^2}\right] = \left[\frac{6(2x-3l)}{l^3} \quad \frac{2(3x-5l)}{l^2} \quad \frac{6(3l-2x)}{l^3} \quad \frac{2(3x-4l)}{l^2}\right]$$

Substituting this expression into Equation 6.23, we obtain

$$[K_e] = EI\int_l^{2l} \begin{bmatrix} \frac{6(2x-3l)}{l^3} \\ \frac{2(3x-5l)}{l^2} \\ \frac{6(3l-2x)}{l^3} \\ \frac{2(3x-4l)}{l^2} \end{bmatrix} \left[\frac{6(2x-3l)}{l^3} \quad \frac{2(3x-5l)}{l^2} \quad \frac{6(3l-2x)}{l^3} \quad \frac{2(3x-4l)}{l^2}\right] dx$$

$$= \frac{EI}{l^6}\int_l^{2l} \begin{bmatrix} 36(l-2x)^2 & 12l(l-2x)(2l-3x) & -36(l-2x)^2 & 12l(l-2x)(l-3x) \\ 12l(l-2x)(2l-3x) & 4l^2(2l-3x)^2 & -12l(l-2x)(2l-3x) & 4l^2(l-3x)(2l-3x) \\ -36(l-2x)^2 & -12l(l-2x)(2l-3x) & 36(l-2x)^2 & -12l(l-2x)(l-3x) \\ 12l(l-2x)(l-3x) & 4l^2(l-3x)(2l-3x) & -12l(l-2x)(l-3x) & 4l^2(l-3x)^2 \end{bmatrix} dx$$

Integrating each term in the matrix, we obtain

$$[K_e] = \frac{EI}{l^3}\begin{bmatrix} 12 & 6l & -12 & 6l \\ 6l & 4l^2 & -6l & 2l^2 \\ -12 & -6l & 12 & -6l \\ 6l & 2l^2 & -6l & 4l^2 \end{bmatrix} \tag{6.24}$$

Equation 6.24 gives the elementary $[K_e]$ matrix or, more specifically, the stiffness matrix for a 2-node beam element.

Like 1D bar elements, this $[K_e]$ matrix applies to any 2-node beam element with a length of l and flexure rigidity of EI.

Example 6.9

For the cantilever beam shown in Figure 6.11, determine the defections and rotation at nodes 2 and 3. The beam is subjected to a distributed load $f = -5$ N/m between nodes 1 and 2, a downward force $P_1 = -15$ N at $x = 4$ m and an upward force $P_2 = 7.5$ N at node 2, and a downward force $P_3 = -25$ N and a downward bending moment $M = 30$ N-m at node 3. Consider that the beam structure is made of a material having a flexure rigidity of $EI = 10^5$ Nm^2.

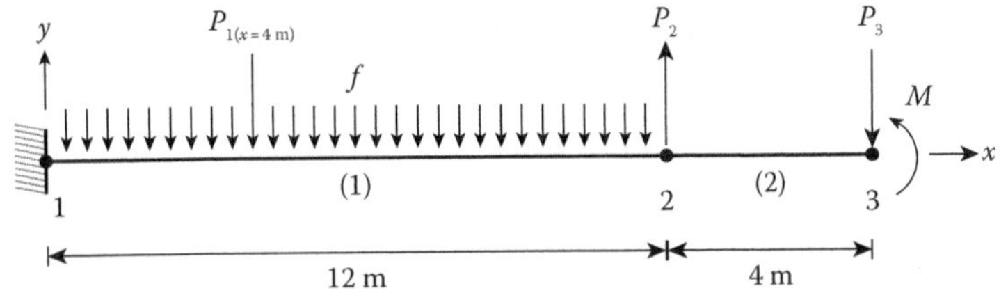

FIGURE 6.11
Beam under transverse loading and bending.

Answer
For this problem, we use two beam elements, elements (1) and (2), for structural discretization. The two elements are linked together by a common node, node 2.

Using Equation 6.24, we obtain the following stiffness matrix for beam (1) with $EI = 10^5$ Nm^2 and $l = 12$ m:

$$[K_e^{(1)}] = 10^3 \begin{bmatrix} 0.69 & 4.17 & -0.69 & 4.17 \\ 4.17 & 33.33 & -4.17 & 16.67 \\ -0.69 & -4.17 & 0.69 & -4.17 \\ 4.17 & 16.67 & -4.17 & 33.33 \end{bmatrix}$$

and the following for beam (2) with $EI = 10^5$ Nm^2 and $l = 4$ m:

$$[K_e^{(2)}] = 10^3 \begin{bmatrix} 18.75 & 37.50 & -18.75 & 37.50 \\ 37.50 & 100.00 & -37.50 & 50.00 \\ -18.75 & -37.50 & 18.75 & -37.50 \\ 37.50 & 50.00 & -37.50 & 100.00 \end{bmatrix}$$

Referring to the global DOF vector, which can be expressed as $\{D\} = \{u_1, u_1', u_2, u_2', u_3, u_3'\}$, we expand these two matrices to

$$[K_e^{(1)}] = 10^3 \begin{bmatrix} 0.69 & 4.17 & -0.69 & 4.17 & 0 & 0 \\ 4.17 & 33.33 & -4.17 & 16.67 & 0 & 0 \\ -0.69 & -4.17 & 0.69 & -4.17 & 0 & 0 \\ 4.17 & 16.67 & -4.17 & 33.33 & 0 & 0 \\ 0 & 0 & 0 & 0 & 0 & 0 \\ 0 & 0 & 0 & 0 & 0 & 0 \end{bmatrix}$$

$$[K_e^{(2)}] = 10^3 \begin{bmatrix} 0 & 0 & 0 & 0 & 0 & 0 \\ 0 & 0 & 0 & 0 & 0 & 0 \\ 0 & 0 & 18.75 & 37.50 & -18.75 & 37.50 \\ 0 & 0 & 37.50 & 100.00 & -37.50 & 50.00 \\ 0 & 0 & -18.75 & -37.50 & 18.75 & -37.50 \\ 0 & 0 & 37.50 & 50.00 & -37.50 & 100.00 \end{bmatrix}$$

By summing them up, we obtain the global stiffness matrix as

$$[K] = 10^3 \begin{bmatrix} 0.69 & 4.17 & -0.69 & 4.17 & 0 & 0 \\ 4.17 & 33.33 & -4.17 & 16.67 & 0 & 0 \\ -0.69 & -4.17 & 19.44 & 33.33 & -18.75 & 37.50 \\ 4.17 & 16.67 & 33.33 & 133.33 & -37.50 & 50.00 \\ 0 & 0 & -18.75 & -37.50 & 18.75 & -37.50 \\ 0 & 0 & 37.50 & 50.00 & -37.50 & 100.00 \end{bmatrix}$$

To determine the elementary load vectors, we express the shape function matrix using the shape functions given in Equation 5.29 (note that these functions are obtained using local coordinates, namely, between $x = 0$ and $x = l$) as

$$[N] = \begin{bmatrix} 1 - \dfrac{3x^2}{l^2} + \dfrac{2x^3}{l^3} & x - \dfrac{2x^2}{l} + \dfrac{x^3}{l^2} & \dfrac{3x^2}{l^2} - \dfrac{2x^3}{l^3} & -\dfrac{x^2}{l} + \dfrac{x^3}{l^2} \end{bmatrix}$$

Then, by referring to Equation 6.22, we determine the elementary load vectors using the following expression:

$$\{P_e\} = -\int_0^l [N]^T f dx - [N]^T|_0^l + \left[\frac{dN}{dx}\right]^T M|_0^l$$

According to the sign conventions set forth in Section 3.5, f, P_1, P_3, and M are positive and P_2 is negative. By substituting the signed values of f, P_1, P_2, P_3, and M along with their relative locations, namely, $x = 4$ for P_1, $x = 0$ for P_2 and $x = 4$ for P_3, and M, we find the following load vector for element (1):

$$\{P_e^{(1)}\} = -\int_0^{12} [N]^T \times (5) dx - [N]^T_{x=4} \times (15) = \begin{Bmatrix} -41.11 \\ -86.67 \\ -33.89 \\ 73.33 \end{Bmatrix}$$

and the following for element (2):

$$\{P_e^{(2)}\} = -[N]^T_{x=0} \times (-7.5) - [N]^T_{x=4} \times (25) + \left[\frac{dN}{dx}\right]^T_{x=4} \times (30) = \begin{Bmatrix} 7.5 \\ 0 \\ -25 \\ 30 \end{Bmatrix}$$

Adding these two load vectors together, we obtain the global load vector:

$$\{P\} = \{-41.11 \quad -86.67 \quad -26.39 \quad 73.33 \quad -25.00 \quad 30.00\}^T$$

Putting these together in the global matrix algebraic equation $[K]\{D\} = \{P\}$, we have

$$10^4 \begin{bmatrix} 0.69 & 4.17 & -0.69 & 4.17 & 0 & 0 \\ 4.17 & 33.33 & -4.17 & 16.67 & 0 & 0 \\ -0.69 & -4.17 & 19.44 & 33.33 & -18.75 & 37.50 \\ 4.17 & 16.67 & 33.33 & 133.33 & -37.50 & 50.00 \\ 0 & 0 & -18.75 & -37.50 & 18.75 & -37.50 \\ 0 & 0 & 37.50 & 50.00 & -37.50 & 100.00 \end{bmatrix} \begin{Bmatrix} u_1 \\ u_1' \\ u_2 \\ u_2' \\ u_3 \\ u_3' \end{Bmatrix} = \begin{Bmatrix} 41.11 \\ 86.67 \\ -26.39 \\ 73.33 \\ -25.00 \\ 30.00 \end{Bmatrix}$$

Since the beam structure has a fixed end at node 1, we have $u_1 = u_1' = 0$ as the boundary conditions. By applying these boundary conditions to the above matrix equation, we strike out the first two rows and columns according to the matrix partition method; thus, we write

$$10^4 \begin{bmatrix} 19.44 & 33.33 & -18.75 & 37.50 \\ 33.33 & 133.33 & -37.50 & 50.00 \\ -18.75 & -37.50 & 18.75 & -37.50 \\ 37.50 & 50.00 & -37.50 & 100.00 \end{bmatrix} \begin{Bmatrix} u_2 \\ u_2' \\ u_3 \\ u_3' \end{Bmatrix} = \begin{Bmatrix} -26.39 \\ 73.33 \\ -25.00 \\ 30.00 \end{Bmatrix}$$

Solving this constrained matrix equation, we obtain

$$\begin{Bmatrix} u_2 \\ u_2' \\ u_3 \\ u_3' \end{Bmatrix} = \begin{Bmatrix} -0.2936 \\ -0.0366 \\ -0.4429 \\ -0.0374 \end{Bmatrix}$$

6.8 The Essence of FEM

In Examples 6.6, 6.7, and 6.9, we follow the same procedure listed at the end of Example 6.4. The fact that a common procedure is used for structures that can be discretized by either bar or beam elements actually captures the essence of the FEM. In other words, in FEM, we first determine elementary $[K_e]$ matrices for the discretized finite elements based on the type of elements and their corresponding shape functions, and then assemble them into the global $[K]$ matrix. After that, with the global load vector $\{P\}$ filled with known and unknown loading conditions, we establish the global matrix equation in the form of $[K]\{D\} = \{P\}$, and reduce it to a constrained matrix equation through matrix partition based on the given boundary conditions. Finally, by solving the reduced matrix equation, we obtain the DOF vector, and using relevant principles and relationships in physics and engineering, we determine other associated engineering unknown variables.

6.9 Exercises

1. Use the following formula,

$$[K_e] = A \int_l \left[\frac{dN}{dx}\right]^T k \left[\frac{dN}{dx}\right] dx$$

to determine the elementary $[K_e]$ matrix for the two 1D 2-node elements given in Figure 6.12 in terms of k, A, and l.

2. Use the same formula given in Exercise 1 to determine the elementary $[K_e]$ matrix for the two 1D 3-node elements given in Figure 6.13 in terms of k, A, and l.

3. The spring loading structure shown in Figure 6.14 is made of two members. The structure is fixed at the left end and is subjected to a point load $P = 150$ lb at the right end, as shown. The lengths of all members are given in the figure. Assuming that all members are made of aluminum with Young's modulus $E = 10 \times 10^6$ lb/in.^{2} and cross section area $A = 0.25$ in.^{2}, determine the displacements at joints 2 and 3.

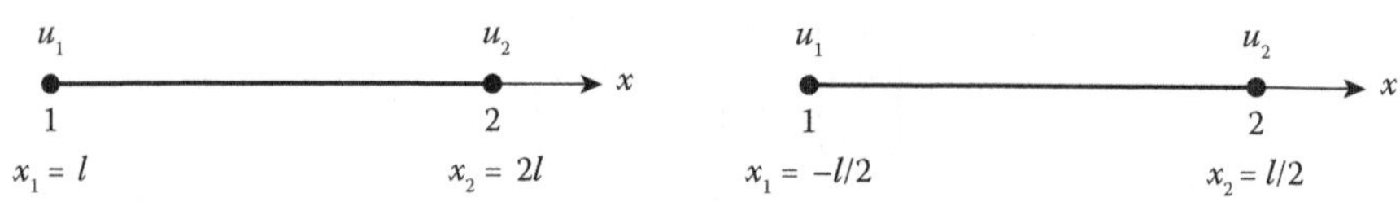

FIGURE 6.12
Two 1D 2-node elements located at different positions.

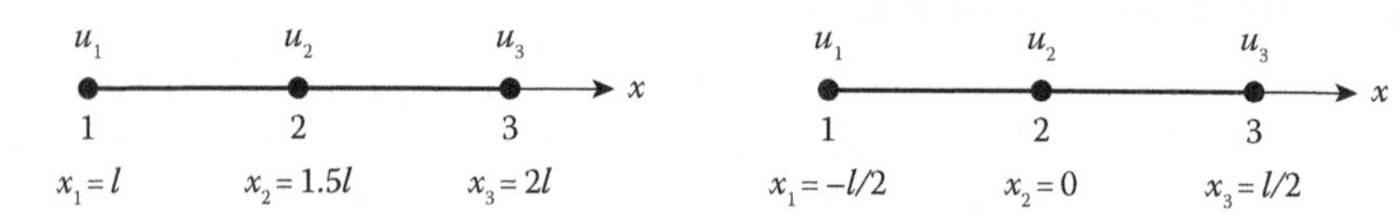

FIGURE 6.13
Two 1D 3-node elements located at different positions.

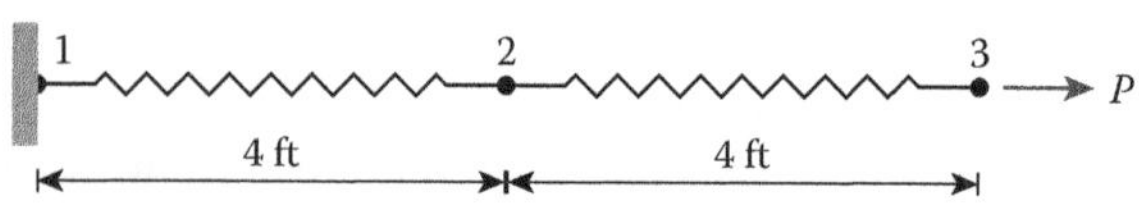

FIGURE 6.14
Spring loading structure made of two bar elements.

4. The spring loading structure shown in Figure 6.15 is made of four members of circular cross section with radius $r = 0.5$ in. The structure is fixed at the left end and is subjected to a point load $P = 275$ lb at the right end, as shown. The lengths of all members are given in the figure. Assuming that all members are made of titanium alloy with Young's modulus $E = 17 \times 10^6$ lb/in.^{2}, determine the displacements at joints 2 through 4.

5. The spring loading structure shown in Figure 6.16 is made of six members. The structure is fixed at both ends and is subjected to a point load $P = 450$ lb, as shown. The lengths of all members are given in the figure. Assuming that all members are made of steel with Young's modulus $E = 30 \times 10^6$ lb/in.^{2} and cross section area $A = 1.5$ in.^{2}, determine the displacements at the three inner joints.

6. The members of the 2D truss shown in Figure 6.17 have a cross section area of 5 cm^2 and are made of steel with Young's modulus $E = 210$ GPa. The truss is subject to a vertical load $P = 1$ KN and a horizontal load $F = 2.5$ KN at joint 3. Determine the deflection of each joint, the stress in each member, and the reaction forces. Use a FEM software tool to model the problem and compare the results.

7. The members of the 2D truss shown in Figure 6.18 have a cross section area of 4 cm^2 and are made of brass with Young's modulus $E = 120$ GPa. The truss is subject to loads $P = 0.75$ KN and $F = 2.0$ KN at joint 2, as shown. Determine the deflection of each joint,

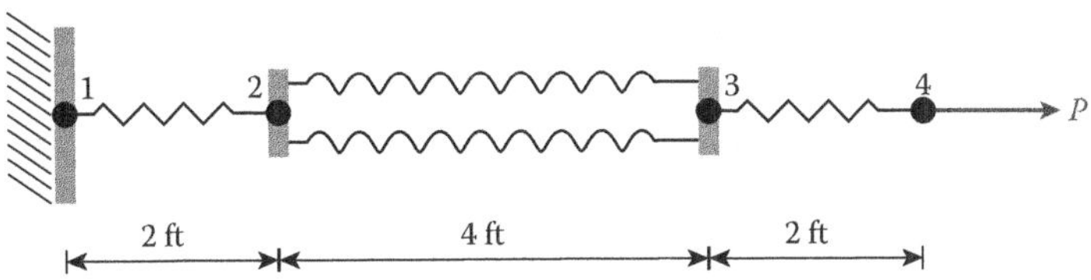

FIGURE 6.15
Spring loading structure made of four bar elements.

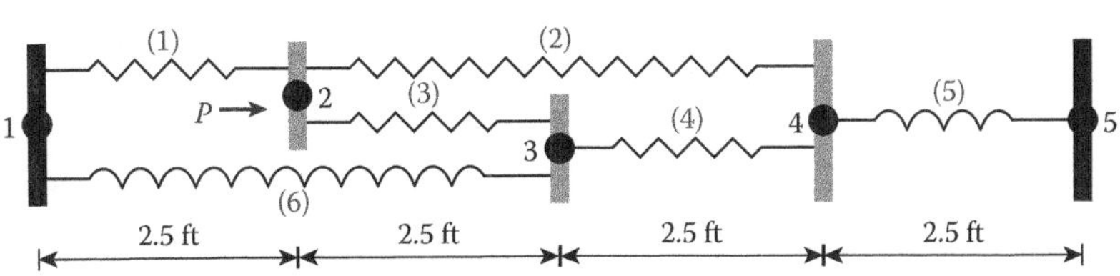

FIGURE 6.16
Spring loading structure made of six bar elements.

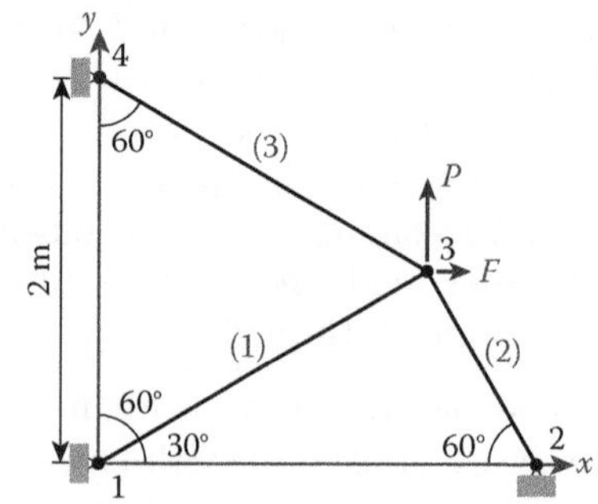

FIGURE 6.17
A 2D truss structure made of three bar elements.

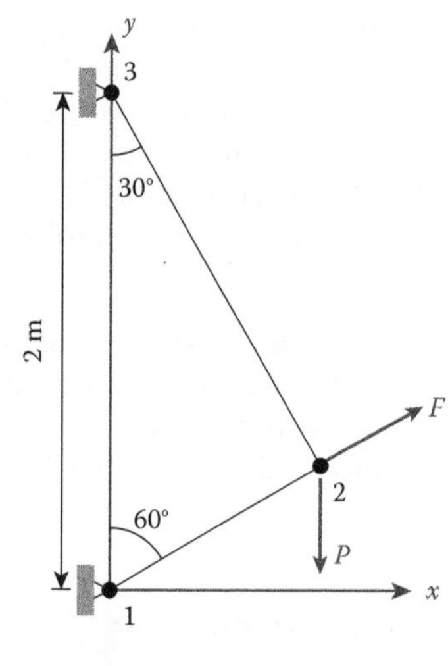

FIGURE 6.18
A 2D truss structure made of two bar elements.

the stress in each member, and the reaction forces. Use a FEM software tool to model the problem and compare the results.

8. The members of the 2D truss shown in Figure 6.19 have a cross section area of 1 in.^{2} and are made of silicon carbide with Young's modulus $E = 65 \times 10^6$ lb/in.^{2}. The truss is subject to load $F =$ 275 lb at joint 2, as shown. Determine the deflection of each joint, the stress in each member, and the reaction forces. Use a FEM software tool to model the problem and compare the results.
9. The members of the 2D truss shown in Figure 6.20 have a cross section area of 1.5 in.^{2} and are made of steel with Young's modulus $E = 30 \times 10^6$ lb/in.^{2}. The truss is subject to loads $P = 200$ lb and

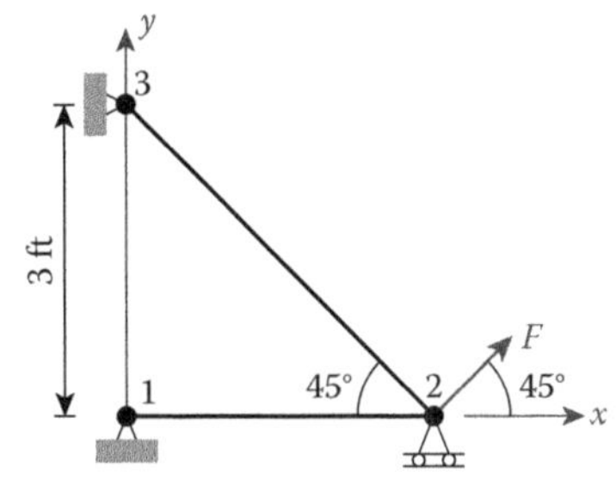

FIGURE 6.19
A 2D truss structure made of two bar elements.

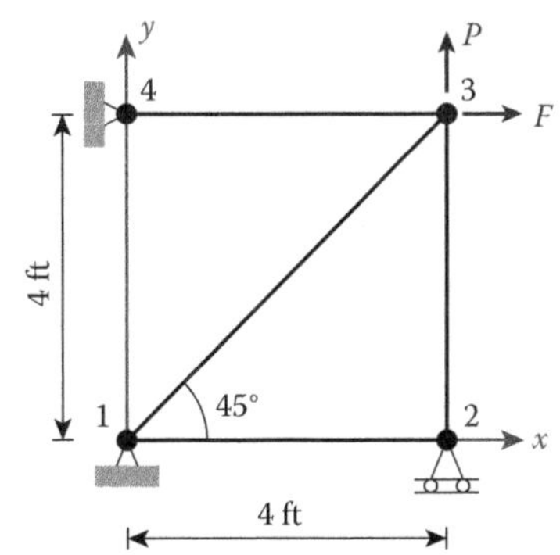

FIGURE 6.20
A 2D truss structure made of four bar elements.

$F = 275$ lb at joint 3, as shown. Determine the deflection of each joint, the stress in each member, and the reaction forces. Use a FEM software tool to model the problem and compare the results.

10. The members of the 2D truss shown in Figure 6.21 have a cross section area of 1.5 in.^{2} and are made of steel with Young's modulus $E = 30 \times 10^6$ lb/in.^{2}. The truss is subject to loads $P = 200$ lb and $F = 275$ lb at joint 3, as shown. Determine the deflection of each joint, the stress in each member, and the reaction forces. Use a FEM software tool to model the problem and compare the results.

11. The members of the 2D truss shown in Figure 6.22 have a cross section area of 2 in.^{2} and are made of aluminum with Young's modulus $E = 10 \times 10^6$ lb/in.^{2}. The truss is subject to loads $P = 1500$ lb and $F = 2750$ lb at joint 3, as shown. Determine the deflection of each joint, the stress in each member, and the reaction forces. Use a FEM software tool to model the problem and compare the results.

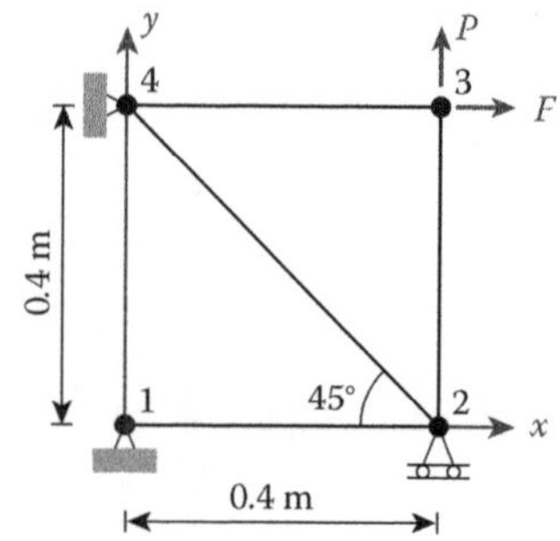

FIGURE 6.21
A 2D truss structure made of four bar elements.

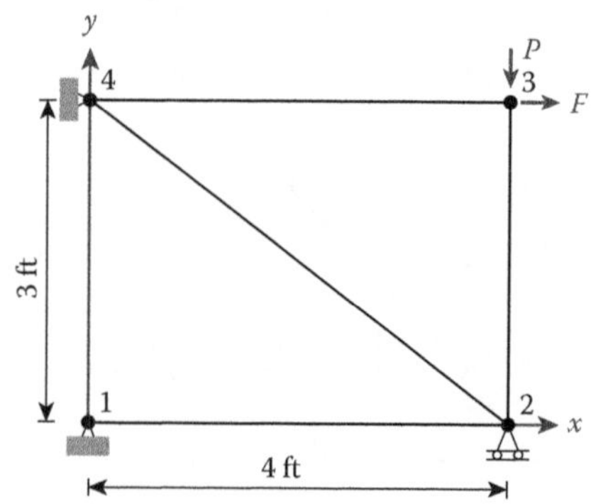

FIGURE 6.22
A 2D truss structure made of four bar elements.

12. The members of the 2D truss shown in Figure 6.23 have a cross section area of 0.5 in.^{2} and are made of titanium alloy with Young's modulus $E = 17 \times 10^6$ lb/in.^{2}. The truss is subject to loads $P =$ 50 lb and $F = 80$ lb at joint 3, as shown. Determine the deflection of each joint, the stress in each member, and the reaction forces. Use a FEM software tool to model the problem and compare the results.

13. The members of the 2D truss shown in Figure 6.24 have a cross section area of 6 mm^2 and are made of steel with Young's modulus $E = 210$ GPa. The truss is subject to loads $P = 150$ N and $F = 300$ N at joint 3, as shown. Determine the deflection of each joint, the stress in each member, and the reaction forces. Use a FEM software tool to model the problem and compare the results.

14. The four joints of the 3D truss shown in Figure 6.25 have the following coordinates: $1(0, 0, -1)$, $2(0, 0, 1)$, $3(0, 1, 0)$, and $4(1.5, 0.25, 0)$, with units in meters. All members have the same cross section area

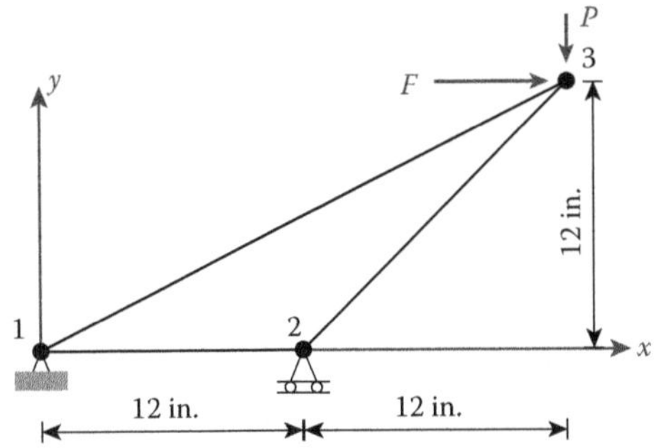

FIGURE 6.23
A 2D truss structure made of three bar elements.

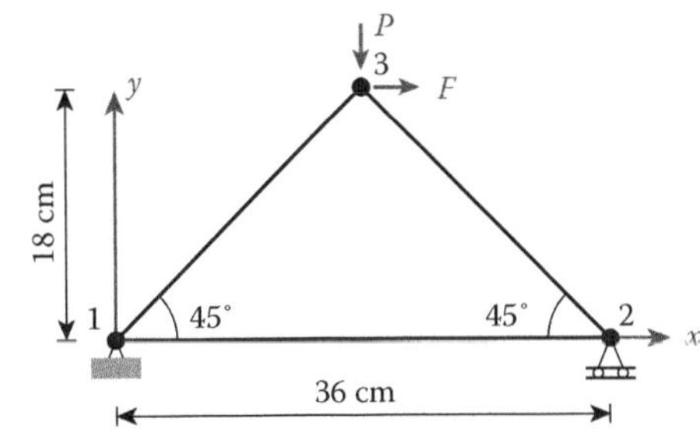

FIGURE 6.24
2D truss structure made of three bar elements.

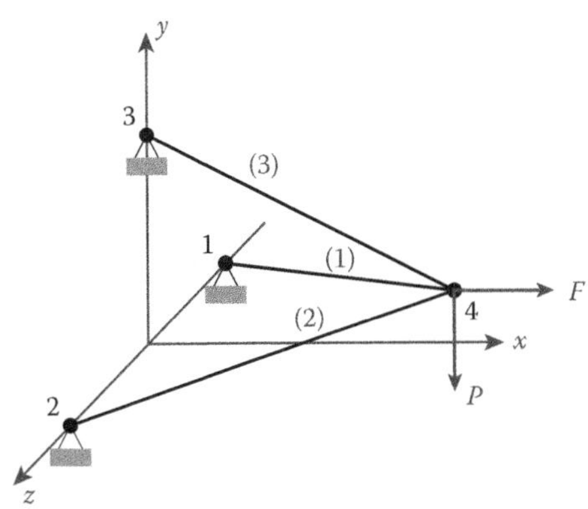

FIGURE 6.25
A 3D truss structure made of three bar elements.

of 10 cm^2 and are made of titanium alloy with Young's modulus $E = 120$ GPa. The truss is subject to a vertical load $P = 2$ KN and a horizontal load $F = 1.5$ KN at joint 4. Determine the deflection of each joint, the stress in each member, and the reaction forces.

Use a FEM software tool to model the problem and compare the results.

15. The four joints of the 3D truss shown in Figure 6.26 have the following coordinates: $1(0.5, 1.5, 0.5)$, $2(0, 0, 0)$, $3(0, 0, 1)$ $4(1, 0, 1)$, and $5(1, 0, 0)$, with units in meters. All members have the same cross section area of 5 cm^2 and are made of steel with Young's modulus $E = 210$ GPa. The truss is subject to a vertical load $P = 5$ KN and a horizontal load $F = 7.5$ KN at joint 1. Determine the deflection of each joint, the stress in each member, and the reaction forces. Use a FEM software tool to model the problem and compare the results.

16. The four joints of the 3D truss shown in Figure 6.27 have the following coordinates: $1(2, 0, 0)$, $2(0, 0, -1)$, $3(0, 1, 0)$, and $4(0, 0, 1)$, with units in meters. All members have the same cross section area of 7.5 cm^2 and are made of brass with Young's modulus $E = 125$ GPa. The truss is subject to a vertical load $P = 2.5$ KN and a horizontal load $F = 5$ KN at joint 1. Determine the deflection of each joint, the

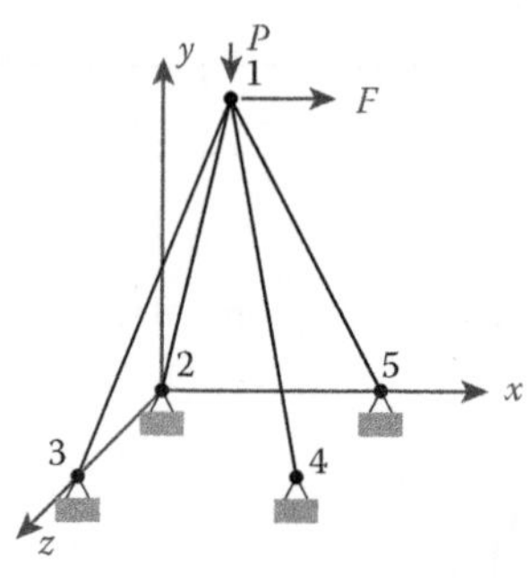

FIGURE 6.26
A 3D truss structure made of four bar elements.

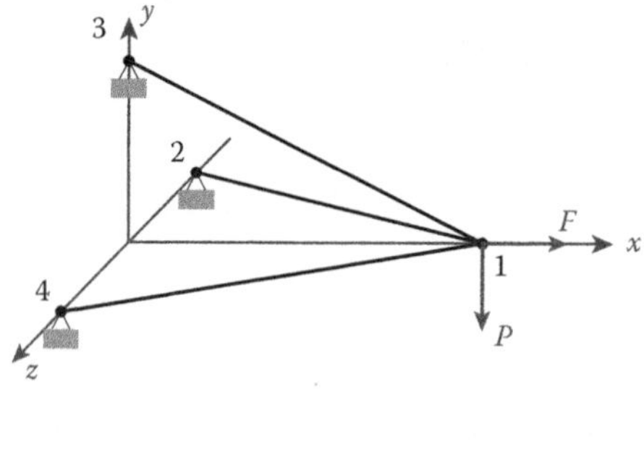

FIGURE 6.27
A 3D truss structure made of three bar elements.

stress in each member, and the reaction forces. Use a FEM software tool to model the problem and compare the results.

17. The four joints of the 3D truss shown in Figure 6.28 have the following coordinates: $1(0, -3, 0)$, $2(2, 0, 0)$, $3(-1, 0, -1)$, and $4(0, 0, 2)$, with units in meters. All members have the same cross section area of 15 cm^2 and are made of aluminum with Young's modulus $E = 70$ GPa. The truss is subject to a vertical load $P = 5$ KN at joint 1. Determine the deflection of each joint, the stress in each member, and the reaction forces. Use a FEM software tool to model the problem and compare the results.

18. Use the formula given in Equation 6.23 to determine the elementary $[K_e]$ matrix for the 2-node beam element shown in Figure 6.29 in terms of Young's modulus, E; the second moment of inertia of the cross section of the beam, I; and length, l.

19. For the bridge structure shown in Figure 6.30 made of beam elements, determine the rotation at nodes 1 through 4. The beam is subjected to a distributed load $f = -15$ lb/in. and a downward force $P = -50$ lb, as shown. Consider that the beam structure is

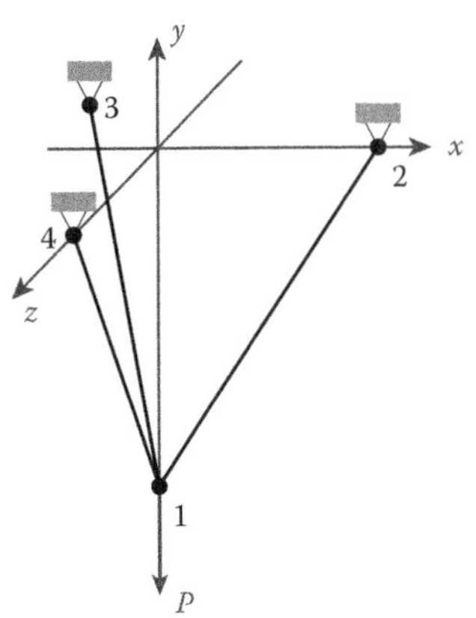

FIGURE 6.28
A 3D truss structure made of three bar elements.

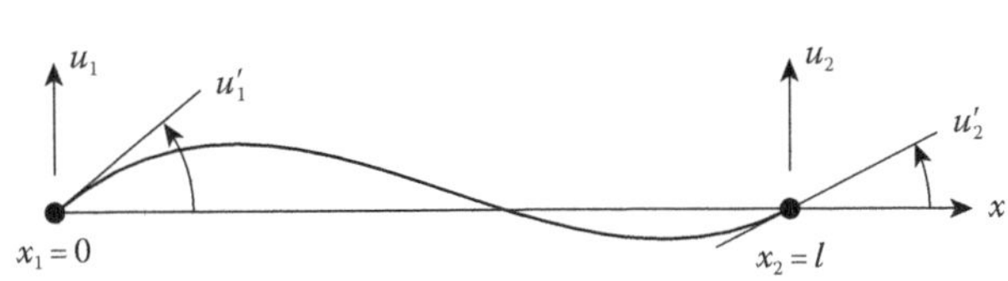

FIGURE 6.29
A 2-node beam element.

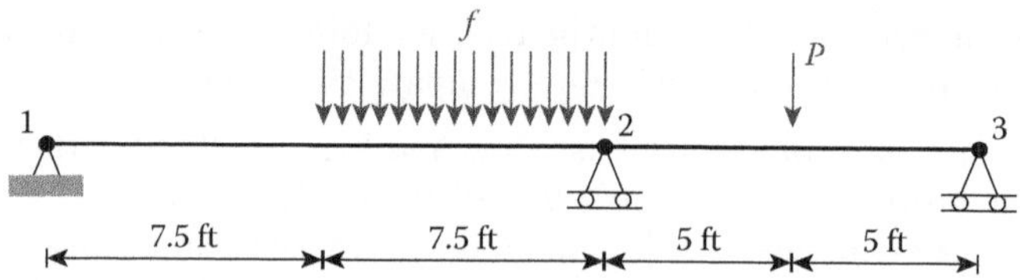

FIGURE 6.30
Bridge structure made of beam elements.

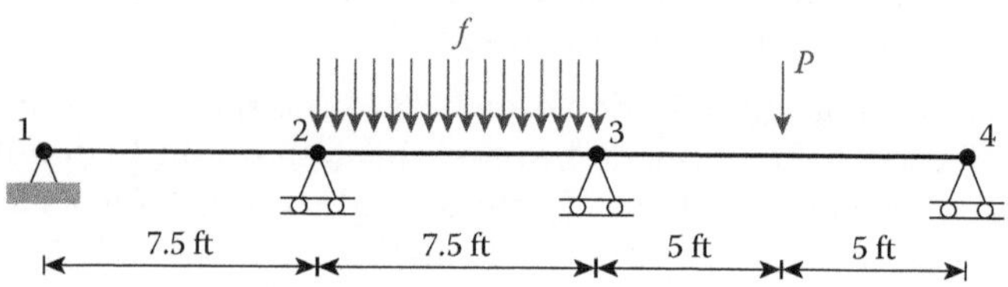

FIGURE 6.31
Bridge structure made of beam elements.

made of a material having flexure rigidity of $EI = 10^9$ lb-in.^{2}. Use a FEM software tool to model the problem and compare the results.

20. For the bridge structure shown in Figure 6.31 made of beam elements, determine the rotation at nodes 1 through 3. The beam is subjected to a distributed load $f = -15$ lb/in. and a downward force $P = -50$ lb, as shown. Consider that the beam structure is made of a material having flexure rigidity of $EI = 10^9$ lb-in.^{2}. Use a FEM software tool to model the problem and compare the results.

Recommended Readings

1. J. N. Reddy. 1993. *An Introduction to the Finite Element Method.* 2nd ed. Boston: McGraw-Hill.
2. David V. Hutton. 2004. *Fundamentals of Finite Element Analysis.* Boston: McGraw-Hill.
3. Jacob Fish and Ted Belytschko. 2007. *A First Course in Finite Elements.* Hoboken, NJ: John Wiley & Sons.

7

Scalar Field Problems in Higher Dimensions

In this chapter, we focus our discussion on scalar field engineering problems in two-dimensional (2D) and three-dimensional (3D) spaces. For scalar field problems, the field quantities of interest are scalar variables, such as temperature, concentration of a certain species, and electrical potential. Since scalar variables are independent of directions, even in 2D and 3D spaces there is only one field quantity at each node of the discretized elements (i.e., nodal DOF = 1). Scalar problems are sometimes referred to as single-variable problems. Because of this, solving single-variable scalar problems of high dimensions is relatively easy to do. In the following sections, we use a single variable u to represent these scalar variables.

7.1 FEM Formulation for 2D Scalar Field Problems

7.1.1 FEM formulation

For scalar field problems in a 2D space, their domains can be discretized into elements of two dimensions. Assuming the orthotropic property, the common form differential equation 6.1 can be expressed in 2D as

$$\frac{\partial}{\partial x}\left[k_x\frac{\partial u}{\partial x}\right]+\frac{\partial}{\partial y}\left[k_y\frac{\partial u}{\partial y}\right]+g=0 \tag{7.1}$$

where $u=u(x,y)$ represents a 2D field quantity. Let $\tilde{u}(x,y)$ be an approximate solution; we write the following residual based on the given differential equation:

$$R=\frac{\partial}{\partial x}\left[k_x\frac{\partial \tilde{u}}{\partial x}\right]+\frac{\partial}{\partial y}\left[k_y\frac{\partial \tilde{u}}{\partial y}\right]+g$$

Assuming the 2D domain has a thickness of t and an area of A, we construct the following weighted integral of residual by introducing a set of weight functions $w(x, y)$:

$$\begin{aligned}\iiint_V wRdV &= \iint_A wRtdA \\ &= \iint_A w\left\{\frac{\partial}{\partial x}\left[k_x\frac{\partial \tilde{u}}{\partial x}\right] + \frac{\partial}{\partial y}\left[k_y\frac{\partial \tilde{u}}{\partial y}\right] + g\right\} tdA = 0\end{aligned}$$

By the product rule of differentiation, we have

$$\begin{aligned} w\frac{\partial}{\partial x}\left[k_x\frac{\partial \tilde{u}}{\partial x}\right] &= -\frac{\partial w}{\partial x}\left[k_x\frac{\partial \tilde{u}}{\partial x}\right] + \frac{\partial}{\partial x}\left(w\left[k_x\frac{\partial \tilde{u}}{\partial x}\right]\right) \\ w\frac{\partial}{\partial y}\left[k_y\frac{\partial \tilde{u}}{\partial y}\right] &= -\frac{\partial w}{\partial y}\left[k_y\frac{\partial \tilde{u}}{\partial y}\right] + \frac{\partial}{\partial y}\left(w\left[k_y\frac{\partial \tilde{u}}{\partial y}\right]\right)\end{aligned}$$

Substituting these relationships into the equation above and rearranging it, we obtain

$$\begin{aligned}&\iint_A \left[\frac{\partial w}{\partial x}\left[k_x\frac{\partial \tilde{u}}{\partial x}\right] + \frac{\partial w}{\partial y}\left[k_y\frac{\partial \tilde{u}}{\partial y}\right]\right] tdA \\ &= \iint_A \left[\frac{\partial}{\partial x}\left(w\left[k_x\frac{\partial \tilde{u}}{\partial x}\right]\right) + \frac{\partial}{\partial y}\left(w\left[k_y\frac{\partial \tilde{u}}{\partial y}\right]\right)\right] tdA + \iint_A wgtdA\end{aligned} \tag{7.2}$$

The integral on the left-hand side of Equation 7.2 can be expressed in a compact form by using the ∇ operator in 2D $\left(\text{i.e., } \nabla = \frac{\partial}{\partial x}\vec{i} + \frac{\partial}{\partial y}\vec{j}\right)$, the dot product expression, and k (for k_x, k_y):

$$\iint_A \left[\frac{\partial w}{\partial x}\left[k_x\frac{\partial \tilde{u}}{\partial x}\right] + \frac{\partial w}{\partial y}\left[k_y\frac{\partial \tilde{u}}{\partial y}\right]\right] tdA = \iint_A \nabla w\cdot[k\nabla\tilde{u}]tdA$$

First, we rewrite the first integral on the right-hand side of Equation 7.2 using the ∇ operator:

$$\begin{aligned}&\iint_A \left[\frac{\partial}{\partial x}\left(w\left[k_x\frac{\partial \tilde{u}}{\partial x}\right]\right) + \frac{\partial}{\partial y}\left(w\left[k_y\frac{\partial \tilde{u}}{\partial y}\right]\right)\right] tdA \\ &= \iint_A \nabla\cdot\left(w\left[k_x\frac{\partial \tilde{u}}{\partial x}\right]\vec{i} + w\left[k_y\frac{\partial \tilde{u}}{\partial y}\right]\vec{j}\right) tdA\end{aligned}$$

then we apply the divergence theorem (see Figure 2.3):

$$\begin{aligned}&\iint_A \nabla\cdot\left(w\left[k_x\frac{\partial \tilde{u}}{\partial x}\right]\vec{i} + w\left[k_y\frac{\partial \tilde{u}}{\partial y}\right]\vec{j}\right) tdA \\ &= \int_L w\left(\left[k_x\frac{\partial \tilde{u}}{\partial x}\right]\vec{i} + \left[k_y\frac{\partial \tilde{u}}{\partial y}\right]\vec{j}\right)\cdot\vec{n}tdL = \int_L w[k\nabla\tilde{u}]\cdot\vec{n}tdL\end{aligned}$$

where $\vec{n} = n_x\vec{i} + n_y\vec{j}$ is the unit normal vector of the boundary line at a given point. Putting all these expressions together, we rewrite Equation 7.2 as

$$\iint_A \nabla w \cdot [k\nabla\tilde{u}]tdxdy = \int_L w[k\nabla\tilde{u}] \cdot \vec{n}tdL + \iint_A wgtdxdy \tag{7.3}$$

By the Galerkin method, we will take the shape functions as the weight functions; thus, we write

$$w_m = N_m \text{ for } m = 1, \ldots, n_e$$

By plugging in these weight functions along with

$$\tilde{u} = [N]\{d_0\}$$

we obtain

$$\iint_A (\nabla N_m \cdot k\nabla[N])tdxdy\{d_0\} = \int_L N_m[k\nabla\tilde{u}] \cdot \vec{n}\}tdL + \iint_A N_m gtdxdy$$

for $m = 1, \ldots, n_e$.

By summing all these n_e equations together (in the same steps used in Section 6.2), we arrive at

$$\iint_A ([\nabla N]^T \cdot k\nabla [N])tdA\{d_0\} = \int_L [N]^T[k\nabla\tilde{u}] \cdot \vec{n}tdL + \iint_A [N]^T gtdA \tag{7.4}$$

in which the coefficient associated with the elementary degrees of freedom (DOF) vector, $\{d_0\}$, is the elementary $[K_e]$ matrix for 2D elements for scalar field problems, that is,

$$[K_e] = \iint_A ([\nabla N]^T \cdot k\nabla [N])tdA \tag{7.5}$$

Note that although this $[K_e]$ matrix has the same meaning as its counterpart in the one-dimensional (1D) domain, because the procedures used to derive it only apply to scalar field problems, it should not be used to calculate the mechanical stiffness matrix. For mechanical problems, due to their vector fields, as well as other material-related issues, such as the Poison's ratio effect and material anisotropy, they are dealt with in a separate chapter (see Chapter 8).

Similar to the 1D situation, the first term on the right-hand side of Equation 7.4 distributes point and edge constraints, for example, a heat flux or a mass flux, to the nodes of the element, and the second term resolves the volume loads (if any), for example, a volume heat source or a volume reaction source, into equivalent nodal quantities. So if we use the load vector $\{P_e\}$ to represent them, we can express Equation 7.4 of 2D scalar problems as

$$[K_e]\{d_0\} = \{P_e\}$$

7.1.2 Elementary $[K_e]$ matrix

Using Equation 7.5, we can find the elementary $[K_e]$ matrix of any 2D elements based on the type and order of the elements and their corresponding shape functions. Once all the elementary $[K_e]$ matrices are known, we will assemble them into the global $[K]$ matrix. To do this, we can go through the same steps as discussed in Section 6.4, which will eventually lead us to the same matrix equation, that is, Equation 6.11,

$$[K]\{D\} = \{P\}$$

in which the global load vector on the right-hand side will be determined by evaluating the integral terms on the right-hand side of Equation 7.4. To solve the matrix equation, we will again apply the matrix partition method based on the given boundary conditions to obtain the unknown DOF.

Of course, this procedure can be handled manually when the number of elements is small, as we saw in the several examples discussed in Chapter 6. But when the physical domain is discretized into a large number of elements, and sometimes with higher-order elements, performing this procedure manually may become too tedious or impossible. Thus, we often turn to a computer program (e.g., a finite element program) to do all these, including geometry building, domain discretization, element selection, $[K_e]$ and $[K]$ matrix evaluation, and matrix equation solving, until the problem is fully solved and relevant parameters of interest are determined. Therefore, from now on we will not complete this procedure manually. Instead, we will just evaluate the $[K_e]$ matrix in order to understand some important issues in performing integrations over the domains defined by the elements.

Example 7.1

For the 2D rectangular element shown in Figure 7.1, determine its elementary $[K_e]$ matrix using Equation 7.5. Assume that the element has a uniform thickness of $t = 0.005$ and a constant $k_x = k_y = k = 1000$ (note that because this example can be applied to different physics problems, such as heat conduction, mass diffusion, fluid flow in porous medium, and electric, without losing generality, we intentionally ignore the units of these values).

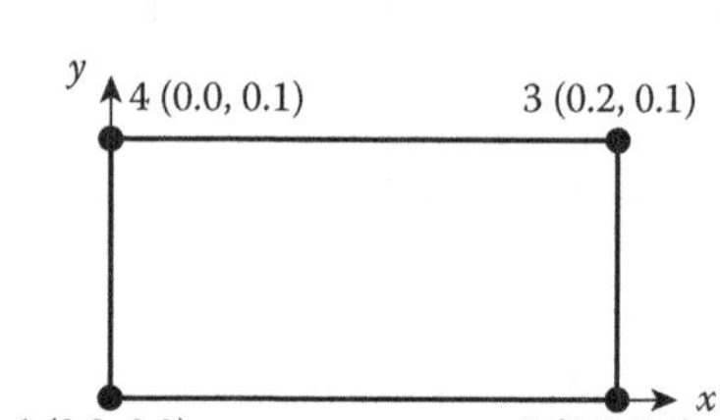

FIGURE 7.1
A 2D rectangular element with a uniform thickness.

Answer

To determine the elementary $[K_e]$ matrix, we first expand Equation 7.5 by using the 2D ∇ operator, $\nabla = \frac{\partial}{\partial x}\vec{i} + \frac{\partial}{\partial y}\vec{j}$:

$$[K_e] = \iint_A \left[\frac{\partial[N]}{\partial x}\vec{i} + \frac{\partial[N]}{\partial y}\vec{j}\right]^T \cdot \left(k_x \frac{\partial[N]}{\partial x}\vec{i} + k_y \frac{\partial[N]}{\partial y}\vec{j}\right) tdA$$
$$= \iint_A \left(\left[\frac{\partial N}{\partial x}\right]^T \vec{i} + \left[\frac{\partial N}{\partial y}\right]^T \vec{j}\right) \cdot \left(k_x \left[\frac{\partial N}{\partial x}\right]\vec{i} + k_y \left[\frac{\partial N}{\partial y}\right]\vec{j}\right) tdA \qquad (7.6)$$
$$= \iint_A \left(\left[\frac{\partial N}{\partial x}\right]^T k_x \left[\frac{\partial N}{\partial x}\right] + \left[\frac{\partial N}{\partial y}\right]^T k_y \left[\frac{\partial N}{\partial y}\right]\right) tdA$$

For the rectangular element, by using the Lagrange interpolation formula (see Section 5.6.2), we calculate its four shape functions as

$$N_1 = \frac{x - x_2}{x_1 - x_2}\frac{y - y_2}{y_1 - y_2} = \frac{(x-0.2)(y-0.1)}{(0-0.2)(0-0.1)} = (1-5x)(1-10y)$$
$$N_2 = \frac{x - x_1}{x_2 - x_1}\frac{y - y_2}{y_1 - y_2} = \frac{(x-0)(y-0.1)}{(0.1-0)(0-0.1)} = 5x(1-10y)$$
$$N_3 = \frac{x - x_1}{x_2 - x_1}\frac{y - y_1}{y_2 - y_1} = \frac{(x-0)(y-0)}{(0.1-0)(0.1-0)} = 50xy$$
$$N_4 = \frac{x - x_2}{x_1 - x_2}\frac{y - y_1}{y_2 - y_1} = \frac{(x-0.1)(y-0)}{(0-0.1)(0.1-0)} = 10(1-5x)y$$

Putting these shape functions into the shape function matrix, we have

$$[N] = \begin{bmatrix}(1-5x)(1-10y) & 5x(1-10y) & 50xy & 10(1-5x)y\end{bmatrix}$$

Taking its first derivative with respect to x and y, we obtain

$$\left[\frac{\partial N}{\partial x}\right] = \begin{bmatrix}50y-5 & 5-50y & 50y & -50y\end{bmatrix}$$
$$\left[\frac{\partial N}{\partial y}\right] = \begin{bmatrix}50x-10 & -50x & 50x & 10-50x\end{bmatrix}$$

Plugging these expressions into Equation 7.6, and integrating it over the rectangular area defined by the element along with $dA = dady$ and the k_x, k_y, t values, we obtain

$$[K_e] = k_x t \int_{x=0}^{0.2}\int_{y=0}^{0.1} \begin{bmatrix}50y-5\\5-50y\\50y\\-50y\end{bmatrix} \begin{bmatrix}50y-5 & 5-50y & 50y & -50y\end{bmatrix} dydx$$
$$+ k_y t \int_{x=0}^{0.2}\int_{y=0}^{0.1} \begin{bmatrix}50x-10\\-50x\\50x\\10-50x\end{bmatrix} \begin{bmatrix}50x-10 & -50x & 50x & 10-50x\end{bmatrix} dydx$$

By multiplying the terms out and integrating them, we obtain

$$[K_e] = \begin{bmatrix} 4.17 & 0.83 & -2.08 & -2.92 \\ -0.83 & 4.17 & -2.92 & -2.08 \\ -2.08 & -2.92 & 4.17 & 0.83 \\ -2.92 & -2.08 & 0.83 & 4.17 \end{bmatrix}$$

Example 7.2

For the 2D triangular element shown in Figure 7.2, determine its elementary $[K_e]$ matrix using Equation 7.5. Assume that the element has a uniform thickness of $t = 0.005$ and a constant $k_x = k_y = k = 1000$ (ignore the units).

Answer

For the triangular element, by using the Lagrange interpolation formula for triangles (see Section 5.6.4), we determine the three shape functions:

$$N_1 = t_1 = \det\begin{bmatrix} 1 & x & y \\ 1 & 0.2 & 0 \\ 1 & 0.2 & 0.1 \end{bmatrix} / \det\begin{bmatrix} 1 & 0 & 0 \\ 1 & 0.2 & 0 \\ 1 & 0.2 & 0.1 \end{bmatrix} = 1 - 5x$$

$$N_2 = t_2 = \det\begin{bmatrix} 1 & 0 & 0 \\ 1 & x & y \\ 1 & 0.2 & 0.1 \end{bmatrix} / \det\begin{bmatrix} 1 & 0 & 0 \\ 1 & 0.2 & 0 \\ 1 & 0.2 & 0.1 \end{bmatrix} = 5x - 10y$$

$$N_3 = t_3 = \det\begin{bmatrix} 1 & 0 & 0 \\ 1 & 0.2 & 0 \\ 1 & x & y \end{bmatrix} / \det\begin{bmatrix} 1 & 0 & 0 \\ 1 & 0.2 & 0 \\ 1 & 0.2 & 0.1 \end{bmatrix} = 10y$$

Putting them into the shape function matrix, we have

$$[N] = \begin{bmatrix} 1 - 5x & 5x - 10y & 10y \end{bmatrix}$$

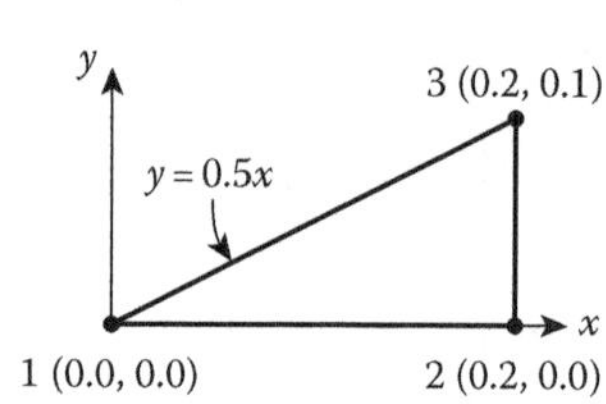

FIGURE 7.2
A 2D triangular element with a uniform thickness.

Taking its first derivative with respect to x and y, we obtain

$$\left[\frac{\partial N}{\partial x}\right] = \begin{bmatrix}-5 & 5 & 0\end{bmatrix}$$

$$\left[\frac{\partial N}{\partial y}\right] = \begin{bmatrix}0 & -10 & 10\end{bmatrix}$$

Plugging these expressions into Equation 7.6, integrating it over the triangular area defined by the element, and substituting the k_x, k_y, t values, we obtain

$$\begin{aligned}[K_e] &= k_x t \int_{x=0}^{0.2}\int_{y=0}^{0.5x} \begin{bmatrix}-5\\5\\0\end{bmatrix} \begin{bmatrix}-5 & 5 & 0\end{bmatrix} dydx \\ &+ k_y t \int_{x=0}^{0.2}\int_{y=0}^{0.5x} \begin{bmatrix}0\\-10\\10\end{bmatrix} \begin{bmatrix}0 & -10 & 10\end{bmatrix} dydx \\ &= \begin{bmatrix}1.25 & -1.25 & 0\\ -1.25 & 6.25 & -5.00\\ 0 & -5.00 & 5.00\end{bmatrix}\end{aligned}$$

These two examples show that to determine the elementary $[K_e]$ matrix for a 2D element, we need to first evaluate the shape function matrix for the element and then perform integration over the areal domain defined by the element. Moreover, because the areal domains of the two elements given here are very regular with easily defined edges, integration over these areal domains can be performed analytically. When elements have irregular shapes, integration over some irregularly shaped areas may become difficult. For these two reasons, it is desirable to have a unified way to express shape functions and perform integration for all elements, regardless of their shapes and locations.

7.2 Types of 2D Scalar Field Problems

Equation 7.4 is developed for a general scalar field problem in 2D space; thus, it is applicable to all scalar field problems in 2D.

For example, the governing differential equation for laminate flow of incompressible and nonviscous fluid can be expressed as

$$\frac{\partial^2 \psi}{\partial x^2} + \frac{\partial^2 \psi}{\partial y^2} = 0$$

where ψ is a steam function. By referring to Equation 7.1, we can just replace ψ for u, and let $g = 0$ and $k_x = k_y = 1$. In this way, we can then use Equation 7.4 to solve laminate flow problems.

For transport of fluid in a porous medium, we have the following governing differential equation:

$$\frac{\partial}{\partial x}\left(k_x\frac{\partial \phi}{\partial x}\right)+\frac{\partial}{\partial y}\left(k_y\frac{\partial \phi}{\partial y}\right)=0$$

where ϕ stands for hydraulic potential (or hydraulic head), and k_x, k_y are hydraulic conductivity. Again, by referring to Equation 7.1, we can see that in substitution of u with ϕ and letting $g = 0$, we can use Equation 7.4 to deal with transport problems in porous media.

Similarly, for electrical and magnetic field problems, their governing differential equations are

$$\epsilon_0\epsilon_r\left(\frac{\partial^2 V}{\partial x^2}+\frac{\partial^2 V}{\partial y^2}\right)=-\rho$$

$$\mu\left(\frac{\partial^2 B}{\partial x^2}+\frac{\partial^2 B}{\partial y^2}\right)=0$$

respectively, where V stands for electrical potential, ϵ_0 for permittivity of the vacuum, ϵ_r for relative permittivity of a medium, ρ for electrical charge density, B for magnetic potential, and μ for permeability of a medium. With proper substitutions and replacements of variables and constants, one can use Equation 7.4 to solve electrical and magnetic problems in 2D.

7.3 FEM Formulation for 3D Scalar Field Problems

7.3.1 FEM formulation

For scalar field problems in 3D space, the common form differential equation 6.1 can be expressed in a compact form as

$$\nabla\cdot[k\nabla u]+g=0$$

where $\nabla=\frac{\partial}{\partial x}\vec{i}+\frac{\partial}{\partial y}\vec{j}+\frac{\partial}{\partial z}\vec{k}$ and $u=u(x,y,z)$ represents a 3D scalar field quantity. Let $\tilde{u}(x,y,z)$ be an approximate solution; we write the following residual based on the given differential equation:

$$R=\nabla\cdot[k\nabla\tilde{u}]+g$$

Then, we construct the following weighted integral of residual by introducing a set of weight functions $w(x,y,z)$:

$$\iiint_V wR\,dV=\iiint_V w\{\nabla\cdot[k\nabla\tilde{u}]+g\}dV=0$$

Assuming an orthotropic property (i.e., k will be replaced by k_x, k_y, k_z in the three orthogonal directions), and by the definition of dot product, we write out all the terms for the above equation:

$$\iiint_V w\left[\frac{\partial}{\partial x}\left[k_x\frac{\partial \tilde{u}}{\partial x}\right]+\frac{\partial}{\partial y}\left[k_y\frac{\partial \tilde{u}}{\partial y}\right]+\frac{\partial}{\partial z}\left[k_z\frac{\partial \tilde{u}}{\partial z}\right]+g\right]dV=0$$

By the product rule of differentiation, we have

$$\begin{aligned}
w\frac{\partial}{\partial x}\left[k_x\frac{\partial \tilde{u}}{\partial x}\right] &= -\frac{\partial w}{\partial x}\left[k_x\frac{\partial \tilde{u}}{\partial x}\right]+\frac{\partial}{\partial x}\left(w\left[k_x\frac{\partial \tilde{u}}{\partial x}\right]\right)\\
w\frac{\partial}{\partial y}\left[k_y\frac{\partial \tilde{u}}{\partial y}\right] &= -\frac{\partial w}{\partial y}\left[k_y\frac{\partial \tilde{u}}{\partial y}\right]+\frac{\partial}{\partial y}\left(w\left[k_y\frac{\partial \tilde{u}}{\partial y}\right]\right)\\
w\frac{\partial}{\partial z}\left[k_z\frac{\partial \tilde{u}}{\partial z}\right] &= -\frac{\partial w}{\partial z}\left[k_z\frac{\partial \tilde{u}}{\partial z}\right]+\frac{\partial}{\partial z}\left(w\left[k_z\frac{\partial \tilde{u}}{\partial z}\right]\right)
\end{aligned}$$

Substituting these relationships into the above equation, we have

$$\begin{aligned}
&\iiint_V \left[\frac{\partial w}{\partial x}\left[k_x\frac{\partial \tilde{u}}{\partial x}\right]+\frac{\partial w}{\partial y}\left[k_y\frac{\partial \tilde{u}}{\partial y}\right]+\frac{\partial w}{\partial z}\left[k_z\frac{\partial \tilde{u}}{\partial z}\right]\right]dV\\
&=\iiint_V \left[\frac{\partial}{\partial x}\left(w\left[k_x\frac{\partial \tilde{u}}{\partial x}\right]\right)+\frac{\partial}{\partial y}\left(w\left[k_y\frac{\partial \tilde{u}}{\partial y}\right]\right)+\frac{\partial}{\partial z}\left(w\left[k_z\frac{\partial \tilde{u}}{\partial z}\right]\right)\right]dV\\
&+\iiint_V wg dV \qquad (7.7)
\end{aligned}$$

The integral on the left-hand side of Equation 7.7 can be simplified into a compact form by using the ∇ operator and dot product expression

$$\iiint_V \left[\frac{\partial w}{\partial x}\left[k_x\frac{\partial \tilde{u}}{\partial x}\right]+\frac{\partial w}{\partial y}\left[k_y\frac{\partial \tilde{u}}{\partial y}\right]+\frac{\partial w}{\partial z}\left[k_z\frac{\partial \tilde{u}}{\partial z}\right]\right]dV=\iiint_V \nabla w\cdot[k\nabla\tilde{u}]dV$$

To the first integral on the right-hand side of Equation 7.7, we apply the divergence theorem (see Equation 2.11):

$$\begin{aligned}
&\iiint_V \left[\frac{\partial}{\partial x}\left(w\left[k_x\frac{\partial \tilde{u}}{\partial x}\right]\right)+\frac{\partial}{\partial y}\left(w\left[k_y\frac{\partial \tilde{u}}{\partial y}\right]\right)+\frac{\partial}{\partial z}\left(w\left[k_z\frac{\partial \tilde{u}}{\partial z}\right]\right)\right]dV\\
&=\iint_S \left[w\left[k_x\frac{\partial \tilde{u}}{\partial x}\right]n_x+w\left[k_y\frac{\partial \tilde{u}}{\partial y}\right]n_y+w\left[k_z\frac{\partial \tilde{u}}{\partial z}\right]n_z\right]dS\\
&=\iint_S w[k\nabla\tilde{u}]\cdot\vec{n}dS
\end{aligned}$$

where $\vec{n}=n_x\vec{i}+n_y\vec{j}+n_z\vec{k}$ is the unit vector of the boundary surface. Putting them together, we express Equation 7.7 as

$$\iiint_V \nabla w\cdot[k\nabla\tilde{u}]dV=\iint_S w[k\nabla\tilde{u}]\cdot\vec{n}dS+\iiint_V wg dV$$

According to the Galerkin method, we have $w_m = N_m$ for $m = 1, \ldots, n_e$. With $\tilde{u} = [N]\{d_0\}$, we obtain

$$\iiint_V (\nabla N_m \cdot k\nabla[N])dV\{d_0\} = \iint_S N_m[k\nabla\tilde{u}] \cdot \vec{n}\}dS + \iiint_V N_m g dV$$

for $m = 1, \ldots, n_e$.

By summing all these n_e equations together (see steps in Section 6.2), we have

$$\iiint_V ([\nabla N]^T \cdot k\nabla[N])dV\{d_0\} = \iint_S [N]^T[k\nabla\tilde{u}] \cdot \vec{n}dS + \iiint_V [N]^T g dV \tag{7.8}$$

along with the elementary $[K_e]$ matrix for 3D elements for scalar field problems:

$$[K_e] = \iiint_V ([\nabla N]^T \cdot k\nabla[N])dV \tag{7.9}$$

As in the 2D case, this $[K_e]$ matrix should not be used to calculate the mechanical stiffness matrix. The two terms on the right-hand side of Equation 7.8 have the same meaning as those in the 1D and 2D cases; namely, the first distributes point and surface constraints to the nodes of the element, and the second resolves the volume loads into equivalent nodal quantities. Similarly, we can also express Equation 7.8 in the following matrix form:

$$[K_e]\{d_0\} = \{P_e\}$$

7.3.2 Elementary $[K_e]$ matrix

Like in the 2D case, Equation 7.9 can be used to find the elementary $[K_e]$ matrix of any 3D elements according to the type and order of the elements and their corresponding shape functions. Following that, the procedure can be used to assemble the global $[K]$ matrix, evaluate the global load vector, and eventually solve the matrix equation $[K]\{D\} = \{P\}$. Again, all these steps are often handled by using a finite element program. However, as with the 2D situation, we will go through some simple examples of evaluating the $[K_e]$ matrix for 3D scalar problems to see how domain integration is done in 3D.

Example 7.3

For the 3D hexahedral element shown in Figure 7.3, determine its elementary $[K_e]$ matrix using Equation 7.9. Assume that the element has constant $k_x = k_y = k_z = k = 1000$ along with the coordinates of their vertices given in the figure (ignore the units).

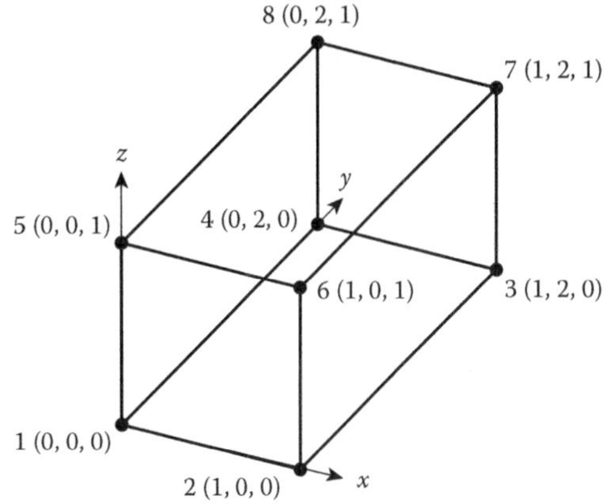

FIGURE 7.3
A 3D hexahedral element.

Answer
To determine the 3D elementary $[K_e]$ matrix for scalar problems, we again expand Equation 7.9 by using the ∇ operator in 3D:

$$[K_e] = \iiint_V \left(\left[\frac{\partial N}{\partial x}\right]^T k_x \left[\frac{\partial N}{\partial x}\right] + \left[\frac{\partial N}{\partial y}\right]^T k_y \left[\frac{\partial N}{\partial y}\right] + \left[\frac{\partial N}{\partial z}\right]^T k_z \left[\frac{\partial N}{\partial z}\right] \right) dV \tag{7.10}$$

For the hexahedral element, by using the Lagrange interpolation formula (see Section 5.6.5), we calculate its eight shape functions as

$$N_1 = \frac{x - x_2}{x_1 - x_2}\frac{y - y_2}{y_1 - y_2}\frac{z - z_2}{z_1 - z_2} = (1 - x)(2 - y)(1 - z)/2$$

$$N_2 = \frac{x - x_1}{x_2 - x_1}\frac{y - y_2}{y_1 - y_2}\frac{z - z_2}{z_1 - z_2} = x(2 - y)(1 - z)/2$$

$$N_3 = \frac{x - x_1}{x_2 - x_1}\frac{y - y_2}{y_1 - y_2}\frac{z - z_1}{z_2 - z_1} = xy(1 - z)/2$$

$$N_4 = \frac{x - x_2}{x_1 - x_2}\frac{y - y_2}{y_1 - y_2}\frac{z - z_1}{z_2 - z_1} = (1 - x)y(1 - z)/2$$

$$N_5 = \frac{x - x_2}{x_1 - x_2}\frac{y - y_1}{y_2 - y_1}\frac{z - z_2}{z_1 - z_2} = (1 - x)(2 - y)z/2$$

$$N_6 = \frac{x - x_1}{x_2 - x_1}\frac{y - y_1}{y_2 - y_1}\frac{z - z_2}{z_1 - z_2} = x(2 - y)z/2$$

$$N_7 = \frac{x - x_1}{x_2 - x_1}\frac{y - y_1}{y_2 - y_1}\frac{z - z_1}{z_2 - z_1} = xyz/2$$

$$N_8 = \frac{x - x_2}{x_1 - x_2}\frac{y - y_1}{y_2 - y_1}\frac{z - z_1}{z_2 - z_1} = (1 - x)yz/2$$

Putting them into the shape function matrix and taking its first derivative with respect to x, y, and z, we obtain

$$\left[\frac{\partial N}{\partial x}\right] = \frac{1}{2}\left[-(2-y)(1-z) \quad (2-y)(1-z) \quad y(1-z) \quad -y(1-z) \quad -(2-y)z \quad (2-y)z \quad yz \quad -yz\right]$$

$$\left[\frac{\partial N}{\partial y}\right] = \frac{1}{2}\left[-(1-x)(1-z) \quad -x(1-z) \quad x(1-z) \quad (1-x)(1-z) \quad -(1-x)z \quad -xz \quad xz \quad (1-x)z\right]$$

$$\left[\frac{\partial N}{\partial z}\right] = \frac{1}{2}\left[-(1-x)(2-y) \quad -x(2-y) \quad -xy \quad -(1-x)y \quad (1-x)(2-y) \quad x(2-y) \quad xy \quad (1-x)y\right]$$

Plugging these expressions into Equation 7.10, and integrating it over the hexahedral volume defined by the hexahedral element, along with substituting the $k_x = k_y = k_z = k$ values, we obtain

$$[K_e] = k\int_{x=0}^{1}\int_{y=0}^{2}\int_{z=0}^{1}\left(\left[\frac{\partial N}{\partial x}\right]^T\left[\frac{\partial N}{\partial x}\right] + \left[\frac{\partial N}{\partial y}\right]^T\left[\frac{\partial N}{\partial y}\right] + \left[\frac{\partial N}{\partial z}\right]^T\left[\frac{\partial N}{\partial z}\right]\right) dzdydx$$

$$= \begin{bmatrix} 500.00 & -83.33 & -83.33 & 166.67 & -83.33 & -208.33 & -125.00 & -83.33 \\ -83.33 & 500.00 & 166.67 & -83.33 & -208.33 & -83.33 & -83.33 & -125.00 \\ -83.33 & 166.67 & 500.00 & -83.33 & -125.00 & -83.33 & -83.33 & -208.33 \\ 166.67 & -83.33 & -83.33 & 500.00 & -83.33 & -125.00 & -208.33 & -83.33 \\ -83.33 & -208.33 & -125.00 & -83.33 & 500.00 & -83.33 & -83.33 & 166.67 \\ -208.33 & -83.33 & -83.33 & -125.00 & -83.33 & 500.00 & 166.67 & -83.33 \\ -125.00 & -83.33 & -83.33 & -208.33 & -83.33 & 166.67 & 500.00 & -83.33 \\ -83.33 & -125.00 & -208.33 & -83.33 & 166.67 & -83.33 & -83.33 & 500.00 \end{bmatrix}$$

Example 7.4

For the 3D tetrahedral element shown in Figure 7.4, determine its elementary $[K_e]$ matrix using Equation 7.9. Assume that the element has a constant $k_x = k_y = k_z = k = 1000$, along with the coordinates of their vertices given in the figure (ignore the units).

Answer

For the tetrahedral element, by using the Lagrange interpolation formula for tetrahedral elements (see Section 5.6.6), we obtain its four shape functions:

$$N_1 = t_1 = \frac{V_1}{V_0} = \frac{1}{6}\det\begin{bmatrix} 1 & x & y & z \\ 1 & 1 & 0 & 0 \\ 1 & 0 & 2 & 0 \\ 1 & 0 & 0 & 1 \end{bmatrix} \Bigg/ \frac{1}{6}\det\begin{bmatrix} 1 & 0 & 0 & 0 \\ 1 & 1 & 0 & 0 \\ 1 & 0 & 2 & 0 \\ 1 & 0 & 0 & 1 \end{bmatrix} = 1 - x - y/2 - z$$

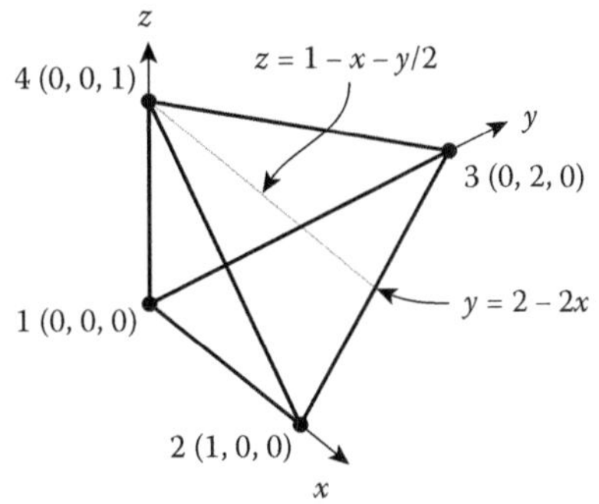

FIGURE 7.4
A 3D tetrahedral element.

$$N_2 = t_2 = \frac{V_2}{V_0} = \frac{1}{6}\det\begin{bmatrix}1 & 0 & 0 & 0\\ 1 & x & y & z\\ 1 & 0 & 2 & 0\\ 1 & 0 & 0 & 1\end{bmatrix} \Big/ \frac{1}{6}\det\begin{bmatrix}1 & 0 & 0 & 0\\ 1 & 1 & 0 & 0\\ 1 & 0 & 2 & 0\\ 1 & 0 & 0 & 1\end{bmatrix} = x$$

$$N_3 = t_3 = \frac{V_3}{V_0} = \frac{1}{6}\det\begin{bmatrix}1 & 0 & 0 & 0\\ 1 & 1 & 0 & 0\\ 1 & x & y & z\\ 1 & 0 & 0 & 1\end{bmatrix} \Big/ \frac{1}{6}\det\begin{bmatrix}1 & 0 & 0 & 0\\ 1 & 1 & 0 & 0\\ 1 & 0 & 2 & 0\\ 1 & 0 & 0 & 1\end{bmatrix} = y/2$$

$$N_4 = t_4 = \frac{V_4}{V_0} = \frac{1}{6}\det\begin{bmatrix}1 & 0 & 0 & 0\\ 1 & 1 & 0 & 0\\ 1 & 0 & 2 & 0\\ 1 & x & y & z\end{bmatrix} \Big/ \frac{1}{6}\det\begin{bmatrix}1 & 0 & 0 & 0\\ 1 & 1 & 0 & 0\\ 1 & 0 & 2 & 0\\ 1 & 0 & 0 & 1\end{bmatrix} = z$$

Putting them into the shape function matrix and taking its first derivative with respect to x, y, and z, we obtain

$$\left[\frac{\partial N}{\partial x}\right] = \begin{bmatrix}-1 & 1 & 0 & 0\end{bmatrix},$$
$$\left[\frac{\partial N}{\partial y}\right] = \begin{bmatrix}-0.5 & 0 & 0.5 & 0\end{bmatrix},$$
$$\left[\frac{\partial N}{\partial z}\right] = \begin{bmatrix}-1 & 0 & 0 & 1\end{bmatrix}$$

Plugging these expressions into Equation 7.10 and integrating it over the tetrahedral domain occupied by the element, along with substitution of the $k_x = k_y = k_z = k$ values, we obtain

$$[K_e] = k_x \int_{x=0}^{1} \int_{y=0}^{2-2x} \int_{z=0}^{1-x-y/2} \begin{bmatrix} -1 \\ 1 \\ 0 \\ 0 \end{bmatrix} \begin{bmatrix} -1 & 1 & 0 & 0 \end{bmatrix} dzdydx$$

$$+ k_y \int_{x=0}^{1} \int_{y=0}^{2-2x} \int_{z=0}^{1-x-y/2} \begin{bmatrix} -0.5 \\ 0 \\ 0.5 \\ 0 \end{bmatrix} \begin{bmatrix} -0.5 & 0 & 0.5 & 0 \end{bmatrix} dzdydx$$

$$+ k_z \int_{x=0}^{1} \int_{y=0}^{2-2x} \int_{z=0}^{1-x-y/2} \begin{bmatrix} -1 \\ 0 \\ 0 \\ 1 \end{bmatrix} \begin{bmatrix} -1 & 0 & 0 & 1 \end{bmatrix} dzdydx$$

$$= \begin{bmatrix} 750.00 & -333.33 & -83.33 & -333.33 \\ -333.33 & 333.33 & 0.00 & 0.00 \\ -83.33 & 0.00 & 83.33 & 0.00 \\ -333.33 & 0.00 & 0.00 & 333.33 \end{bmatrix}$$

As we can see from these 3D cases, to determine the elementary $[K_e]$ matrix, one needs to first evaluate the shape function matrix for the element and perform integration over the volumetric domain defined by the element. Thus, the issues and challenges related to the odd shape of the element in 2D exist here also. So the best way to overcome these issues and challenges is to take advantage of the concept of isoparametric elements for shape function development and Gauss quadrature for numerical integration, which we discuss in later chapters.

7.4 Types of 3D Scalar Field Problems

In a similar manner, Equation 7.8 is developed for a general-case scalar field problem in 3D space. The discussions in Section 7.2 can be extended to other scalar field 3D situations. That is, with proper substitutions and replacements of variables and constants, we can use Equation 7.8 to solve all scalar field problems, including the laminate flow, transport in porous media, and electric problems in 3D.

7.5 Exercises

1. For the 2D rectangular element shown in Figure 7.5, determine its elementary $[K_e]$ matrix. Assume that the element has a uniform thickness of $t = 0.01$ and a constant $k_x = k_y = k = 100$ (ignore the units for these values).

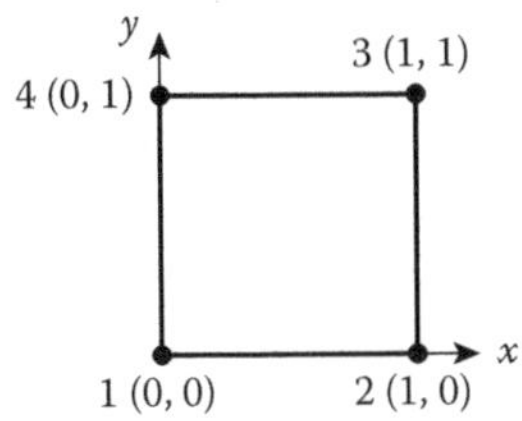

FIGURE 7.5
A 2D rectangular element with a uniform thickness.

2. For the 2D rectangular element shown in Figure 7.6, determine its elementary $[K_e]$ matrix. Assume that the element has a uniform thickness of $t = 0.01$ and a constant $k_x = k_y = k = 100$ (ignore the units for these values).
3. For the 2D triangular element shown in Figure 7.7, determine its elementary $[K_e]$ matrix. Assume that the element has a uniform thickness of $t = 0.01$ and a constant $k_x = k_y = k = 100$ (ignore the units for these values).
4. For the 2D triangular element shown in Figure 7.8, determine its elementary $[K_e]$ matrix. Assume that the element has a uniform

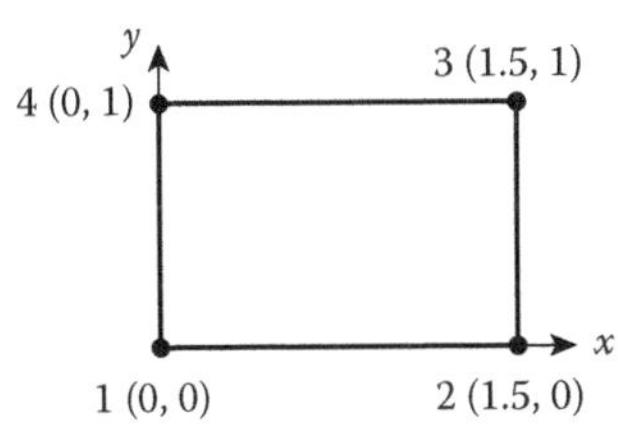

FIGURE 7.6
A 2D rectangular element with a uniform thickness.

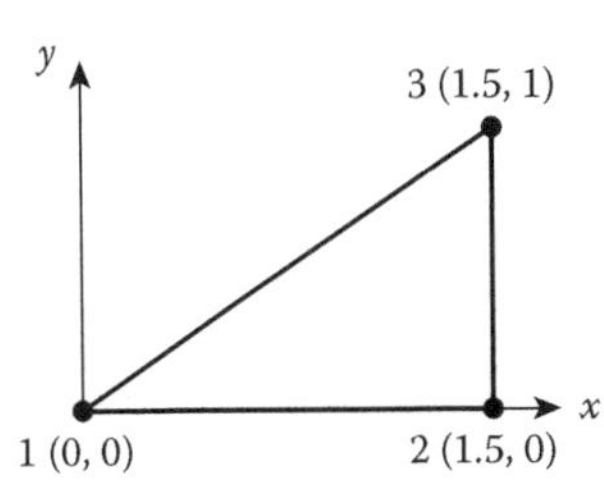

FIGURE 7.7
A 2D triangular element with a uniform thickness.

thickness of $t = 0.01$ and a constant $k_x = k_y = k = 100$ (ignore the units for these values).

5. For the 3D hexahedral element shown in Figure 7.9, determine its elementary $[K_e]$ matrix. Assume that the element has a constant $k_x = k_y = k_z = k = 1000$ (ignore the units for these values).

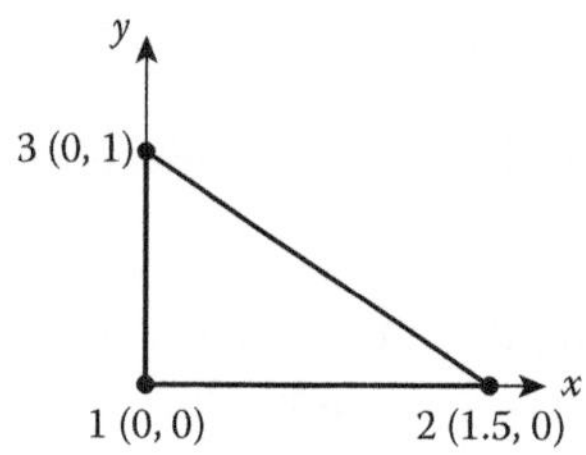

FIGURE 7.8
A 2D triangular element with a uniform thickness.

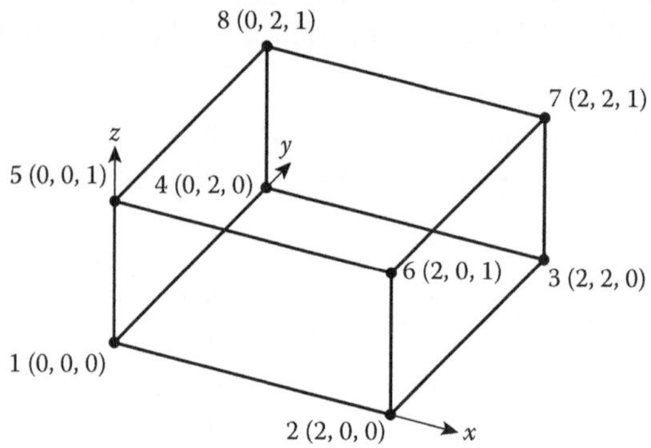

FIGURE 7.9
A 3D hexahedral element.

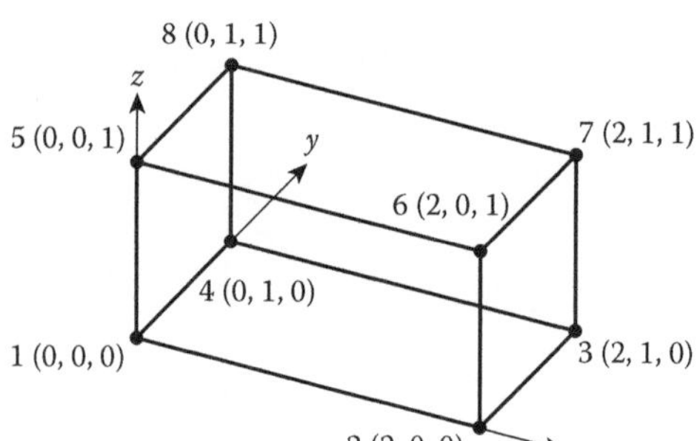

FIGURE 7.10
A 3D hexahedral element.

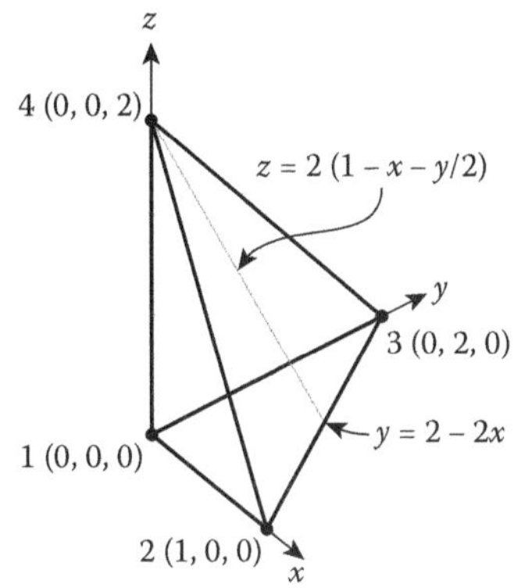

FIGURE 7.11
A 3D tetrahedral element.

6. For the 3D hexahedral element shown in Figure 7.10, determine its elementary $[K_e]$ matrix. Assume that the element has a constant $k_x = k_y = k_z = k = 1000$ (ignore the units for these values).
7. For the 3D tetrahedral element shown in Figure 7.11, determine its elementary $[K_e]$ matrix. Assume that the element has a constant $k_x = k_y = k_z = k = 1000$ (ignore the units for these values).

Recommended Readings

1. J. N. Reddy. 1993. *An Introduction to the Finite Element Method.* 2nd ed. Boston: McGraw-Hill.
2. Robert D. Cook, David S. Malkus, Michael E. Plesha, and Robert J. Witt. 2002. *Concepts and Applications of Finite Element Analysis.* 4th ed. Hoboken, NJ: John Wiley & Sons.
3. Saeed Moaveni. 2008. *Finite Element Analysis, Theory and Application with ANSYS.* Upper Saddle River, NJ: Prentice Hall.
4. David V. Hutton. 2004. *Fundamentals of Finite Element Analysis.* Boston: McGraw-Hill.
5. Tirupathi R. Chandrupatla and Ashok D. Belegundu. 2002. *Introduction to Finite Elements in Engineering.* 3rd ed. Upper Saddle River, NJ: Prentice Hall.
6. Jacob Fish and Ted Belytschko. 2007. *A First Course in Finite Elements.* Hoboken, NJ: John Wiley & Sons.

8

Vector Field Problems in Higher Dimensions

For vector field problems, we concentrate our discussion on problems of solid mechanics. Due to the directional dependence of the field quantity, the finite element method (FEM) formulations developed for scalar field problems cannot be used. Moreover, although we have seen twice the partial differential equations (PDEs) and FEM formulations for mechanical structures, such as bars and beams, because we have neglected the Poisson's ratio effect and material anisotropy, these PDEs and FEM formulations cannot be applied to problems of solid mechanics either. Thus, in this chapter we develop PDEs of equilibrium for solid mechanical structures and the corresponding FEM formulations in three-dimensional (3D) and two-dimensional (2D) spaces.

8.1 3D Solid Mechanics Problems

8.1.1 Free-body diagram and PDEs of equilibrium

We begin by considering a free-body diagram of an arbitrary, infinitesimal cube, shown in Figure 8.1, with dimensions dx, dy, and dz along the three Cartesian axes, x, y, and z, respectively. Each surface of the cube has three stress components as marked in the figure. Thus, we write the following three stress vectors:

$$
\begin{aligned}
S_x &= \sigma_x \vec{i} + \tau_{xy}\vec{j} + \tau_{xz}\vec{k} \\
S_y &= \tau_{yx}\vec{i} + \sigma_y\vec{j} + \tau_{yz}\vec{k} \\
S_z &= \tau_{zx}\vec{i} + \tau_{zy}\vec{j} + \sigma_z\vec{k}
\end{aligned}
$$

where $\tau_{xy} = \tau_{yx}, \tau_{xz} = \tau_{zx}$, and $\tau_{yz} = \tau_{zy}$. To establish the force equilibrium for this infinitesimal cube, we calculate the net force in each of the three axes by multiplying the differential stresses in the opposite surfaces as

$$
\begin{aligned}
\sum F_x :& \left(\sigma_x + \frac{\partial \sigma_x}{\partial x}dx - \sigma_x\right) dydz + \left(\tau_{xy} + \frac{\partial \tau_{xy}}{\partial y}dy - \tau_{xy}\right) dxdz \\
&+ \left(\tau_{xz} + \frac{\partial \tau_{xz}}{\partial z}dz - \tau_{xz}\right) dxdy + f_x dxdydz
\end{aligned}
$$

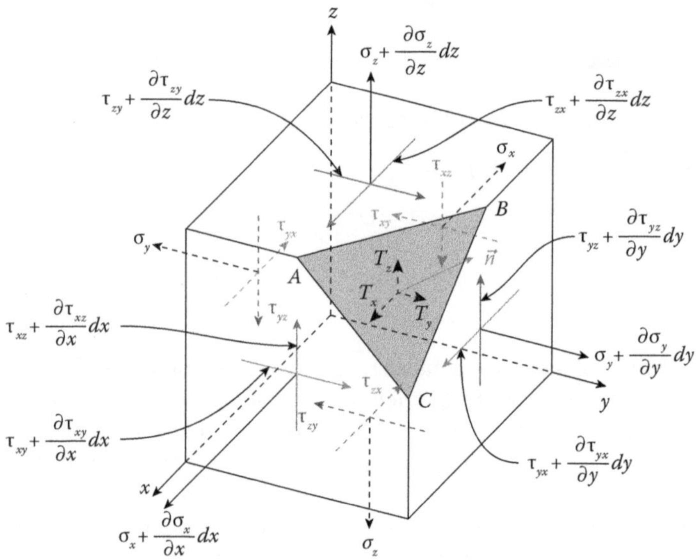

FIGURE 8.1
A 3D free-body diagram in Cartesian coordinates.

$$\sum F_y : \left(\sigma_y + \frac{\partial \sigma_y}{\partial y} dy - \sigma_y\right) dxdz + \left(\tau_{xy} + \frac{\partial \tau_{xy}}{\partial x} dx - \tau_{xy}\right) dydz$$
$$+ \left(\tau_{yz} + \frac{\partial \tau_{yz}}{\partial z} dz - \tau_{yz}\right) dxdy + f_y dxdydz$$

$$\sum F_z : \left(\sigma_z + \frac{\partial \sigma_z}{\partial z} dz - \sigma_z\right) dxdy + \left(\tau_{xz} + \frac{\partial \tau_{xz}}{\partial x} dx - \tau_{xz}\right) dydz$$
$$+ \left(\tau_{yz} + \frac{\partial \tau_{yz}}{\partial y} dy - \tau_{yz}\right) dydz + f_z dxdydz$$

where f_x, f_y, and f_z are the three components of the volume force in Cartesian coordinates. By considering Newton's second law of motion, we express the following three equilibrium equations (after multiplying $1/dxdydz$ on both sides of the equations):

$$\begin{aligned}
\sum F_x = ma_x &: \frac{\partial \sigma_x}{\partial x} + \frac{\partial \tau_{xy}}{\partial y} + \frac{\partial \tau_{xz}}{\partial z} + f_x = \rho \frac{\partial^2 u}{\partial t^2} \\
\sum F_y = ma_y &: \frac{\partial \tau_{xy}}{\partial x} + \frac{\partial \sigma_y}{\partial y} + \frac{\partial \tau_{yz}}{\partial z} + f_y = \rho \frac{\partial^2 v}{\partial t^2} \\
\sum F_z = ma_z &: \frac{\partial \tau_{xz}}{\partial x} + \frac{\partial \tau_{yz}}{\partial y} + \frac{\partial \sigma_z}{\partial z} + f_z = \rho \frac{\partial^2 w}{\partial t^2}
\end{aligned} \tag{8.1}$$

where $\rho(= m/dxdydz)$ is the mass density of the material, and u, v, and w are displacements in the x, y, and z directions, respectively, and t is time.

These are the PDEs of equilibrium in Cartesian coordinates for governing 3D solid mechanical problems. Note that if we ignore all components except σ_x, we can reduce this set of equations to a one-dimensional (1D) equation as

$$\frac{\partial \sigma_x}{\partial x} + f_x = \rho \frac{\partial^2 u}{\partial t^2}$$

which is the same as the 1D hanging bar equation, Equation 3.2, after considering $\sigma_x = E\epsilon_x = E\dfrac{\partial u}{\partial x}$. Now we can see that the mechanical situation in the PDE of a hanging bar is indeed much simplified.

By selecting an arbitrary plane defined by points A, B, and C, with a normal vector of $\vec{n} = n_x\vec{i} + n_y\vec{j} + n_z\vec{k}$, we calculate tractions in this plane by the projections of the three stress vectors, namely, the dot products of the stress vectors and $\vec{n}$ as

$$\begin{aligned} T_x &= \vec{n} \cdot S_x = \sigma_x n_x + \tau_{xy} n_y + \tau_{xz} n_z \\ T_y &= \vec{n} \cdot S_y = \tau_{xy} n_x + \sigma_y n_y + \tau_{yz} n_z \\ T_z &= \vec{n} \cdot S_z = \tau_{xz} n_x + \tau_{yz} n_y + \sigma_z n_z \end{aligned} \tag{8.2}$$

8.1.2 Weighted integral of residual

We now consider a stationary (or static) condition (so the time effect is ignored) by constructing the weighted integral of residual to Equation 8.1. With weight functions expressed in a vector $\{w\} = \{w_x \; w_y \; w_z\}^T$, we write

$$\begin{aligned} \iiint_V \Bigg[& w_x \left(\frac{\partial \sigma_x}{\partial x} + \frac{\partial \tau_{xy}}{\partial y} + \frac{\partial \tau_{xz}}{\partial z} + f_x \right) + w_y \left(\frac{\partial \tau_{xy}}{\partial x} + \frac{\partial \sigma_y}{\partial y} + \frac{\partial \tau_{yz}}{\partial z} + f_y \right) \\ & + w_z \left(\frac{\partial \tau_{xz}}{\partial x} + \frac{\partial \tau_{yz}}{\partial y} + \frac{\partial \sigma_z}{\partial z} + f_z \right) \Bigg] dV = 0 \end{aligned} \tag{8.3}$$

By the product rule of differentiation, we can express

$$\begin{aligned} w_x \frac{\partial \sigma_x}{\partial x} &= -\sigma_x \frac{\partial w_x}{\partial x} + \frac{\partial}{\partial x}(\sigma_x w_x) \\ w_x \frac{\partial \tau_{xy}}{\partial y} &= -\tau_{xy} \frac{\partial w_x}{\partial y} + \frac{\partial}{\partial y}(\tau_{xy} w_x) \\ w_x \frac{\partial \tau_{xz}}{\partial z} &= -\tau_{xz} \frac{\partial w_x}{\partial z} + \frac{\partial}{\partial z}(\tau_{xz} w_x) \\ w_y \frac{\partial \tau_{xy}}{\partial x} &= -\tau_{xy} \frac{\partial w_y}{\partial x} + \frac{\partial}{\partial x}(\tau_{xy} w_y) \\ w_y \frac{\partial \sigma_y}{\partial y} &= -\sigma_y \frac{\partial w_y}{\partial y} + \frac{\partial}{\partial y}(\sigma_y w_y) \\ w_y \frac{\partial \tau_{yz}}{\partial z} &= -\tau_{yz} \frac{\partial w_y}{\partial z} + \frac{\partial}{\partial z}(\tau_{yz} w_y) \end{aligned}$$

$$w_z \frac{\partial \tau_{xz}}{\partial x} = -\tau_{xz} \frac{\partial w_z}{\partial x} + \frac{\partial}{\partial x}(\tau_{xz} w_z)$$
$$w_z \frac{\partial \tau_{yz}}{\partial y} = -\tau_{yz} \frac{\partial w_z}{\partial y} + \frac{\partial}{\partial y}(\tau_{yz} w_z)$$
$$w_z \frac{\partial \sigma_z}{\partial z} = -\sigma_z \frac{\partial w_z}{\partial z} + \frac{\partial}{\partial z}(\sigma_z w_z)$$

Substituting these relationships into Equation 8.3, we obtain

$$\begin{aligned} -\iiint_V &\left[\sigma_x \frac{\partial w_x}{\partial x} + \sigma_y \frac{\partial w_y}{\partial y} + \sigma_z \frac{\partial w_z}{\partial z} + \tau_{yz}\left(\frac{\partial w_y}{\partial z} + \frac{\partial w_z}{\partial y}\right) + \tau_{xz}\left(\frac{\partial w_x}{\partial z} + \frac{\partial w_z}{\partial x}\right)\right. \\ &\left. + \tau_{xy}\left(\frac{\partial w_x}{\partial y} + \frac{\partial w_y}{\partial x}\right)\right] dV \\ + \iiint_V &\left[\frac{\partial}{\partial x}(\sigma_x w_x + \tau_{xy} w_y + \tau_{xz} w_z)\right. \\ &\left. + \frac{\partial}{\partial y}(\tau_{xy} w_x + \sigma_y w_y + \tau_{yz} w_z) + \frac{\partial}{\partial z}(\tau_{xz} w_x + \tau_{yz} w_y + \sigma_z w_z)\right] dV \\ + \iiint_V &(w_x f_x + w_y f_y + w_z f_z)\} dV = 0 \end{aligned} \tag{8.4}$$

To simplify this equation, let us introduce some new expressions. We first express the stress and strain components in vectors as

$$\{\sigma\} = \left\{\sigma_x \quad \sigma_y \quad \sigma_z \quad \tau_{yz} \quad \tau_{xz} \quad \tau_{xy}\right\}^T \quad \text{and}$$
$$\{\epsilon\} = \left\{\epsilon_x \quad \epsilon_y \quad \epsilon_z \quad \gamma_{yz} \quad \gamma_{xz} \quad \gamma_{xy}\right\}^T$$

By the definition of strains, we can write the following relationships for the strains in terms of the displacements in a matrix form:

$$\{\epsilon\} = \begin{Bmatrix} \epsilon_x \\ \epsilon_y \\ \epsilon_z \\ \gamma_{yz} \\ \gamma_{xz} \\ \gamma_{xy} \end{Bmatrix} = \begin{Bmatrix} \dfrac{\partial u_x}{\partial x} \\ \dfrac{\partial u_y}{\partial y} \\ \dfrac{\partial u_z}{\partial z} \\ \dfrac{\partial u_y}{\partial z} + \dfrac{\partial u_z}{\partial y} \\ \dfrac{\partial u_x}{\partial z} + \dfrac{\partial u_z}{\partial x} \\ \dfrac{\partial u_x}{\partial y} + \dfrac{\partial u_y}{\partial x} \end{Bmatrix}$$

where u_x, u_y, and u_z are displacement components in the x, y, and z directions, respectively. Based on this matrix expression, we introduce a new differential operator in a matrix form:

$$\nabla_s = \begin{bmatrix} \frac{\partial}{\partial x} & 0 & 0 \\ 0 & \frac{\partial}{\partial y} & 0 \\ 0 & 0 & \frac{\partial}{\partial z} \\ 0 & \frac{\partial}{\partial z} & \frac{\partial}{\partial y} \\ \frac{\partial}{\partial z} & 0 & \frac{\partial}{\partial x} \\ \frac{\partial}{\partial y} & \frac{\partial}{\partial x} & 0 \end{bmatrix} \quad \text{or} \quad \nabla_s^T = \begin{bmatrix} \frac{\partial}{\partial x} & 0 & 0 & 0 & \frac{\partial}{\partial z} & \frac{\partial}{\partial y} \\ 0 & \frac{\partial}{\partial y} & 0 & \frac{\partial}{\partial z} & 0 & \frac{\partial}{\partial x} \\ 0 & 0 & \frac{\partial}{\partial z} & \frac{\partial}{\partial y} & \frac{\partial}{\partial x} & 0 \end{bmatrix} \tag{8.5}$$

Moreover, we express the displacements, volume forces, and weight functions in vector forms as

$$\{d\} = \begin{Bmatrix} u_x \\ u_y \\ u_z \end{Bmatrix}, \quad \{f\} = \begin{Bmatrix} f_x \\ f_y \\ f_z \end{Bmatrix}, \quad \{w\} = \begin{Bmatrix} w_x \\ w_y \\ w_z \end{Bmatrix}$$

Then, we can write the following matrix equations:

$$\{\epsilon\} = \begin{bmatrix} \frac{\partial}{\partial x} & 0 & 0 \\ 0 & \frac{\partial}{\partial y} & 0 \\ 0 & 0 & \frac{\partial}{\partial z} \\ 0 & \frac{\partial}{\partial z} & \frac{\partial}{\partial y} \\ \frac{\partial}{\partial z} & 0 & \frac{\partial}{\partial x} \\ \frac{\partial}{\partial y} & \frac{\partial}{\partial x} & 0 \end{bmatrix} \begin{Bmatrix} u_x \\ u_y \\ u_z \end{Bmatrix} = \nabla_s\{d\} \quad \text{and} \quad \nabla_s\{w\} = \begin{Bmatrix} \frac{\partial w_x}{\partial x} \\ \frac{\partial w_y}{\partial y} \\ \frac{\partial w_z}{\partial z} \\ \frac{\partial w_y}{\partial z} + \frac{\partial w_z}{\partial y} \\ \frac{\partial w_x}{\partial z} + \frac{\partial w_z}{\partial x} \\ \frac{\partial w_x}{\partial y} + \frac{\partial w_y}{\partial x} \end{Bmatrix} \tag{8.6}$$

With the above preparation, we now go back to simplify Equation 8.4. Using Equation 8.6 along with the stress vector expression, we simplify the first integral into a compact matrix form as

$$-\iiint_V \{\nabla_s\{w\}\}^T\{\sigma\}dV$$

For the second integral, first let

$$F_x = \sigma_x w_x + \tau_{xy} w_y + \tau_{xz} w_z$$
$$F_y = \tau_{xy} w_x + \sigma_y w_y + \tau_{yz} w_z$$
$$F_z = \tau_{xz} w_x + \tau_{yz} w_y + \sigma_z w_z$$

and then we apply the divergence theorem (see Equation 2.11 in Chapter 2) with $\vec{n} = n_x \vec{i} + n_y \vec{j} + n_z \vec{k}$:

$$\iiint_V \left[\frac{\partial F_x}{\partial x} + \frac{\partial F_y}{\partial y} + \frac{\partial F_z}{\partial z} \right] dV = \iint_A F \cdot \vec{n} dA = \iint_A [F_x n_x + F_y n_y + F_z n_z] dA$$

Thus, we rewrite the second integral, after regrouping and substitution of the traction expressions, as

$$\begin{aligned}
&\iint_A [(\sigma_x w_x + \tau_{xy} w_y + \tau_{xz} w_z) n_x + (\tau_{xy} w_x + \sigma_y w_y + \tau_{yz} w_z) n_y \\
&\quad + (\tau_{xz} w_x + \tau_{yz} w_y + \sigma_z w_z) n_z] dA \\
&= \iint_A [w_x(\sigma_x n_x + \tau_{xy} n_y + \tau_{xz} n_z) + w_y(\tau_{xy} n_x + \sigma_y n_y + \tau_{yz} n_z) \\
&\quad + w_z(\tau_{xz} n_x + \tau_{yz} n_y + \sigma_z n_z)] dA \\
&= \iint_A [w_x T_x + w_y T_y + w_z T_z] dA = \iint_A \{w\}^T \{T\} dA + \sum \{w\}^T P
\end{aligned}$$

where P represents point loads on the boundary surfaces, if any.

The last integral in Equation 8.4 can be expressed in compact form as

$$\iiint_V (w_x f_x + w_y f_y + w_z f_z) dV = \iiint_V \{w\}^T \{f\} dV$$

Putting all these together, we have

$$\iiint_V \{\nabla_s \{w\}\}^T \{\sigma\} dV = \iiint_V \{w\}^T \{f\} dV + \iint_A \{w\}^T \{T\} dA + \sum \{w\}^T P \tag{8.7}$$

For any given material, stresses are related to strains according to a generalized Hooke's law, which can be expressed as

$$\{\sigma\} = [C]\{\epsilon\} = \begin{bmatrix} c_{11} & c_{12} & c_{13} & c_{14} & c_{15} & c_{16} \\ c_{12} & c_{22} & c_{23} & c_{24} & c_{25} & c_{26} \\ c_{13} & c_{23} & c_{33} & c_{34} & c_{35} & c_{36} \\ c_{14} & c_{24} & c_{34} & c_{44} & c_{45} & c_{46} \\ c_{15} & c_{25} & c_{35} & c_{45} & c_{55} & c_{56} \\ c_{16} & c_{26} & c_{36} & c_{46} & c_{56} & c_{66} \end{bmatrix} \{\epsilon\}$$

where $[C]$ is the material property matrix, with c_{ij} representing properties of an anisotropic material. For an isotropic material (i.e., a material with the same and homogeneous properties in all directions), $[C]$ is a much simpler matrix:

$$[C] = \frac{E}{(1+\nu)(1-2\nu)} \begin{bmatrix} 1-\nu & \nu & \nu & 0 & 0 & 0 \\ \nu & 1-\nu & \nu & 0 & 0 & 0 \\ \nu & \nu & 1-\nu & 0 & 0 & 0 \\ 0 & 0 & 0 & 0.5-\nu & 0 & 0 \\ 0 & 0 & 0 & 0 & 0.5-\nu & 0 \\ 0 & 0 & 0 & 0 & 0 & 0.5-\nu \end{bmatrix} \tag{8.8}$$

where E is Young's modulus and ν is Poisson's ratio of the material. With this expression, we can write the matrix form stress–strain relationship as

$$\begin{Bmatrix} \sigma_x \\ \sigma_y \\ \sigma_z \\ \tau_{yz} \\ \tau_{xz} \\ \tau_{xy} \end{Bmatrix} = \frac{E}{(1+\nu)(1-2\nu)} \begin{bmatrix} 1-\nu & \nu & \nu & 0 & 0 & 0 \\ \nu & 1-\nu & \nu & 0 & 0 & 0 \\ \nu & \nu & 1-\nu & 0 & 0 & 0 \\ 0 & 0 & 0 & 0.5-\nu & 0 & 0 \\ 0 & 0 & 0 & 0 & 0.5-\nu & 0 \\ 0 & 0 & 0 & 0 & 0 & 0.5-\nu \end{bmatrix} \begin{Bmatrix} \epsilon_x \\ \epsilon_y \\ \epsilon_z \\ \gamma_{yz} \\ \gamma_{xz} \\ \gamma_{xy} \end{Bmatrix} \tag{8.9}$$

or an inverse strain–stress relationship as

$$\begin{Bmatrix} \epsilon_x \\ \epsilon_y \\ \epsilon_z \\ \gamma_{yz} \\ \gamma_{xz} \\ \gamma_{xy} \end{Bmatrix} = \frac{1}{E} \begin{bmatrix} 1 & -\nu & -\nu & 0 & 0 & 0 \\ -\nu & 1 & -\nu & 0 & 0 & 0 \\ -\nu & -\nu & 1 & 0 & 0 & 0 \\ 0 & 0 & 0 & 2(1+\nu) & 0 & 0 \\ 0 & 0 & 0 & 0 & 2(1+\nu) & 0 \\ 0 & 0 & 0 & 0 & 0 & 2(1+\nu) \end{bmatrix} \begin{Bmatrix} \sigma_x \\ \sigma_y \\ \sigma_z \\ \tau_{yz} \\ \tau_{xz} \\ \tau_{xy} \end{Bmatrix} \tag{8.10}$$

8.1.3 FEM formulation

We will now develop the FEM formulation for 3D solid mechanical problems using Equation 8.7 with an element having elementary DOF $= n_e$. Referring to Equations 5.32 and 5.35, we can express the three field quantities in the x, y, and z directions in terms of the elementary shape functions and degrees of freedom (DOF), respectively, as

$$\tilde{u}_x = \sum_{m=1}^{n_e} N_m u_{mx}, \tilde{u}_y = \sum_{m=1}^{n_e} N_m u_{my}, \tilde{u}_z = \sum_{m=1}^{n_e} N_m u_{mz}$$

and in a matrix form as

$$\begin{Bmatrix} \tilde{u}_x \\ \tilde{u}_y \\ \tilde{u}_z \end{Bmatrix} = \begin{bmatrix} N_1 & 0 & 0 & N_2 & 0 & 0 & N_3 & 0 & 0 & \cdots \\ 0 & N_1 & 0 & 0 & N_2 & 0 & 0 & N_3 & 0 & \cdots \\ 0 & 0 & N_1 & 0 & 0 & N_2 & 0 & 0 & N_3 & \cdots \end{bmatrix} \begin{Bmatrix} u_{1x} \\ u_{1y} \\ u_{1z} \\ u_{2x} \\ u_{2y} \\ u_{2z} \\ u_{3x} \\ u_{3y} \\ u_{3z} \\ \vdots \end{Bmatrix}$$

$$= [N]\{d_0\} \tag{8.11}$$

The shape function matrix $[N]$ for a 3D vector field element with elementary DOF $= n_e$ is a $3 \times 3n_e$ matrix, and the DOF vector $\{d_o\}$ is a $3n_e \times 1$ vector.

By the Galerkin method, we select the shape function matrix as the weight vector. Thus, using the following expressions,

$$\{d\} = [N]\{d_0\}, \; \{w\} = [N]$$

along with Equation 8.6, we further express the stress–strain relationship as

$$\{\sigma\} = [C]\{\epsilon\} = [C]\nabla_s\{d\} = [C]\nabla_s[N]\{d_0\}$$

Then, the term on the left side of Equation 8.7 can be expressed as

$$\iiint_V \{\nabla_s\{w\}\}^T\{\sigma\}dV = \iiint_V \{\nabla_s[N]\}^T[C](\nabla_s[N])dV\{d_0\}$$

Therefore, we have the following finite element formulation for 3D solid mechanical problems in a matrix form:

$$\iiint_V \{\nabla_s[N]\}^T[C](\nabla_s[N])dV\{d_0\} = \iiint_V [N]^T\{f\}dV + \iint_S [N]^T\{T\}dS + \sum [N]^T P \tag{8.12}$$

Similarly, the coefficient of the DOF vector $\{d_0\}$ is the elementary $[K_e]$ matrix:

$$[K_e] = \iiint_V \{\nabla_s[N]\}^T[C](\nabla_s[N])dV \tag{8.13}$$

where $[C]$ is given in Equation 8.8.

8.1.4 Elementary $[K_e]$ matrix for solid mechanics problems

To solve the 3D vector field solid mechanics problem, we can follow the same procedure as discussed in Chapter 7, namely, (1) find the elementary $[K_e]$ matrix using Equation 8.13 based on the type and order of the elements and their corresponding shape functions, (2) assemble them into the global $[K]$ matrix, (3) determine the global load vector, (4) establish the global matrix equation, $[K]\{D\} = \{P\}$, and (5) solve this matrix equation by applying the matrix partition method based on the given boundary conditions to obtain the unknown DOF. Next, we will go through an example to see how the elementary $[K_e]$ is developed for 3D elements for problems of solid mechanics.

Example 8.1

For the 3D hexahedral element shown in Figure 8.2, determine its elementary $[K_e]$ matrix using Equation 8.13. Assume that the element is made of an isotropic material with $E = 200$ GPa and $\nu = 0.3$. The coordinates of the nodes of the element (with units of meters) are given in the figure.

Answer

For the hexahedral element, since the element is the same as that in Figure 7.3, we have the same shape functions, namely,

$$N_1 = (1-x)(2-y)(1-z)/2, \qquad N_2 = x(2-y)(1-z)/2,$$
$$N_3 = xy(1-z)/2, \qquad N_4 = (1-x)y(1-z)/2,$$
$$N_5 = (1-x)(2-y)z/2, \qquad N_6 = x(2-y)z/2,$$
$$N_7 = xyz/2, \qquad N_8 = (1-x)yz/2$$

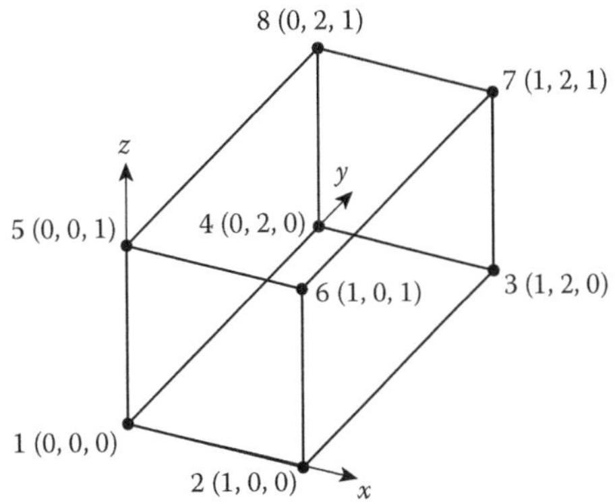

FIGURE 8.2
A 3D hexahedral element.

Referring to Equation 8.11, we know that the shape function matrix for this 8-node 3D solid mechanical element is a 3×24 matrix in the following form:

$$[N] = \begin{bmatrix} N_1 & 0 & 0 & N_2 & 0 & 0 & N_3 & 0 & 0 & \cdots & N_7 & 0 & 0 & N_8 & 0 & 0 \\ 0 & N_1 & 0 & 0 & N_2 & 0 & 0 & N_3 & 0 & \cdots & 0 & N_7 & 0 & 0 & N_8 & 0 \\ 0 & 0 & N_1 & 0 & 0 & N_2 & 0 & 0 & N_3 & \cdots & 0 & 0 & N_7 & 0 & 0 & N_8 \end{bmatrix}$$

With this matrix, we calculate $\nabla_s[N]$ using the expression given in Equation 8.5:

$$\nabla_s[N] = \begin{bmatrix} \frac{\partial N_1}{\partial x} & 0 & 0 & \frac{\partial N_2}{\partial x} & 0 & 0 & \cdots & \frac{\partial N_7}{\partial x} & 0 & 0 & \frac{\partial N_8}{\partial x} & 0 & 0 \\ 0 & \frac{\partial N_1}{\partial y} & 0 & 0 & \frac{\partial N_2}{\partial y} & 0 & \cdots & 0 & \frac{\partial N_7}{\partial y} & 0 & 0 & \frac{\partial N_8}{\partial y} & 0 \\ 0 & 0 & \frac{\partial N_1}{\partial z} & 0 & 0 & \frac{\partial N_2}{\partial z} & \cdots & & 0 & 0\frac{\partial N_7}{\partial z} & 0 & 0 & \frac{\partial N_8}{\partial z} \\ 0 & \frac{\partial N_1}{\partial z} & \frac{\partial N_1}{\partial y} & 0 & \frac{\partial N_2}{\partial z} & \frac{\partial N_2}{\partial y} & \cdots & 0 & \frac{\partial N_7}{\partial z} & \frac{\partial N_7}{\partial y} & 0 & \frac{\partial N_8}{\partial z} & \frac{\partial N_8}{\partial y} \\ \frac{\partial N_1}{\partial z} & 0 & \frac{\partial N_1}{\partial x} & \frac{\partial N_2}{\partial z} & 0 & \frac{\partial N_2}{\partial x} & \cdots & \frac{\partial N_7}{\partial z} & 0 & \frac{\partial N_7}{\partial x} & \frac{\partial N_8}{\partial z} & 0 & \frac{\partial N_8}{\partial x} \\ \frac{\partial N_1}{\partial y} & \frac{\partial N_1}{\partial x} & 0 & \frac{\partial N_2}{\partial y} & \frac{\partial N_2}{\partial x} & 0 & \cdots & \frac{\partial N_7}{\partial y} & \frac{\partial N_7}{\partial x} & 0 & \frac{\partial N_8}{\partial y} & \frac{\partial N_8}{\partial x} & 0 \end{bmatrix}$$

where

$$\frac{\partial N_1}{\partial x} = -(2-y)(1-z)/2, \ \frac{\partial N_2}{\partial x} = (2-y)(1-z)/2, \ \frac{\partial N_3}{\partial x} = y(1-z)/2$$

$$\frac{\partial N_4}{\partial x} = -y(1-z)/2, \ \frac{\partial N_5}{\partial x} = -(2-y)z/2, \ \frac{\partial N_6}{\partial x} = (2-y)z/2, \ \frac{\partial N_7}{\partial x} = yz/2$$

$$\frac{\partial N_8}{\partial x} = -yz/2, \ \frac{\partial N_1}{\partial y} = -(1-x)(1-z)/2, \ \frac{\partial N_2}{\partial y} = -x(1-z)/2$$

$$\frac{\partial N_3}{\partial y} = x(1-z)/2, \ \frac{\partial N_4}{\partial y} = -(1-x)(1-z)/2, \ \frac{\partial N_5}{\partial y} = -(1-x)z/2$$

$$\frac{\partial N_6}{\partial y} = -xz/2, \ \frac{\partial N_7}{\partial y} = xz/2, \ \frac{\partial N_8}{\partial y} = (1-x)z/2$$

$$\frac{\partial N_1}{\partial z} = -(1-x)(2-y)/2, \ \frac{\partial N_2}{\partial z} = -x(2-y)/2, \ \frac{\partial N_3}{\partial z} = -xy/2, \ \frac{\partial N_4}{\partial z} = (1-x)y/2$$

$$\frac{\partial N_5}{\partial z} = (1-x)(2-y)/2, \ \frac{\partial N_6}{\partial z} = x(2-y)/2, \ \frac{\partial N_7}{\partial z} = xy/2, \ \frac{\partial N_8}{\partial z} = (1-x)y/2$$

in this 6×24 matrix. Moreover, using Equation 8.8 along with $E = 200$ GPa and $\nu = 0.3$, we calculate the material property matrix:

$$[C] = 10^{11}\begin{bmatrix} 2.69 & 1.15 & 1.15 & 0 & 0 & 0 \\ 1.15 & 2.69 & 1.15 & 0 & 0 & 0 \\ 1.15 & 1.15 & 2.69 & 0 & 0 & 0 \\ 0 & 0 & 0 & 0.77 & 0 & 0 \\ 0 & 0 & 0 & 0 & 0.77 & 0 \\ 0 & 0 & 0 & 0 & 0 & 0.77 \end{bmatrix}$$

Putting all these into Equation 8.13 and integrating it over the hexahedral volume defined by the hexahedral element, along with $dV = dxdydz$, we obtain the following 24×24 elementary $[K_e]$ matrix for an 8-node 3D solid mechanical element:

$$[K_e] = \int_{x=0}^{1}\int_{y=0}^{2}\int_{z=0}^{1} \underset{24\times 6}{\{\nabla_s[N]\}^T} \underset{6\times 6}{[C]} \underset{6\times 24}{\{\nabla_s[N]\}} \, dzdydx$$

$$= 10^{10}\begin{bmatrix} 8.12 & 1.60 & 3.21 & \cdots & -0.16 & -0.32 \\ 1.60 & 4.91 & 1.60 & \cdots & -1.18 & -1.60 \\ 3.21 & 1.60 & 8.12 & \cdots & -1.60 & -2.78 \\ \vdots & \vdots & \vdots & \ddots & \vdots & \vdots \\ -0.16 & -1.18 & -1.60 & \cdots & 4.91 & 1.60 \\ -0.32 & -1.60 & -2.78 & \cdots & 1.60 & 8.12 \end{bmatrix}_{24\times 24}$$

Example 8.2

For the 3D tetrahedral element shown in Figure 8.3, determine its elementary $[K_e]$ matrix using Equation 8.13. Assume that the element is made of an isotropic material with $E = 200$ GPa and $\nu = 0.3$. The coordinates of the nodes of the elements (with units of meters) are given in the figure.

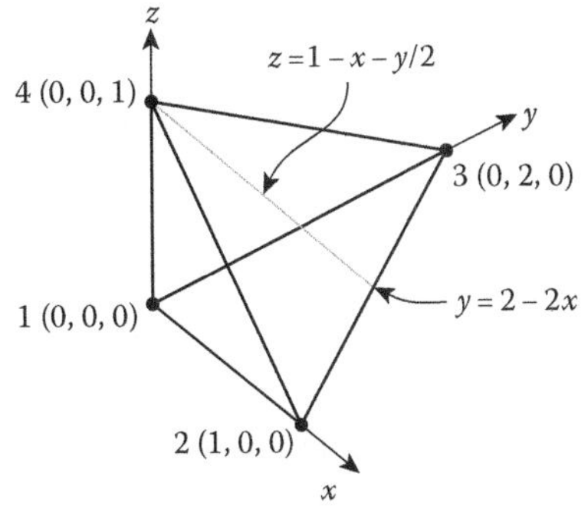

FIGURE 8.3
A three-dimensional tetrahedral element.

Answer

For the tetrahedral element, since the element is the same as that in Figure 7.4, we have the same shape functions as

$$N_1 = 1 - x - y/2 - z, \quad N_2 = x, \quad N_3 = y/2, \quad N_4 = z$$

With these expressions, we calculate the 6×12 $\nabla_s[N]$:

$$\nabla_s[N] = \begin{bmatrix} -1 & 0 & 0 & 1 & 0 & 0 & 0 & 0 & 0 & 0 & 0 & 0 \\ 0 & -0.5 & 0 & 0 & 0 & 0 & 0 & 0.5 & 0 & 0 & 0 & 0 \\ 0 & 0 & -1 & 0 & 0 & 0 & 0 & 0 & 0 & 0 & 0 & 1 \\ 0 & -1 & -0.5 & 0 & 0 & 0 & 0 & 0 & 0.5 & 0 & 1 & 0 \\ -1 & 0 & -1 & 0 & 0 & 1 & 0 & 0 & 0 & 1 & 0 & 0 \\ -0.5 & -1 & 0 & 0 & 1 & 0 & 0.5 & 0 & 0 & 0 & 0 & 0 \end{bmatrix}$$

Plugging this expression and the $[C]$ matrix into Equation 8.13 and integrating it over the tetrahedral volume defined by the element, we obtain the following 12×12 elementary $[K_e]$ matrix for a 4-node 3D solid mechanical element:

$$[K_e] = \int_{x=0}^{1} \int_{y=0}^{2-2x} \int_{z=0}^{1-x-y/2} \underset{12\times 6}{\{\nabla_s[N]\}^T} \; \underset{6\times 6}{[C]} \; \underset{6\times 12}{\{\nabla_s[N]\}} \; dzdydx$$

$$= 10^{10} \begin{bmatrix} 12.18 & 3.21 & 6.41 & \cdots & -0 & -3.85 \\ 3.21 & 7.37 & 3.21 & \cdots & -2.56 & -1.92 \\ 6.41 & 3.21 & 12.18 & \cdots & -1.28 & -8.97 \\ \vdots & \vdots & \vdots & \ddots & \vdots & \vdots \\ 0 & -2.56 & -1.28 & \cdots & 2.56 & 0 \\ -3.85 & -1.92 & -8.97 & \cdots & 0 & 8.97 \end{bmatrix}_{12\times 12}$$

By comparing these two examples with Examples 7.3 and 7.4, we can see that although the general procedure to calculate the 3D elementary $[K_e]$ matrix for a solid mechanics (vector field) problem is similar to that for a scalar field problem, there exist several distinct differences.

1. The $[N]$ matrix is different. For a scalar field 3D problem, the $[N]$ matrix is a one-row matrix, but for a 3D solid mechanics problem, it is a three-row matrix.
2. The way to calculate the shape function derivative is different. For scalar field, we calculate $\partial[N]/\partial x, \partial[N]/\partial y$, and $\partial[N]/\partial z$ directly, but for solid mechanics, we apply the ∇_s operator to determine $\nabla_s[N]$.
3. The material property is handled differently in the actual $[K_e]$ formula. For scalar field, the material properties of a homogeneous domain can be represented by constants, but for solid mechanics, even a homogeneous isotropic material, its properties need to be expressed in a 6×6 $[C]$ matrix due to the Poisson's ratio effect.

Aside from these differences, these is something in common in both situations, namely, the difficulty in performing integration when elements have odd shapes and varying shape function expressions due to their different locations. This again points to the need to have a unified way to write shape functions and perform numerical integration based on the concept of isoparametric elements and Gauss quadrature.

8.2 2D Solid Mechanics Problems

There are situations where a 3D solid mechanics problem can be simplified as a 2D problem. For example, when a mechanical structure is thin in its third dimension (say, along the z axis) in comparison with the other two dimensions, and if the loading and deformations of the structure occur only within the plane of the sheet structure, the stresses in the third dimension, $\sigma_z, \tau_y z, \tau_x z$, are negligible. Another example is that when the structure is very long in its longitudinal z direction compared with the x, y dimensions, the loading, deformations, and even the cross section area of this structure remain unchanged over the entire longitudinal length. In this case, the strains in the third dimension, $\epsilon_z, \gamma_y z, \gamma_x z$, are negligible. We call the first situation plane stress and the second one plane strain. Of course, unlike scalar field problems, mechanical problems are vector field problems; thus, reducing a 3D vector field problem to a 2D one cannot be done by simply neglecting the third dimension.

8.2.1 Plane stress situation

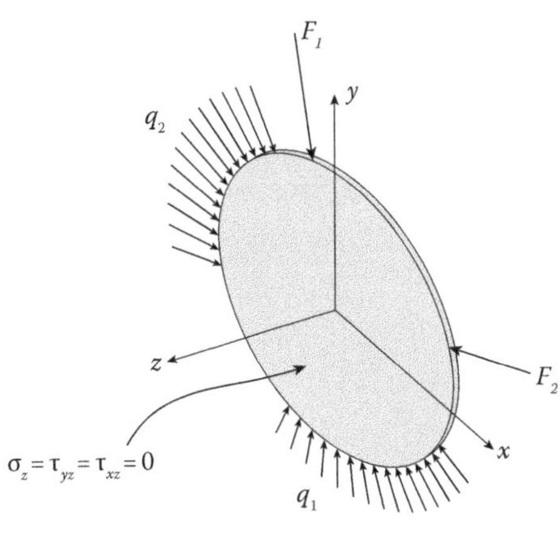

FIGURE 8.4
Plane stress situation.

When a structure is very thin in the z direction relative to the dimensions along the x, y directions, we may regard it as a 2D structure.

If the loads and constraints subjected to around the edge of the 2D structure are within the plane of the structure (e.g., the x-y plane) and distributed uniformly over the thickness of this thin 2D structure, the resulting deformations are expected to occur within the same plane (note that in this situation, out-of-plane deformations are considered negligible). Then, the right and left surfaces of this thin structure become stress-free, as shown in Figure 8.4.

Thus, we have the following on the two free surfaces:

$$\sigma_z = \tau_{yz} = \tau_{xz} = 0$$

Since the 2D structure is very thin, it is reasonable to assume that all these stress components are also negligible (or zero) throughout the 2D structure. This situation is commonly referred to as the plane stress situation. In other words, a plane stress situation is one in which only three of the six stress components exist, and these existing stress components all appear within a single plane (e.g., the x-y plane in the case depicted in Figure 8.4).

For isotropic materials, by applying these zero stress expressions to Equation 8.10, we express the reduced strain–stress relationship for a 2D plane stress situation as

$$\begin{Bmatrix} \epsilon_x \\ \epsilon_y \\ \gamma_{xy} \end{Bmatrix} = \frac{1}{E} \begin{bmatrix} 1 & -\nu & 0 \\ -\nu & 1 & 0 \\ 0 & 0 & 2(1+\nu) \end{bmatrix} \begin{Bmatrix} \sigma_x \\ \sigma_y \\ \tau_{xy} \end{Bmatrix}$$

which, after inversing, can be expressed in an equivalent stress–strain relationship as

$$\begin{Bmatrix} \sigma_x \\ \sigma_y \\ \tau_{xy} \end{Bmatrix} = \frac{E}{(1-\nu^2)} \begin{bmatrix} 1 & \nu & 0 \\ \nu & 1 & 0 \\ 0 & 0 & (1-\nu)/2 \end{bmatrix} \begin{Bmatrix} \epsilon_x \\ \epsilon_y \\ \gamma_{xy} \end{Bmatrix}$$

In the plane stress situation depicted in Figure 8.4, the fact that these three stress components are zero does not automatically make the corresponding strains zero. From equation 8.10, we find that

$$\epsilon_z = -\nu(\sigma_x + \sigma_y)/E, \quad \gamma_{yz} = \gamma_{xz} = 0$$

Moreover, referring to the reduced stress–strain relationship, we express the reduced material property matrix $[C]$ for a 2D plane stress solid mechanics problem as

$$[C] = \frac{E}{(1-\nu^2)} \begin{bmatrix} 1 & \nu & 0 \\ \nu & 1 & 0 \\ 0 & 0 & (1-\nu)/2 \end{bmatrix} \tag{8.14}$$

8.2.2 Plane strain situation

As defined in Chapter 3, strains measure the relative change in length, that is, the change in length (either elongation or shortening) of a structure divided by the original length of the structure.

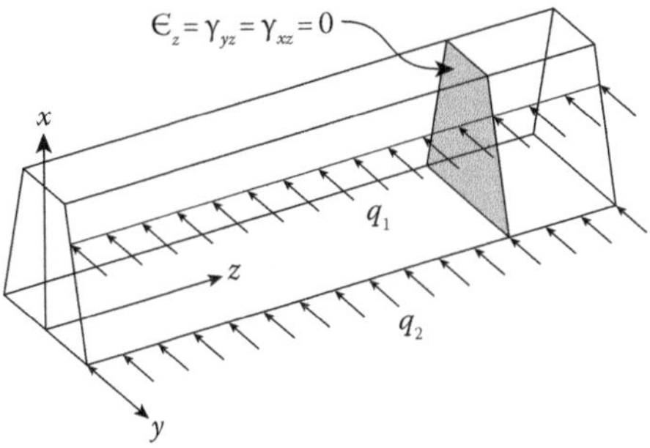

FIGURE 8.5
Plane strain situation.

When a structure with a constant cross section area is very long in its longitudinal direction (say, the z direction) compared with the x, y dimensions, such as the levee structure shown in Figure 8.5, the z-related strains (e.g., ϵ_z, γ_{yz}, and γ_{xz}) become negligible because any finite change in length divided by a very large length will make these strains negligible. Under such a condition, when the loading and constraints are perpendicular to the longitudinal axis and they do not vary along the length, this structural problem can be simplified by considering a thin section perpendicular to the longitudinal axis. For instance, the shaded section in the figure is one such section. The resulting problem is a 2D plane strain problem due to

$$\epsilon_z = \gamma_{yz} = \gamma_{xz} = 0$$

In other words, a plane strain situation is one in which only three of the six strain components exist, and these existing stress components all appear within a single plane (e.g., the x-y plane in the case depicted in Figure 8.5).

For isotropic materials, by applying these zero-strain expressions to Equation 8.9, we reduce it to a 2D stress–strain relationship for a plane strain situation:

$$\begin{Bmatrix} \sigma_x \\ \sigma_y \\ \tau_{xy} \end{Bmatrix} = \frac{E}{(1+\nu)(1-2\nu)} \begin{bmatrix} 1-\nu & \nu & 0 \\ \nu & 1-\nu & 0 \\ 0 & 0 & 0.5-\nu \end{bmatrix} \begin{Bmatrix} \epsilon_x \\ \epsilon_y \\ \gamma_{xy} \end{Bmatrix}$$

which, after inversing, yields the strain–stress relationship for a plane strain problem:

$$\begin{Bmatrix} \epsilon_x \\ \epsilon_y \\ \gamma_{xy} \end{Bmatrix} = \frac{(1+\nu)}{E} \begin{bmatrix} 1-\nu & -\nu & 0 \\ -\nu & 1-\nu & 0 \\ 0 & 0 & 2 \end{bmatrix} \begin{Bmatrix} \sigma_x \\ \sigma_y \\ \tau_{xy} \end{Bmatrix}$$

Similarly, of the three stress components corresponding to the three zero strains, only the shear components are zero and the normal stress is not:

$$\sigma_z = E\nu(\epsilon_x + \epsilon_y)/[(1+\nu)(1-2\nu)], \quad \tau_{yz} = \tau_{xz} = 0$$

Referring to the reduced stress–strain relationship, we express the reduced material property matrix $[C]$ for a 2D plane strain solid mechanics problem as

$$[C] = \frac{E}{(1+\nu)(1-2\nu)} \begin{bmatrix} 1-\nu & \nu & 0 \\ \nu & 1-\nu & 0 \\ 0 & 0 & 0.5-\nu \end{bmatrix} \tag{8.15}$$

8.2.3 FEM formulation for 2D solid mechanics

For a 2D solid mechanics problem, the DOF, force, and weight vectors can be reduced to

$$\{d\} = \begin{Bmatrix} u_x \\ u_y \end{Bmatrix}, \{f\} = \begin{Bmatrix} f_x \\ f_y \end{Bmatrix}, \{w\} = \begin{Bmatrix} w_x \\ w_y \end{Bmatrix}$$

and the stress and strain vectors reduced to

$$\{\sigma\} = \begin{Bmatrix} \sigma_x \\ \sigma_y \\ \tau_{xy} \end{Bmatrix}, \{\epsilon\} = \begin{Bmatrix} \epsilon_x \\ \epsilon_y \\ \gamma_{xy} \end{Bmatrix} = \begin{Bmatrix} \dfrac{\partial u_x}{\partial x} \\ \dfrac{\partial u_y}{\partial y} \\ \dfrac{\partial u_x}{\partial y} + \dfrac{\partial u_y}{\partial x} \end{Bmatrix} = \nabla_{s2}\{d\}$$

where ∇_{s2} is the 2D reduced differential operator matrix, which is expressed as

$$\nabla_{s2} = \begin{bmatrix} \dfrac{\partial}{\partial x} & 0 \\ 0 & \dfrac{\partial}{\partial y} \\ \dfrac{\partial}{\partial y} & \dfrac{\partial}{\partial x} \end{bmatrix} \quad \text{or} \quad \nabla_{s2}^T = \begin{bmatrix} \dfrac{\partial}{\partial x} & 0 & \dfrac{\partial}{\partial y} \\ 0 & \dfrac{\partial}{\partial y} & \dfrac{\partial}{\partial x} \end{bmatrix} \tag{8.16}$$

With the above information, the PDEs given in Equation 8.1 can be reduced to

$$\frac{\partial \sigma_x}{\partial x} + \frac{\partial \tau_{xy}}{\partial y} + f_x = 0$$
$$\frac{\partial \tau_{xy}}{\partial x} + \frac{\partial \sigma_y}{\partial y} + f_y = 0$$

and the tractions in Equation 8.2 reduced to

$$\sigma_x n_x + \tau_{xy} n_y = T_x$$
$$\tau_{xy} n_x + \sigma_y n_y = T_y$$

Thus, Equation 8.4 can be simplified to its 2D counterpart as

$$
\begin{aligned}
&-\iint_A \left[\sigma_x \frac{\partial w_x}{\partial x} + \sigma_y \frac{\partial w_y}{\partial y} + \tau_{xy}\left(\frac{\partial w_x}{\partial y} + \frac{\partial w_y}{\partial x}\right)\right] tdA \\
&+ \iint_A \left[\frac{\partial}{\partial x}(\sigma_x w_x + \tau_{xy} w_y) + \frac{\partial}{\partial y}(\tau_{xy} w_x + \sigma_y w_y)\right] tdA \\
&+ \iint_A (w_x f_x + w_y f_y)\} tdA = 0
\end{aligned}
\tag{8.17}
$$

where t is the thickness of the 2D structure. By applying the ∇_{s2} operator to the first integral and the divergence theorem to the second integral, and expressing the equation in a compact form, we obtain

$$
\iint_A \{\nabla_{s2}\{w\}\}^T \{\sigma\} tdA = \iint_A \{w\}^T \{f\} tdA + \int_L \{w\}^T \{T\} tdL + \sum \{w\}^T P
\tag{8.18}
$$

For this 2D solid mechanics problem, referring to Equations 5.32 and 5.34, we can approximate the two field quantities in the x, y directions in terms of the elementary shape functions and DOF vector as

$$
\tilde{u}_x = \sum_{m=1}^{n_e} N_m u_{mx},\ \tilde{u}_y = \sum_{m=1}^{n_e} N_m u_{my}
$$

or in a matrix form as

$$
\begin{Bmatrix} \tilde{u} \\ \tilde{v} \end{Bmatrix} = \begin{bmatrix} N_1 & 0 & N_2 & 0 & N_3 & 0 & \cdots \\ 0 & N_1 & 0 & N_2 & 0 & N_3 & \cdots \end{bmatrix} \begin{Bmatrix} u_{1x} \\ u_{1y} \\ u_{2x} \\ u_{2y} \\ u_{3x} \\ u_{3y} \\ \vdots \end{Bmatrix} = [N]\{d_0\}
\tag{8.19}
$$

The shape function matrix $[N]$ for a 2D solid mechanics element with elementary DOF $= n_e$ is a $2 \times 2n_e$ matrix and the DOF vector $\{d_o\}$ is a $2n_e \times 1$ vector.

By the Galerkin method, we select the shape function matrix as the weight vector. Thus, using the following expressions,

$$
\{d\} = [N]\{d_0\},\ \{w\} = [N]
$$

we express

$$
\{\sigma\} = [C]\{\epsilon\} = [C]\nabla_{s2}\{d\} = [C]\nabla_{s2}[N]\{d_0\}
$$

Then, by substituting these relationships into Equation 8.18, we obtain the following finite element formulation for a 2D solid mechanical problem,

$$\begin{aligned}\iint_A \{\nabla_{s2}[N]\}^T[C](\nabla_{s2}[N])tdA\{d_0\} = &\iint_A [N]^T\{f\}tdA \\ &+ \int_L [N]^T\{T\}tdL + \sum [N]^T P\end{aligned} \tag{8.20}$$

along with the elementary $[K_e]$ matrix:

$$[K_e] = \iint_A \{\nabla_{s2}[N]\}^T[C](\nabla_{s2}[N])tdA \tag{8.21}$$

Note that in calculating the $[K_e]$ matrix for a 2D solid mechanics problem using this equation, when the problem is a plane stress problem, we need to use the $[C]$ matrix given in Equation 8.14, and when the problem is a plane strain one, we will use the $[C]$ matrix given in Equation 8.15.

Example 8.3

For the 2D rectangular element shown in Figure 8.6, determine its elementary $[K_e]$ matrix using Equation 8.21. Assume that the element is made of an isotropic material with $E = 200$ GPa and $\nu = 0.3$ and has a uniform thickness of $t = 0.005$ m. The coordinates of the nodes of the element (with units of meters) are given in the figure.

Answer

For the rectangular element, since this element is the same as the one in Figure 7.1, we have the same set of shape functions:

$$N_1 = (1-5x)(1-10y),\ N_2 = 5x(1-10y),\ N_3 = 50xy,\ N_4 = 10(1-5x)y$$

Referring to Equation 8.19, we know that the shape function matrix for this 4-node 2D solid mechanical element is a 2×8 matrix in the following form:

$$[N] = \begin{bmatrix} N_1 & 0 & N_2 & 0 & N_3 & 0 & N_4 & 0 \\ 0 & N_1 & 0 & N_2 & 0 & N_3 & 0 & N_4 \end{bmatrix}$$

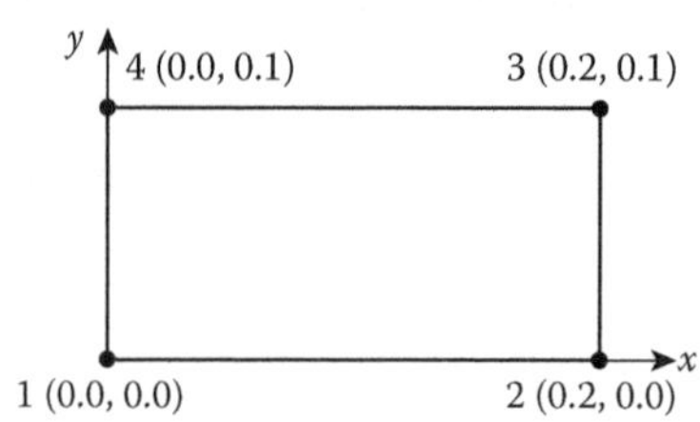

FIGURE 8.6
A 2D rectangular element with a uniform thickness.

With this matrix, we calculate the $3 \times 8\, \nabla_{s2}[N]$ matrix:

$$\nabla_{s2}[N] = \begin{bmatrix} 50y-5 & 0 & 5-50y & 0 & 50y & 0 & -50y & 0 \\ 0 & 50x-10 & 0 & -50x & 0 & 50x & 0 & 10-50x \\ 50x-10 & 50y-5 & -50x & 5-50y & 50x & 50y & 10-50x & -50y \end{bmatrix}$$

Moreover, using Equations 8.14 and 8.15, along with $E = 200$ GPa and $\nu = 0.3$, we calculate the material property matrix,

$$[C] = 10^{11} \times \begin{bmatrix} 2.20 & 0.66 & 0 \\ 0.66 & 2.20 & 0 \\ 0 & 0 & 0.77 \end{bmatrix}$$

for a plane stress problem and

$$[C] = 10^{11} \times \begin{bmatrix} 2.69 & 1.15 & 0 \\ 1.15 & 2.69 & 0 \\ 0 & 0 & 0.77 \end{bmatrix}$$

for a plane strain problem.

Putting all these into Equation 8.21, along with $t = 0.005$ and $dA = dxdy$, and integrating it over the rectangular area of the element, we obtain the following 8×8 elementary $[K_e]$ matrix for the rectangular element for plane stress solid mechanics problems,

$$[K_e] = \int_{x=0}^{2} \int_{y=0}^{1} \underset{8\times 3}{\{\nabla_{s2}[N]\}^T} \quad \underset{3\times 3}{[C]} \quad \underset{3\times 8}{\{\nabla_{s2}[N]\}} \; tdydx$$

$$= 10^8 \times \begin{bmatrix} 4.396 & 1.786 & -0.549 & -0.137 & -2.198 & -1.786 & -1.648 & 0.137 \\ 1.786 & 7.967 & 0.137 & 3.022 & -1.786 & -3.984 & -0.137 & -7.005 \\ -0.549 & 0.137 & 4.396 & -1.786 & -1.648 & -0.137 & -2.198 & 1.786 \\ -0.137 & 3.022 & -1.786 & 7.967 & 0.137 & -7.005 & 1.786 & -3.984 \\ -2.198 & -1.786 & -1.648 & 0.137 & 4.396 & 1.786 & -0.549 & -0.137 \\ -1.786 & -3.984 & -0.137 & -7.005 & 1.786 & 7.967 & 0.137 & 3.022 \\ -1.648 & -0.137 & -2.198 & 1.786 & -0.549 & 0.137 & 4.396 & -1.786 \\ 0.137 & -7.005 & 1.786 & -3.984 & -0.137 & 3.022 & -1.786 & 7.967 \end{bmatrix}$$

and the following 8×8 elementary $[K_e]$ matrix for the rectangular element for plane strain solid mechanics problems:

$$[K_e] = 10^8 \times \begin{bmatrix} 4.808 & 2.404 & -0.962 & 0.481 & -2.404 & -2.404 & -1.442 & -0.481 \\ 2.404 & 9.615 & -0.481 & 3.846 & -2.404 & -4.808 & 0.481 & -8.654 \\ -0.962 & -0.481 & 4.808 & -2.404 & -1.442 & 0.481 & -2.404 & 2.404 \\ 0.481 & 3.846 & -2.404 & 9.615 & -0.481 & -8.654 & 2.404 & -4.808 \\ -2.404 & -2.404 & -1.442 & -0.481 & 4.808 & 2.404 & -0.962 & 0.481 \\ -2.404 & -4.808 & 0.481 & -8.654 & 2.404 & 9.615 & -0.481 & 3.846 \\ -1.442 & 0.481 & -2.404 & 2.404 & -0.962 & -0.481 & 4.808 & -2.404 \\ -0.481 & -8.654 & 2.404 & -4.808 & 0.481 & 3.846 & -2.404 & 9.615 \end{bmatrix}$$

Example 8.4

For the 2D triangular element shown in Figure 8.7, determine its elementary $[K_e]$ matrix using Equation 8.21. Assume that the element is made of an isotropic material with $E = 200$ GPa and $\nu = 0.3$ and has a uniform thickness of $t = 0.005$ m. The coordinates of the nodes of the element (with units of meters) are given in the figure.

Answer

For the triangular element, since this element is the same as the one in Figure 7.2, we have the same set of shape functions as

$$N_1 = 1 - 5x, \quad N_2 = 5x - 10y, \quad N_3 = 10y$$

With these expressions, we calculate the 3×6 $\nabla_{s2}[N]$ matrix:

$$\nabla_s[N] = \begin{bmatrix} -5 & 0 & 5 & 0 & 0 & 0 \\ 0 & 0 & 0 & -10 & 0 & 10 \\ 0 & -5 & -10 & 5 & 10 & 0 \end{bmatrix}$$

Plugging this expression, along with $t = 0.005$ and the $[C]$ matrix, into Equation 8.21 and integrating it over the triangular area of the element, we obtain the following 6×6 elementary $[K_e]$ matrix for the triangular element for plane stress solid mechanics problems,

$$[K_e] = \int_{x=0}^{2} \int_{y=0}^{0.5x} \underset{6\times 3}{\{\nabla_{s2}[N]\}^T} \underset{3\times 3}{[C]} \underset{3\times 6}{\{\nabla_{s2}[N]\}} \, t dy dx$$

$$= 10^9 \times \begin{bmatrix} 2.747 & 0.000 & -2.747 & 1.648 & 0.000 & -1.648 \\ 0.000 & 0.962 & 1.923 & -0.962 & -1.923 & 0.000 \\ -2.747 & 1.923 & 6.593 & -3.571 & -3.846 & 1.648 \\ 1.648 & -0.962 & -3.571 & 11.951 & 1.923 & -10.989 \\ 0.000 & -1.923 & -3.846 & 1.923 & 3.846 & 0.000 \\ -1.648 & 0.000 & 1.648 & -10.989 & 0.000 & 10.989 \end{bmatrix}$$

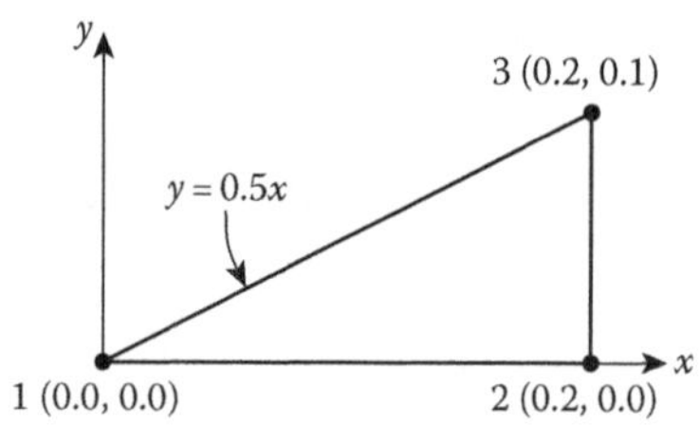

FIGURE 8.7
A 2D triangular element with a uniform thickness.

and the following 6×6 elementary $[K_e]$ matrix for the triangular element for plane strain solid mechanics problems:

$$[K_e] = 10^9 \times \begin{bmatrix} 3.365 & 0.000 & -3.365 & 2.885 & 0.000 & -2.885 \\ 0.000 & 0.962 & 1.923 & -0.962 & -1.923 & 0.000 \\ -3.365 & 1.923 & 7.212 & -4.808 & -3.846 & 2.885 \\ 2.885 & -0.962 & -4.808 & 14.423 & 1.923 & -13.462 \\ 0.000 & -1.923 & -3.846 & 1.923 & 3.846 & 0.000 \\ -2.885 & 0.000 & 2.885 & -13.462 & 0.000 & 13.462 \end{bmatrix}$$

From Examples 8.3 and 8.4, we note that the elementary $[K_e]$ matrix for a plane stress situation is different from that for a plane strain situation. Quantitatively, the plane strain results, on average, are higher than the plane stress results. Thus, it is important to know when to perform which analysis, as the unintended differences may lead to serious consequences.

8.3 Exercises

1. For the 3D hexahedral element shown in Figure 8.8, determine its elementary $[K_e]$ matrix following the steps discussed in Example 8.1. Assume that the element is made of an isotropic material with $E = 200$ GPa and $\nu = 0.3$. The coordinates of the nodes of the elements (with units of centimeters) are given in the figure.
2. For the 3D hexahedral element shown in Figure 8.9, determine its elementary $[K_e]$ matrix following the steps discussed in Example 8.1. Assume that the element is made of an isotropic material with $E = 200$ GPa and $\nu = 0.3$. The coordinates of the nodes of the elements (with units of centimeters) are given in the figure.

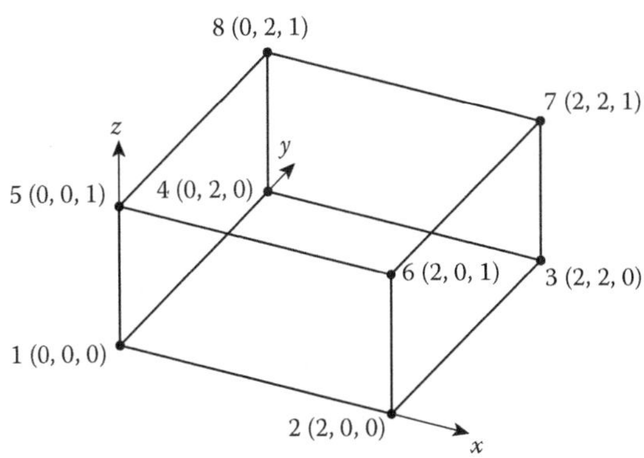

FIGURE 8.8
A 3D hexahedral element.

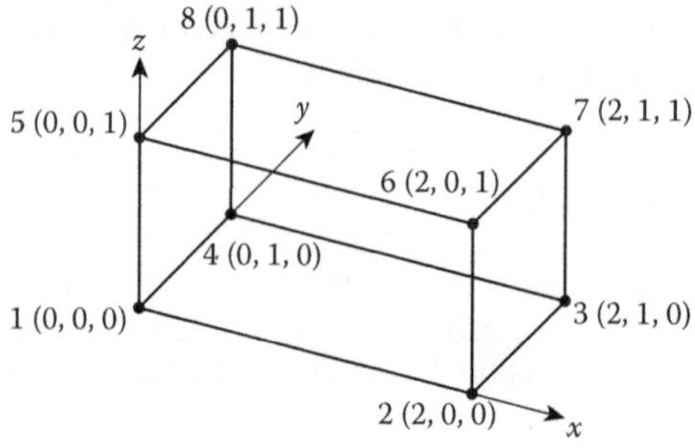

FIGURE 8.9
A 3D hexahedral element.

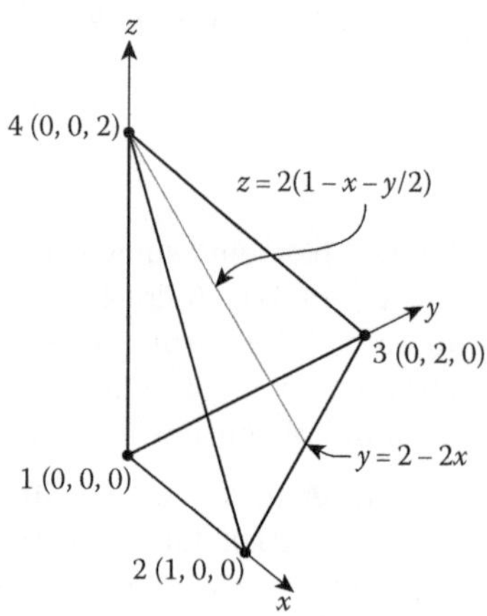

FIGURE 8.10
A 3D tetrahedral element.

3. For the 3D tetrahedral element shown in Figure 8.10, determine its elementary $[K_e]$ matrix following the steps discussed in Example 8.1. Assume that the element is made of an isotropic material with $E = 200$ GPa and $\nu = 0.3$. The coordinates of the nodes of the elements (with units of centimeters) are given in the figure.

4. In analyzing a thin structural problem with no out-of-plane stresses or displacements, an engineer confidently simplified it to a 2D problem and employed a finite element software to perform the analysis. Without the engineer's notice, the software has plane strain as the default setting for 2D structural problems. Use the knowledge you have learned in this chapter to describe the problem that the engineer's negligence has caused. Can you be more quantitative in estimating the errors in the results?

5. For the 2D rectangular element shown in Figure 8.11, determine its elementary $[K_e]$ matrix for both the plane stress and plane strain situations following the steps discussed in Example 8.2. Assume that the element is made of an isotropic material with $E = 210$ GPa and $\nu = 0.33$ and has a uniform thickness of $t = 0.1$ cm. The coordinates of the nodes of the elements (with units of centimeters) are given in the figure.

6. For the 2D rectangular element shown in Figure 8.12, determine its elementary $[K_e]$ matrix for both the plane stress and plane strain situations following the steps discussed in Example 8.2. Assume that the element is made of an isotropic material with $E = 210$ GPa and $\nu = 0.33$ and has a uniform thickness of $t = 0.1$ cm. The coordinates of the nodes of the elements (with units of centimeters) are given in the figure.

7. For the 2D triangular element shown in Figure 8.13, determine its elementary $[K_e]$ matrix for both the plane stress and plane strain situations following the steps discussed in Example 8.2. Assume that the element is made of an isotropic material with $E = 210$ GPa and $\nu = 0.33$ and has a uniform thickness of $t = 0.1$ cm. The coordinates

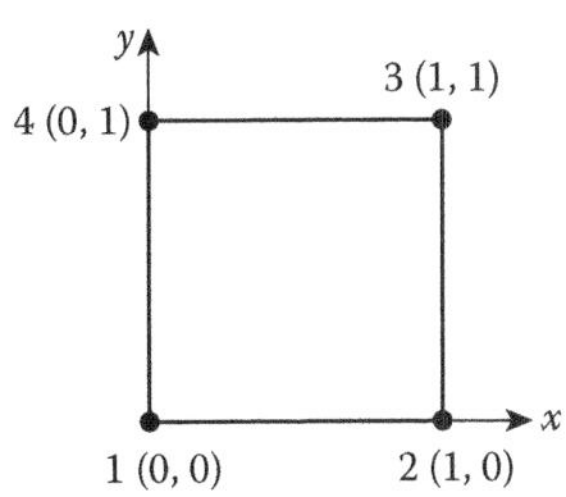

FIGURE 8.11
A 2D rectangular element with a uniform thickness.

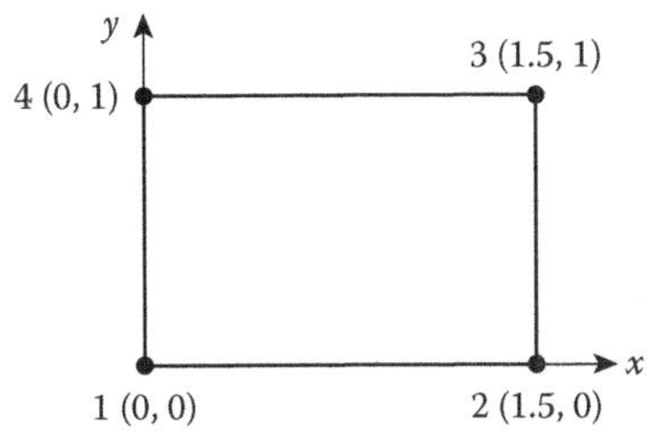

FIGURE 8.12
A 2D rectangular element with a uniform thickness.

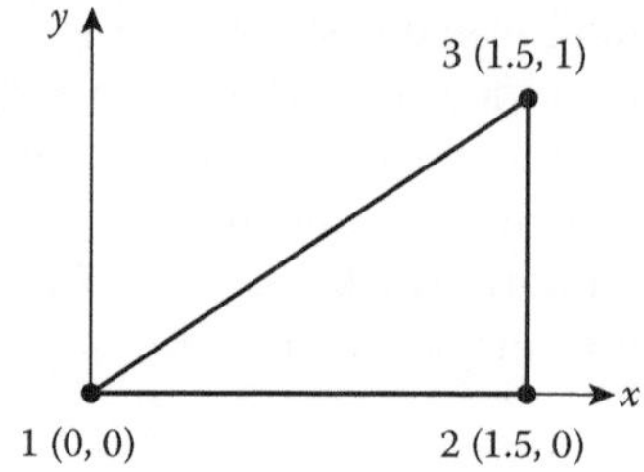

FIGURE 8.13
A 2D triangular element with a uniform thickness.

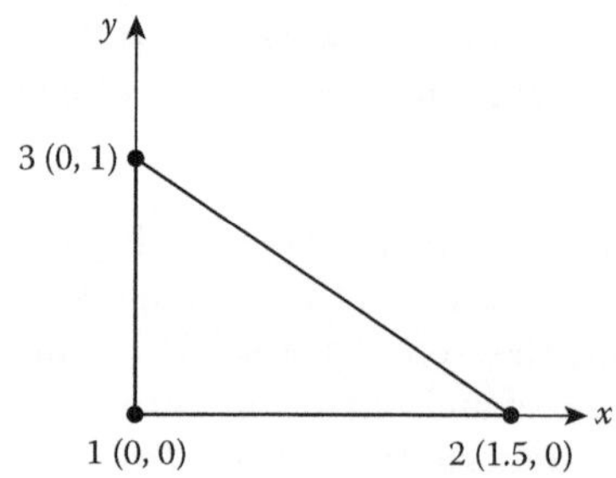

FIGURE 8.14
A 2D triangular element with a uniform thickness.

of the nodes of the elements (with units of centimeters) are given in the figure.

8. For the 2D triangular element shown in Figure 8.14, determine its elementary $[K_e]$ matrix for both the plane stress and plane strain situations following the steps discussed in Example 8.2. Assume that the element is made of an isotropic material with $E = 210$ GPa and $\nu = 0.33$ and has a uniform thickness of $t = 0.1$ cm. The coordinates of the nodes of the elements (with units of centimeters) are given in the figure.

Recommended Readings

1. J. N. Reddy. 1993. *An Introduction to the Finite Element Method.* 2nd ed. Boston: McGraw-Hill.
2. S. P. Timoshenko and J. N. Goodier. 1970. *Theory of Elasticity.* New York: McGraw-Hill.
3. Pei Chi Chou and Nicholas J. Pagano. 1967. *Elasticity Tensor, Dyadic and Engineering Approaches.* New York: Dover.

9

Axisymmetric Scalar and Vector Field Problems

When a structure can be formed by rotating a section with respect to an axis, such a structure is said to have axial symmetric geometry. Sometimes, we call it axisymmetric structure, for short. For an axisymmetric structure, when its loading and constraints also have the same axial symmetric characteristic, we can simplify the analysis of the structure by considering a radial section of the structure. Axisymmetry can occur in both scalar field problems and vector field problems. Because of some major differences in scalar field and vector field problems, we discuss their finite element method (FEM) formulations separately in this chapter.

9.1 Axisymmetric Scalar Field Problems

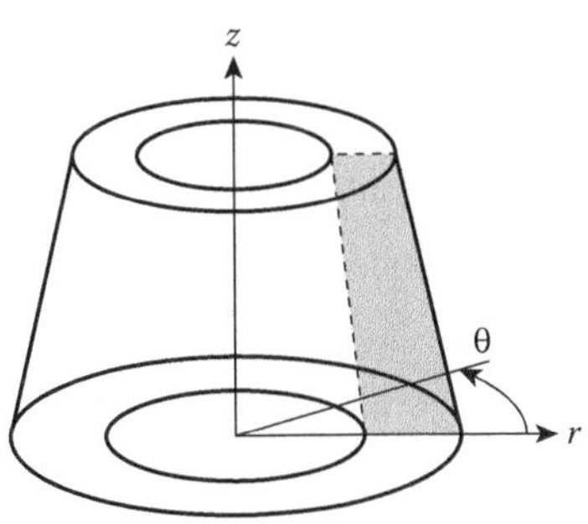

FIGURE 9.1
Axisymmetric situation.

When the geometry of a domain and the loading and constraint conditions are all symmetric about an axis, say the z axis, as shown in Figure 9.1, it is often sufficient to analyze the problem as axisymmetric by isolating a 2D radial section (e.g., the shaded section in Figure 9.1). In this section, we learn how to set up the FEM formulation for scalar field problems that have the axisymmetric characteristic. For scalar field problems, we are often concerned about one degree of freedom (DOF) per node, such as temperature in a heat transfer or conduction problem, concentration of a substance in a mass transport problem, or potential in an electrical problem.

9.1.1 PDE in cylindrical coordinates

Before we develop the finite element formulation for an axisymmetric situation, let us first express the ∇ operator and the divergence of a field in a 3D cylindrical coordinate system:

$$\nabla = \frac{\partial}{\partial r}\vec{a_r} + \frac{1}{r}\frac{\partial}{\partial \theta}\vec{a_\theta} + \frac{\partial}{\partial z}\vec{a_z}$$
$$\nabla \cdot F = \frac{1}{r}\frac{\partial (rF_r)}{\partial r} + \frac{1}{r}\frac{\partial F_\theta}{\partial \theta} + \frac{\partial F_z}{\partial z}$$

Recall that the governing partial differential equation (PDE) for 3D scalar field problems in Cartesian coordinates (x, y, z) can be expressed as

$$\nabla \cdot [k\nabla u] + g = 0$$

we now rewrite this PDE in cylindrical coordinates (r, θ, z). First, by using the above ∇ and divergence expressions and assuming an orthotropic material property, we write

$$k\nabla u = k_r\frac{\partial u}{\partial r}\vec{a_r} + \frac{k_\theta}{r}\frac{\partial u}{\partial \theta}\vec{a_\theta} + k_z\frac{\partial u}{\partial z}\vec{a_z}$$

and

$$\nabla \cdot [k\nabla u] = \frac{1}{r}\frac{\partial}{\partial r}\left(rk_r\frac{\partial u}{\partial r}\right) + \frac{1}{r}\frac{\partial}{\partial \theta}\left(\frac{k_\theta}{r}\frac{\partial u}{\partial \theta}\right) + \frac{\partial}{\partial z}\left(k_z\frac{\partial u}{\partial z}\right)$$

With this expression, we rewrite the PDE in Cartesian coordinates as one in cylindrical coordinates:

$$\frac{1}{r}\frac{\partial}{\partial r}\left(rk_r\frac{\partial u}{\partial r}\right) + \frac{1}{r}\frac{\partial}{\partial \theta}\left(\frac{k_\theta}{r}\frac{\partial}{\partial \theta}\right) + \frac{\partial}{\partial z}\left(k_z\frac{\partial u}{\partial z}\right) + g = 0$$

9.1.2 Axisymmetry and FEM formulation

For an axisymmetric problem, the field quantity u does not change with θ; thus, the above PDE is simplified to a 2D equation:

$$\frac{1}{r}\frac{\partial}{\partial r}\left(rk_r\frac{\partial u}{\partial r}\right) + \frac{\partial}{\partial z}\left(k_z\frac{\partial u}{\partial z}\right) + g = 0 \tag{9.1}$$

where $u = u(r, z)$ represents a 2D field quantity. This means that an axisymmetric problem can be equivalently dealt with by considering a 2D radial section (e.g., the shaded section in Figure 9.1) and solving it as a 2D problem.

Let $\tilde{u}(r, z)$ be an approximate solution; we write the following residual:

$$R = \frac{1}{r}\frac{\partial}{\partial r}\left(rk_r\frac{\partial \tilde{u}}{\partial r}\right) + \frac{\partial}{\partial z}\left(k_z\frac{\partial \tilde{u}}{\partial z}\right) + g$$

Considering the 2D section has an area of S, we construct the following weighted integral by introducing a set of weight functions $w(x, y)$:

$$\iiint_V wRdV = \int_0^{2\pi} d\theta \iint_A wR\, rdA$$
$$= 2\pi \iint_A \left\{ \frac{w}{r}\frac{\partial}{\partial r}\left(rk_r\frac{\partial \tilde{u}}{\partial r}\right) + w\frac{\partial}{\partial z}\left(k_z\frac{\partial \tilde{u}}{\partial z}\right) + wg \right\} rdA = 0$$

By the product rule of differentiation, we have

$$\frac{\partial}{\partial r}\left[w\left(rk_r\frac{\partial \tilde{u}}{\partial r}\right)\right] = w\frac{\partial}{\partial r}\left(rk_r\frac{\partial \tilde{u}}{\partial r}\right) + \frac{\partial w}{\partial r}\left(rk_r\frac{\partial \tilde{u}}{\partial r}\right)$$
$$\frac{\partial}{\partial z}\left[w\left(k_z\frac{\partial \tilde{u}}{\partial z}\right)\right] = w\frac{\partial}{\partial z}\left(k_z\frac{\partial \tilde{u}}{\partial z}\right) + \frac{\partial w}{\partial z}\left(k_z\frac{\partial \tilde{u}}{\partial z}\right)$$

Substituting these relationships into the above equation and eliminating the constant (2π), we arrive at

$$\iint_A \left[\frac{\partial w}{\partial r}\left(k_r\frac{\partial \tilde{u}}{\partial r}\right) + \frac{\partial w}{\partial z}\left(k_z\frac{\partial \tilde{u}}{\partial z}\right)\right] rdA$$
$$= \iint_A \left(\frac{1}{r}\frac{\partial}{\partial r}\left[w\left(rk_r\frac{\partial \tilde{u}}{\partial r}\right)\right] + \frac{\partial}{\partial z}\left[w\left(k_z\frac{\partial \tilde{u}}{\partial z}\right)\right]\right) rdA + \iint_A wgrdA \tag{9.2}$$

Again, the integral on the left-hand side of Equation 9.2 can be expressed in a compact form by using the 2D cylindrical ∇ operator $\left(\text{i.e., } \nabla = \frac{\partial}{\partial r}\vec{a_r} + \frac{\partial}{\partial z}\vec{a_z}\right)$, the dot product expression, and k (for k_r, k_z, assuming an orthotropic property) as

$$\iint_A \left[\frac{\partial w}{\partial r}\left(k_r\frac{\partial \tilde{u}}{\partial r}\right) + \frac{\partial w}{\partial z}\left(k_z\frac{\partial \tilde{u}}{\partial z}\right)\right] rdA = \iint_A \nabla w \cdot [k\nabla \tilde{u}] rdA$$

To the first integral on the right-hand side of Equation 9.2, we apply the divergence theorem:

$$\iint_A \left(\frac{1}{r}\frac{\partial}{\partial r}\left[w\left(rk_r\frac{\partial \tilde{u}}{\partial r}\right)\right] + \frac{\partial}{\partial z}\left[w\left(k_z\frac{\partial \tilde{u}}{\partial z}\right)\right]\right) rdA$$
$$= \iint_A \nabla \cdot \left[w\left(k_r\frac{\partial \tilde{u}}{\partial r}\right)\vec{a_r} + w\left(k_z\frac{\partial \tilde{u}}{\partial z}\right)\vec{a_z}\right] rdA$$
$$= \int_L w\left(k_r\frac{\partial \tilde{u}}{\partial r}\vec{a_r} + k_z\frac{\partial \tilde{u}}{\partial z}\vec{a_z}\right)\cdot \vec{n}rdL = \int_L w[k\nabla \tilde{u}]\cdot \vec{n}rdL$$

where $\vec{n} = n_r\vec{a_r} + n_z\vec{a_z}$ is the unit normal vector of the boundary line L at a given point. Putting all these expressions together, we rewrite Equation 9.2 as

$$\iint_A \nabla w \cdot [k\nabla\tilde{u}]rdA = \int_L w[k\nabla\tilde{u}] \cdot \vec{n}rdL + \iint_A wg\,rdA \tag{9.3}$$

Using the Galerkin method, we have $w_m = N_m$ for $m = 1, ..., n_e$. With $\tilde{u} = [N]\{d_0\}$, we obtain

$$\iint_A (\nabla N_m \cdot k\nabla[N])rdA\{d_0\} = \int_L N_m[k\nabla\tilde{u}] \cdot \vec{n}\}rdL + \iint_A N_m grdA$$

for $m = 1, \ldots, n_e$.

By summing all these n_e equations together (see steps in Section 6.2), we obtain the following for axisymmetric scalar field problems,

$$\iint_A ([\nabla N]^T \cdot k\nabla[N])rdA\{d_0\} = \int_L [N]^T[k\nabla\tilde{u}] \cdot \vec{n}rdL + \iint_A [N]^T grdA \tag{9.4}$$

and the elementary $[K_e]$ matrix:

$$[K_e] = \iint_A ([\nabla N]^T \cdot k\nabla[N])rdA \tag{9.5}$$

Example 9.1

For the 2D rectangular element shown in Figure 9.2, determine its elementary $[K_e]$ matrix using Equation 9.5. Assume that the element is intended for solving axisymmetric scalar problems with constant $k_r = k_z = k = 1000$ and the coordinates of their nodes given in the figure (note that because this example can be applied to different physics problems, such as heat conduction, mass diffusion, fluid flow in porous medium, and as electric, without losing generality, we intentionally ignore the units of these values).

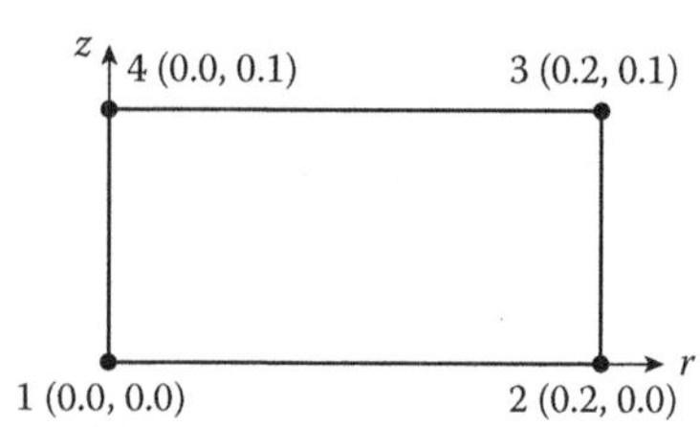

FIGURE 9.2
A 2D rectangular element with a uniform thickness.

Answer

To determine the elementary $[K_e]$ matrix for a 2D axisymmetric scalar problem, we first expand Equation 9.5 by using the 2D cylindrical ∇ operator, $\nabla = \dfrac{\partial}{\partial r}\vec{a_r} + \dfrac{\partial}{\partial z}\vec{a_z}$:

$$[K_e] = \iint_A \left(\left[\frac{\partial N}{\partial r}\right]^T k_r \left[\frac{\partial N}{\partial r}\right] + \left[\frac{\partial N}{\partial z}\right]^T k_z \left[\frac{\partial N}{\partial z}\right] \right) r dA \tag{9.6}$$

For the rectangular element, since this element is the same as the one in Figure 8.6, we have the same set of shape functions (after replacing x with r and y with z); thus, we express the shape function matrix as

$$[N] = \begin{bmatrix}(1-5r)(1-10z) & 5r(1-10z) & 50rz & 10(1-5r)z\end{bmatrix}$$

Taking its first derivative with respect to r and z, we have

$$\left[\frac{\partial N}{\partial r}\right] = \begin{bmatrix}50z-5 & 5-50z & 50z & -50z\end{bmatrix}$$

$$\left[\frac{\partial N}{\partial z}\right] = \begin{bmatrix}50r-10 & -50r & 50r & 10-50r\end{bmatrix}$$

Plugging these expressions into Equation 9.6, and integrating it over the rectangular area defined by the element, along with substituting the $k_r = k_z = k$ value, we obtain

$$[K_e] = k_r \int_{r=0}^{0.2}\int_{z=0}^{0.1} \begin{bmatrix}50z-5\\ 5-50z\\ 50z\\ -50z\end{bmatrix} \begin{bmatrix}50z-5 & 5-50z & 50z & -50z\end{bmatrix} rdrdz$$

$$+ k_z \int_{r=0}^{0.2}\int_{z=0}^{0.1} \begin{bmatrix}50r-10\\ -50r\\ 50r\\ 10-50r\end{bmatrix} \begin{bmatrix}50r-10 & -50r & 50r & 10-50r\end{bmatrix} rdzdr$$

$$= \begin{bmatrix}50.00 & 16.67 & -41.67 & -25.00\\ 16.67 & 116.67 & -91.67 & -41.67\\ -41.67 & -91.67 & 116.67 & 16.67\\ -25.00 & -41.67 & 16.67 & 50.00\end{bmatrix}$$

Example 9.2

For the 2D triangular element shown in Figure 9.3, determine its elementary $[K_e]$ matrix using Equation 9.5. Assume that the element is intended for solving axisymmetric scalar problems with constant $k_r = k_z = k = 1000$ and the coordinates of their nodes given in the figure (ignore the units).

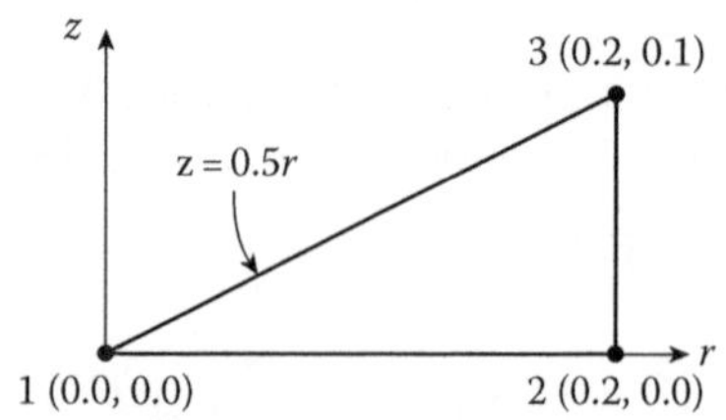

FIGURE 9.3
A 2D triangular element with a uniform thickness.

Answer
For the triangular element, since it is the same as the one in Figure 8.7, we have the same set of shape functions (after replacing x with r and y with z):

$$[N] = \begin{bmatrix} 1-5r & 5r-10z & 10z \end{bmatrix}$$

Taking its first derivative with respect to r and z, we obtain

$$\left[\frac{\partial N}{\partial r}\right] = \begin{bmatrix} -5 & 5 & 0 \end{bmatrix}, \quad \left[\frac{\partial N}{\partial z}\right] = \begin{bmatrix} 0 & -10 & 10 \end{bmatrix}$$

Plugging these expressions into Equation 9.6, along with $dA = drdz$, integrating it over the triangular area of the element, and substituting the $k_r = k_z = k$ value, we obtain

$$\begin{aligned} [K_e] &= k \int_{r=0}^{0.2} \int_{z=0}^{0.5r} \left(\begin{bmatrix} -5 \\ 5 \\ 0 \end{bmatrix} \begin{bmatrix} -5 & 5 & 0 \end{bmatrix} + \begin{bmatrix} 0 \\ -10 \\ 10 \end{bmatrix} \begin{bmatrix} 0 & -10 & 10 \end{bmatrix} \right) rdzdr \\ &= \begin{bmatrix} 33.33 & -33.33 & 0 \\ -33.33 & 166.67 & -133.33 \\ 0 & -133.33 & 133.33 \end{bmatrix} \end{aligned}$$

In comparing Equations 7.5 and 9.5, we note that the two equations look very much alike, but the results of the corresponding elements in Section 7.1.2 and here are quite different, although the corresponding elements are of exactly the same shape, size, and location. The reason for this is that the way we solve an axisymmetric problem treats the structure as a 3D domain; thus, the integrand in Equation 9.5 contains r, which accounts for the volume of a rotational 3D structural domain. By contrast, the integrand in Equation 7.5 contains t, which accounts for the volume of a uniformly thin 2D domain.

9.2 Axisymmetric Vector Field Problems

For vector fields, we are mainly concerned about the problems of solid mechanics, in which the geometry of the structural domains and the loading and constraint conditions are all symmetric about an axis, say the z axis. These situations can be treated as axisymmetric problems by analyzing a 2D radial section of the structure. Since solid mechanics are vector field problems, the finite element formulation developed in Section 9.1 for scalar field problems cannot be used. We need to develop PDEs and a finite element formulation for axisymmetric problems of solid mechanics.

9.2.1 PDEs of equilibrium in cylindrical coordinates

We begin by reexamining the stress and strain relationships and developing the PDEs of equilibrium in cylindrical coordinates.

In cylindrical coordinates, r, θ, z, the stress and strain can be expressed in vector forms by their corresponding components as

$$\{\sigma\} = \left\{\sigma_r \quad \sigma_\theta \quad \sigma_z \quad \tau_{rz} \quad \tau_{r\theta} \quad \tau_{\theta z}\right\}^T$$
$$\{\epsilon\} = \left\{\epsilon_r \quad \epsilon_\theta \quad \epsilon_z \quad \gamma_{rz} \quad \gamma_{r\theta} \quad \gamma_{\theta z}\right\}^T$$

These strain components can be related to the components of the displacement fields, u_r, u_θ, u_z in the r, θ, z directions, respectively, by the following relationships:

$$\epsilon_r = \frac{\partial u_r}{\partial r}, \qquad \sigma_\theta = \frac{u_r}{r} + \frac{\partial u_\theta}{r\partial\theta}, \qquad \epsilon_z = \frac{\partial u_z}{\partial z},$$
$$\gamma_{r\theta} = \frac{\partial u_r}{r\partial\theta} + \frac{\partial u_\theta}{\partial r} - \frac{u_\theta}{r}, \quad \gamma_{rz} = \frac{\partial u_r}{\partial z} + \frac{\partial u_z}{\partial r}, \quad \gamma_{\theta z} = \frac{\partial u_\theta}{\partial z} + \frac{\partial u_z}{r\partial\theta}$$

In the free-body diagram, shown in Figure 9.4, of an arbitrary, infinitesimal block in cylindrical coordinates, each surface of the block has three stress components, as marked in the figure with $\tau_{rz} = \tau_{zr}, \tau_{r\theta} = \tau_{\theta r}$, and $\tau_{\theta z} = \tau_{z\theta}$. By considering the force equilibrium of this block with dimensions $dr, d\theta$, and dz along the three cylindrical axes, we express the following by ignoring acceleration:

$$\begin{aligned}\sum F_r = 0 : &\left(\sigma_r + \frac{\partial\sigma_r}{\partial r}dr - \sigma_r\right) rd\theta dz + \left(\tau_{r\theta} + \frac{\partial\tau_{r\theta}}{r\partial\theta}rd\theta - \tau_{r\theta}\right)\cos\frac{d\theta}{2}drdz \\ &- \left(\sigma_\theta + \frac{\partial\sigma_\theta}{r\partial\theta}rd\theta + \sigma_\theta\right)\sin\frac{d\theta}{2}drdz + \left(\tau_{rz} + \frac{\partial\tau_{rz}}{\partial z}dz - \tau_{rz}\right)drrd\theta \\ &+ f_r rd\theta drdz = 0\end{aligned}$$

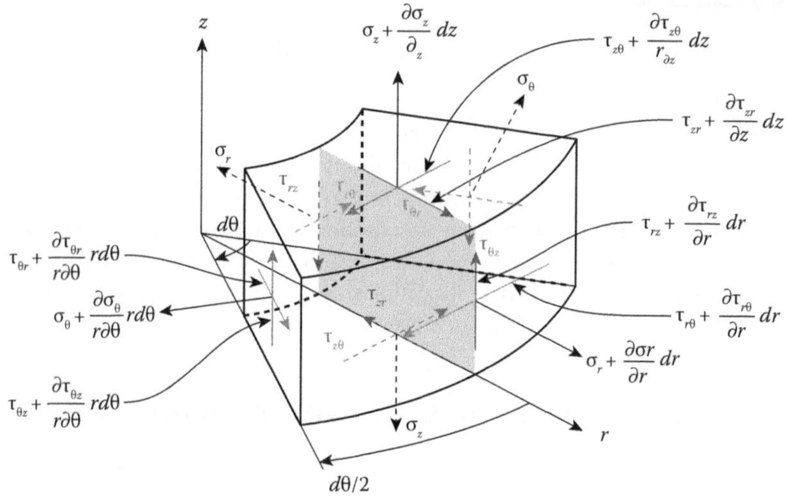

FIGURE 9.4
A 3D free-body diagram in cylindrical coordinates.

$$\sum F_\theta = 0: \left(\sigma_\theta + \frac{\partial \sigma_\theta}{r\partial\theta} r d\theta - \sigma_\theta\right) \cos\frac{d\theta}{2} dr dz$$
$$+ \left(\tau_{r\theta} + \frac{\partial \tau_{r\theta}}{r\partial\theta} r d\theta + \tau_{r\theta}\right) \sin\frac{d\theta}{2} dr dz + \left(\tau_{r\theta} + \frac{\partial \tau_{r\theta}}{\partial r} dr - \tau_{r\theta}\right) r d\theta dz$$
$$+ \left(\tau_{\theta z} + \frac{\partial \tau_{\theta z}}{\partial z} dz - \tau_{\theta z}\right) r d\theta dr + f_\theta r d\theta dr dz = 0$$
$$\sum F_z = 0: \left(\sigma_z + \frac{\partial \sigma_z}{\partial z} dz - \sigma_z\right) dr r d\theta + \left(\tau_{rz} + \frac{\partial \tau_{rz}}{\partial r} dr - \tau_{rz}\right) r d\theta dz$$
$$+ \left(\tau_{\theta z} + \frac{\partial \tau_{\theta z}}{r\partial\theta} r d\theta - \tau_{\theta z}\right) dr dz + f_z r d\theta dr dz = 0$$

where f_r, f_θ, f_z are the three components of the volume force in cylindrical coordinates. Since $d\theta$ is very small, we have $\sin(d\theta/2) \approx d\theta/2$ and $\cos(d\theta/2) \approx 1$. Thus, applying these expressions to the above equations and neglecting the two extremely small terms (i.e., $[\partial\sigma_\theta/\partial\theta] d\theta d\theta dr dz$ and $[\partial\tau_{r\theta}/\partial\theta] d\theta d\theta dr dz$), we simplify them into the following PDEs of equilibrium in cylindrical coordinates (after multiplying $1/r dr d\theta dz$ on both sides of these equations):

$$\begin{aligned} \sum F_r = 0: &\quad \frac{\partial \sigma_r}{\partial r} + \frac{\partial \tau_{r\theta}}{r\partial\theta} + \frac{\partial \tau_{rz}}{\partial z} - \frac{\sigma_\theta}{r} + f_r = 0 \\ \sum F_\theta = 0: &\quad \frac{\partial \tau_{r\theta}}{\partial r} + \frac{\partial \sigma_\theta}{r\partial\theta} + \frac{\partial \tau_{\theta z}}{\partial z} + \frac{\tau_{r\theta}}{r} + f_\theta = 0 \\ \sum F_z = 0: &\quad \frac{\partial \tau_{rz}}{\partial r} + \frac{\partial \tau_{\theta z}}{r\partial\theta} + \frac{\partial \sigma_z}{\partial z} + f_z = 0 \end{aligned} \tag{9.7}$$

In an axisymmetric situation, any radial section of the structure will remain in the same section plane after deformation and all variables are independent of θ; thus, we have $\tau_{r\theta} = \tau_{z\theta} = \gamma_{r\theta} = \gamma_{z\theta} = 0$ and $v = 0$. Then, the stress and strain vectors are reduced to

$$\{\sigma\} = \{\sigma_r \quad \sigma_\theta \quad \sigma_z \quad \tau_{rz}\}^T$$
$$\{\epsilon\} = \{\epsilon_r \quad \epsilon_\theta \quad \epsilon_z \quad \gamma_{rz}\}^T$$

the PDEs of equilibrium are reduced to

$$\begin{aligned} &\frac{\partial \sigma_r}{\partial r} + \frac{\partial \tau_{rz}}{\partial z} - \frac{\sigma_\theta}{r} + f_r = 0 \\ &\frac{\partial \tau_{rz}}{\partial r} + \frac{\partial \sigma_z}{\partial z} + f_z = 0 \end{aligned} \tag{9.8}$$

and the displacement, volume force, and weight function vectors are reduced to

$$\{d\} = \begin{Bmatrix} u_r \\ u_z \end{Bmatrix}, \quad \{f\} = \begin{Bmatrix} f_r \\ f_z \end{Bmatrix}, \quad \{w\} = \begin{Bmatrix} w_r \\ w_z \end{Bmatrix}$$

With the above information, we express the reduced strain–displacement relationships in a matrix form as

$$\{\epsilon\} = \{\epsilon_r \quad \epsilon_\theta \quad \epsilon_z \quad \gamma_{rz}\}^T = \left\{ \frac{\partial u_r}{\partial r} \quad \frac{u_r}{r} \quad \frac{\partial u_z}{\partial z} \quad \frac{\partial u_r}{\partial z} + \frac{\partial u_z}{\partial r} \right\}^T$$

By introducing the following differential operator matrix,

$$\nabla_{sa} = \begin{bmatrix} \frac{\partial}{\partial r} & 0 \\ \frac{1}{r} & 0 \\ 0 & \frac{\partial}{\partial z} \\ \frac{\partial}{\partial z} & \frac{\partial}{\partial r} \end{bmatrix} \quad \text{or} \quad \nabla_{sa}^T = \begin{bmatrix} \frac{\partial}{\partial r} & \frac{1}{r} & 0 & \frac{\partial}{\partial z} \\ 0 & 0 & \frac{\partial}{\partial z} & \frac{\partial}{\partial r} \end{bmatrix} \tag{9.9}$$

we write the following matrix equations:

$$\{\epsilon\} = \begin{bmatrix} \frac{\partial}{\partial r} & 0 \\ \frac{1}{r} & 0 \\ 0 & \frac{\partial}{\partial z} \\ \frac{\partial}{\partial z} & \frac{\partial}{\partial r} \end{bmatrix} \begin{Bmatrix} u_r \\ u_z \end{Bmatrix} = \nabla_{sa}\{d\} \quad \text{and} \quad \nabla_{sa}\{w\} = \begin{Bmatrix} \frac{\partial w_r}{\partial r} \\ \frac{w_r}{r} \\ \frac{\partial w_z}{\partial z} \\ \frac{\partial w_r}{\partial z} + \frac{\partial w_z}{\partial r} \end{Bmatrix} \tag{9.10}$$

Assuming an isotropic material and referring to Equation 8.9, we have the following stress and strain relationships:

$$\begin{Bmatrix} \sigma_r \\ \sigma_\theta \\ \sigma_z \\ \tau_{rz} \end{Bmatrix} = \frac{E}{(1+\nu)(1-2\nu)} \begin{bmatrix} 1-\nu & \nu & \nu & 0 \\ \nu & 1-\nu & \nu & 0 \\ \nu & \nu & 1-\nu & 0 \\ 0 & 0 & 0 & 0.5-\nu \end{bmatrix} \begin{Bmatrix} \epsilon_r \\ \epsilon_\theta \\ \epsilon_z \\ \gamma_{rz} \end{Bmatrix}$$

Then the material property matrix $[C]$ for an axisymmetric solid mechanics problem becomes

$$[C] = \frac{E}{(1+\nu)(1-2\nu)} \begin{bmatrix} 1-\nu & \nu & \nu & 0 \\ \nu & 1-\nu & \nu & 0 \\ \nu & \nu & 1-\nu & 0 \\ 0 & 0 & 0 & 0.5-\nu \end{bmatrix} \tag{9.11}$$

9.2.2 FEM formulation for axisymmetric solid mechanics

By constructing the weighted integral of residual to Equation 9.8 using the weight function vector, we write

$$\iiint_V \left[w_r \left(\frac{\partial \sigma_r}{\partial r} + \frac{\partial \tau_{rz}}{\partial z} - \frac{\sigma_\theta}{r} + f_r \right) + w_z \left(\frac{\partial \tau_{rz}}{\partial r} + \frac{\partial \sigma_z}{\partial z} + f_z \right) \right] dV = 0 \tag{9.12}$$

By the product rule of differentiation, we can express

$$\begin{aligned} w_r \frac{\partial \sigma_r}{\partial r} &= -\sigma_r \frac{\partial w_r}{\partial r} + \frac{\partial}{\partial r}(\sigma_r w_r) \\ w_r \frac{\partial \tau_{rz}}{\partial z} &= -\tau_{rz} \frac{\partial w_r}{\partial z} + \frac{\partial}{\partial z}(\tau_{rz} w_r) \\ w_z \frac{\partial \tau_{rz}}{\partial r} &= -\tau_{rz} \frac{\partial w_z}{\partial r} + \frac{\partial}{\partial r}(\tau_{rz} w_z) \\ w_z \frac{\partial \sigma_z}{\partial z} &= -\sigma_z \frac{\partial w_z}{\partial z} + \frac{\partial}{\partial z}(\sigma_z w_z) \end{aligned}$$

Substituting these expressions to Equation 9.12, we have

$$\begin{aligned} &\iiint_V \left[-\sigma_r \frac{\partial w_r}{\partial r} - \sigma_z \frac{\partial w_z}{\partial z} - \tau_{rz} \left(\frac{\partial w_r}{\partial z} + \frac{\partial w_z}{\partial r} \right) - \frac{\sigma_\theta w_r}{r} \right] dV \\ &+ \iiint_V \left[\frac{\partial}{\partial r}(\sigma_r w_r + \tau_{rz} w_z) + \frac{\partial}{\partial z}(\tau_{rz} w_r + \sigma_z w_z) \right] dV \\ &+ \iiint_V (w_r f_r + w_z f_z) dV = 0 \end{aligned}$$

After rearranging it, substituting $rdrd\theta dz$ for dV, and integrating for θ from 0 to 2π, we obtain

$$\begin{aligned}
2\pi \iint_A \left[\sigma_r \frac{\partial w_r}{\partial r} + \frac{\sigma_\theta w_r}{r} + \sigma_z \frac{\partial w_z}{\partial z} + \tau_{rz}(\frac{\partial w_r}{\partial z} + \frac{\partial w_z}{\partial r})\right] rdrdz \\
= 2\pi \iint_A \left[\frac{\partial}{\partial r}(\sigma_r w_r + \tau_{rz} w_z) + \frac{\partial}{\partial z}(\tau_{rz} w_r + \sigma_z w_z)\right] rdrdz \\
+ 2\pi \iint_A (w_r f_r + w_z f_z) rdzdr
\end{aligned} \tag{9.13}$$

in which the constant 2π can be eliminated.

By using Equation 9.10 along with the reduced stress vector, we simplify the first integral in Equation 9.13 into a compact matrix form as

$$-\iint_A \{\nabla_{sa}\{w\}\}^T \{\sigma\} rdA$$

For the second integral, we apply the divergence theorem, with $\vec{n} = n_r \vec{a_r} + n_z \vec{a_z}$:

$$\begin{aligned}
\iint_A \left[\frac{\partial}{\partial r}(\sigma_r w_r + \tau_{rz} w_z) + \frac{\partial}{\partial z}(\tau_{rz} w_r + \sigma_z w_z)\right] rdA \\
= \int_L [(\sigma_r w_r + \tau_{rz} w_z) n_r + (\tau_{rz} w_r + \sigma_z w_z) n_z] rdL \\
= \int_L [w_r(\sigma_r n_r + \tau_{rz} n_z) + w_z(\tau_{rz} n_r + \sigma_z n_z)] rdL \\
= \int_L [w_r T_r + w_z T_z] rdL = \int_L \{w\}^T \{T\} rdL + \sum \{w\}^T P
\end{aligned}$$

where T is traction vector and P is point load on the boundary of the 2D domain.

The last integral in Equation 9.13 can be expressed in a compact form as

$$\iint_A (w_r f_r + w_z f_z) rdA = \iint_A \{w\}^T \{f\} rdA$$

Putting all these together, we have

$$\iint_A \{\nabla_{sa}\{w\}\}^T \{\sigma\} rdA = \iint_A \{w\}^T \{f\} rdA + \int_L \{w\}^T \{T\} rdL + \sum \{w\}^T P \tag{9.14}$$

Referring to Equation 5.32, we can express the two field quantities in the r and z directions in terms of the elementary shape functions and DOF vector as

$$\tilde{u}_r = \sum_{m=1}^{n_e} N_m u_{mr}, \quad \tilde{u}_z = \sum_{m=1}^{n_e} N_m w_{mz}$$

for a 2D element having elementary DOF $= n_e$. Putting these expressions together in accordance with the displacement vector, $\{d\} = \{\tilde{u}_r\ \tilde{u}_z\}^T$, we obtain the following matrix equation:

$$\begin{Bmatrix} \tilde{u}_r \\ \tilde{u}_z \end{Bmatrix} = \begin{bmatrix} N_1 & 0 & N_2 & 0 & N_3 & 0 & \cdots \\ 0 & N_1 & 0 & N_2 & 0 & N_3 & \cdots \end{bmatrix} \begin{Bmatrix} u_{1r} \\ u_{1z} \\ u_{2r} \\ u_{2z} \\ u_{3r} \\ u_{3z} \\ \vdots \end{Bmatrix} = [N]\{d_0\} \quad (9.15)$$

By substituting the above shape function matrix, the stress–strain relationship $\{\sigma\} = [C]\{\epsilon\} = [C]\nabla_{sa}[N]\{d_0\}$, and $\{w\} = [N]$ (per the Galerkin method) into Equation 9.14, we obtain

$$\iint_A \{\nabla_{sa}^T[N]\}[C](\nabla_{sa}[N])rdA\{d_0\} = \iint_A [N]^T\{f\}rdA + \int_L [N]^T\{T\}rdL + \sum [N]^T P \quad (9.16)$$

and the elementary $[K_e]$ matrix,

$$[K_e] = \iint_A \{\nabla_{sa}[N]\}^T[C](\nabla_{sa}[N])rdA \quad (9.17)$$

where $[C]$ is given in Equation 9.11.

Example 9.3

For the 2D rectangular element shown in Figure 9.2, determine its elementary $[K_e]$ matrix using Equation 9.17. Assume that the element is made of an isotropic material with $E = 200$ GPa and $\nu = 0.3$.

Answer

For the rectangular element, we directly copy the shape functions of that in Figure 9.2 here:

$$N_1 = (1-5r)(1-10z),\ N_2 = 5r(1-10z),\ N_3 = 50rz,\ N_4 = 10(1-5r)z$$

Referring to Equation 9.15, we know that the shape function matrix for this 4-node 2D solid mechanical element is a 2×8 matrix, which can be expressed as

$$[N] = \begin{bmatrix} N_1 & 0 & N_2 & 0 & N_3 & 0 & N_4 & 0 \\ 0 & N_1 & 0 & N_2 & 0 & N_3 & 0 & N_4 \end{bmatrix}$$

With this matrix, we calculate $\nabla_{sa}[N]$, which is a 4×8 matrix:

$$\nabla_{sa}[N] = \begin{bmatrix} 50z-50 & 0 & 5-50z & 0 & 50z & 0 & -50z & 0 \\ (1-5r)(1-10z)/r & 0 & 5-50z & 0 & 50z & 0 & 10z(1-5r)/r & 0 \\ 0 & 50r-10 & 0 & -50r & 0 & 50r & 0 & 10-50r \\ 50r-10 & 50z-5 & -50r & 5-50z & 50r & 50z & 10-50r & -50z \end{bmatrix}$$

Moreover, using Equation 9.11, along with $E = 200$ GPa and $\nu = 0.3$, we calculate the material property matrix:

$$[C] = 10^{11} \times \begin{bmatrix} 2.69 & 1.15 & 1.15 & 0 \\ 1.15 & 2.69 & 1.15 & 0 \\ 1.15 & 1.15 & 2.69 & 0 \\ 0 & 0 & 0 & 0.77 \end{bmatrix}$$

Putting all these into Equation 9.17 along with $dA = drdz$, and integrating it over the rectangular area of the element, we obtain the following 8×8 elementary $[K_e]$ matrix for a 4-node 2D axisymmetric element for solid mechanics:

$$[K_e] = \int_{r=0}^{1}\int_{z=0}^{1} \underset{8\times 4}{\{\nabla_{sa}[N]\}^T} \quad \underset{4\times 4}{[C]} \quad \underset{4\times 8}{\{\nabla_{sa}[N]\}} \quad rdzdr$$

$$= 10^9 \times \begin{bmatrix} \infty & -0.64 & 2.56 & 0.64 & -2.56 & -3.21 & \infty & 3.21 \\ -0.64 & 10.26 & -1.28 & 7.69 & -6.41 & -9.62 & -3.21 & -8.33 \\ 2.56 & -1.28 & 20.51 & -10.26 & -1.28 & 5.13 & -2.56 & 6.41 \\ 0.64 & 7.69 & -10.26 & 28.21 & -5.13 & -26.28 & 3.21 & -9.62 \\ -2.56 & -6.41 & -1.28 & -5.13 & 20.51 & 10.26 & 2.56 & 1.28 \\ -3.21 & -9.62 & 5.13 & -26.28 & 10.26 & 28.21 & -0.64 & 7.69 \\ \infty & -3.21 & -2.56 & 3.21 & 2.56 & -0.64 & \infty & 0.64 \\ 3.21 & -8.33 & 6.41 & -9.62 & 1.28 & 7.69 & 0.64 & 10.26 \end{bmatrix}$$

Note that this $[K_e]$ matrix contains several terms of infinity. The reason is that these terms contain $1/r^2$ because the geometric domain includes the edge of $r = 0$, which in turn causes division by zero when we evaluate them by integration analytically. This problem can be avoided by performing numerical integration instead. This is another reason why Gauss quadrature numerical integration is necessary.

Example 9.4

For the 2D triangular element shown in Figure 9.3, determine its elementary $[K_e]$ matrix using Equation 9.17. Assume that the element is made of an isotropic material with $E = 200$ GPa and $\nu = 0.3$.

Answer

For the triangular element, we have the following shape functions by copying the ones for the element shown in Figure 9.3:

$$N_1 = 1 - 5r, \quad N_2 = 5r - 10z, \quad N_3 = 10z$$

With these expressions, we calculate the 4×6 $\nabla_{sa}[N]$ matrix:

$$\nabla_{sa}[N] = \begin{bmatrix} -5 & 0 & 5 & 0 & 0 & 0 \\ (1-5r)/r & 0 & (5r-10z)/r & 0 & 10z/r & 0 \\ 0 & 0 & 0 & -10 & 0 & 10 \\ 0 & -5 & -10 & 5 & 10 & 0 \end{bmatrix}$$

Plugging this expression and the $[C]$ matrix into Equation 9.17 and integrating it over the triangular area of the element, we obtain the following 6×6 elementary $[K_e]$ matrix for a 3-node 2D solid mechanical element for an axisymmetric problem:

$$[K_e] = \int_{r=0}^{1} \int_{z=0}^{0.5r} \underset{6\times 4}{\{\nabla_{sa}[N]\}^T} \underset{4\times 4}{[C]} \underset{4\times 6}{\{\nabla_{sa}[N]\}} \, rdzdr$$

$$= 10^9 \times \begin{bmatrix} 14.10 & 0 & -6.73 & 3.85 & 0.32 & -3.85 \\ 0 & 2.56 & 5.13 & -2.56 & -5.13 & 0 \\ -6.73 & 5.13 & 26.07 & -16.67 & -6.84 & 11.54 \\ 3.85 & -2.56 & -16.67 & 38.46 & 1.28 & -35.90 \\ 0.32 & -5.13 & -6.84 & 1.28 & 13.25 & 3.85 \\ -3.85 & 0 & 11.54 & -35.90 & 3.85 & 35.90 \end{bmatrix}$$

When comparing Equations 9.17 and 8.21, we note that these two equations differ in several ways. First, the differential operator is different: for axisymmetric solid mechanics, ∇_{sa} is given in Equation 9.9, while for 2D solid mechanics, ∇_{s2} is given in Equation 8.16. Second, the material property $[C]$ matrix is different: $[C]$ is a 4×4 matrix as given in Equation 9.11 for axisymmetric problems, and it is a 3×3 matrix as given by Equation 8.14 (for plane stress) or Equation 8.15 (for plane strain). Third, the integrand is different: it contains r to account for the volume of a rotational 3D domain for axisymmetric situations, but it uses t to account for the volume of a uniformly thin 2D domain.

9.3 Exercises

1. For the 2D rectangular element shown in Figure 9.5, determine its elementary $[K_e]$ matrix following the steps discussed in Example 9.1. Assume that the element is intended for solving axisymmetric scalar problems with constant $k_r = k_z = k = 1000$ and the coordinates of their nodes given in the figure (ignore the units of these values).

2. For the 2D rectangular element shown in Figure 9.6, determine its elementary $[K_e]$ matrix following the steps discussed in Example 9.1. Assume that the element is intended for solving axisymmetric scalar problems with constant $k_r = k_z = k = 1000$

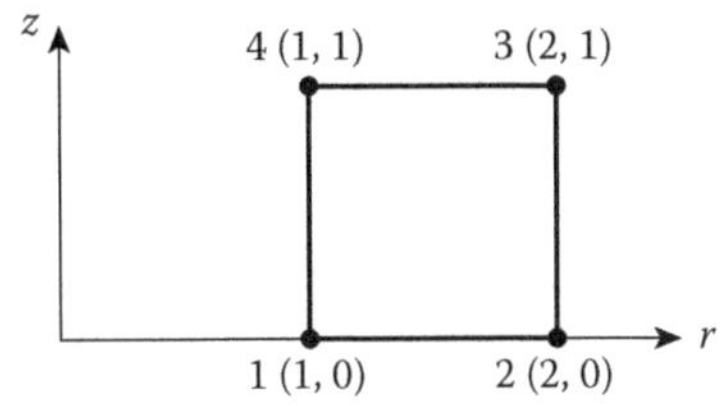

FIGURE 9.5
A 2D rectangular element with a uniform thickness.

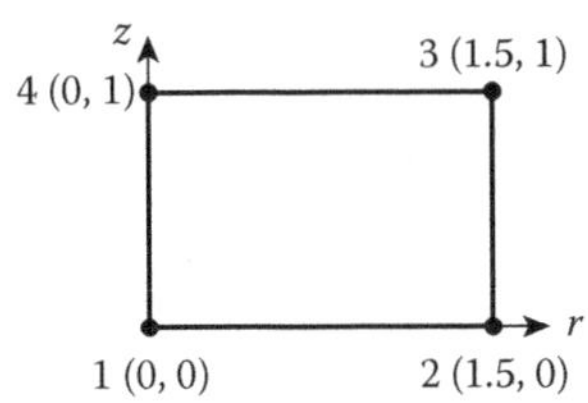

FIGURE 9.6
A 2D rectangular element with a uniform thickness.

and the coordinates of their nodes given in the figure (ignore the units of these values).

3. For the 2D triangular element shown in Figure 9.7, determine its elementary $[K_e]$ matrix following the steps discussed in Example 9.1. Assume that the element is intended for solving axisymmetric scalar problems with constant $k_r = k_z = k = 1000$ and the coordinates of their nodes given in the figure (ignore the units of these values).

4. For the 2D triangular element shown in Figure 9.8, determine its elementary $[K_e]$ matrix following the steps discussed in Example 9.1. Assume that the element is intended for solving axisymmetric scalar

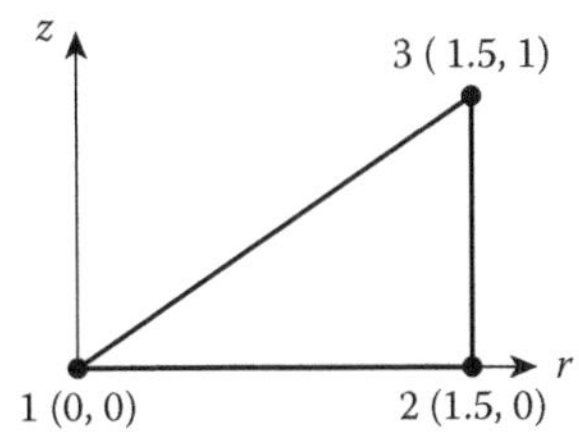

FIGURE 9.7
A 2D triangular element with a uniform thickness.

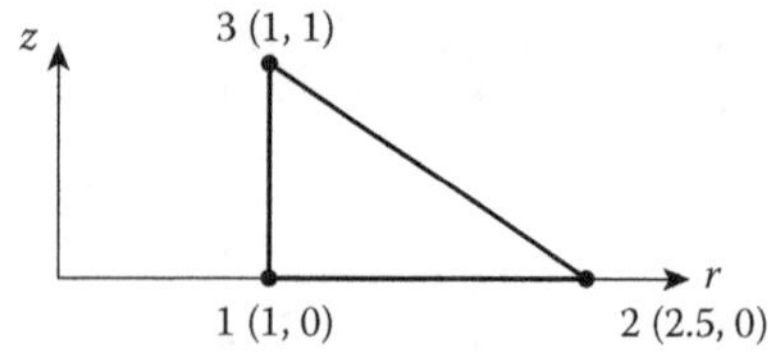

FIGURE 9.8
A 2D triangular element with a uniform thickness.

problems with constant $k_r = k_z = k = 1000$ and the coordinates of their nodes given in the figure (ignore the units of these values).

5. For the 2D rectangular element shown in Figure 9.5, determine its elementary $[K_e]$ matrix following the steps discussed in Example 9.2. Assume that the element is intended for solving axisymmetric solid mechanics problems with its material made of an isotropic material with $E = 200$ GPa and $\nu = 0.3$.
6. For the 2D rectangular element shown in Figure 9.6, determine its elementary $[K_e]$ matrix following the steps discussed in Example 9.2. Assume that the element is intended for solving axisymmetric solid mechanics problems with its material made of an isotropic material with $E = 200$ GPa and $\nu = 0.3$.
7. For the 2D triangular element shown in Figure 9.7, determine its elementary $[K_e]$ matrix following the steps discussed in Example 9.2. Assume that the element is intended for solving axisymmetric solid mechanics problems with its material made of an isotropic material with $E = 200$ GPa and $\nu = 0.3$.
8. For the 2D triangular element shown in Figure 9.8, determine its elementary $[K_e]$ matrix following the steps discussed in Example 9.2. Assume that the element is intended for solving axisymmetric solid mechanics problems with its material made of an isotropic material with $E = 200$ GPa and $\nu = 0.3$.

Recommended Readings

1. S. P. Timoshenko and J. N. Goodier. 1970. *Theory of Elasticity.* New York: McGraw-Hill.
2. Pei Chi Chou and Nicholas J. Pagano. 1967. *Elasticity Tensor, Dyadic and Engineering Approaches.* New York: Dover.

10

Isoparametric Elements

In the previous several chapters, we noted that integration over the domains defined by the elements is necessary in calculating the elementary $[K_e]$ matrices. In those examples given, we intentionally used elements with regular shapes such that the integration bounds can be easily defined and that the actual integration over the domains can be determined directly in an analytic way. In a real situation, however, it is impossible to do so because the shape of elements can be very complicated (e.g., see Figures 5.2 and 5.3), making it difficult and sometimes impossible to define the integration bounds. Thus, it is desirable to have elements of the same type transformed into a standard element with a fixed shape at a fixed location. In this way, all elements of the same type can be represented by a common element having the same parameters (i.e., the shape and vertex coordinates). Isoparametric elements are such elements that just serve this purpose. Additionally, isoparametric elements use the same set of shape functions to interpolate the field quantity and to transform an arbitrarily shaped element to the corresponding isoparametric element.

10.1 Isoparametric Elements for Slender Structures

The isoparametric element for slender structures in a natural coordinate system, ξ, is defined as a thin and long element with two ends located at $\xi = -1$ and $\xi = 1$, as shown in Figure 10.1.

When the element consists of only two end nodes, it is a linear element. For higher-order elements, more nodes are added with even spacing between nodes. For example, the quadratic (3-node) isoparametric element will have an additional node at $\xi = 0$; the cubic (4-node) isoparametric element will have two additional nodes, one at $\xi = -1/3$ and the other at $\xi = 1/3$; and so on.

10.1.1 Shape and mapping functions for bar elements

10.1.1.1 The 2-node isoparametric bar element

In its natural coordinate system, the 2-node bar element has its two ends located at $\xi = -1$ and $\xi = 1$, as shown in Figure 10.2.

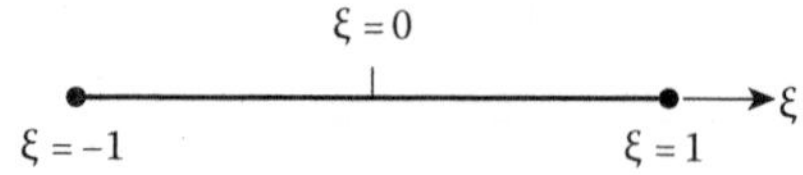

FIGURE 10.1
Isoparametric one-dimensional (1D) element.

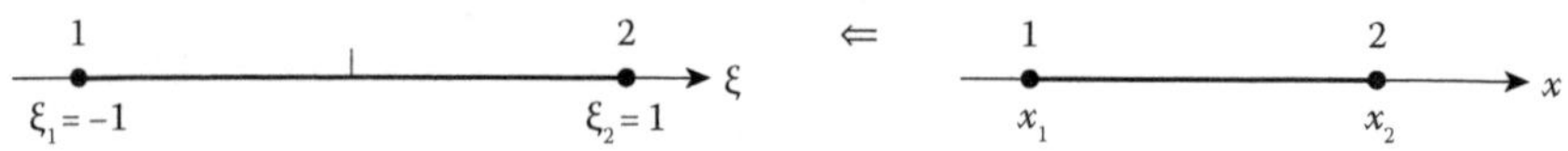

FIGURE 10.2
Isoparametric transformation of a 2-node bar element.

By using the Lagrange formula (see Section 5.6.1), we write the following two shape functions for the isoparametric element:

$$\begin{aligned} N_1 &= \prod_{i=1(i\neq 1)}^{2} \frac{\xi - \xi_i}{\xi_1 - \xi_i} = \frac{(\xi - \xi_2)}{(\xi_1 - \xi_2)} = \frac{1}{2}(1-\xi) \\ N_2 &= \prod_{i=1(i\neq 2)}^{2} \frac{\xi - \xi_i}{\xi_2 - \xi_i} = \frac{(\xi - \xi_1)}{(\xi_2 - \xi_1)} = \frac{1}{2}(1+\xi) \end{aligned} \tag{10.1}$$

which can be put together in a shape function matrix:

$$[N] = \left[\frac{1}{2}(1-\xi) \quad \frac{1}{2}(1+\xi)\right] \tag{10.2}$$

For most isoparametric elements, their shape functions are used not only for interpolating the field quantity, but also for transforming an arbitrary element in the x coordinates to the isoparametric element in the ξ coordinates. For example, the 2-node arbitrary bar element located between x_1 and x_2 (in Figure 10.2) can be transformed to the isoparametric element by using the following mapping function:

$$x = \sum_{m=1}^{2} N_m x_m = N_1 x_1 + N_2 x_2 = \frac{1}{2}(1-\xi)x_1 + \frac{1}{2}(1+\xi)x_2 \tag{10.3}$$

Clearly, this mapping function yields $x = x_1$ when $\xi = -1$, and $x = x_2$ when $\xi = 1$. In this way, an arbitrary element located between x_1 and x_2 in the x coordinates is transformed to the isoparametric element in the ξ coordinates. The benefits of doing this include (1) all 2-node bar elements can be dealt with using the same set of shape functions as those given in Equation 10.1, and (2) integration over the elementary domain will be performed in a fixed range from −1 to 1. The information on the location of the original element is passed on through the mapping function given in Equation 10.3.

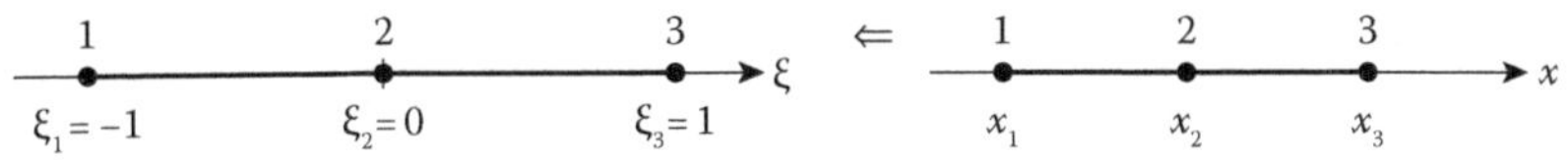

FIGURE 10.3
Isoparametric transformation of a 3-node bar element.

10.1.1.2 The 3-node isoparametric bar element

The 3-node isoparametric bar element is an element with three nodes located at $\xi_1 = -1$, $\xi_2 = 0$, and $\xi_3 = 1$ in the ξ coordinate system (see Figure 10.3).

Using the Lagrange formula, we express its shape functions as

$$\begin{aligned} N_1 &= \prod_{i=1(i\neq 1)}^{3} \frac{\xi-\xi_i}{\xi_1-\xi_i} = \frac{(\xi-\xi_2)(\xi-\xi_3)}{(\xi_1-\xi_2)(\xi_1-\xi_3)} = \frac{1}{2}(-\xi+\xi^2) \\ N_2 &= \prod_{i=1(i\neq 2)}^{3} \frac{\xi-\xi_i}{\xi_2-\xi_i} = \frac{(\xi-\xi_1)(\xi-\xi_3)}{(\xi_2-\xi_1)(\xi_2-\xi_3)} = 1-\xi^2 \\ N_3 &= \prod_{i=1(i\neq 3)}^{3} \frac{\xi-\xi_i}{\xi_3-\xi_i} = \frac{(\xi-\xi_1)(\xi-\xi_2)}{(\xi_3-\xi_1)(\xi_3-\xi_2)} = \frac{1}{2}(\xi+\xi^2) \end{aligned} \tag{10.4}$$

and the shape function matrix

$$[N] = \left[\frac{1}{2}(-\xi+\xi^2) \quad 1-\xi^2 \quad \frac{1}{2}(\xi+\xi^2)\right] \tag{10.5}$$

With these shape functions, we construct the following mapping function,

$$x = \sum_{m=1}^{3} N_m x_m = \frac{1}{2}(-\xi+\xi^2)x_1 + (1-\xi^2)x_2 + \frac{1}{2}(\xi+\xi^2)x_3 \tag{10.6}$$

for transforming an arbitrary element in the x coordinate system to the ξ coordinate system, as shown in Figure 10.3.

10.1.1.3 n_e-Node isoparametric bar element

As a general extension, for a bar element with n_e nodes, we first determine its shape functions, N_m for $m = 1, 2, \ldots, n_e$, by using the Lagrange formula (Equation 5.13):

$$N_m = \prod_{i=1(i\neq m)}^{n_e} \frac{\xi-\xi_i}{\xi_m-\xi_i}$$

With the obtained shape functions, we write the mapping function in terms of the nodal coordinates (x_m, for $m = 1, 2, \ldots, n_e$),

$$x = \sum_{m=1}^{n_e} N_m x_m$$

for transforming an arbitrary bar element in the x coordinate system to the corresponding isoparametric one in the ξ coordinate system.

10.1.2 Elementary $[K_e]$ matrix for bar elements

It is now clear that the isoparametric transformation provides us with standard elements. But how is the evaluation of the elementary $[K_e]$ matrix handled such that the same results are ensured after the transformation?

To determine the elementary $[K_e]$ matrix for bar elements, we use Equation 6.5, that is,

$$[K_e] = A \int_l \left[\frac{dN}{dx}\right]^T k \left[\frac{dN}{dx}\right] dx$$

Since the shape functions for isoparametric elements are expressed as functions of ξ, we apply the chain rule of differentiation:

$$\left[\frac{dN}{dx}\right] = \left[\frac{dN}{d\xi}\right] \frac{d\xi}{dx} = \frac{1}{J}\left[\frac{dN}{d\xi}\right]$$

where $J = dx/d\xi$ is called the Jacobian of transformation from an arbitrary element to its corresponding isoparametric one. The Jacobian of isoparametric transformation is a scalar factor in a 1D situation that can be determined by using the mapping function as

$$[J] = \frac{dx}{d\xi} = \sum_{m=1}^{n_e} \frac{dN_m}{d\xi} x_m$$

Putting the above relationship into the $[K_e]$ equation along with $dx = Jd\xi$, we have

$$[K_e] = A \int_0^l \left[\frac{dN}{dx}\right]^T k \left[\frac{dN}{dx}\right] dx = A \int_{-1}^1 \frac{1}{J^2} \left[\frac{dN}{d\xi}\right]^T k \left[\frac{dN}{d\xi}\right] Jd\xi$$
$$= \frac{1}{J}\left(A \int_{-1}^1 \left[\frac{dN}{d\xi}\right]^T k \left[\frac{dN}{d\xi}\right] d\xi\right) = \frac{[K_e^{iso}]}{J}$$

Note that the integration bounds are transformed from 0 and l to -1 and 1, respectively. In the above equation, $[K_e^{iso}]$ represents the elementary $[K_e]$ matrix of an isoparametric element in the natural coordinate system, which is a constant matrix due to its fixed shape and size. It is clear that the $[K_e]$ matrix of an arbitrary bar element equals $[K_e^{iso}]$ divided by the Jacobian (J) of the isoparametric transformation.

Example 10.1

Determine the $[K_e]$ matrix of a 2-node bar element located between $x_1 = l$ and $x_2 = 2l$ having a uniform cross section area of A and a constant material property of k.

Answer

By using the mapping function given in Equation 10.3 for the 2-node bar element, we calculate the Jacobian:

$$J = \frac{dx}{d\xi} = \frac{x_2 - x_1}{2} = \frac{l}{2}$$

With the shape function matrix given in Equation 10.2, we express

$$\left[\frac{dN}{d\xi}\right] = \left[\frac{dN_1}{d\xi} \quad \frac{dN_2}{d\xi}\right] = \left[-\frac{1}{2} \quad \frac{1}{2}\right]$$

Substituting this relationship into the $[K_e]$ matrix expression along with $dx = Jd\xi$ and $J = l/2$, we obtain the following elementary $[K_e]$ for 2-node bar elements:

$$[K_e] = \frac{kA}{J}\int_{-1}^{1}\begin{bmatrix} -\frac{1}{2} \\ \frac{1}{2} \end{bmatrix}\left[-\frac{1}{2} \quad \frac{1}{2}\right] d\xi = \frac{kA}{4J}\int_{-1}^{1}\begin{bmatrix} 1 & -1 \\ -1 & 1 \end{bmatrix} d\xi$$

$$= \frac{kA}{2J}\begin{bmatrix} 1 & -1 \\ -1 & 1 \end{bmatrix} = \frac{kA}{l}\begin{bmatrix} 1 & -1 \\ -1 & 1 \end{bmatrix}$$

This result is the same as that in Example 6.1 in Section 6.2.1, although the two elements have different locations. It is as expected because the Jacobian (J) is a constant in this case, and it is proportional to the length of the element. So as long as a 2-node bar element has a length of l and material property of kA, it will have the same $[K_e]$ matrix as given above. This result also proves that transforming an arbitrary element into the isoparametric element will not change the values of its $[K_e]$ matrix.

Example 10.2

Determine the $[K_e]$ matrix of a 3-node bar element located at $x_1 = l$, $x_2 = 3l/2$, and $x_3 = 2l$ having a uniform cross section area of A and a constant material property of k.

Answer

By using the mapping function given in Equation 10.6 for the 3-node bar element, we calculate the Jacobian:

$$J = \frac{dx}{d\xi} = \frac{x_3 - x_1}{2} + \xi(x_1 - 2x_2 + x_3) = \frac{l}{2}$$

With the shape functions given in Equation 10.5, we express

$$\left[\frac{dN}{d\xi}\right] = [(-1+2\xi)/2 \quad -2\xi \quad (1+2\xi)/2]$$

Substituting this expression into the $[K_e]$ matrix expression along with $dx = Jd\xi$ and $J = l/2$, we obtain the following elementary $[K_e]$ for 3-node bar elements:

$$\begin{aligned}
[K_e] &= \frac{kA}{J}\int_{-1}^{1}\begin{bmatrix}(-1+2\xi)/2\\ -2\xi\\ (1+2\xi)/2\end{bmatrix}[(-1+2\xi)/2 \quad -2\xi \quad (1+2\xi)/2]\,d\xi\\
&= \frac{kA}{4J}\int_{-1}^{1}\begin{bmatrix}(1-2\xi)^2 & 4\xi(1-2\xi) & 4\xi^2-1\\ 4\xi(1-2\xi) & 16\xi^2 & -4\xi(1+2\xi)\\ 4\xi^2-1 & -4\xi(1+2\xi) & (1+2\xi)^2\end{bmatrix}d\xi\\
&= \frac{kA}{3l}\begin{bmatrix}7 & -8 & 1\\ -8 & 16 & -8\\ 1 & -8 & 7\end{bmatrix}
\end{aligned}$$

This result is the same as that in Example 6.2 in Section 6.2.1, which is, again, as expected because the Jacobian (J) is also a constant in this case. Thus, as long as a 3-node bar element has a length of l and material property of kA, this result applies to all such elements.

10.1.3 Shape and mapping functions for beam elements

The 2-node isoparametric beam element is defined as an element with two end nodes at $\xi_1 = -1$ and $\xi_2 = 1$ in the ξ coordinate system (note that this is the same as in the 2-node bar element case). By using the Hermite interpolation formula and following the steps in Example 5.8 in Section 5.7.2), we obtain the following four shape functions:

$$\begin{aligned}
N_1 &= \frac{(1-\xi)^2(\xi+2)}{4}, \quad N_2 = \frac{(1-\xi)^2(1+\xi)}{4}\\
N_3 &= \frac{(1+\xi)^2(2-\xi)}{4}, \quad N_4 = \frac{(\xi-1)(1+\xi)^2}{4}
\end{aligned} \tag{10.7}$$

For the mapping function, although N_1 and N_3 can be used to map a beam element located between x_1 and x_2 in the x coordinate to the natural ξ coordinate between -1 and 1, doing so will introduce a nonconstant Jacobian. Thus, we choose a simpler mapping function. In view of the fact that geometrically, a beam element is like a 2-node bar element and has only two end nodes, we take the hint of this similarity to use the same mapping function as that used for a 2-node bar element for the beam element. Thus, for an arbitrary beam located at $x_1 = 0$ and $x_2 = l$ in the x coordinate, we have the following mapping function and the Jacobian of isoparametric transformation:

$$x = \frac{1}{2}(1-\xi)x_1 + \frac{1}{2}(1+\xi)x_2 = \frac{l}{2}(1+\xi) \text{ and } J = \frac{dx}{d\xi} = \frac{l}{2} \tag{10.8}$$

For the beam element, since the DOF vector contains derivatives, we need to include the Jacobian factor when performing transformation

$$\begin{Bmatrix} u_1(x) \\ u_1'(x) \\ u_2(x) \\ u_2'(x) \end{Bmatrix} \rightarrow \begin{Bmatrix} u_1(\xi) \\ Ju_1'(\xi) \\ u_2(\xi) \\ Ju_2'(\xi) \end{Bmatrix}$$

Thus, the interpolation of the field quantity can be written as

$$\tilde{u} = \sum_{m=1}^{4} N_m u_m = [N] \begin{Bmatrix} u_1(\xi) \\ Ju_1'(\xi) \\ u_2(\xi) \\ Ju_2'(\xi) \end{Bmatrix} = [N_1 \quad JN_2 \quad N_3 \quad JN_4] \begin{Bmatrix} u_1(\xi) \\ u_1'(\xi) \\ u_2(\xi) \\ u_2'(\xi) \end{Bmatrix}$$

With the above expression along with $J = l/2$, we obtain the following shape function matrix for isoparametric beam elements:

$$[N] = \left[\frac{(1-\xi)^2(\xi+2)}{4} \quad \frac{(1-\xi)^2(1+\xi)l}{8} \quad \frac{(1+\xi)^2(2-\xi)}{4} \quad \frac{(\xi-1)(1+\xi)^2 l}{8} \right] \tag{10.9}$$

10.1.4 Elementary $[K_e]$ matrix for beam elements

For the elementary $[K_e]$ matrix, referring to Equation 6.23, we express

$$[K_e] = EI \int_0^l \left[\frac{d^2N}{dx^2}\right]^T \left[\frac{d^2N}{dx^2}\right] dx$$

By applying twice the chain rule of differentiation to the shape function matrix, we have

$$\left[\frac{d^2N}{dx^2}\right] = \left[\frac{d^2N}{d\xi^2}\right] \left(\frac{d\xi}{dx}\right)^2 = \frac{1}{J^2}\left[\frac{d^2N}{d\xi^2}\right]$$

Substituting this expression into the $[K_e]$ matrix equation above, along with $dx = Jd\xi$ and $J = l/2$, we obtain

$$\begin{aligned}[K_e] &= EI \int_0^l \left[\frac{d^2N}{dx^2}\right]^T \left[\frac{d^2N}{dx^2}\right] dx = EI \int_{-1}^{1} \frac{1}{J^4} \left[\frac{d^2N}{d\xi^2}\right]^T \left[\frac{d^2N}{d\xi^2}\right] Jd\xi \\ &= \frac{EI}{J^3} \int_{-1}^{1} \left[\frac{d^2N}{d\xi^2}\right]^T \left[\frac{d^2N}{d\xi^2}\right] d\xi = \frac{[K_e^{iso}]}{J^3}\end{aligned}$$

where $[K_e^{iso}]$ represents the elementary $[K_e]$ matrix for the isoparametric beam element. Clearly, unlike in the bar element cases, the $[K_e]$ matrix for beam elements equals $[K_e^{iso}]$ divided by J^3.

Example 10.3

Determine the $[K_e]$ matrix of a 2-node beam element located at $x_1 = 0$ and $x_2 = l$ having flexure rigidity EI.

Answer

Using the shape function matrix given in Equation 10.9, we calculate

$$\left[\frac{d^2N}{d\xi^2}\right] = \begin{bmatrix} \frac{3\xi}{2} & \frac{(3\xi-1)l}{4} & \frac{-3\xi}{2} & \frac{(3\xi+1)l}{4} \end{bmatrix}$$

Substituting this expression into the $[K_e]$ expression, along with $J = l/2$, we obtain

$$[K_e] = \frac{EI}{16J^3}\int_{-1}^{1}\begin{bmatrix} 6\xi \\ (3\xi-1)l \\ -6\xi \\ (3\xi+1)l \end{bmatrix}\begin{bmatrix} 6\xi & (3\xi-1)l & -6\xi & (3\xi+1)l \end{bmatrix} d\xi$$

$$= \frac{EI}{2l^3}\int_{-1}^{1}\begin{bmatrix} 36\xi^2 & 6l\xi(3\xi-1) & -36\xi^2 & 6l\xi(3\xi+1) \\ 6l\xi(3\xi-1) & l^2(3\xi-1)^2 & -6l\xi(3\xi-1) & l^2(9\xi^2-1) \\ -36\xi^2 & -6l\xi(3\xi-1) & 36\xi^2 & -6l\xi(3\xi+1) \\ 6l\xi(3\xi+1) & l^2(9\xi^2-1) & -6l\xi(3\xi+1) & l^2(3\xi+1)^2) \end{bmatrix} d\xi$$

$$= \frac{EI}{l^3}\begin{bmatrix} 12 & 6l & -12 & 6l \\ 6l & 4l^2 & -6l & 2l^2 \\ -12 & -6l & 12 & -6l \\ 6l & 2l^2 & -6l & 4l^2 \end{bmatrix}$$

This result is the same as that in Equation 6.24, although the two elements have different locations. This is as expected because the two beams have the same length, which results in the same constant Jacobian. So, as long as a 2-node beam element has a length of l and flexure rigidity of EI, this $[K_e]$ matrix result applies to all such elements.

10.2 Isoparametric Elements for 2D Structures

For isoparametric elements in two-dimensional (2D) space, we often consider two elements: one is the square element and the other the right angle isosceles triangle defined in the natural coordinate system, ξ, η. For the isoparametric square element, its four vertex nodes are located at $(\xi = \pm 1, \eta = \pm 1)$.

Of course, like any quadrilateral elements, it can be made of just four vertex nodes, nine nodes (including the 8-node serendipity one), or more, depending on the order of the interpolation. For the isoparametric triangular element, it has its three vertex nodes at $(\xi = 0, \eta = 0), (\xi = 1, \eta = 0)$, and $(\xi = 1, \eta = 0)$. In the same way, this element can have just 3 vertex nodes, or 6 nodes, 10 nodes, or more, depending on the order of the interpolation.

10.2.1 Shape and mapping functions

10.2.1.1 The 4-node isoparametric square element

Figure 10.4 shows the isoparametric square element with its four vertex nodes located at $(-1,-1), (1,-1), (1,1)$, and $(-1,1)$ in the natural coordinate system, ξ and η.

Using the Lagrange formula (see Section 5.6.2) with $n_\xi = n_\eta = 2$ and $\xi_1 = -1, \xi_2 = 1, \eta_1 = -1$, and $\eta_2 = 1$, we express the following shape functions:

$$\begin{aligned} N_1 = L_{1,1} &= \frac{\xi-\xi_2}{\xi_1-\xi_2}\frac{\eta-\eta_2}{\eta_1-\eta_2} = \frac{(1-\xi)(1-\eta)}{4} \\ N_2 = L_{2,1} &= \frac{\xi-\xi_1}{\xi_2-\xi_1}\frac{\eta-\eta_2}{\eta_1-\eta_2} = \frac{(1+\xi)(1-\eta)}{4} \\ N_3 = L_{2,2} &= \frac{\xi-\xi_1}{\xi_2-\xi_1}\frac{\eta-\eta_1}{\eta_2-\eta_1} = \frac{(1+\xi)(1+\eta)}{4} \\ N_4 = L_{1,2} &= \frac{\xi-\xi_2}{\xi_1-\xi_2}\frac{\eta-\eta_1}{\eta_2-\eta_1} = \frac{(1-\xi)(1+\eta)}{4} \end{aligned} \tag{10.10}$$

With these shape functions, we write the mapping functions

$$\begin{aligned} x &= \sum_{m=1}^{4} N_m x_m = N_1x_1 + N_2x_2 + N_3x_3 + N_4x_4 \\ y &= \sum_{m=1}^{4} N_m y_m = N_1y_1 + N_2y_2 + N_3y_3 + N_4y_4 \end{aligned} \tag{10.11}$$

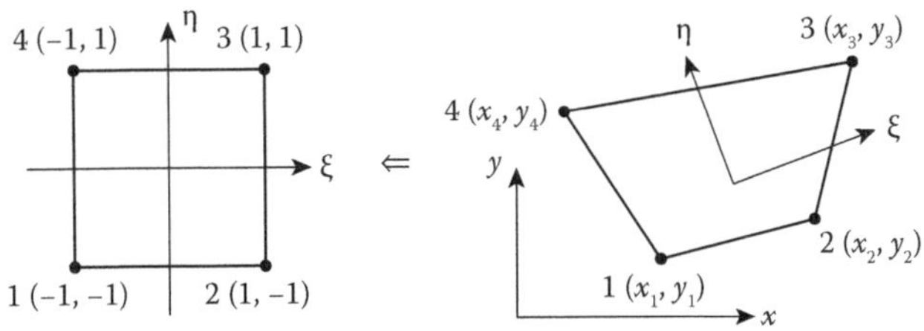

FIGURE 10.4
Isoparametric transformation of a 4-node quadrilateral element.

for transforming an arbitrary quadrilateral element with vertices at (x_1, y_1), (x_2, y_2), (x_3, y_3), and (x_4, y_4) into the 4-node isoparametric square element, as shown in Figure 10.4. With this transformation, the elementary domain in the natural coordinate system, ξ and η, is now within the bounds of $-1 \leq \xi \leq 1$ and $-1 \leq \eta \leq 1$.

10.2.1.2 n_e-Node isoparametric square element

In general, when the isoparametric square element has n_e nodes, we express its shape function matrix as

$$[N] = \begin{bmatrix} N_1 & N_2 & N_3 & N_4 & \cdots & N_{n_e} \end{bmatrix}$$

where the individual shape functions are determined by using the Lagrange formula for quadrilateral elements discussed in Section 5.6.2. With these shape functions, we have the mapping functions for isoparametric transformation as

$$x = \sum_{m=1}^{n_e} N_m x_m, \quad y = \sum_{m=1}^{n_e} N_m y_m$$

10.2.1.3 The 3-node isoparametric triangular element

Figure 10.5 shows the isoparametric triangular element with its three vertex nodes located at $(0,0), (1,0)$, and $(0,1)$ in the natural coordinate system, (ξ, η).

Using the Lagrange formula for triangles along with the following calculated areas (see Section 5.6.4),

$$A_0 = 1/2, \; A_1 = (1 - \xi - \eta)/2, \; A_2 = \xi/2, \; A_3 = \eta/2$$

we obtain the three shape functions

$$N_1 = A_1/A_0 = 1 - \xi - \eta, \quad N_2 = A_2/A_0 = \xi, \quad N_3 = A_3/A_0 = \eta \tag{10.12}$$

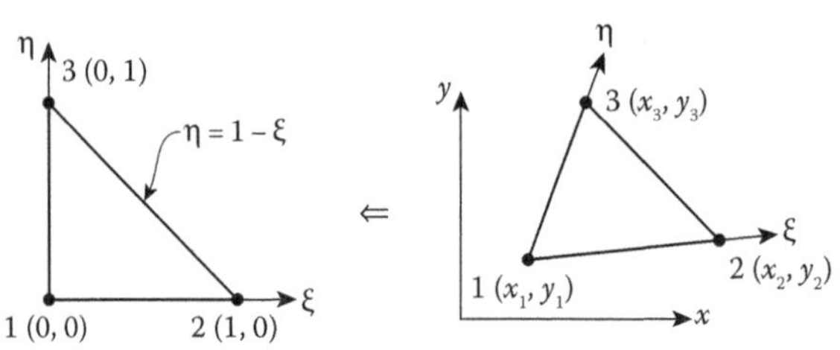

FIGURE 10.5
Isoparametric transformation of a 3-node triangular element.

And with that, we write the mapping functions

$$\begin{aligned} x &= \sum_{m=1}^{3} N_m x_m = N_1 x_1 + N_2 x_2 + N_3 x_3 \\ y &= \sum_{m=1}^{3} N_m y_m = N_1 y_1 + N_2 y_2 + N_3 y_3 \end{aligned} \tag{10.13}$$

for transforming an arbitrary triangular element with vertex nodes at (x_1, y_1), (x_2, y_2), and (x_3, y_3) into the corresponding 3-node isoparametric triangular element, as shown in Figure 10.5. With this isoparametric transformation, the elementary domain in the natural coordinate system, ξ and η, is now within the bounds of $0 \leq \xi \leq 1$ and $0 \leq \eta \leq 1 - \xi$.

10.2.1.4 n_e-Node isoparametric triangular element

In a similar way, when the isoparametric triangular element has n_e nodes, we can express the shape function matrix as

$$[N] = \begin{bmatrix} N_1 & N_2 & N_3 & N_4 & \cdots & N_{n_e} \end{bmatrix}$$

where the individual shape functions are determined by using the Lagrange formula for triangular elements discussed in Section 5.6.4. With these shape functions, we write the mapping functions for isoparametric transformation:

$$x = \sum_{m=1}^{n_e} N_m x_m, \quad y = \sum_{m=1}^{n_e} N_m y_m$$

10.2.2 Elementary $[K_e]$ matrix for scalar field problems

We now discuss the evaluation of the elementary $[K_e]$ matrix based on the isoparametric transformation for 2D scalar field problems. Referring to Equation 7.5, we know that the elementary $[K_e]$ matrix can be expressed as

$$\begin{aligned} [K_e] &= \iint_A ([\nabla N]^T \cdot k\nabla [N]) t dA \\ &= \iint_A \left(\left[\frac{\partial N}{\partial x}\right]^T k \left[\frac{\partial N}{\partial x}\right] + \left[\frac{\partial N}{\partial y}\right]^T k \left[\frac{\partial N}{\partial y}\right] \right) t dA \end{aligned}$$

For 2D isoparametric elements, since their shape function matrices $[N]$ are expressed in terms of ξ and η, to find $\partial N/\partial x$ and $\partial N/\partial y$, we first apply the chain rule of differentiation to obtain the following derivatives:

$$\frac{\partial N}{\partial \xi} = \frac{\partial N}{\partial x}\frac{\partial x}{\partial \xi} + \frac{\partial N}{\partial y}\frac{\partial y}{\partial \xi}, \quad \frac{\partial N}{\partial \eta} = \frac{\partial N}{\partial x}\frac{\partial x}{\partial \eta} + \frac{\partial N}{\partial y}\frac{\partial y}{\partial \eta}$$

In a matrix form, these expressions can be condensed to

$$\begin{Bmatrix} \dfrac{\partial N}{\partial \xi} \\ \dfrac{\partial N}{\partial \eta} \end{Bmatrix} = \begin{bmatrix} \dfrac{\partial x}{\partial \xi} & \dfrac{\partial y}{\partial \xi} \\ \dfrac{\partial x}{\partial \eta} & \dfrac{\partial y}{\partial \eta} \end{bmatrix} \begin{Bmatrix} \dfrac{\partial N}{\partial x} \\ \dfrac{\partial N}{\partial y} \end{Bmatrix} = [J] \begin{Bmatrix} \dfrac{\partial N}{\partial x} \\ \dfrac{\partial N}{\partial y} \end{Bmatrix}$$

where

$$[J] = \begin{bmatrix} \dfrac{\partial x}{\partial \xi} & \dfrac{\partial y}{\partial \xi} \\ \dfrac{\partial x}{\partial \eta} & \dfrac{\partial y}{\partial \eta} \end{bmatrix}$$

is the Jacobian matrix of isoparametric transformation, which is a 2×2 matrix in a 2D situation.

Knowing the Jacobian matrix, $[J]$, we express

$$\begin{Bmatrix} \dfrac{\partial N}{\partial x} \\ \dfrac{\partial N}{\partial y} \end{Bmatrix} = [J]^{-1} \begin{Bmatrix} \dfrac{\partial N}{\partial \xi} \\ \dfrac{\partial N}{\partial \eta} \end{Bmatrix} = [\Gamma] \begin{Bmatrix} \dfrac{\partial N}{\partial \xi} \\ \dfrac{\partial N}{\partial \eta} \end{Bmatrix}$$

Here, $[\Gamma]$ is the inverse of the Jacobian matrix, which can be written out in a 2×2 matrix as

$$[\Gamma] = \begin{bmatrix} \Gamma_{11} & \Gamma_{12} \\ \Gamma_{21} & \Gamma_{22} \end{bmatrix}$$

Then, we write

$$\frac{\partial N}{\partial x} = \Gamma_{11}\frac{\partial N}{\partial \xi} + \Gamma_{12}\frac{\partial N}{\partial \eta}, \quad \frac{\partial N}{\partial y} = \Gamma_{21}\frac{\partial N}{\partial \xi} + \Gamma_{22}\frac{\partial N}{\partial \eta}$$

Substituting these two relationships into the $[K_e]$ matrix and integrating over the isoparametric square domain, along with $dA = \det[J]d\xi d\eta$ (see Equation B.3 in Appendix B), we obtain the following elementary $[K_e]$ matrix for quadrilateral elements:

$$\begin{aligned} [K_e] = & \int_{-1}^{1}\int_{-1}^{1} \left(\left[\Gamma_{11}\frac{\partial N}{\partial \xi} + \Gamma_{12}\frac{\partial N}{\partial \eta}\right]^T k \left[\Gamma_{11}\frac{\partial N}{\partial \xi} + \Gamma_{12}\frac{\partial N}{\partial \eta}\right]\right) t \det[J] d\eta d\xi \\ & + \int_{-1}^{1}\int_{-1}^{1} \left(\left[\Gamma_{21}\frac{\partial N}{\partial \xi} + \Gamma_{22}\frac{\partial N}{\partial \eta}\right]^T k \left[\Gamma_{21}\frac{\partial N}{\partial \xi} + \Gamma_{22}\frac{\partial N}{\partial \eta}\right]\right) t \det[J] d\eta d\xi \end{aligned} \tag{10.14}$$

For triangular elements, by integrating over the isoparametric triangular domain, we have

$$[K_e] = \int_0^1 \int_0^{1-\xi} \left(\left[\Gamma_{11} \frac{\partial N}{\partial \xi} + \Gamma_{12} \frac{\partial N}{\partial \eta} \right]^T k \left[\Gamma_{11} \frac{\partial N}{\partial \xi} + \Gamma_{12} \frac{\partial N}{\partial \eta} \right] \right) t \det[J] d\eta d\xi$$
$$+ \int_0^1 \int_0^{1-\xi} \left(\left[\Gamma_{21} \frac{\partial N}{\partial \xi} + \Gamma_{22} \frac{\partial N}{\partial \eta} \right]^T k \left[\Gamma_{21} \frac{\partial N}{\partial \xi} + \Gamma_{22} \frac{\partial N}{\partial \eta} \right] \right) t \det[J] d\eta d\xi \tag{10.15}$$

Equations 10.14 and 10.15 provide the formulas to determine the elementary $[K_e]$ matrices for 2D scalar field problems for quadrilateral and triangular elements, respectively. They are developed based on the isoparametric transformation.

To obtain the actual value for any given element, we need to know the shape function matrix of the corresponding isoparametric element in its natural coordinate system, the Jacobian matrix of transformation ($[J]$), and its inverse matrix, $[\Gamma]$. In the following sections, we will see how this is done for an arbitrary quadrilateral element and a triangular element.

10.2.2.1 The 4-node quadrilateral elements

For 4-node quadrilateral elements, referring to Equation 10.10, we have the following shape function matrix $[N]$ for the isoparametric element:

$$[N] = \left[\frac{(1-\xi)(1-\eta)}{4} \quad \frac{(1+\xi)(1-\eta)}{4} \quad \frac{(1+\xi)(1+\eta)}{4} \quad \frac{(1-\xi)(1+\eta)}{4} \right] \tag{10.16}$$

The Jacobian matrix of isoparametric transformation is determined using the mapping functions given in Equation 10.11 as

$$[J] = \begin{bmatrix} \dfrac{\partial x}{\partial \xi} & \dfrac{\partial y}{\partial \xi} \\ \dfrac{\partial x}{\partial \eta} & \dfrac{\partial y}{\partial \eta} \end{bmatrix} = \frac{1}{4} \begin{bmatrix} -(1-\eta) & (1-\eta) & (1+\eta) & -(1+\eta) \\ -(1-\xi) & -(1+\xi) & (1+\xi) & (1-\xi) \end{bmatrix} \begin{bmatrix} x_1 & y_1 \\ x_2 & y_2 \\ x_3 & y_3 \\ x_4 & y_4 \end{bmatrix} \tag{10.17}$$

With this $[J]$ matrix, we calculate its inverse, the $[\Gamma]$ matrix, as

$$[\Gamma] = [J]^{-1} = \begin{bmatrix} \Gamma_{11} & \Gamma_{12} \\ \Gamma_{21} & \Gamma_{22} \end{bmatrix}$$

10.2.2.2 The 3-node isoparametric triangular elements

For 3-node triangular elements, using the shape functions given in Equation 10.12, we have the following shape function matrix for the isoparametric element:

$$[N] = \begin{bmatrix} 1-\xi-\eta & \xi & \eta \end{bmatrix} \tag{10.18}$$

The Jacobian matrix is determined by using the mapping functions given in Equation 10.13:

$$[J] = \begin{bmatrix} \dfrac{\partial x}{\partial \xi} & \dfrac{\partial y}{\partial \xi} \\ \dfrac{\partial x}{\partial \eta} & \dfrac{\partial y}{\partial \eta} \end{bmatrix} = \begin{bmatrix} -1 & 1 & 0 \\ -1 & 0 & 1 \end{bmatrix} \begin{bmatrix} x_1 & y_1 \\ x_2 & y_2 \\ x_3 & y_3 \end{bmatrix} = \begin{bmatrix} x_2 - x_1 & y_2 - y_1 \\ x_3 - x_1 & y_3 - y_1 \end{bmatrix} \tag{10.19}$$

With this $[J]$ matrix, we further calculate its inverse, the $[\Gamma]$ matrix.

Example 10.4

For the 2D rectangular and triangular elements shown in Figure 10.6, determine their elementary $[K_e]$ matrices using Equations 10.14 and 10.15. Assume that the elements have a constant property, $kt = 5$.

Answer

For the rectangular element, by using Equation 10.17, along with the nodal coordinates given in the figure, we calculate the Jacobian matrix:

$$[J] = \frac{1}{4}\begin{bmatrix} -(1-\eta) & (1-\eta) & (1+\eta) & -(1+\eta) \\ -(1-\xi) & -(1+\xi) & (1+\xi) & (1-\xi) \end{bmatrix} \begin{bmatrix} 0 & 0 \\ 0.2 & 0 \\ 0.2 & 0.1 \\ 0 & 0.1 \end{bmatrix} = \begin{bmatrix} 0.1 & 0 \\ 0 & 0.05 \end{bmatrix}$$

From this, we find

$$[\Gamma] = [J]^{-1} = \begin{bmatrix} 10 & 0 \\ 0 & 20 \end{bmatrix}$$

Then, we have $\det[J] = 1/200$, $\Gamma_{11} = 10$, $\Gamma_{22} = 20$, and $\Gamma_{12} = \Gamma_{21} = 0$. From the shape function matrix given in Equation 10.16, we express

$$\left[\frac{\partial N}{\partial \xi}\right] = \frac{1}{4}\left[-(1-\eta) \quad (1-\eta) \quad (1+\eta) \quad -(1+\eta)\right]$$

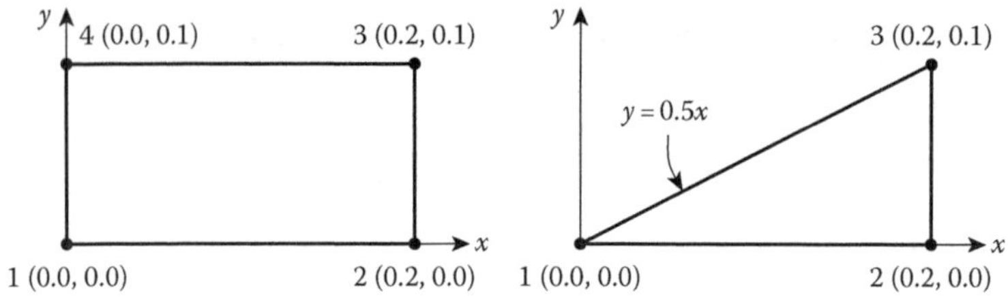

FIGURE 10.6
Two-dimensional rectangular and triangular elements with a uniform thickness.

$$\left[\frac{\partial N}{\partial \eta}\right] = \frac{1}{4}\begin{bmatrix}-(1-\xi) & -(1+\xi) & (1+\xi) & (1-\xi)\end{bmatrix}$$

Putting all these into Equation 10.14, we have

$$[K_e] = kt\int_{-1}^{1}\int_{-1}^{1}\left(\left[\Gamma_{11}\frac{\partial N}{\partial \xi}\right]^T\left[\Gamma_{11}\frac{\partial N}{\partial \xi}\right] + \left[\Gamma_{22}\frac{\partial N}{\partial \eta}\right]^T\left[\Gamma_{22}\frac{\partial N}{\partial \eta}\right]\right)\det[J]d\eta d\xi$$

$$= \frac{100\times 5}{16\times 200}\int_{-1}^{1}\int_{-1}^{1}\begin{bmatrix}-(1-\eta)\\(1-\eta)\\(1+\eta)\\-(1+\eta)\end{bmatrix}\begin{bmatrix}-(1-\eta) & (1-\eta) & (1+\eta) & -(1+\eta)\end{bmatrix}d\eta d\xi$$

$$+\frac{400\times 5}{16\times 200}\int_{-1}^{1}\int_{-1}^{1}\begin{bmatrix}-(1-\xi)\\-(1+\xi)\\(1+\xi)\\(1-\xi)\end{bmatrix}\begin{bmatrix}-(1-\xi) & -(1+\xi) & (1+\xi) & (1-\xi)\end{bmatrix}d\eta d\xi$$

By multiplying out the matrix terms and completing the two integrations, we obtain

$$[K_e] = \begin{bmatrix}4.17 & 0.83 & -2.08 & -2.92\\0.83 & 4.17 & -2.92 & -2.08\\-2.08 & -2.92 & 4.17 & 0.83\\-2.92 & -2.08 & 0.83 & 4.17\end{bmatrix}$$

Similarly, for the triangular element, by using Equation 10.19, along with the nodal coordinates given in the figure, we calculate

$$[J] = \begin{bmatrix}0.2 & 0\\0.2 & 0.1\end{bmatrix},\quad [\Gamma] = \begin{bmatrix}5 & 0\\-10 & 10\end{bmatrix}$$

Then, we have $\det[J] = 1/50$, $\Gamma_{11} = 5$, $\Gamma_{12} = 0$, $\Gamma_{21} = -10$, $\Gamma_{22} = 10$. From the shape function matrix given in Equation 10.18, we have

$$\left[\frac{\partial N}{\partial \xi}\right] = \begin{bmatrix}-1 & 1 & 0\end{bmatrix},\quad \left[\frac{\partial N}{\partial \eta}\right] = \begin{bmatrix}-1 & 0 & 1\end{bmatrix}$$

Putting all these into Equation 10.15, we have

$$[K_e] = \frac{25\times 5}{50}\int_0^1\int_0^{1-\xi}\begin{bmatrix}-1\\1\\0\end{bmatrix}\begin{bmatrix}-1 & 1 & 0\end{bmatrix}d\eta d\xi$$

$$+\frac{100\times 5}{50}\int_0^1\int_0^{1-\xi}\left(-\begin{bmatrix}-1\\1\\0\end{bmatrix}+\begin{bmatrix}-1\\0\\1\end{bmatrix}\right)\left(-\begin{bmatrix}-1 & 1 & 0\end{bmatrix}+\begin{bmatrix}-1 & 0 & 1\end{bmatrix}\right)d\eta d\xi$$

$$= \begin{bmatrix}1.25 & -1.25 & 0\\-1.25 & 6.25 & -5.00\\0 & -5.00 & 5.00\end{bmatrix}$$

The results are the same as those in Examples 7.1 and 7.2 in Section 7.1.2. This is as expected because the corresponding elements are the same, thus confirming that isoparametric transformation does not affect the outcomes.

10.2.2.3 Axisymmetric situation

For axisymmetric scalar field problems, we can go through the same procedure by letting ξ point to the radial direction and η the axial direction. For example, for n_e-node elements, we have the following mapping functions:

$$r = \sum_{m=1}^{n_e} N_m x_m, \quad z = \sum_{m=1}^{n_e} N_m z_m$$

Referring to Equations 9.4, 10.14, and 10.15, we write the following elementary $[K_e]$ matrix for quadrilateral elements for axisymmetric scalar field problems,

$$\begin{aligned}[K_e] = &\int_{-1}^{1}\int_{-1}^{1}\left(\left[\Gamma_{11}\frac{\partial N}{\partial \xi} + \Gamma_{12}\frac{\partial N}{\partial \eta}\right]^T k \left[\Gamma_{11}\frac{\partial N}{\partial \xi} + \Gamma_{12}\frac{\partial N}{\partial \eta}\right]\right) \\ &\times \left[\sum_{m=1}^{n_e} N_m x_m\right] \det[J] d\eta d\xi \\ &+ \int_{-1}^{1}\int_{-1}^{1}\left(\left[\Gamma_{21}\frac{\partial N}{\partial \xi} + \Gamma_{22}\frac{\partial N}{\partial \eta}\right]^T k \left[\Gamma_{21}\frac{\partial N}{\partial \xi} + \Gamma_{22}\frac{\partial N}{\partial \eta}\right]\right) \\ &\times \left[\sum_{m=1}^{n_e} N_m x_m\right] \det[J] d\eta d\xi\end{aligned} \tag{10.20}$$

and the following for triangular elements for axisymmetric scalar field problems:

$$\begin{aligned}[K_e] = &\int_{0}^{1}\int_{0}^{1-\xi}\left(\left[\Gamma_{11}\frac{\partial N}{\partial \xi} + \Gamma_{12}\frac{\partial N}{\partial \eta}\right]^T k \left[\Gamma_{11}\frac{\partial N}{\partial \xi} + \Gamma_{12}\frac{\partial N}{\partial \eta}\right]\right) \\ &\times \left[\sum_{m=1}^{n_e} N_m x_m\right] \det[J] d\eta d\xi \\ &+ \int_{0}^{1}\int_{0}^{1-\xi}\left(\left[\Gamma_{21}\frac{\partial N}{\partial \xi} + \Gamma_{22}\frac{\partial N}{\partial \eta}\right]^T k \left[\Gamma_{21}\frac{\partial N}{\partial \xi} + \Gamma_{22}\frac{\partial N}{\partial \eta}\right]\right) \\ &\times \left[\sum_{m=1}^{n_e} N_m x_m\right] \det[J] d\eta d\xi\end{aligned} \tag{10.21}$$

Example 10.5

For the 2D rectangular and triangular elements shown in Figure 10.7, determine their elementary $[K_e]$ matrices using Equations 10.20 and 10.21. Assume that the elements have a constant property of $k = 1000$.

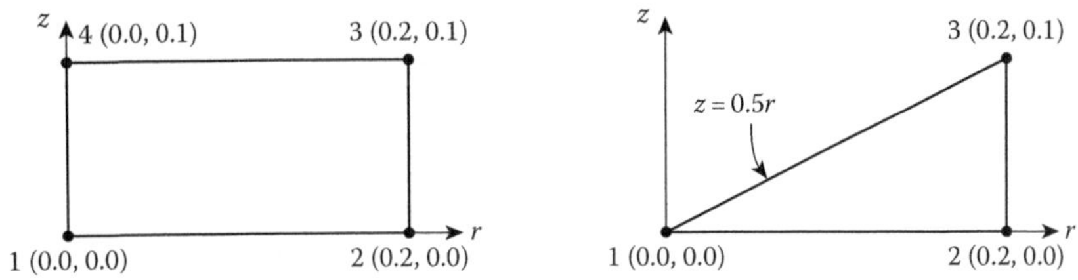

FIGURE 10.7
Two-dimensional rectangular and triangular elements.

Answer
Since the two elements are the same as those in Example 10.4, we have the same $[J]$ and $[\Gamma]$ matrices for the corresponding elements. Thus, for the rectangular element, we have

$$[J] = \begin{bmatrix} 0.1 & 0 \\ 0 & 0.05 \end{bmatrix}, \quad [\Gamma] = \begin{bmatrix} 10 & 0 \\ 0 & 20 \end{bmatrix}$$

Thus, $\det[J] = 1/200$, $\Gamma_{11} = 10$, $\Gamma_{22} = 20$, and $\Gamma_{12} = \Gamma_{21} = 0$. Moreover, by using the shape functions given in Equation 10.16, we calculate

$$r = \sum_{m=1}^{4} N_m x_m = \frac{1+\xi}{10}$$

Putting all these into Equation 10.20, along with $k = 1000$, we have

$$[K_e] = \frac{25}{8}\int_{-1}^{1}\int_{-1}^{1} \begin{bmatrix} -(1-\eta) \\ (1-\eta) \\ (1+\eta) \\ -(1+\eta) \end{bmatrix} \left[-(1-\eta) \quad (1-\eta) \quad (1+\eta) \quad -(1+\eta)\right](1+\xi)d\eta d\xi$$

$$+\frac{25}{2}\int_{-1}^{1}\int_{-1}^{1} \begin{bmatrix} -(1-\xi) \\ -(1+\xi) \\ (1+\xi) \\ (1-\xi) \end{bmatrix} \left[-(1-\xi) \quad -(1+\xi) \quad (1+\xi) \quad (1-\xi)\right](1+\xi)d\eta d\xi$$

$$= \begin{bmatrix} 50.00 & 16.67 & -41.67 & -25.00 \\ 16.67 & 116.67 & -91.67 & -41.67 \\ -41.67 & -91.67 & 116.67 & 16.67 \\ -25.00 & -41.67 & 16.67 & 50.00 \end{bmatrix}$$

Similarly, for the triangular element, we have

$$[J] = \begin{bmatrix} 0.2 & 0 \\ 0.2 & 0.1 \end{bmatrix}, \quad [\Gamma] = \begin{bmatrix} 5 & 0 \\ -10 & 10 \end{bmatrix}$$

and $\det[J] = 1/50$, $\Gamma_{11} = 5$, $\Gamma_{12} = 0$, $\Gamma_{21} = -10$, $\Gamma_{22} = 10$. Using the shape functions given in Equation 10.18, we calculate

$$r = \sum_{m=1}^{3} N_m x_m = \frac{\xi + \eta}{5}$$

Putting all these into Equation 10.21, along with $k = 1000$, we have

$$[K_e] = 100 \int_0^1 \int_0^{1-\xi} \begin{bmatrix} -1 \\ 1 \\ 0 \end{bmatrix} \begin{bmatrix} -1 & 1 & 0 \end{bmatrix} (\xi + \eta) d\eta d\xi$$
$$+ 400 \int_0^1 \int_0^{1-\xi} \left(- \begin{bmatrix} -1 \\ 1 \\ 0 \end{bmatrix} + \begin{bmatrix} -1 \\ 0 \\ 1 \end{bmatrix} \right) \left(- \begin{bmatrix} -1 & 1 & 0 \end{bmatrix} + \begin{bmatrix} -1 & 0 & 1 \end{bmatrix} \right)$$
$$\times (\xi + \eta) d\eta d\xi$$
$$= \begin{bmatrix} 33.33 & -33.33 & 0 \\ -33.33 & 166.67 & -133.33 \\ 0 & -133.33 & 133.33 \end{bmatrix}$$

Since the elements in this example are the same as in Examples 9.1 and 9.2 in Section 9.1.2, the results are the same as well, thus further confirming that isoparametric transformation does not affect the outcomes. However, the differences between these two axisymmetric cases and the two 2D cases in Example 10.4 highlight that an axisymmetric solution is equivalent to a three-dimensional (3D) solution.

10.2.3 Elementary $[K_e]$ matrix for vector field problems

For vector field problems, the above development cannot be used. In this section, we discuss the evaluation of the elementary $[K_e]$ matrix based on isoparametric transformation for 2D vector field problems. Again, we will limit our discussion to problems of solid mechanics. To determine the $[K_e]$ matrix for vector field solid mechanics problems, we need to reevaluate the left-hand term in Equation 8.18, namely,

$$\iint_S \{\nabla_{s2}\{w\}\}^T \{\sigma\} t dS \tag{10.22}$$

By using Equation 8.16, we express

$$\nabla_{s2}\{w\} = \begin{bmatrix} \frac{\partial}{\partial x} & 0 \\ 0 & \frac{\partial}{\partial y} \\ \frac{\partial}{\partial y} & \frac{\partial}{\partial x} \end{bmatrix} \begin{Bmatrix} w_x \\ w_y \end{Bmatrix} = [A_2] \begin{Bmatrix} \frac{\partial w_x}{\partial x} \\ \frac{\partial w_x}{\partial y} \\ \frac{\partial w_y}{\partial x} \\ \frac{\partial w_y}{\partial y} \end{Bmatrix}, \text{ and } \{\epsilon\} = \nabla_{s2}\{d\} = [A_2] \begin{Bmatrix} \frac{\partial u_x}{\partial x} \\ \frac{\partial u_x}{\partial y} \\ \frac{\partial u_y}{\partial x} \\ \frac{\partial u_y}{\partial y} \end{Bmatrix}$$

where

$$[A_2] = \begin{bmatrix} 1 & 0 & 0 & 0 \\ 0 & 0 & 0 & 1 \\ 0 & 1 & 1 & 0 \end{bmatrix} \tag{10.23}$$

Using the Jacobian matrix of isoparametric transformation $[J]$ and its inverse $[\Gamma]$, we express

$$\left\{ \begin{matrix} \dfrac{\partial u_x}{\partial x} \\ \dfrac{\partial u_x}{\partial y} \end{matrix} \right\} = [J]^{-1} \left\{ \begin{matrix} \dfrac{\partial u_x}{\partial \xi} \\ \dfrac{\partial u_x}{\partial \eta} \end{matrix} \right\}, \quad \left\{ \begin{matrix} \dfrac{\partial u_y}{\partial x} \\ \dfrac{\partial u_y}{\partial y} \end{matrix} \right\} = [J]^{-1} \left\{ \begin{matrix} \dfrac{\partial u_y}{\partial \xi} \\ \dfrac{\partial u_y}{\partial \eta} \end{matrix} \right\}$$

or

$$\left\{ \begin{matrix} \dfrac{\partial u_x}{\partial x} \\ \dfrac{\partial u_x}{\partial y} \end{matrix} \right\} = \begin{bmatrix} \Gamma_{11} & \Gamma_{12} \\ \Gamma_{21} & \Gamma_{22} \end{bmatrix} \left\{ \begin{matrix} \dfrac{\partial u_x}{\partial \xi} \\ \dfrac{\partial u_x}{\partial \eta} \end{matrix} \right\}, \quad \left\{ \begin{matrix} \dfrac{\partial u_y}{\partial x} \\ \dfrac{\partial u_y}{\partial y} \end{matrix} \right\} = \begin{bmatrix} \Gamma_{11} & \Gamma_{12} \\ \Gamma_{21} & \Gamma_{22} \end{bmatrix} \left\{ \begin{matrix} \dfrac{\partial u_y}{\partial \xi} \\ \dfrac{\partial u_y}{\partial \eta} \end{matrix} \right\}$$

Putting them together, we can write

$$\left\{ \begin{matrix} \dfrac{\partial u_x}{\partial x} \\ \dfrac{\partial u_x}{\partial y} \\ \dfrac{\partial u_y}{\partial x} \\ \dfrac{\partial u_y}{\partial y} \end{matrix} \right\} = \begin{bmatrix} \Gamma_{11} & \Gamma_{12} & 0 & 0 \\ \Gamma_{21} & \Gamma_{22} & 0 & 0 \\ 0 & 0 & \Gamma_{11} & \Gamma_{12} \\ 0 & 0 & \Gamma_{21} & \Gamma_{22} \end{bmatrix} \left\{ \begin{matrix} \dfrac{\partial u_x}{\partial \xi} \\ \dfrac{\partial u_x}{\partial \eta} \\ \dfrac{\partial u_y}{\partial \xi} \\ \dfrac{\partial u_y}{\partial \eta} \end{matrix} \right\} = [\Gamma_{e2}] \left\{ \begin{matrix} \dfrac{\partial u_x}{\partial \xi} \\ \dfrac{\partial u_x}{\partial \eta} \\ \dfrac{\partial u_y}{\partial \xi} \\ \dfrac{\partial u_y}{\partial \eta} \end{matrix} \right\}$$

Here, $[\Gamma_{e2}]$ represents the 4×4 matrix expanded based on the 2×2 $[\Gamma]$ matrix for 2D vector field problems.

For 2D elements having n_e nodes, with the following mapping functions,

$$x = \sum_{m=1}^{n_e} N_m x_m, \quad y = \sum_{m=1}^{n_e} N_m y_m$$

we first calculate the Jacobian matrix $[J]$ and its inverse matrix $[\Gamma]$, as well as the expanded $[\Gamma_{e2}]$. Then, using the following field quantity interpolation functions,

$$u_x = \sum_{m=1}^{n_e} N_m u_{mx}, \quad u_y = \sum_{m=1}^{n_e} N_m u_{my}$$

we express

$$\begin{Bmatrix} \frac{\partial u_x}{\partial \xi} \\ \frac{\partial u_x}{\partial \eta} \\ \frac{\partial u_y}{\partial \xi} \\ \frac{\partial u_y}{\partial \eta} \end{Bmatrix} = \begin{bmatrix} \frac{\partial N_1}{\partial \xi} & 0 & \frac{\partial N_2}{\partial \xi} & 0 & \cdots & \frac{\partial N_{n_e}}{\partial \xi} & 0 \\ \frac{\partial N_1}{\partial \eta} & 0 & \frac{\partial N_2}{\partial \eta} & 0 & \cdots & \frac{\partial N_{n_e}}{\partial \eta} & 0 \\ 0 & \frac{\partial N_1}{\partial \xi} & 0 & \frac{\partial N_2}{\partial \xi} & \cdots & 0 & \frac{\partial N_{n_e}}{\partial \xi} \\ 0 & \frac{\partial N_1}{\partial \eta} & 0 & \frac{\partial N_2}{\partial \eta} & \cdots & 0 & \frac{\partial N_{n_e}}{\partial \eta} \end{bmatrix} \begin{Bmatrix} u_{1x} \\ u_{1y} \\ u_{2x} \\ u_{2y} \\ \vdots \\ u_{n_e x} \\ u_{n_e y} \end{Bmatrix}$$

$$= [\partial N_2] \begin{Bmatrix} u_{1x} \\ u_{1y} \\ u_{2x} \\ u_{2y} \\ \vdots \\ u_{n_e x} \\ u_{n_e y} \end{Bmatrix}$$

Here, $[\partial N_2]$ represents the $4 \times 2n_e$ shape function matrix derivative. With these compact expressions, we express the strain vector as

$$\{\epsilon\} = \nabla_{s2}\{d\} = \left[A_2\right] \left[\Gamma_{e2}\right] \left[\partial N_2\right] \{d_0\}$$

In similar steps, we have

$$\nabla_{s2}\{w\} = \left[A_2\right] \left[\Gamma_{e2}\right] \left[\partial N_2\right]$$

Putting them all back into Equation 10.22, along with $\{\sigma\} = [C]\{\epsilon\}$ and $dA = \det[J]d\eta d\xi$ (see Equation B.3 in Appendix B) and integrating over the isoparametric square domain, we obtain the following $[K_e]$ for 2D quadrilateral elements based on isoparametric transformation for 2D solid mechanics problems:

$$[K_e] = \int_{-1}^{1} \int_{-1}^{1} \left[\left[A_2\right] \left[\Gamma_{e2}\right] \left[\partial N_2\right]\right]^T [C] \left[\left[A_2\right] \left[\Gamma_{e2}\right] \left[\partial N_2\right]\right] \det\left[J\right] t d\eta d\xi \tag{10.24}$$

For triangular elements, we have

$$[K_e] = \int_{0}^{1} \int_{0}^{1-\xi} \left[\left[A_2\right] \left[\Gamma_{e2}\right] \left[\partial N_2\right]\right]^T [C] \left[\left[A_2\right] \left[\Gamma_{e2}\right] \left[\partial N_2\right]\right] \det\left[J\right] t d\eta d\xi \tag{10.25}$$

So, for 2D solid mechanics problems, to find the elementary $[K_e]$ matrix based on the isoparametric transformation, we just need to find the $[\Gamma_{e2}]$ and $[\partial N_2]$ for a given element.

Example 10.6

For the 2D rectangular and triangular elements shown in Figure 10.8 (note that coordinates are in units of meters), determine their elementary $[K_e]$ matrices using Equations 10.24 and 10.25. Assume that the elements are made of an isotropic material with $E = 200$ GPa and $\nu = 0.3$ with a uniform thickness of $t = 0.005$ m.

Answer

Referring to the examples discussed above, we have the following for the rectangular element:

$$[J] = \begin{bmatrix} 0.1 & 0 \\ 0 & 0.05 \end{bmatrix}, \quad \det[J] = \frac{1}{200}, \quad [\Gamma] = \begin{bmatrix} 10 & 0 \\ 0 & 20 \end{bmatrix}$$

Then, we have

$$[\Gamma_{e2}] = \begin{bmatrix} 10 & 0 & 0 & 0 \\ 0 & 20 & 0 & 0 \\ 0 & 0 & 10 & 0 \\ 0 & 0 & 0 & 20 \end{bmatrix}$$

Moreover, with the shape functions given in Equation 10.16, we calculate

$$[\partial N_2] = \frac{1}{4}\begin{bmatrix} \eta-1 & 0 & 1-\eta & 0 & 1+\eta & 0 & -1-\eta & 0 \\ \xi-1 & 0 & -1-\xi & 0 & \xi+1 & 0 & 1-\xi & 0 \\ 0 & \eta-1 & 0 & 1-\eta & 0 & 1+\eta & 0 & -1-\eta \\ 0 & \xi-1 & 0 & -1-\xi & 0 & 1+\xi & 0 & 1-\xi \end{bmatrix}$$

Substituting these expressions, along with $[A_2]$ (Equation 10.23), $[C]$ for plane stress (Equation 8.14), and the values of E, ν, and t, into

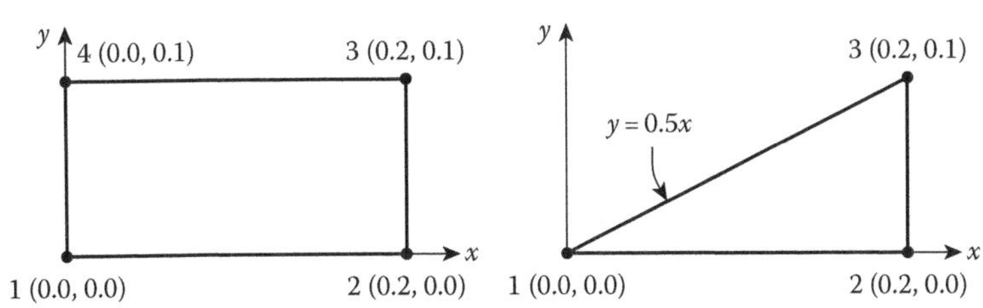

FIGURE 10.8
Two-dimensional rectangular and triangular elements with a uniform thickness.

Equation 10.24, we have

$$[K_e] = \frac{0.005}{200} \int_{-1}^{1} \int_{-1}^{1} [[A_2]\,[\Gamma_{e2}]\,[\partial N_2]]^T\,[C]\,[[A_2]\,[\Gamma_{e2}]\,[\partial N_2]]\,d\eta d\xi$$

$$= 10^9 \times \begin{bmatrix} 0.440 & 0.179 & -0.055 & -0.014 & -0.220 & -0.179 & -0.165 & 0.014 \\ 0.179 & 0.797 & 0.014 & 0.302 & -0.179 & -0.398 & -0.014 & -0.701 \\ -0.055 & 0.014 & 0.440 & -0.179 & -0.165 & -0.014 & -0.220 & 0.179 \\ -0.014 & 0.302 & -0.179 & 0.797 & 0.014 & -0.701 & 0.179 & -0.398 \\ -0.220 & -0.179 & -0.165 & 0.014 & 0.440 & 0.179 & -0.055 & -0.014 \\ -0.179 & -0.398 & -0.014 & -0.701 & 0.179 & 0.797 & 0.014 & 0.302 \\ -0.165 & -0.014 & -0.220 & 0.179 & -0.055 & 0.014 & 0.440 & -0.179 \\ 0.014 & -0.701 & 0.179 & -0.398 & -0.014 & 0.302 & -0.179 & 0.797 \end{bmatrix}$$

Similarly, for the triangular element, we have

$$[J] = \begin{bmatrix} 0.2 & 0 \\ 0.2 & 0.1 \end{bmatrix}, \quad \det[J] = \frac{1}{50}, \quad [\Gamma] = \begin{bmatrix} 5 & 0 \\ -10 & 10 \end{bmatrix}$$

and

$$[\Gamma_{e2}] = \begin{bmatrix} 5 & 0 & 0 & 0 \\ -10 & 10 & 0 & 0 \\ 0 & 0 & 5 & 0 \\ 0 & 0 & -10 & 10 \end{bmatrix}$$

Moreover, with the shape functions given in Equation 10.18, we calculate

$$[\partial N_2] = \begin{bmatrix} -1 & 0 & 1 & 0 & 0 & 0 \\ -1 & 0 & 0 & 0 & 1 & 0 \\ 0 & -1 & 0 & 1 & 0 & 0 \\ 0 & -1 & 0 & 0 & 0 & 1 \end{bmatrix}$$

Substituting these expressions, along with $[A_2]$ (Equation 10.23), $[C]$ for plane stress (Equation 8.14), and the values of E, ν, and t, into Equation 10.25, we have

$$[K_e] = \frac{0.005}{50} \int_{0}^{1} \int_{0}^{1-\xi} [[A_2]\,[\Gamma_{e2}]\,[\partial N_2]]^T\,[C]\,[[A_2]\,[\Gamma_{e2}]\,[\partial N_2]]\,d\eta d\xi$$

$$= 10^9 \times \begin{bmatrix} 0.275 & 0.000 & -0.275 & 0.165 & 0.000 & -0.165 \\ 0.000 & 0.096 & 0.192 & -0.096 & -0.192 & 0.000 \\ -0.275 & 0.192 & 0.659 & -0.357 & -0.385 & 0.165 \\ 0.165 & -0.096 & -0.357 & 1.195 & 0.192 & -1.099 \\ 0.000 & -0.192 & -0.385 & 0.192 & 0.385 & 0.000 \\ -0.165 & 0.000 & 0.165 & -1.099 & 0.000 & 1.099 \end{bmatrix}$$

Comparing these results with those in Examples 8.3 and 8.4, it is clear the results are the same, which is as expected because the problems are the same.

10.2.3.1 Axisymmetric situation

For axisymmetric problems, referring to Equation 9.9, we express

$$\nabla_{sa}\{w\} = \begin{bmatrix} \frac{\partial}{\partial r} & 0 \\ \frac{1}{r} & 0 \\ 0 & \frac{\partial}{\partial z} \\ \frac{\partial}{\partial z} & \frac{\partial}{\partial r} \end{bmatrix} \begin{Bmatrix} w_r \\ w_z \end{Bmatrix} = [A_a] \begin{Bmatrix} \frac{\partial w_r}{\partial r} \\ \frac{w_r}{r} \\ \frac{\partial w_r}{\partial z} \\ \frac{\partial w_z}{\partial r} \\ \frac{\partial w_z}{\partial z} \end{Bmatrix}, \text{ and } \{\epsilon\} = \nabla_{sa}\{d\} = [A_a] \begin{Bmatrix} \frac{\partial u_r}{\partial r} \\ \frac{u_r}{r} \\ \frac{\partial u_r}{\partial z} \\ \frac{\partial u_z}{\partial r} \\ \frac{\partial u_z}{\partial z} \end{Bmatrix}$$

where

$$[A_a] = \begin{bmatrix} 1 & 0 & 0 & 0 & 0 \\ 0 & 1 & 0 & 0 & 0 \\ 0 & 0 & 0 & 0 & 1 \\ 0 & 0 & 1 & 1 & 0 \end{bmatrix} \tag{10.26}$$

For 2D elements having n_e nodes, with the following mapping functions,

$$r = \sum_{m=1}^{n_e} N_m r_m, \quad z = \sum_{m=1}^{n_e} N_m z_m$$

we calculate the Jacobian matrix $[J]$:

$$[J] = \begin{bmatrix} \frac{\partial r}{\partial \xi} & \frac{\partial z}{\partial \xi} \\ \frac{\partial r}{\partial \eta} & \frac{\partial z}{\partial \eta} \end{bmatrix}$$

With the inverse of the Jacobian matrix, $[\Gamma]$, we have

$$\begin{Bmatrix} \frac{\partial u_r}{\partial r} \\ \frac{\partial u_z}{\partial z} \end{Bmatrix} = \begin{bmatrix} \Gamma_{11} & \Gamma_{12} \\ \Gamma_{21} & \Gamma_{22} \end{bmatrix} \begin{Bmatrix} \frac{\partial u_r}{\partial \xi} \\ \frac{\partial u_r}{\partial \eta} \end{Bmatrix}, \quad \begin{Bmatrix} \frac{\partial u_r}{\partial r} \\ \frac{\partial u_z}{\partial z} \end{Bmatrix} = \begin{bmatrix} \Gamma_{11} & \Gamma_{12} \\ \Gamma_{21} & \Gamma_{22} \end{bmatrix} \begin{Bmatrix} \frac{\partial u_z}{\partial \xi} \\ \frac{\partial u_z}{\partial \eta} \end{Bmatrix}$$

Moreover, with the mapping function for r, we express

$$\frac{u_r}{r} = \frac{u_r}{\sum_{m=1}^{n_e} N_m r_m}$$

Putting them together, we write

$$\begin{Bmatrix} \dfrac{\partial u_r}{\partial r} \\ \dfrac{u_r}{r} \\ \dfrac{\partial u_r}{\partial z} \\ \dfrac{\partial u_z}{\partial r} \\ \dfrac{\partial u_z}{\partial z} \end{Bmatrix} = \begin{bmatrix} \Gamma_{11} & 0 & \Gamma_{12} & 0 & 0 \\ 0 & \dfrac{1}{\sum_{m=1}^{n_e} N_m x_m} & 0 & 0 & 0 \\ \Gamma_{21} & 0 & \Gamma_{22} & 0 & 0 \\ 0 & 0 & 0 & \Gamma_{11} & \Gamma_{12} \\ 0 & 0 & 0 & \Gamma_{21} & \Gamma_{22} \end{bmatrix} \begin{Bmatrix} \dfrac{\partial u_r}{\partial \xi} \\ u_r \\ \dfrac{\partial u_r}{\partial \eta} \\ \dfrac{\partial u_z}{\partial \xi} \\ \dfrac{\partial u_z}{\partial \eta} \end{Bmatrix} = [\Gamma_{ea}] \begin{Bmatrix} \dfrac{\partial u_r}{\partial \xi} \\ u_r \\ \dfrac{\partial u_r}{\partial \eta} \\ \dfrac{\partial u_z}{\partial \xi} \\ \dfrac{\partial u_z}{\partial \eta} \end{Bmatrix}$$

Here, $[\Gamma_{ea}]$ represents the 5×5 matrix expanded based on the 2×2 $[\Gamma]$ matrix.

With the following field quantity interpolation functions,

$$u_r = \sum_{m=1}^{n_e} N_m u_{mr}, \quad u_z = \sum_{m=1}^{n_e} N_m u_{mz}$$

we have

$$\begin{Bmatrix} \dfrac{\partial u_r}{\partial \xi} \\ u_r \\ \dfrac{\partial u_r}{\partial \eta} \\ \dfrac{\partial u_z}{\partial \xi} \\ \dfrac{\partial u_z}{\partial \eta} \end{Bmatrix} = \begin{bmatrix} \dfrac{\partial N_1}{\partial \xi} & 0 & \dfrac{\partial N_2}{\partial \xi} & 0 & \cdots & \dfrac{\partial N_{n_e}}{\partial \xi} & 0 \\ N_1 & 0 & N_2 & 0 & \cdots & N_{n_e} & 0 \\ \dfrac{\partial N_1}{\partial \eta} & 0 & \dfrac{\partial N_2}{\partial \eta} & 0 & \cdots & \dfrac{\partial N_{n_e}}{\partial \eta} & 0 \\ 0 & \dfrac{\partial N_1}{\partial \xi} & 0 & \dfrac{\partial N_2}{\partial \xi} & \cdots & 0 & \dfrac{\partial N_{n_e}}{\partial \xi} \\ 0 & \dfrac{\partial N_1}{\partial \eta} & 0 & \dfrac{\partial N_2}{\partial \eta} & \cdots & 0 & \dfrac{\partial N_{n_e}}{\partial \eta} \end{bmatrix} \begin{Bmatrix} u_{1r} \\ u_{1z} \\ u_{2r} \\ u_{2z} \\ \vdots \\ u_{n_e r} \\ u_{n_e z} \end{Bmatrix}$$

$$= [\partial N_a] \begin{Bmatrix} u_{1r} \\ u_{1z} \\ u_{2r} \\ u_{2z} \\ \vdots \\ u_{n_e r} \\ u_{n_e z} \end{Bmatrix}$$

Here, $[\partial N_a]$ represents the $5 \times 2n_e$ shape function matrix derivative.

Using these matrices, we express the strain vector as

$$\{\epsilon\} = \nabla_{sa}\{d\} = [A_a]\,[\Gamma_{ea}]\,[\partial N_a]\,\{d_0\}$$

and

$$\nabla_{sa}\{w\} = [A_a]\,[\Gamma_{ea}]\,[\partial N_a]$$

Putting them all in the term on the left-hand side of Equation 9.14, along with $\{\sigma\} = [C]\{\epsilon\}$ and $dA = \det[J]d\xi d\eta$, and integrating over the isoparametric square domain, we obtain the following $[K_e]$ for 2D quadrilateral elements for axisymmetric solid mechanics problems:

$$[K_e] = \int_{-1}^{1}\int_{-1}^{1} [[A_a]\,[\Gamma_{ea}]\,[\partial N_a]]^T\,[C]\,[[A_a]\,[\Gamma_{ea}]\,[\partial N_a]] \times \det[J]\left[\sum_{m=1}^{n_e} N_m x_m\right] d\eta d\xi \tag{10.27}$$

For triangular elements, we have

$$[K_e] = \int_{0}^{1}\int_{0}^{1-\xi} [[A_a]\,[\Gamma_{ea}]\,[\partial N_a]]^T\,[C]\,[[A_a]\,[\Gamma_{ea}]\,[\partial N_a]] \times \det[J]\left[\sum_{m=1}^{n_e} N_m x_m\right] d\eta d\xi \tag{10.28}$$

So, for axisymmetric solid mechanics problems, to find the elementary $[K_e]$ matrix based on the isoparametric transformation, we need to find the $[\Gamma_{ea}]$ and $[\partial N_a]$ for a given element.

Example 10.7

For the 2D rectangular and triangular elements shown in Figure 10.9, determine their elementary $[K_e]$ matrices using Equations 10.27 and 10.28. Assume that the elements are made of an isotropic material with $E = 200$ GPa and $\nu = 0.3$.

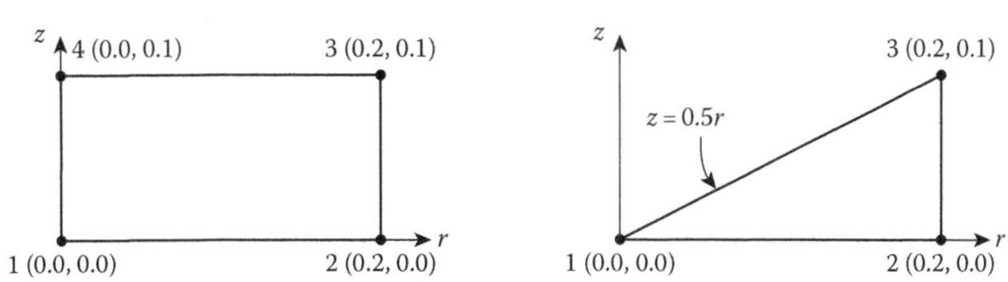

FIGURE 10.9
Two-dimensional rectangular and triangular elements.

Answer

Referring to the examples discussed above, we have the following for the rectangular element:

$$[J]=\begin{bmatrix}0.1 & 0\\ 0 & 0.05\end{bmatrix},\quad \det[J]=\frac{1}{200},\quad [\Gamma]=\begin{bmatrix}10 & 0\\ 0 & 20\end{bmatrix},\quad r=\sum_{m=1}^{4}N_m x_m=\frac{1+\xi}{10}$$

Then, we express

$$[\Gamma_{ea}]=\begin{bmatrix}10 & 0 & 0 & 0 & 0\\ 0 & 10/(\xi+1) & 0 & 0 & 0\\ 0 & 0 & 20 & 0 & 0\\ 0 & 0 & 0 & 10 & 0\\ 0 & 0 & 0 & 0 & 20\end{bmatrix}$$

Moreover, we calculate

$$[\partial N_a]=\frac{1}{4}\begin{bmatrix}\eta-1 & 0 & 1-\eta & 0 & 1+\eta & 0 & -1-\eta & 0\\ (1-\xi)(1-\eta) & 0 & (1+\xi)(1-\eta) & 0 & (1+\xi)(1+\eta) & 0 & (1-\xi)(1+\eta) & 0\\ \xi-1 & 0 & -1-\xi & 0 & \xi+1 & 0 & 1-\xi & 0\\ 0 & \eta-1 & 0 & 1-\eta & 0 & 1+\eta & 0 & -1-\eta\\ 0 & \xi-1 & 0 & -1-\xi & 0 & 1+\xi & 0 & 1-\xi\end{bmatrix}$$

Substituting these expressions, along with $[A_a]$ (Equation 10.26), $[C]$ for the axisymmetric situation (Equation 9.11), and the values of E and ν, into Equation 10.27, we have

$$[K_e]=\frac{1}{2000}\int_{-1}^{1}\int_{-1}^{1}\left[[A_a]\,[\Gamma_{ea}]\,[\partial N_a]\right]^T[C]\left[[A_a]\,[\Gamma_{ea}]\,[\partial N_a]\right](1+\xi)d\eta d\xi$$

$$=10^9\times\begin{bmatrix}\infty & -0.64 & 2.56 & 0.64 & -2.56 & -3.21 & \infty & 3.21\\ -0.64 & 10.26 & -1.28 & 7.69 & -6.41 & -9.62 & -3.21 & -8.33\\ 2.56 & -1.28 & 20.51 & -10.26 & -1.28 & 5.13 & -2.56 & 6.41\\ 0.64 & 7.69 & -10.26 & 28.21 & -5.13 & -26.28 & 3.21 & -9.62\\ -2.56 & -6.41 & -1.28 & -5.13 & 20.51 & 10.26 & 2.56 & 1.28\\ -3.21 & -9.62 & 5.13 & -26.28 & 10.26 & 28.21 & -0.64 & 7.69\\ \infty & -3.21 & -2.56 & 3.21 & 2.56 & -0.64 & \infty & 0.64\\ 3.21 & -8.33 & 6.41 & -9.62 & 1.28 & 7.69 & 0.64 & 10.26\end{bmatrix}$$

Similarly, for the triangular element, we have

$$[J]=\begin{bmatrix}0.2 & 0\\ 0.2 & 0.1\end{bmatrix},\quad \det[J]=\frac{1}{50},\quad [\Gamma]=\begin{bmatrix}5 & 0\\ -10 & 10\end{bmatrix},\quad r=\sum_{m=1}^{3}N_m x_m=\frac{\xi+\eta}{5}$$

Then, we write

$$[\Gamma_{ea}]=\begin{bmatrix}5 & 0 & 0 & 0 & 0\\ 0 & 5/(\xi+\eta) & 0 & 0 & 0\\ -10 & 0 & 10 & 0 & 0\\ 0 & 0 & 0 & 5 & 0\\ 0 & 0 & 0 & -10 & 10\end{bmatrix}$$

Moreover, we have

$$[\partial N_a] = \begin{bmatrix} -1 & 0 & 1 & 0 & 0 & 0 \\ 1-\xi-\eta & 0 & \xi & 0 & \eta & 0 \\ -1 & 0 & 0 & 0 & 1 & 0 \\ 0 & -1 & 0 & 1 & 0 & 0 \\ 0 & -1 & 0 & 0 & 0 & 1 \end{bmatrix}$$

Substituting these expressions, along with $[A_a]$ (Equation 10.26), $[C]$ for the axisymmetric situation (Equation 9.11), and the values of E and ν, into Equation 10.28, we have

$$[K_e] = \frac{1}{250}\int_0^1 \int_0^{1-\xi} [[A_a]\,[\Gamma_{ea}]\,[\partial N_a]]^T\,[C]\,[[A_a]\,[\Gamma_{ea}]\,[\partial N_a]]\,(\xi+\eta)d\eta d\xi$$

$$= 10^9 \times \begin{bmatrix} 14.10 & 0 & -6.73 & 3.85 & 0.32 & -3.85 \\ 0 & 2.56 & 5.13 & -2.56 & -5.13 & 0 \\ -6.73 & 5.13 & 26.07 & -16.67 & -6.84 & 11.54 \\ 3.85 & -2.56 & -16.67 & 38.46 & 1.28 & -35.90 \\ 0.32 & -5.13 & -6.84 & 1.28 & 13.25 & 3.85 \\ -3.85 & 0 & 11.54 & -35.90 & 3.85 & 35.90 \end{bmatrix}$$

Comparing these results with those in Examples 9.3 and 9.4 in Section 9.2.2, we can see that the results are the same as expected because we solved the same problems. However, the result for the rectangular element still contains several terms of infinity. This fact suggests that the isoparametric transformation does not alleviate the problem of division by zero in integrating terms containing $1/r^2$ over a geometric domain that includes the edge of $r = 0$. We will reexamine this issue in Example 11.3 in Section 11.2 when we discuss Gauss quadrature for numerical integration.

10.3 Isoparametric Elements for 3D Structures

For isoparametric elements in a 3D space, we mainly consider two elements: one is the right angle hexahedral element and the other the right angle tetrahedron defined in the natural coordinate system, ξ, η, ζ. For the isoparametric hexahedral element, its eight vertex nodes are located at ($\xi = \pm 1, \eta = \pm 1, \zeta = \pm 1$). Of course, like any hexahedral elements, it can have just 8 vertex nodes, or 27 nodes, or more depending on the order of the interpolation. For the isoparametric tetrahedral element, it has its four vertex nodes at $(0, 0, 0), (1, 0, 0), (0, 1, 0)$, and $(0, 0, 1)$. In the same way, this element can have just 4 vertex nodes, or 10 nodes, or more depending on the order of the interpolation.

10.3.1 Shape and mapping functions

10.3.1.1 The 8-node isoparametric hexahedral element

The 8-node isoparametric hexahedral element in the natural coordinate system, ξ, η, ζ, is defined as a hexahedral element with eight vertex nodes located at $\xi = \pm 1, \eta = \pm 1$, and $\zeta = \pm 1$, as shown in Figure 10.10.

Using the Lagrange formula (see Section 5.6.5) with $n_\xi = n_\eta = n_\zeta = 2$ and $\xi_1 = \eta_1 = \zeta_1 = -1, \xi_2 = \eta_2 = \zeta_2 = 1$, we obtain the following shape functions:

$$
\begin{aligned}
N_1 = L_{1,1,1} &= \frac{\xi - \xi_2}{\xi_1 - \xi_2}\frac{\eta - \eta_2}{\eta_1 - \eta_2}\frac{\zeta - \zeta_2}{\zeta_1 - \zeta_2} = \frac{(1-\xi)(1-\eta)(1-\zeta)}{8} \\
N_2 = L_{2,1,1} &= \frac{\xi - \xi_1}{\xi_2 - \xi_1}\frac{\eta - \eta_2}{\eta_1 - \eta_2}\frac{\zeta - \zeta_2}{\zeta_1 - \zeta_2} = \frac{(1+\xi)(1-\eta)(1-\zeta)}{8} \\
N_3 = L_{2,2,1} &= \frac{\xi - \xi_1}{\xi_2 - \xi_1}\frac{\eta - \eta_1}{\eta_2 - \eta_1}\frac{\zeta - \zeta_2}{\zeta_1 - \zeta_2} = \frac{(1+\xi)(1+\eta)(1-\zeta)}{8} \\
N_4 = L_{1,2,1} &= \frac{\xi - \xi_2}{\xi_1 - \xi_2}\frac{\eta - \eta_1}{\eta_2 - \eta_1}\frac{\zeta - \zeta_2}{\zeta_1 - \zeta_2} = \frac{(1-\xi)(1+\eta)(1-\zeta)}{8} \\
N_5 = L_{1,1,2} &= \frac{\xi - \xi_2}{\xi_1 - \xi_2}\frac{\eta - \eta_2}{\eta_1 - \eta_2}\frac{\zeta - \zeta_1}{\zeta_2 - \zeta_1} = \frac{(1-\xi)(1-\eta)(1+\zeta)}{8} \\
N_6 = L_{2,1,2} &= \frac{\xi - \xi_1}{\xi_2 - \xi_1}\frac{\eta - \eta_2}{\eta_1 - \eta_2}\frac{\zeta - \zeta_1}{\zeta_2 - \zeta_1} = \frac{(1+\xi)(1-\eta)(1+\zeta)}{8} \\
N_7 = L_{2,2,2} &= \frac{\xi - \xi_1}{\xi_2 - \xi_1}\frac{\eta - \eta_1}{\eta_2 - \eta_1}\frac{\zeta - \zeta_1}{\zeta_2 - \zeta_1} = \frac{(1+\xi)(1+\eta)(1+\zeta)}{8} \\
N_8 = L_{1,2,2} &= \frac{\xi - \xi_2}{\xi_1 - \xi_2}\frac{\eta - \eta_1}{\eta_2 - \eta_1}\frac{\zeta - \zeta_1}{\zeta_2 - \zeta_1} = \frac{(1-\xi)(1+\eta)(1+\zeta)}{8}
\end{aligned}
\tag{10.29}
$$

which are often put together as the shape function matrix

$$[N] = \begin{bmatrix} N_1 & N_2 & N_3 & N_4 & N_5 & N_6 & N_7 & N_8 \end{bmatrix}$$

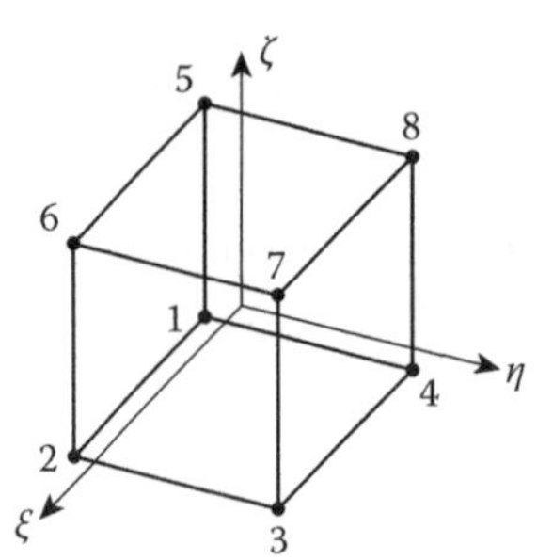

Node 1: (−1, −1, −1) Node 5: (−1, −1, 1)
Node 2: (1, −1, −1) Node 6: (1, −1, 1)
Node 3: (1, 1, −1) Node 7: (1, 1, 1)
Node 4: (−1, 1, −1) Node 8: (−1, 1, 1)

FIGURE 10.10
The 8-node isoparametric hexahedral element.

With these shape functions, we write the mapping functions as

$$x = \sum_{m=1}^{8} N_m x_m, \quad y = \sum_{m=1}^{8} N_m y_m, \quad z = \sum_{m=1}^{8} N_m z_m \tag{10.30}$$

for transforming an arbitrary hexahedral element with vertex nodes at (x_1, y_1, z_1), (x_2, y_2, z_2), (x_3, y_3, z_3), (x_1, y_1, z_3), (x_4, y_4, z_4), (x_5, y_5, z_5) (x_6, y_6, z_6), (x_7, y_7, z_7), and (x_8, y_8, z_8) into the 8-node isoparametric hexahedral element. After this transformation, the elementary domain is now within the bounds of $-1 \leq \xi \leq 1$, $-1 \leq \eta \leq 1$, and $-1 \leq \zeta \leq 1$.

10.3.1.2 n_e-Node isoparametric hexahedral element

In general, when the isoparametric hexahedral element has n_e nodes, we can express its shape function matrix as

$$[N] = \begin{bmatrix} N_1 & N_2 & N_3 & N_4 & \cdots & N_{n_e} \end{bmatrix}$$

where the individual shape functions are determined by using the Lagrange formula for hexahedral elements discussed in Section 5.6.5. With these shape functions, we write the mapping functions for isoparametric transformation:

$$x = \sum_{m=1}^{n_e} N_m x_m, \quad y = \sum_{m=1}^{n_e} N_m y_m \quad z = \sum_{m=1}^{n_e} N_m z_m$$

10.3.1.3 The 4-node isoparametric tetrahedral element

The 4-node isoparametric tetrahedral element in the natural coordinate system, ξ, η, ζ, is defined as the right angle tetrahedron with four vertex nodes located at $(0, 0, 0), (1, 0, 0), (0, 1, 0)$, and $(0, 0, 1)$, as shown in Figure 10.11.

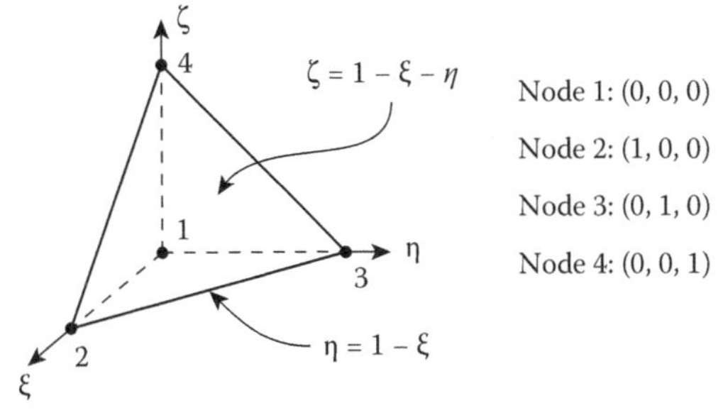

FIGURE 10.11
A 4-node isoparametric tetrahedral element.

Using the Lagrange formula for tetrahedral elements (see Section 5.6.6), along with the calculated volumes,

$$\begin{aligned} V_0 &= 1/6, V_1 = (1-\xi-\eta-\zeta)/6 \\ V_2 &= \xi/6, V_3 = \eta/6, V_4 = \zeta/6 \end{aligned}$$

we express the following shape functions,

$$\begin{aligned} N_1 &= V_1/V_0 = 1-\xi-\eta-\zeta, \ N_2 = V_2/V_0 = \xi \\ N_3 &= V_3/V_0 = \eta, \qquad N_4 = V_4/V_0 = \zeta \end{aligned} \tag{10.31}$$

and the mapping functions,

$$x = \sum_{m=1}^{4} N_m x_m, \ y = \sum_{m=1}^{4} N_m y_m, \ z = \sum_{m=1}^{4} N_m z_m \tag{10.32}$$

for transforming an arbitrary tetrahedral element with vertex nodes at (x_1, y_1, z_1), (x_2, y_2, z_2), (x_3, y_3, z_3), and (x_4, y_4, z_4) into the corresponding 4-node isoparametric tetrahedral element. After this transformation, the elementary domain is now within the bounds of $0 \le \xi \le 1$, $0 \le \eta \le 1-\xi$, and $0 \le \zeta \le 1-\xi-\eta$.

10.3.1.4 n_e-Node isoparametric tetrahedral element

In a similar way, when the isoparametric tetrahedral element has n_e nodes, we can express the shape function matrix as

$$[N] = \begin{bmatrix} N_1 & N_2 & N_3 & N_4 & \cdots & N_{n_e} \end{bmatrix}$$

where the individual shape functions are determined by using the Lagrange formula for tetrahedral elements discussed in Section 5.6.6. With these shape functions, we write the mapping functions for isoparametric transformation:

$$x = \sum_{m=1}^{n_e} N_m x_m, \quad y = \sum_{m=1}^{n_e} N_m y_m \quad z = \sum_{m=1}^{n_e} N_m z_m$$

10.3.2 Elementary $[K_e]$ matrix for scalar field problems

For 3D scalar field problems, referring to Equation 7.9, we know that the elementary $[K_e]$ matrix can be expressed as

$$\begin{aligned} [K_e] &= \iiint_V ([\nabla N]^T \cdot k\nabla [N]) dV \\ &= \iiint_V \left(\left[\frac{\partial N}{\partial x}\right]^T k_x \left[\frac{\partial N}{\partial x}\right] + \left[\frac{\partial N}{\partial y}\right]^T k_y \left[\frac{\partial N}{\partial y}\right] + \left[\frac{\partial N}{\partial z}\right]^T k_z \left[\frac{\partial N}{\partial z}\right] \right) dV \end{aligned}$$

Since the shape function matrix $[N]$ is now expressed in terms of ξ, η, and ζ, we again apply the chain rule of differentiation to obtain the following derivatives:

$$\frac{\partial N}{\partial \xi} = \frac{\partial N}{\partial x}\frac{\partial x}{\partial \xi} + \frac{\partial N}{\partial y}\frac{\partial y}{\partial \xi} + \frac{\partial N}{\partial z}\frac{\partial z}{\partial \xi}$$
$$\frac{\partial N}{\partial \eta} = \frac{\partial N}{\partial x}\frac{\partial x}{\partial \eta} + \frac{\partial N}{\partial y}\frac{\partial y}{\partial \eta} + \frac{\partial N}{\partial z}\frac{\partial z}{\partial \eta}$$
$$\frac{\partial N}{\partial \zeta} = \frac{\partial N}{\partial x}\frac{\partial x}{\partial \zeta} + \frac{\partial N}{\partial y}\frac{\partial y}{\partial \zeta} + \frac{\partial N}{\partial z}\frac{\partial z}{\partial \zeta}$$

Condensing them into a matrix form, we have

$$\begin{Bmatrix} \dfrac{\partial N}{\partial \xi} \\ \dfrac{\partial N}{\partial \eta} \\ \dfrac{\partial N}{\partial \zeta} \end{Bmatrix} = \begin{bmatrix} \dfrac{\partial x}{\partial \xi} & \dfrac{\partial y}{\partial \xi} & \dfrac{\partial z}{\partial \xi} \\ \dfrac{\partial x}{\partial \eta} & \dfrac{\partial y}{\partial \eta} & \dfrac{\partial z}{\partial \eta} \\ \dfrac{\partial x}{\partial \zeta} & \dfrac{\partial y}{\partial \zeta} & \dfrac{\partial z}{\partial \zeta} \end{bmatrix} \begin{Bmatrix} \dfrac{\partial N}{\partial x} \\ \dfrac{\partial N}{\partial y} \\ \dfrac{\partial N}{\partial z} \end{Bmatrix} = [J] \begin{Bmatrix} \dfrac{\partial N}{\partial x} \\ \dfrac{\partial N}{\partial y} \\ \dfrac{\partial N}{\partial z} \end{Bmatrix} \tag{10.33}$$

where

$$[J] = \begin{bmatrix} \dfrac{\partial x}{\partial \xi} & \dfrac{\partial y}{\partial \xi} & \dfrac{\partial z}{\partial \xi} \\ \dfrac{\partial x}{\partial \eta} & \dfrac{\partial y}{\partial \eta} & \dfrac{\partial z}{\partial \eta} \\ \dfrac{\partial x}{\partial \zeta} & \dfrac{\partial y}{\partial \zeta} & \dfrac{\partial z}{\partial \zeta} \end{bmatrix}$$

is the Jacobian matrix of isoparametric transform, which is a 3×3 matrix in a 3D situation.

For a 3D element with n_e nodes, we express its mapping functions in terms of shape functions and nodal coordinates as

$$x = \sum_{m=1}^{n_e} N_m x_m, \quad y = \sum_{m=1}^{n_e} N_m y_m, \quad z = \sum_{m=1}^{n_e} N_m z_m$$

for $m = 1, 2, \ldots, n_e$. Applying these relationships to Equation 10.33, we calculate

$$[J] = \begin{bmatrix} \dfrac{\partial N_1}{\partial \xi} & \dfrac{\partial N_2}{\partial \xi} & \dfrac{\partial N_3}{\partial \xi} & \dfrac{\partial N_4}{\partial \xi} & \dfrac{\partial N_5}{\partial \xi} & \cdots & \dfrac{\partial N_{n_e}}{\partial \xi} \\ \dfrac{\partial N_1}{\partial \eta} & \dfrac{\partial N_2}{\partial \eta} & \dfrac{\partial N_3}{\partial \eta} & \dfrac{\partial N_4}{\partial \eta} & \dfrac{\partial N_5}{\partial \eta} & \cdots & \dfrac{\partial N_{n_e}}{\partial \eta} \\ \dfrac{\partial N_1}{\partial \zeta} & \dfrac{\partial N_2}{\partial \zeta} & \dfrac{\partial N_3}{\partial \zeta} & \dfrac{\partial N_4}{\partial \zeta} & \dfrac{\partial N_5}{\partial \zeta} & \cdots & \dfrac{\partial N_{n_e}}{\partial \zeta} \end{bmatrix} \begin{bmatrix} x_1 & y_1 & z_1 \\ x_2 & y_2 & z_2 \\ x_3 & y_3 & z_3 \\ x_4 & y_4 & z_4 \\ x_5 & y_5 & z_5 \\ \vdots & \vdots & \vdots \\ x_{n_e} & y_{n_e} & z_{n_e} \end{bmatrix} \tag{10.34}$$

Then, we have

$$\begin{Bmatrix} \dfrac{\partial N}{\partial x} \\ \dfrac{\partial N}{\partial y} \\ \dfrac{\partial N}{\partial z} \end{Bmatrix} = [J]^{-1} \begin{Bmatrix} \dfrac{\partial N}{\partial \xi} \\ \dfrac{\partial N}{\partial \eta} \\ \dfrac{\partial N}{\partial \zeta} \end{Bmatrix} = [\Gamma] \begin{Bmatrix} \dfrac{\partial N}{\partial \xi} \\ \dfrac{\partial N}{\partial \eta} \\ \dfrac{\partial N}{\partial \zeta} \end{Bmatrix}$$

in which $[\Gamma]$ is the inverse of the Jacobian matrix, which can be expressed as

$$[\Gamma] = \begin{bmatrix} \Gamma_{11} & \Gamma_{12} & \Gamma_{13} \\ \Gamma_{21} & \Gamma_{22} & \Gamma_{23} \\ \Gamma_{31} & \Gamma_{32} & \Gamma_{33} \end{bmatrix}$$

Then, we write

$$\begin{aligned} \frac{\partial N}{\partial x} &= \Gamma_{11}\frac{\partial N}{\partial \xi} + \Gamma_{12}\frac{\partial N}{\partial \eta} + \Gamma_{13}\frac{\partial N}{\partial \zeta} \\ \frac{\partial N}{\partial y} &= \Gamma_{21}\frac{\partial N}{\partial \xi} + \Gamma_{22}\frac{\partial N}{\partial \eta} + \Gamma_{23}\frac{\partial N}{\partial \zeta} \\ \frac{\partial N}{\partial z} &= \Gamma_{31}\frac{\partial N}{\partial \xi} + \Gamma_{32}\frac{\partial N}{\partial \eta} + \Gamma_{33}\frac{\partial N}{\partial \zeta} \end{aligned}$$

Substituting these relationships into the $[K_e]$ matrix and integrating over the isoparametric hexahedral domain, along with $dV = \det[J] d\xi d\eta d\zeta$ (see Equation B.4 in Appendix B), we obtain the following elementary $[K_e]$ for hexahedral elements for scalar field problems,

$$\begin{aligned} [K_e] = &\iiint_{-1}^{1} \left(\left[\Gamma_{11}\frac{\partial N}{\partial \xi} + \Gamma_{12}\frac{\partial N}{\partial \eta} + \Gamma_{13}\frac{\partial N}{\partial \zeta} \right]^T \right. \\ &\qquad \left. \times k \left[\Gamma_{11}\frac{\partial N}{\partial \xi} + \Gamma_{12}\frac{\partial N}{\partial \eta} + \Gamma_{13}\frac{\partial N}{\partial \zeta} \right] \right) \det[J] d\zeta d\eta d\xi \\ &+ \iiint_{-1}^{1} \left(\left[\Gamma_{21}\frac{\partial N}{\partial \xi} + \Gamma_{22}\frac{\partial N}{\partial \eta} + \Gamma_{23}\frac{\partial N}{\partial \zeta} \right]^T \right. \\ &\qquad \left. \times k \left[\Gamma_{21}\frac{\partial N}{\partial \xi} + \Gamma_{22}\frac{\partial N}{\partial \eta} + \Gamma_{23}\frac{\partial N}{\partial \zeta} \right] \right) \det[J] d\zeta d\eta d\xi \\ &+ \iiint_{-1}^{1} \left(\left[\Gamma_{31}\frac{\partial N}{\partial \xi} + \Gamma_{32}\frac{\partial N}{\partial \eta} + \Gamma_{33}\frac{\partial N}{\partial \zeta} \right]^T \right. \\ &\qquad \left. \times k \left[\Gamma_{31}\frac{\partial N}{\partial \xi} + \Gamma_{32}\frac{\partial N}{\partial \eta} + \Gamma_{33}\frac{\partial N}{\partial \zeta} \right] \right) \det[J] d\zeta d\eta d\xi \end{aligned} \tag{10.35}$$

and the following for tetrahedral elements by integrating over the isoparametric tetrahedral domain:

$$\begin{aligned}[K_e] = \int_0^1 \int_0^{1-\xi} \int_0^{1-\xi-\eta} & \left(\left[\Gamma_{11} \frac{\partial N}{\partial \xi} + \Gamma_{12} \frac{\partial N}{\partial \eta} + \Gamma_{13} \frac{\partial N}{\partial \zeta} \right]^T \right. \\ & \left. \times k \left[\Gamma_{11} \frac{\partial N}{\partial \xi} + \Gamma_{12} \frac{\partial N}{\partial \eta} + \Gamma_{13} \frac{\partial N}{\partial \zeta} \right] \right) \\ & \times \det[J] d\zeta d\eta d\xi \\ + \int_0^1 \int_0^{1-\xi} \int_0^{1-\xi-\eta} & \left(\left[\Gamma_{21} \frac{\partial N}{\partial \xi} + \Gamma_{22} \frac{\partial N}{\partial \eta} + \Gamma_{23} \frac{\partial N}{\partial \zeta} \right]^T \right. \\ & \left. \times k \left[\Gamma_{21} \frac{\partial N}{\partial \xi} + \Gamma_{22} \frac{\partial N}{\partial \eta} + \Gamma_{23} \frac{\partial N}{\partial \zeta} \right] \right) \\ & \times \det[J] d\zeta d\eta d\xi \\ + \int_0^1 \int_0^{1-\xi} \int_0^{1-\xi-\eta} & \left(\left[\Gamma_{31} \frac{\partial N}{\partial \xi} + \Gamma_{32} \frac{\partial N}{\partial \eta} + \Gamma_{33} \frac{\partial N}{\partial \zeta} \right]^T \right. \\ & \left. \times k \left[\Gamma_{31} \frac{\partial N}{\partial \xi} + \Gamma_{32} \frac{\partial N}{\partial \eta} + \Gamma_{33} \frac{\partial N}{\partial \zeta} \right] \right) \\ & \times \det[J] d\zeta d\eta d\xi \end{aligned} \tag{10.36}$$

Example 10.8

For the 3D hexahedral and tetrahedral elements shown in Figure 10.12, determine their elementary $[K_e]$ matrices using Equations 10.35 and 10.36. Assume that the elements have a constant $k = 1000$.

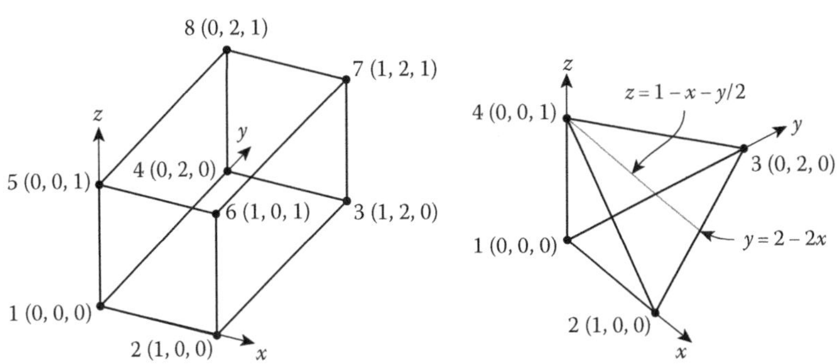

FIGURE 10.12
Three dimensional hexahedral and tetrahedral elements.

Answer

By applying Equation 10.34 to a hexahedral element, we obtain the following:

$$[J] = \begin{bmatrix} \frac{\partial N_1}{\partial \xi} & \frac{\partial N_2}{\partial \xi} & \frac{\partial N_3}{\partial \xi} & \frac{\partial N_4}{\partial \xi} & \frac{\partial N_5}{\partial \xi} & \frac{\partial N_6}{\partial \xi} & \frac{\partial N_7}{\partial \xi} & \frac{\partial N_8}{\partial \xi} \\ \frac{\partial N_1}{\partial \eta} & \frac{\partial N_2}{\partial \eta} & \frac{\partial N_3}{\partial \eta} & \frac{\partial N_4}{\partial \eta} & \frac{\partial N_5}{\partial \eta} & \frac{\partial N_6}{\partial \eta} & \frac{\partial N_7}{\partial \eta} & \frac{\partial N_8}{\partial \eta} \\ \frac{\partial N_1}{\partial \zeta} & \frac{\partial N_2}{\partial \zeta} & \frac{\partial N_3}{\partial \zeta} & \frac{\partial N_4}{\partial \zeta} & \frac{\partial N_5}{\partial \zeta} & \frac{\partial N_6}{\partial \zeta} & \frac{\partial N_7}{\partial \zeta} & \frac{\partial N_8}{\partial \zeta} \end{bmatrix} \begin{bmatrix} x_1 & y_1 & z_1 \\ x_2 & y_2 & z_2 \\ x_3 & y_3 & z_3 \\ x_4 & y_4 & z_4 \\ x_5 & y_5 & z_5 \\ x_6 & y_6 & z_6 \\ x_7 & y_7 & z_7 \\ x_8 & y_8 & z_8 \end{bmatrix} \tag{10.37}$$

where

$$\begin{aligned}
&\frac{\partial N_1}{\partial \xi} = -\frac{(1-\eta)(1-\zeta)}{8}, \quad \frac{\partial N_2}{\partial \xi} = \frac{(1-\eta)(1-\zeta)}{8}, \quad \frac{\partial N_3}{\partial \xi} = \frac{(1+\eta)(1-\zeta)}{8} \\
&\frac{\partial N_4}{\partial \xi} = -\frac{(1+\eta)(1-\zeta)}{8}, \quad \frac{\partial N_5}{\partial \xi} = -\frac{(1-\eta)(1+\zeta)}{8}, \quad \frac{\partial N_6}{\partial \xi} = \frac{(1-\eta)(1+\zeta)}{8} \\
&\frac{\partial N_7}{\partial \xi} = \frac{(1+\eta)(1+\zeta)}{8}, \quad \frac{\partial N_8}{\partial \xi} = -\frac{(1+\eta)(1+\zeta)}{8} \\
&\frac{\partial N_1}{\partial \eta} = -\frac{(1-\xi)(1-\zeta)}{8}, \quad \frac{\partial N_2}{\partial \eta} = -\frac{(1+\xi)(1-\zeta)}{8}, \quad \frac{\partial N_3}{\partial \eta} = \frac{(1+\xi)(1-\zeta)}{8} \\
&\frac{\partial N_4}{\partial \eta} = \frac{(1-\xi)(1-\zeta)}{8}, \quad \frac{\partial N_5}{\partial \eta} = -\frac{(1-\xi)(1+\zeta)}{8}, \quad \frac{\partial N_6}{\partial \eta} = -\frac{(1+\xi)(1+\zeta)}{8} \\
&\frac{\partial N_7}{\partial \eta} = \frac{(1+\xi)(1+\zeta)}{8}, \quad \frac{\partial N_8}{\partial \eta} = \frac{(1-\xi)(1+\zeta)}{8} \\
&\frac{\partial N_1}{\partial \zeta} = -\frac{(1-\xi)(1-\eta)}{8}, \quad \frac{\partial N_2}{\partial \zeta} = -\frac{(1+\xi)(1-\eta)}{8}, \quad \frac{\partial N_3}{\partial \zeta} = -\frac{(1+\xi)(1+\eta)}{8} \\
&\frac{\partial N_4}{\partial \zeta} = -\frac{(1-\xi)(1+\eta)}{8}, \quad \frac{\partial N_5}{\partial \zeta} = \frac{(1-\xi)(1-\eta)}{8}, \quad \frac{\partial N_6}{\partial \zeta} = \frac{(1+\xi)(1-\eta)}{8} \\
&\frac{\partial N_7}{\partial \zeta} = \frac{(1+\xi)(1+\eta)}{8}, \quad \frac{\partial N_8}{\partial \zeta} = \frac{(1-\xi)(1+\eta)}{8}
\end{aligned} \tag{10.38}$$

based on the shape functions given in Equation 10.29. Substituting the nodal coordinates given in the figure into Equation 10.37, we obtain

$$[J] = \begin{bmatrix} 0.5 & 0 & 0 \\ 0 & 1 & 0 \\ 0 & 0 & 0.5 \end{bmatrix}$$

With that, we find

$$\det[J] = \frac{1}{4}, \quad [\Gamma] = \begin{bmatrix} 2 & 0 & 0 \\ 0 & 1 & 0 \\ 0 & 0 & 2 \end{bmatrix}$$

Moreover, with the terms given in Equation 10.38, we assemble the following shape function derivative matrices:

$$\left[\frac{\partial N}{\partial \xi}\right] = \left[\frac{\partial N_1}{\partial \xi} \quad \frac{\partial N_2}{\partial \xi} \quad \frac{\partial N_3}{\partial \xi} \quad \frac{\partial N_4}{\partial \xi} \quad \frac{\partial N_5}{\partial \xi} \quad \frac{\partial N_6}{\partial \xi} \quad \frac{\partial N_7}{\partial \xi} \quad \frac{\partial N_8}{\partial \xi}\right]$$

$$\left[\frac{\partial N}{\partial \eta}\right] = \left[\frac{\partial N_1}{\partial \eta} \quad \frac{\partial N_2}{\partial \eta} \quad \frac{\partial N_3}{\partial \eta} \quad \frac{\partial N_4}{\partial \eta} \quad \frac{\partial N_5}{\partial \eta} \quad \frac{\partial N_6}{\partial \eta} \quad \frac{\partial N_7}{\partial \eta} \quad \frac{\partial N_8}{\partial \eta}\right]$$

$$\left[\frac{\partial N}{\partial \zeta}\right] = \left[\frac{\partial N_1}{\partial \zeta} \quad \frac{\partial N_2}{\partial \zeta} \quad \frac{\partial N_3}{\partial \zeta} \quad \frac{\partial N_4}{\partial \zeta} \quad \frac{\partial N_5}{\partial \zeta} \quad \frac{\partial N_6}{\partial \zeta} \quad \frac{\partial N_7}{\partial \zeta} \quad \frac{\partial N_8}{\partial \zeta}\right]$$

Putting all these into Equation 10.35, we obtain

$$[K_e] = k \iiint_{-1}^{1} \left(\Gamma_{11}^2 \left[\frac{\partial N}{\partial \xi}\right]^T \left[\frac{\partial N}{\partial \xi}\right] + \Gamma_{22}^2 \left[\frac{\partial N}{\partial \eta}\right]^T \left[\frac{\partial N}{\partial \eta}\right] + \Gamma_{33}^2 \left[\frac{\partial N}{\partial \zeta}\right]^T \left[\frac{\partial N}{\partial \zeta}\right]\right) \times \det[J] d\zeta d\eta d\xi$$

$$= \frac{1000}{4} \iiint_{-1}^{1} \left(4 \left[\frac{\partial N}{\partial \xi}\right]^T \left[\frac{\partial N}{\partial \xi}\right] + \left[\frac{\partial N}{\partial \eta}\right]^T \left[\frac{\partial N}{\partial \eta}\right] + 4 \left[\frac{\partial N}{\partial \zeta}\right]^T \left[\frac{\partial N}{\partial \zeta}\right]\right) d\zeta d\eta d\xi$$

$$= \begin{bmatrix} 500.0 & -83.3 & -83.3 & 166.7 & -83.3 & -208.3 & -125.0 & -83.3 \\ -83.3 & 500.0 & 166.7 & -83.3 & -208.3 & -83.3 & -83.3 & -125.0 \\ -83.3 & 166.7 & 500.0 & -83.3 & -125.0 & -83.3 & -83.3 & -208.3 \\ 166.7 & -83.3 & -83.3 & 500.0 & -83.3 & -125.0 & -208.3 & -83.3 \\ -83.3 & -208.3 & -125.0 & -83.3 & 500.0 & -83.3 & -83.3 & 166.7 \\ -208.3 & -83.3 & -83.3 & -125.0 & -83.3 & 500.0 & 166.7 & -83.3 \\ -125.0 & -83.3 & -83.3 & -208.3 & -83.3 & 166.7 & 500.0 & -83.3 \\ -83.3 & -125.0 & -208.3 & -83.3 & 166.7 & -83.3 & -83.3 & 500.0 \end{bmatrix}$$

Similarly, for the tetrahedral element, by applying Equation 10.34 to a tetrahedral element along with the shape functions given in Equation 10.31, we obtain the following Jacobian matrix of transformation:

$$[J] = \begin{bmatrix} -1 & 1 & 0 & 0 \\ -1 & 0 & 1 & 0 \\ -1 & 0 & 0 & 1 \end{bmatrix} \begin{bmatrix} x_1 & y_1 & z_1 \\ x_2 & y_2 & z_2 \\ x_3 & y_3 & z_3 \\ x_4 & y_4 & z_4 \end{bmatrix} \tag{10.39}$$

Substituting the nodal coordinates given in the figure, we have

$$[J] = \begin{bmatrix} 1 & 0 & 0 \\ 0 & 2 & 0 \\ 0 & 0 & 1 \end{bmatrix}, \quad \det[J] = 2, \quad [\Gamma] = \begin{bmatrix} 1 & 0 & 0 \\ 0 & 0.5 & 0 \\ 0 & 0 & 1 \end{bmatrix}$$

Moreover, with these individual shape functions we calculate

$$\left[\frac{\partial N}{\partial \xi}\right] = \begin{bmatrix}-1 & 1 & 0 & 0\end{bmatrix}, \quad \left[\frac{\partial N}{\partial \eta}\right] = \begin{bmatrix}-1 & 0 & 1 & 0\end{bmatrix}, \quad \left[\frac{\partial N}{\partial \zeta}\right] = \begin{bmatrix}-1 & 0 & 0 & 1\end{bmatrix}$$

Plugging these expressions into Equation 10.36 and integrating it over the isoparametric tetrahedral domain, along with the k value, we obtain

$$\begin{aligned}
[K_e] &= k\int_0^1\int_0^{1-\xi}\int_0^{1-\xi-\eta}\left(\left[\Gamma_{11}\frac{\partial N}{\partial \xi}\right]^T\left[\Gamma_{11}\frac{\partial N}{\partial \xi}\right]\right)\det[J]d\zeta d\eta d\xi \\
&+ k\int_0^1\int_0^{1-\xi}\int_0^{1-\xi-\eta}\left(\left[\Gamma_{22}\frac{\partial N}{\partial \eta}\right]^T\left[\Gamma_{22}\frac{\partial N}{\partial \eta}\right]\right)\det[J]d\zeta d\eta d\xi \\
&+ k\int_0^1\int_0^{1-\xi}\int_0^{1-\xi-\eta}\left(\left[\Gamma_{33}\frac{\partial N}{\partial \zeta}\right]^T\left[\Gamma_{33}\frac{\partial N}{\partial \zeta}\right]\right)\det[J]d\zeta d\eta d\xi \\
&= 2000\int_0^1\int_0^{1-\xi}\int_0^{1-\xi-\eta}\begin{bmatrix}-1\\1\\0\\0\end{bmatrix}\begin{bmatrix}-1 & 1 & 0 & 0\end{bmatrix}d\zeta d\eta d\xi \\
&+ 500\int_0^1\int_0^{1-\xi}\int_0^{1-\xi-\eta}\begin{bmatrix}-1\\0\\1\\0\end{bmatrix}\begin{bmatrix}-1 & 0 & 1 & 0\end{bmatrix}d\zeta d\eta d\xi \\
&+ 2000\int_0^1\int_0^{1-\xi}\int_0^{1-\xi-\eta}\begin{bmatrix}-1\\0\\0\\1\end{bmatrix}\begin{bmatrix}-1 & 0 & 0 & 1\end{bmatrix}d\zeta d\eta d\xi \\
&= \begin{bmatrix}750.00 & -333.33 & -83.33 & -333.33\\ -333.33 & 333.33 & 0 & 0\\ -83.33 & 0 & 83.33 & 0\\ -333.33 & 0 & 0 & 333.33\end{bmatrix}
\end{aligned}$$

Comparing the results from this example with those in Examples 7.3 and 7.4 in Section 7.3.2, we can see that they are exactly the same. This is as expected because the corresponding elements are the same.

10.3.3 Elementary $[K_e]$ matrix for vector field problems

To determine the elementary $[K_e]$ matrix for 3D isoparametric elements for solid mechanics problems, we go back to reevaluate the left-hand term in Equation 8.7, namely,

$$\iiint_V \{\nabla_s\{w\}\}^T\{\sigma\}dV \tag{10.40}$$

By using Equation 8.6, we write

$$\nabla_s\{w\} = \begin{bmatrix} \frac{\partial}{\partial x} & 0 & 0 \\ 0 & \frac{\partial}{\partial y} & 0 \\ 0 & 0 & \frac{\partial}{\partial z} \\ 0 & \frac{\partial}{\partial z} & \frac{\partial}{\partial y} \\ \frac{\partial}{\partial z} & 0 & \frac{\partial}{\partial x} \\ \frac{\partial}{\partial y} & \frac{\partial}{\partial x} & 0 \end{bmatrix} \begin{Bmatrix} w_x \\ w_y \\ w_z \end{Bmatrix} = [A_3] \begin{Bmatrix} \frac{\partial w_x}{\partial x} \\ \frac{\partial w_x}{\partial y} \\ \frac{\partial w_x}{\partial z} \\ \frac{\partial w_y}{\partial x} \\ \frac{\partial w_y}{\partial y} \\ \frac{\partial w_y}{\partial z} \\ \frac{\partial w_z}{\partial x} \\ \frac{\partial w_z}{\partial y} \\ \frac{\partial w_z}{\partial z} \end{Bmatrix}, \text{ and } \{\epsilon\} = \nabla_s\{d\} = [A_3] \begin{Bmatrix} \frac{\partial u_x}{\partial x} \\ \frac{\partial u_x}{\partial y} \\ \frac{\partial u_x}{\partial z} \\ \frac{\partial u_y}{\partial x} \\ \frac{\partial u_y}{\partial y} \\ \frac{\partial u_y}{\partial z} \\ \frac{\partial u_z}{\partial x} \\ \frac{\partial u_z}{\partial y} \\ \frac{\partial u_z}{\partial z} \end{Bmatrix}$$

where

$$[A_3] = \begin{bmatrix} 1 & 0 & 0 & 0 & 0 & 0 & 0 & 0 & 0 \\ 0 & 0 & 0 & 0 & 1 & 0 & 0 & 0 & 0 \\ 0 & 0 & 0 & 0 & 0 & 0 & 0 & 0 & 1 \\ 0 & 1 & 0 & 1 & 0 & 0 & 0 & 0 & 0 \\ 0 & 0 & 0 & 0 & 0 & 1 & 0 & 1 & 0 \\ 0 & 0 & 1 & 0 & 0 & 0 & 1 & 0 & 0 \end{bmatrix} \tag{10.41}$$

For a 3D element with n_e nodes, the Jacobian matrix of isoparametric transformation is given in Equation 10.34. With a known $[J]$, we express its inverse $[\Gamma]$ as

$$[\Gamma] = \begin{bmatrix} \Gamma_{11} & \Gamma_{12} & \Gamma_{13} \\ \Gamma_{21} & \Gamma_{22} & \Gamma_{23} \\ \Gamma_{31} & \Gamma_{32} & \Gamma_{33} \end{bmatrix}$$

Then, we write

$$\begin{Bmatrix} \frac{\partial u_x}{\partial x} \\ \frac{\partial u_x}{\partial y} \\ \frac{\partial u_x}{\partial z} \end{Bmatrix} = [\Gamma] \begin{Bmatrix} \frac{\partial u_x}{\partial \xi} \\ \frac{\partial u_x}{\partial \eta} \\ \frac{\partial u_x}{\partial \zeta} \end{Bmatrix}, \quad \begin{Bmatrix} \frac{\partial u_y}{\partial x} \\ \frac{\partial u_y}{\partial y} \\ \frac{\partial u_y}{\partial z} \end{Bmatrix} = [\Gamma] \begin{Bmatrix} \frac{\partial u_y}{\partial \xi} \\ \frac{\partial u_y}{\partial \eta} \\ \frac{\partial u_y}{\partial \zeta} \end{Bmatrix}, \quad \begin{Bmatrix} \frac{\partial u_z}{\partial x} \\ \frac{\partial u_z}{\partial y} \\ \frac{\partial u_z}{\partial z} \end{Bmatrix} = [\Gamma] \begin{Bmatrix} \frac{\partial u_z}{\partial \xi} \\ \frac{\partial u_z}{\partial \eta} \\ \frac{\partial u_z}{\partial \zeta} \end{Bmatrix}$$

Putting them together, we have

$$\begin{Bmatrix} \dfrac{\partial u_x}{\partial x} \\ \dfrac{\partial u_x}{\partial y} \\ \dfrac{\partial u_x}{\partial z} \\ \dfrac{\partial u_y}{\partial x} \\ \dfrac{\partial u_y}{\partial y} \\ \dfrac{\partial u_y}{\partial z} \\ \dfrac{\partial u_z}{\partial x} \\ \dfrac{\partial u_z}{\partial y} \\ \dfrac{\partial u_z}{\partial z} \end{Bmatrix} = \begin{bmatrix} \Gamma_{11} & \Gamma_{12} & \Gamma_{13} & 0 & 0 & 0 & 0 & 0 & 0 \\ \Gamma_{21} & \Gamma_{22} & \Gamma_{23} & 0 & 0 & 0 & 0 & 0 & 0 \\ \Gamma_{31} & \Gamma_{32} & \Gamma_{33} & 0 & 0 & 0 & 0 & 0 & 0 \\ 0 & 0 & 0 & \Gamma_{11} & \Gamma_{12} & \Gamma_{13} & 0 & 0 & 0 \\ 0 & 0 & 0 & \Gamma_{21} & \Gamma_{22} & \Gamma_{23} & 0 & 0 & 0 \\ 0 & 0 & 0 & \Gamma_{31} & \Gamma_{32} & \Gamma_{33} & 0 & 0 & 0 \\ 0 & 0 & 0 & 0 & 0 & 0 & \Gamma_{11} & \Gamma_{12} & \Gamma_{13} \\ 0 & 0 & 0 & 0 & 0 & 0 & \Gamma_{21} & \Gamma_{22} & \Gamma_{23} \\ 0 & 0 & 0 & 0 & 0 & 0 & \Gamma_{31} & \Gamma_{32} & \Gamma_{33} \end{bmatrix} \begin{Bmatrix} \dfrac{\partial u_x}{\partial \xi} \\ \dfrac{\partial u_x}{\partial \eta} \\ \dfrac{\partial u_x}{\partial \zeta} \\ \dfrac{\partial u_y}{\partial \xi} \\ \dfrac{\partial u_y}{\partial \eta} \\ \dfrac{\partial u_y}{\partial \zeta} \\ \dfrac{\partial u_x}{\partial \xi} \\ \dfrac{\partial u_z}{\partial \eta} \\ \dfrac{\partial u_z}{\partial \zeta} \end{Bmatrix}$$

$$= [\Gamma_{e3}] \begin{Bmatrix} \dfrac{\partial u_x}{\partial \xi} \\ \dfrac{\partial u_x}{\partial \eta} \\ \dfrac{\partial u_x}{\partial \zeta} \\ \dfrac{\partial u_y}{\partial \xi} \\ \dfrac{\partial u_y}{\partial \eta} \\ \dfrac{\partial u_y}{\partial \zeta} \\ \dfrac{\partial u_x}{\partial \xi} \\ \dfrac{\partial u_z}{\partial \eta} \\ \dfrac{\partial u_z}{\partial \zeta} \end{Bmatrix}$$

in which $[\Gamma_{e3}]$ represents the 9×9 matrix expanded based on the 3×3 $[\Gamma]$ matrix for 3D vector field problems.

With the interpolation functions

$$u_x = \sum_{m=1}^{n_e} N_m u_{mx}, \quad u_y = \sum_{m=1}^{n_e} N_m u_{my}, \quad u_z = \sum_{m=1}^{n_e} N_m u_{mz}$$

for $m = 1, 2, \ldots, n_e$, we write

$$\left\{\begin{matrix} \frac{\partial u_x}{\partial \xi} \\ \frac{\partial u_x}{\partial \eta} \\ \frac{\partial u_x}{\partial \zeta} \\ \frac{\partial u_y}{\partial \xi} \\ \frac{\partial u_y}{\partial \eta} \\ \frac{\partial u_y}{\partial \zeta} \\ \frac{\partial u_z}{\partial \xi} \\ \frac{\partial u_z}{\partial \eta} \\ \frac{\partial u_z}{\partial \zeta} \end{matrix}\right\} = \begin{bmatrix} \frac{\partial N_1}{\partial \xi} & 0 & 0 & \frac{\partial N_2}{\partial \xi} & 0 & 0 & \cdots & \frac{\partial N_{n_e}}{\partial \xi} & 0 & 0 \\ \frac{\partial N_1}{\partial \eta} & 0 & 0 & \frac{\partial N_2}{\partial \eta} & 0 & 0 & \cdots & \frac{\partial N_{n_e}}{\partial \eta} & 0 & 0 \\ \frac{\partial N_1}{\partial \zeta} & 0 & 0 & \frac{\partial N_2}{\partial \zeta} & 0 & 0 & \cdots & \frac{\partial N_{n_e}}{\partial \zeta} & 0 & 0 \\ 0 & \frac{\partial N_1}{\partial \xi} & 0 & 0 & \frac{\partial N_2}{\partial \xi} & 0 & \cdots & 0 & \frac{\partial N_{n_e}}{\partial \xi} & 0 \\ 0 & \frac{\partial N_1}{\partial \eta} & 0 & 0 & \frac{\partial N_2}{\partial \eta} & 0 & \cdots & 0 & \frac{\partial N_{n_e}}{\partial \eta} & 0 \\ 0 & \frac{\partial N_1}{\partial \zeta} & 0 & 0 & \frac{\partial N_2}{\partial \zeta} & 0 & \cdots & 0 & \frac{\partial N_{n_e}}{\partial \zeta} & 0 \\ 0 & 0 & \frac{\partial N_1}{\partial \xi} & 0 & 0 & \frac{\partial N_2}{\partial \xi} & \cdots & 0 & 0 & \frac{\partial N_{n_e}}{\partial \xi} \\ 0 & 0 & \frac{\partial N_1}{\partial \eta} & 0 & 0 & \frac{\partial N_2}{\partial \eta} & \cdots & 0 & 0 & \frac{\partial N_{n_e}}{\partial \eta} \\ 0 & 0 & \frac{\partial N_1}{\partial \zeta} & 0 & 0 & \frac{\partial N_2}{\partial \zeta} & \cdots & 0 & 0 & \frac{\partial N_{n_e}}{\partial \zeta} \end{bmatrix}$$

$$\times \left\{\begin{matrix} u_{1x} \\ u_{1y} \\ u_{1z} \\ u_{2x} \\ u_{2y} \\ u_{2z} \\ u_{3x} \\ u_{3y} \\ u_{3z} \\ u_{4x} \\ u_{4y} \\ u_{4z} \\ u_{5x} \\ u_{5y} \\ u_{5z} \\ \vdots \\ u_{n_e x} \\ u_{n_e y} \\ u_{n_e z} \end{matrix}\right\}$$

Let $[\partial N_3]$ represent the above $9 \times 3n_e$ shape function matrix derivative; then by using these matrices, we can express the strain vector as

$$\{\epsilon\} = \nabla_s\{d\} = [A_3]\,[\Gamma_{e3}]\,[\partial N_3]\,\{d_0\}$$

In similar steps, we have

$$\nabla_s\{w\} = [A_3]\,[\Gamma_{e3}]\,[\partial N_3]$$

Putting them all back into Equation 10.40, along with $\{\sigma\} = [C]\{\epsilon\}$ and $dxdydz = \det[J]d\zeta d\eta d\xi$, and integrating it over the isoparametric hexahedral domain, we obtain the following for 3D hexahedral elements for solid mechanics problems,

$$[K_e] = \int_{-1}^{1}\int_{-1}^{1}\int_{-1}^{1} [[A_3]\,[\Gamma_{e3}]\,[\partial N_3]]^T\,[C]\,[[A_3]\,[\Gamma_{e3}]\,[\partial N_3]]\,\det[J]\,d\zeta d\eta d\xi \tag{10.42}$$

and the following for tetrahedral elements:

$$[K_e] = \int_{0}^{1}\int_{0}^{1-\xi}\int_{0}^{1-\xi-\eta} [[A_3]\,[\Gamma_{e3}]\,[\partial N_3]]^T\,[C]\,[[A_3]\,[\Gamma_{e3}]\,[\partial N_3]] \times \det[J]\,d\zeta d\eta d\xi \tag{10.43}$$

Example 10.9

For the 3D hexahedral and tetrahedral elements shown in Figure 10.13 (with coordinates in units of meters), determine their elementary $[K_e]$ matrices using Equations 10.42 and 10.43. Assume that the elements are made of an isotropic material with $E = 200$ GPa and $\nu = 0.3$.

Answer
Referring to Example 10.8, we have the following for the hexahedral element:

$$[J] = \begin{bmatrix} 0.5 & 0 & 0 \\ 0 & 1 & 0 \\ 0 & 0 & 0.5 \end{bmatrix}, \quad \det[J] = \frac{1}{4}, \quad [\Gamma] = \begin{bmatrix} 2 & 0 & 0 \\ 0 & 1 & 0 \\ 0 & 0 & 2 \end{bmatrix}$$

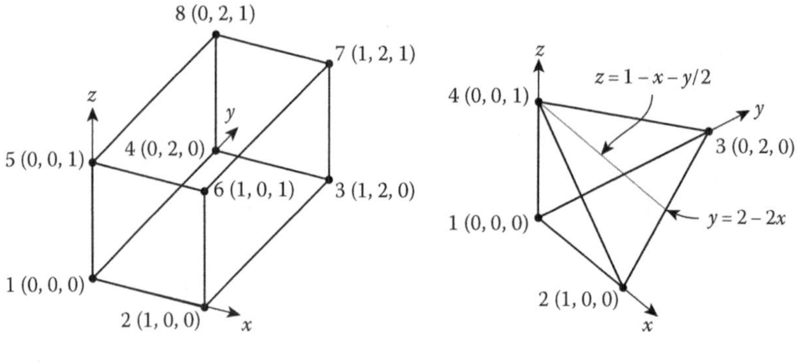

FIGURE 10.13
Three dimensional hexahedral and tetrahedral elements for solid mechanics problems.

Then, we express

$$[\Gamma_{e3}] = \begin{bmatrix} 2 & 0 & 0 & 0 & 0 & 0 & 0 & 0 & 0 \\ 0 & 1 & 0 & 0 & 0 & 0 & 0 & 0 & 0 \\ 0 & 0 & 2 & 0 & 0 & 0 & 0 & 0 & 0 \\ 0 & 0 & 0 & 2 & 0 & 0 & 0 & 0 & 0 \\ 0 & 0 & 0 & 0 & 1 & 0 & 0 & 0 & 0 \\ 0 & 0 & 0 & 0 & 0 & 2 & 0 & 0 & 0 \\ 0 & 0 & 0 & 0 & 0 & 0 & 2 & 0 & 0 \\ 0 & 0 & 0 & 0 & 0 & 0 & 0 & 1 & 0 \\ 0 & 0 & 0 & 0 & 0 & 0 & 0 & 0 & 2 \end{bmatrix}$$

Moreover, with the shape functions given in Equation 10.29, we calculate

$$[\partial N_3] = \begin{bmatrix} \frac{\partial N_1}{\partial \xi} & 0 & 0 & \frac{\partial N_2}{\partial \xi} & 0 & 0 & \cdots & \frac{\partial N_8}{\partial \xi} & 0 & 0 \\ \frac{\partial N_1}{\partial \eta} & 0 & 0 & \frac{\partial N_2}{\partial \eta} & 0 & 0 & \cdots & \frac{\partial N_8}{\partial \eta} & 0 & 0 \\ \frac{\partial N_1}{\partial \zeta} & 0 & 0 & \frac{\partial N_2}{\partial \zeta} & 0 & 0 & \cdots & \frac{\partial N_8}{\partial \zeta} & 0 & 0 \\ 0 & \frac{\partial N_1}{\partial \xi} & 0 & 0 & \frac{\partial N_2}{\partial \xi} & 0 & \cdots & 0 & \frac{\partial N_8}{\partial \xi} & 0 \\ 0 & \frac{\partial N_1}{\partial \eta} & 0 & 0 & \frac{\partial N_2}{\partial \eta} & 0 & \cdots & 0 & \frac{\partial N_8}{\partial \eta} & 0 \\ 0 & \frac{\partial N_1}{\partial \zeta} & 0 & 0 & \frac{\partial N_2}{\partial \zeta} & 0 & \cdots & 0 & \frac{\partial N_8}{\partial \zeta} & 0 \\ 0 & 0 & \frac{\partial N_1}{\partial \xi} & 0 & 0 & \frac{\partial N_2}{\partial \xi} & \cdots & 0 & 0 & \frac{\partial N_8}{\partial \xi} \\ 0 & 0 & \frac{\partial N_1}{\partial \eta} & 0 & 0 & \frac{\partial N_2}{\partial \eta} & \cdots & 0 & 0 & \frac{\partial N_8}{\partial \eta} \\ 0 & 0 & \frac{\partial N_1}{\partial \zeta} & 0 & 0 & \frac{\partial N_2}{\partial \zeta} & \cdots & 0 & 0 & \frac{\partial N_8}{\partial \zeta} \end{bmatrix}$$

where the individual shape function derivatives are given in Equation 10.38.

Substituting these expressions, along with $[A_3]$ (Equation 10.41), $[C]$ for 3D solid mechanics (Equation 8.8), and the values of E and ν, into Equation 10.42, we have

$$[K_e] = \frac{1}{4}\int_{-1}^{1}\int_{-1}^{1}\int_{-1}^{1} [[A_3]\,[\Gamma_{e3}]\,[\partial N_3]]^T\,[C]\,[[A_3]\,[\Gamma_{e3}]\,[\partial N_3]]\,d\zeta d\eta d\xi$$

$$= 10^{10}\begin{bmatrix} 8.12 & 1.60 & 3.21 & \cdots & -0.16 & -0.32 \\ 1.60 & 4.91 & 1.60 & \cdots & -1.18 & -1.60 \\ 3.21 & 1.60 & 8.12 & \cdots & -1.60 & -2.78 \\ \vdots & \vdots & \vdots & \ddots & \vdots & \vdots \\ -0.16 & -1.18 & -1.60 & \cdots & 4.91 & 1.60 \\ -0.32 & -1.60 & -2.78 & \cdots & 1.60 & 8.12 \end{bmatrix}$$

Similarly, for the tetrahedral element, we have

$$[J] = \begin{bmatrix} 1 & 0 & 0 \\ 0 & 2 & 0 \\ 0 & 0 & 1 \end{bmatrix}, \quad \det[J] = 2, \quad [\Gamma] = \begin{bmatrix} 1 & 0 & 0 \\ 0 & 0.5 & 0 \\ 0 & 0 & 1 \end{bmatrix}$$

Then, we express

$$[\Gamma_{e3}] = \begin{bmatrix} 1 & 0 & 0 & 0 & 0 & 0 & 0 & 0 & 0 \\ 0 & 0.5 & 0 & 0 & 0 & 0 & 0 & 0 & 0 \\ 0 & 0 & 1 & 0 & 0 & 0 & 0 & 0 & 0 \\ 0 & 0 & 0 & 1 & 0 & 0 & 0 & 0 & 0 \\ 0 & 0 & 0 & 0 & 0.5 & 0 & 0 & 0 & 0 \\ 0 & 0 & 0 & 0 & 0 & 1 & 0 & 0 & 0 \\ 0 & 0 & 0 & 0 & 0 & 0 & 1 & 0 & 0 \\ 0 & 0 & 0 & 0 & 0 & 0 & 0 & 0.5 & 0 \\ 0 & 0 & 0 & 0 & 0 & 0 & 0 & 0 & 1 \end{bmatrix}$$

Using the shape functions given in Equation 10.31, we calculate

$$[\partial N_3] = \begin{bmatrix} -1 & 0 & 0 & 1 & 0 & 0 & 0 & 0 & 0 & 0 & 0 & 0 \\ -1 & 0 & 0 & 0 & 0 & 0 & 1 & 0 & 0 & 0 & 0 & 0 \\ -1 & 0 & 0 & 0 & 0 & 0 & 0 & 0 & 0 & 1 & 0 & 0 \\ 0 & -1 & 0 & 0 & 1 & 0 & 0 & 0 & 0 & 0 & 0 & 0 \\ 0 & -1 & 0 & 0 & 0 & 0 & 0 & 1 & 0 & 0 & 0 & 0 \\ 0 & -1 & 0 & 0 & 0 & 0 & 0 & 0 & 0 & 0 & 1 & 0 \\ 0 & 0 & -1 & 0 & 0 & 1 & 0 & 0 & 0 & 0 & 0 & 0 \\ 0 & 0 & -1 & 0 & 0 & 0 & 0 & 0 & 1 & 0 & 0 & 0 \\ 0 & 0 & -1 & 0 & 0 & 0 & 0 & 0 & 0 & 0 & 0 & 1 \end{bmatrix}$$

Substituting these expressions, along with $[A_3]$ (Equation 10.41), $[C]$ for 3D solid mechanics (Equation 8.8), and the values of E and ν, into Equation 10.43, we have

$$[K_e] = 2\int_0^1 \int_0^{1-\xi} \int_0^{1-\xi-\eta} \left[[A_3]\,[\Gamma_{e3}]\,[\partial N_3]\right]^T [C] \left[[A_3]\,[\Gamma_{e3}]\,[\partial N_3]\right] d\zeta d\eta d\xi$$

$$= 10^{10} \begin{bmatrix} 12.18 & 3.21 & 6.41 & \cdots & -0 & -3.85 \\ 3.21 & 7.37 & 3.21 & \cdots & -2.56 & -1.92 \\ 6.41 & 3.21 & 12.18 & \cdots & -1.28 & -8.97 \\ \vdots & \vdots & \vdots & \ddots & \vdots & \vdots \\ 0 & -2.56 & -1.28 & \cdots & 2.56 & 0 \\ -3.85 & -1.92 & -8.97 & \cdots & 0 & 8.97 \end{bmatrix}$$

These results are exactly the same as those in Examples 8.1 and 8.2 in Section 8.1.4, as expected, because the corresponding elements are the same.

10.4 Exercises

1. Determine the $[K_e]$ matrix for the 2-node bar elements shown in Figure 10.14 in terms of E, A, and l.

2. Determine the $[K_e]$ matrix for the 3-node bar elements shown in Figure 10.15 in terms of E, A, and l.

3. Determine the $[K_e]$ matrix for the two 3-node bar elements shown in Figure 10.16 with a slightly off-centered middle node in terms of E, A, and l. Also, try to solve this problem using the method discussed in Chapter 6.

4. Follow the discussion in Section 10.1.4 and in Example 10.3 to determine the elementary $[K_e]$ matrix for the two 2-node beam elements shown in Figure 10.17 in terms of E, I, and l and compare the results of the two elements.

5. For the 2D square and rectangular elements shown in Figure 10.18 to be used for 2D scalar problems, determine their elementary $[K_e]$ matrices. Assume that the elements have a constant property of $kt = 4$ (ignore the units).

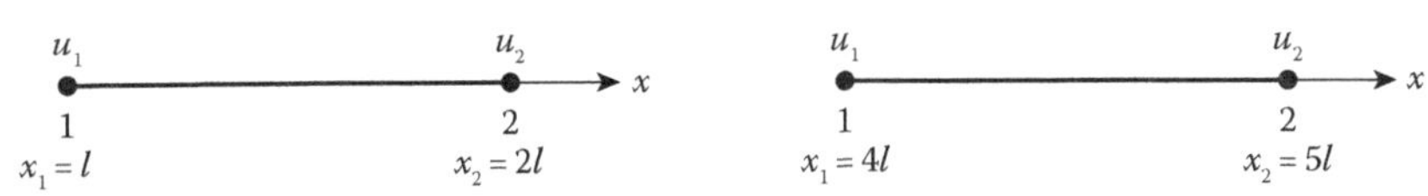

FIGURE 10.14
Two 1D 2-node elements located at different positions.

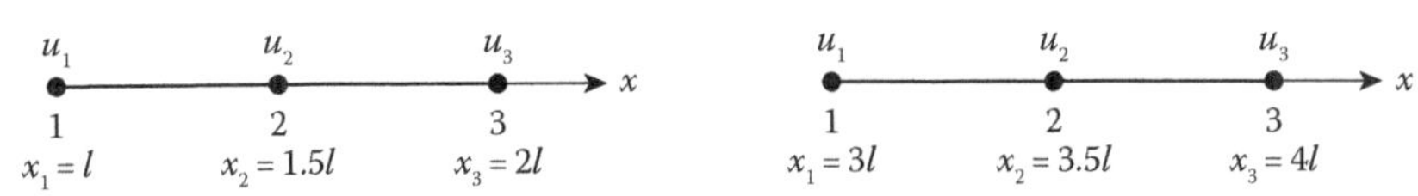

FIGURE 10.15
Two 1D 3-node elements located at different positions.

FIGURE 10.16
Two 1D 3-node elements located at different positions.

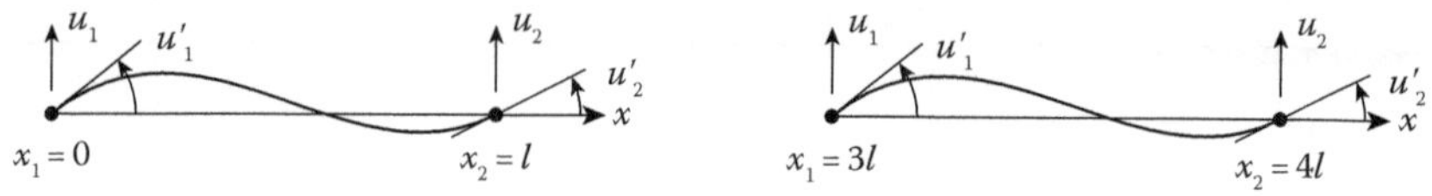

FIGURE 10.17
Two 2-node beam elements at different locations.

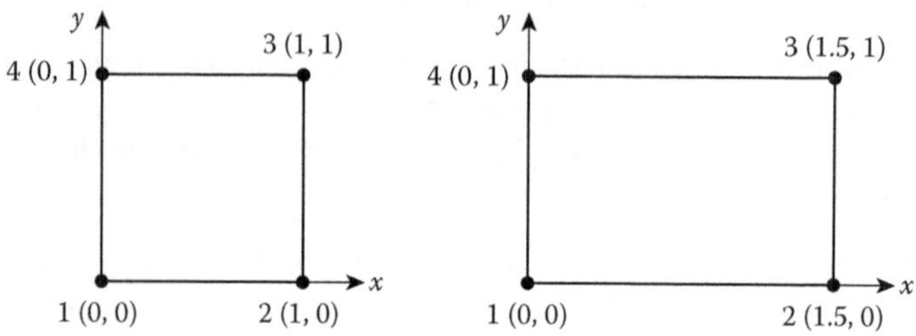

FIGURE 10.18
Two 2D rectangular elements with a uniform thickness.

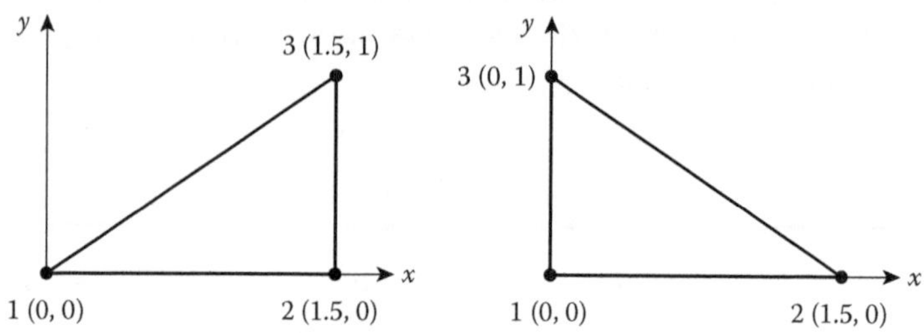

FIGURE 10.19
Two 2D triangular elements with a uniform thickness.

6. For the two 2D triangular elements shown in Figure 10.19 to be used for 2D scalar problems, determine their elementary $[K_e]$ matrices. Assume that the elements have a constant property of $kt = 4$ (ignore the units).
7. For the two 2D rectangular elements shown in Figure 10.20 to be used for scalar axisymmetric problems, determine their elementary $[K_e]$ matrices. Assume that the elements have a constant property of $k = 500$ (ignore the units).
8. For the two 2D triangular elements shown in Figure 10.21 to be used for scalar axisymmetric problems, determine their elementary $[K_e]$ matrices. Assume that the elements have a constant property of $k = 500$ (ignore the units).

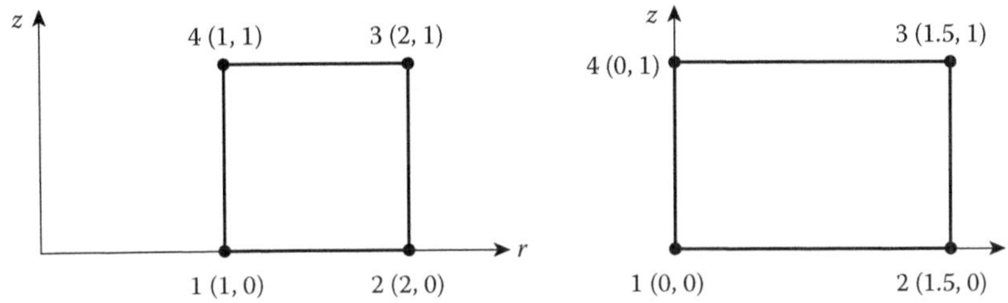

FIGURE 10.20
Two 2D rectangular elements with a uniform thickness.

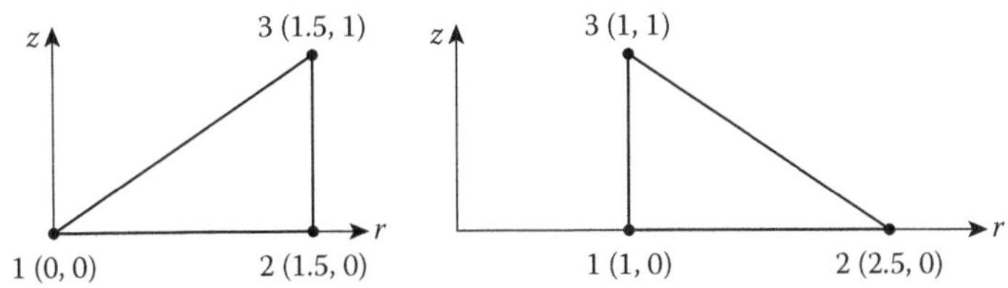

FIGURE 10.21
Two 2D triangular elements with a uniform thickness.

9. For the 2D square and rectangular elements shown in Figure 10.18 to be used for 2D solid mechanics problems, determine their elementary $[K_e]$ matrices. Assume that the elements are made of an isotropic material with $E = 200$ GPa and $\nu = 0.3$. Consider both the plane stress and plane strain situations.
10. For the two 2D triangular elements shown in Figure 10.19 to be used for 2D solid mechanics problems, determine their elementary $[K_e]$ matrices. Assume that the elements are made of an isotropic material with $E = 200$ GPa and $\nu = 0.3$. Consider both the plane stress and plane strain situations.
11. For the two 2D rectangular elements shown in Figure 10.20 to be used for axisymmetric solid mechanics problems, determine their elementary $[K_e]$ matrices. Assume that the elements are made of an isotropic material with $E = 200$ GPa and $\nu = 0.3$.
12. For the two 2D triangular elements shown in Figure 10.21 to be used for axisymmetric solid mechanics problems, determine their elementary $[K_e]$ matrices. Assume that the elements are made of an isotropic material with $E = 200$ GPa and $\nu = 0.3$.
13. For the 3D hexahedral element shown in Figure 10.22 to be used for 3D scalar problems, determine its elementary $[K_e]$ matrix. Assume that the element has a constant $k = 1000$ (ignore the units).

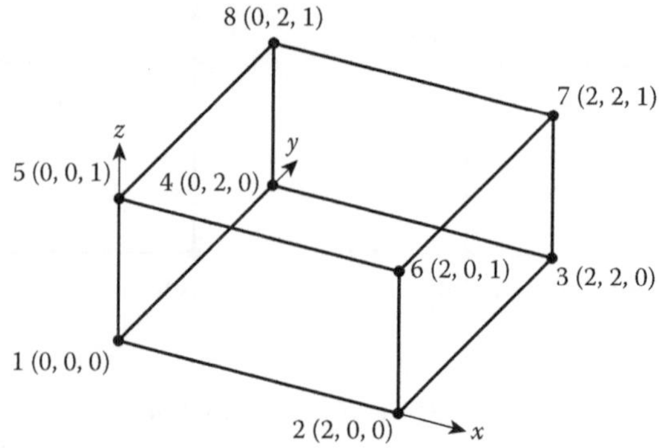

FIGURE 10.22
A 3D hexahedral element.

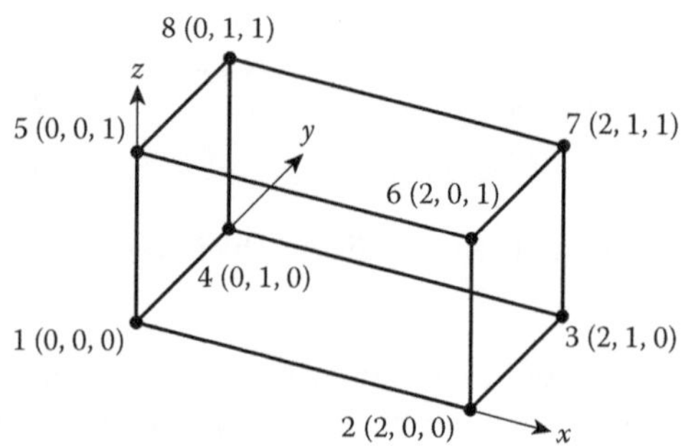

FIGURE 10.23
A 3D hexahedral element.

14. For the 3D hexahedral element shown in Figure 10.23 to be used for 3D scalar problems, determine its elementary $[K_e]$ matrix. Assume that the element has a constant $k = 1000$ (ignore the units).
15. For the 3D tetrahedral element shown in Figure 10.24 to be used for 3D scalar problems, determine its elementary $[K_e]$ matrix. Assume that the element has a constant $k = 1000$ (ignore the units).
16. For the 3D hexahedral element shown in Figure 10.22 to be used for 3D solid mechanics problems, determine its elementary $[K_e]$ matrix. Assume that the element is made of an isotropic material with $E = 200$ GPa and $\nu = 0.3$.
17. For the 3D hexahedral element shown in Figure 10.23 to be used for 3D solid mechanics problems, determine its elementary $[K_e]$ matrix. Assume that the element is made of an isotropic material with $E = 200$ GPa and $\nu = 0.3$.

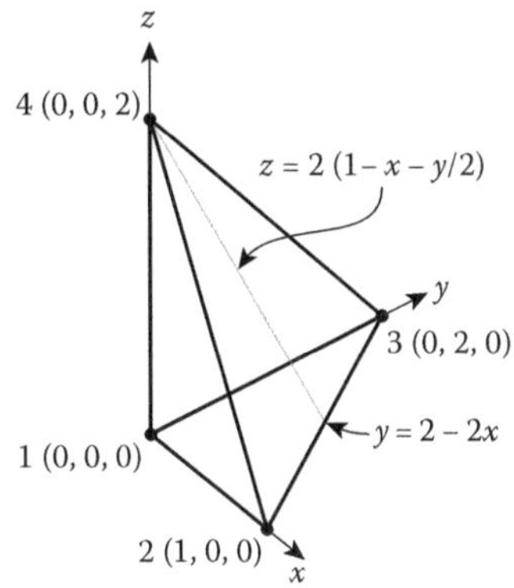

FIGURE 10.24
A 3D tetrahedral element.

18. For the 3D tetrahedral element shown in Figure 10.24 to be used for 3D solid mechanics problems, determine its elementary $[K_e]$ matrix. Assume that the element is made of an isotropic material with $E = 200$ GPa and $\nu = 0.3$.

Recommended Readings

1. J. N. Reddy. 1993. *An Introduction to the Finite Element Method.* 2nd ed. Boston: McGraw-Hill.
2. Robert D. Cook, David S. Malkus, Michael E. Plesha, and Robert J. Witt. 2002. *Concepts and Applications of Finite Element Analysis.* 4th ed. Hoboken, NJ: John Wiley & Sons.

11

Gauss Quadrature and Numerical Integration

As we learned in Chapters 7 through 10, integration over the domain of an element is a necessary step for evaluating the elementary $[K_e]$ matrix and other relevant vectors. Although isoparametric elements offer uniform elements with well-defined boundaries as integration bounds, they still leave us with integrations to perform. Performing integrations using a computer program is actually not an easy task. Moreover, in Chapters 9 and 10 we encountered terms of infinity in the elementary $[K_e]$ matrix of axisymmetric elements for vector field problems. To address all these issues, it is necessary to have a numerical approach to perform integrations. The Gauss quadrature method, named after Carl Friedrich Gauss (1777–1855), a German mathematician, is one such approach: it approximates an integration with the weighted sum of the integrand evaluated at some predetermined locations. In this chapter, we discuss how Gauss quadrature works.

Because of the isoparametric transformation, we can define all integrations in domains defined by isoparametric elements. Thus, the integration bounds for various elements are as follows:

1. For one-dimensional (1D) elements: $\int_{-1}^{1} f(\xi)d\xi$
2. For two-dimensional (2D) quadrilateral elements: $\int_{-1}^{1} d\xi \int_{-1}^{1} f(\xi,\eta)d\eta$
3. For 2D triangular elements: $\int_{0}^{1} d\xi \int_{0}^{1-\xi} f(\xi,\eta)d\eta$
4. For three-dimensional (3D) hexahedral elements: $\int_{-1}^{1} d\xi \int_{-1}^{1} d\eta \int_{-1}^{1} f(\xi,\eta,\zeta)d\zeta$
5. For 3D tetrahedral elements: $\int_{0}^{1} d\xi \int_{0}^{1-\xi} d\eta \int_{0}^{1-\xi-\eta} f(\xi,\eta,\zeta)d\zeta$

11.1 Gauss Quadrature

The general idea behind Gauss quadrature is to reduce the difficulty level of calculation by expressing integration as a sum of a series of multiplications. We begin by examining integration in a 1D situation. For the integral $\int_{-1}^{1} f(\xi)d\xi$, we ask, can we approximate it as a sum of a series of multiplications such that

$$\int_{-1}^{1} f(\xi)d\xi \approx \sum_{i=1}^{n} f(\xi_i)w_i$$

for $i = 1, \ldots, n$?

This kind of numerical approximation is called Gauss quadrature. So the above question can be rephrased as, can we find a series of Gauss points with values of ξ_i and weights of w_i to satisfy the above approximation? The answer is yes, but the goodness of approximation depends on how many Gauss points, along with associated weights, we will use. In the following sections, we examine cases with different numbers of Gauss points.

11.1.1 A 1-point Gauss quadrature

We will now expand on this idea and see how this procedure is actually carried out. For the case of one Gauss point along with one weight factor, we express

$$\int_{-1}^{1} f(\xi)d\xi \approx w_1 f(\xi_1)$$

Since we have two parameters that need to be determined, namely, ξ_1 and w_1, we select a polynomial function with two constants as $f(\xi) = a_0 + a_1\xi$ to approximate the integrand function (note that the same polynomial term selection criterion discussed in Section 5.4 applies here). With substitution, we have

$$\int_{-1}^{1} (a_0 + a_1\xi)d\xi \approx w_1(a_0 + a_1\xi_1)$$

After integrating and rearranging it, we obtain

$$\int_{-1}^{1} (a_0 + a_1\xi)d\xi = 2a_0 \approx w_1(a_0 + a_1\xi_1)$$

which leads to

$$(2 - w_1)a_0 + \xi_1 a_1 = 0$$

For this to be true for any arbitrary values of a_0, a_1, we set

$$w_1 = 2, \quad \xi_1 = 0$$

Thus, we have

$$\int_{-1}^{1} f(\xi)d\xi \approx 2f(0) \tag{11.1}$$

This is the result of 1-point Gauss quadrature, in which $\xi = 0$ is the location of the Gauss point and $w_1 = 2$ is the weight factor.

Figure 11.1 illustrates the meaning of Equation 11.1. Instead of integrating the function $f(\xi)$ from -1 to 1 (the result should be the shaded areas under the integrand curve), we approximate it by the area of a rectangle having a height determined by the integrand function $f(\xi)$ evaluated at the Gauss point ($\xi = 0$) and a width determined by the weight factor ($w_1 = 2$). This single weight factor equals the width of the integration domain.

11.1.2 A 2-point Gauss quadrature

If we are concerned about the goodness of such an approximation, let us consider adding more Gauss points. For a 2-point case, we select two location points, ξ_1, ξ_2, along with two weights, w_1, w_2. Thus, we express

$$\int_{-1}^{1} f(\xi)d\xi \approx w_1 f(\xi_1) + w_2 f(\xi_2)$$

Since we now have four parameters that need to be determined, we select a four-term polynomial function: $f(\xi) = a_0 + a_1\xi + a_2\xi^2 + a_3\xi^3$. By plugging this function in the above equation, we find

$$\int_{-1}^{1} (a_0 + a_1\xi + a_2\xi^2 + a_3\xi^3)d\xi \approx w_1(a_0 + a_1\xi_1 + a_2\xi_1^2 + a_3\xi_1^3) + w_2(a_0 + a_1\xi_1 + a_2\xi_2^2 + a_3\xi_2^3)$$

Integrating the left-hand side and rearranging the right-hand side, we arrive at

$$2a_0 + \frac{2}{3}a_2 \approx a_0(w_1 + w_2) + a_1(w_1\xi_1 + w_2\xi_2) + a_2(w_1\xi_1^2 + w_2\xi_2^2) + a_3(w_1\xi_1^3 + w_2\xi_2^3)$$

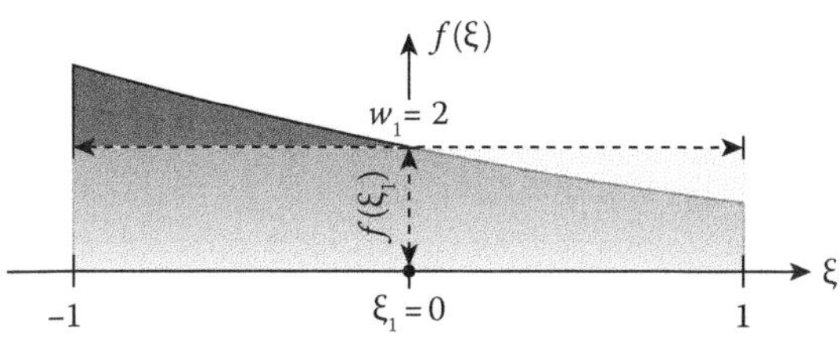

FIGURE 11.1
A 1-point Gauss quadrature.

For this to be true for any arbitrary values of a_i, $i = 0, \ldots, 3$, we set

$$w_1 + w_2 = 2,\;\; w_1\xi_1 + w_2\xi_2 = 0,\;\; w_1\xi_1^2 + w_2\xi_2^2 = \frac{2}{3},\;\; w_1\xi_1^3 + w_2\xi_2^3 = 0$$

By solving these four algebraic equations together, we obtain the following,

$$w_1 = w_2 = 1, \xi_1 = -1/\sqrt{3},\;\; \xi_2 = 1/\sqrt{3}$$

as the point locations and weight factors for the 2-point Gauss quadrature. Thus, we have

$$\int_{-1}^{1} f(\xi)d\xi \approx \sum_{i}^{2} f(\xi_i)w_i = f(-1/\sqrt{3}) + f(1/\sqrt{3}) \tag{11.2}$$

Figure 11.2 illustrates the meaning of Equation 11.2. In this case, the shaded area under the curve is now approximated by two rectangles with the same width (or weight) of 1. The height of the first rectangle is $f(\xi = -1/\sqrt{3})$ taken at Gauss point $\xi = -1/\sqrt{3}$, and that of the second rectangle is $f(\xi = 1/\sqrt{3})$ taken at Gauss point $\xi = 1/\sqrt{3}$. The sum of the two weight factors equals the width of the integration domain.

11.1.3 A 3-point Gauss quadrature

If we want to use three Gauss points, then we will need three weight factors to go with them. Thus, we express

$$\int_{-1}^{1} f(\xi)d\xi \approx w_1 f(\xi_1) + w_2 f(\xi_2) + w_3 f(\xi_3)$$

Since we have six parameters that need to be determined, namely, w_1, w_2, w_3 and ξ_1, ξ_2, ξ_3, we select a six-term polynomial function:

$$f(\xi) = a_0 + a_1\xi + a_2\xi^2 + a_3\xi^3 + a_4\xi^4 + a_5\xi^5$$

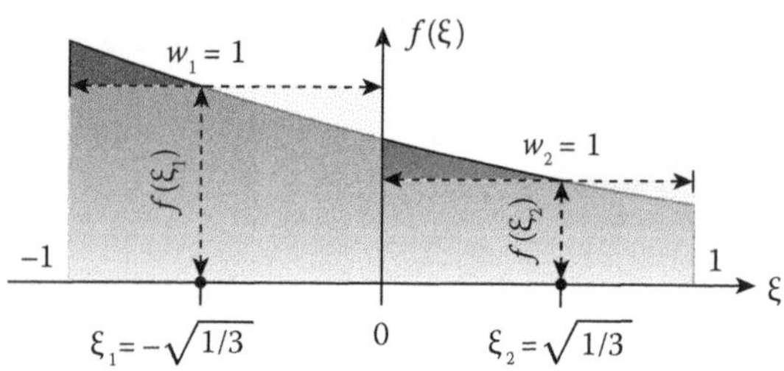

FIGURE 11.2
A 2-point Gauss quadrature.

By plugging this function into the above equation, we have

$$\begin{aligned}\int_{-1}^{1}&(a_0 + a_1\xi + a_2\xi^2 + a_3\xi^3 + a_4\xi^4 + a_5\xi^5)d\xi \\ &\approx w_1(a_0 + a_1\xi_1 + a_2\xi_1^2 + a_3\xi_1^3 + a_4\xi_1^4 + a_5\xi_1^5) \\ &\quad + w_2(a_0 + a_2\xi_2 + a_3\xi_2^2 + a_3\xi_2^3 + a_4\xi_2^4 + a_5\xi_2^5) \\ &\quad + w_3(a_0 + a_1\xi_3 + a_2\xi_3^3 + a_3\xi_3^3 + a_4\xi_3^4 + a_5\xi_3^5)\end{aligned}$$

Integrating and expressing it in a matrix form, we have

$$\begin{bmatrix}2 & 0 & \frac{2}{3} & 0 & \frac{2}{5} & 0\end{bmatrix}\begin{Bmatrix}a_0\\a_1\\a_2\\a_3\\a_4\\a_5\end{Bmatrix} = \begin{bmatrix}w_1 & w_2 & w_3\end{bmatrix}\begin{bmatrix}1 & \xi_1 & \xi_1^2 & \xi_1^3 & \xi_1^4 & \xi_1^5\\1 & \xi_2 & \xi_2^2 & \xi_2^3 & \xi_2^4 & \xi_2^5\\1 & \xi_3 & \xi_3^2 & \xi_3^3 & \xi_3^4 & \xi_3^5\end{bmatrix}\begin{Bmatrix}a_0\\a_1\\a_2\\a_3\\a_4\\a_5\end{Bmatrix}$$

For this to be true for any arbitrary values of a_i, $i = 0, \ldots, 5$, we set

$$\begin{bmatrix}2 & 0 & \frac{2}{3} & 0 & \frac{2}{5} & 0\end{bmatrix} = \begin{bmatrix}w_1 & w_2 & w_3\end{bmatrix}\begin{bmatrix}1 & \xi_1 & \xi_1^2 & \xi_1^3 & \xi_1^4 & \xi_1^5\\1 & \xi_2 & \xi_2^2 & \xi_2^3 & \xi_2^4 & \xi_2^5\\1 & \xi_3 & \xi_3^2 & \xi_3^3 & \xi_3^4 & \xi_3^5\end{bmatrix}$$

This produces the following six algebra equations:

$$\begin{aligned}w_1 + w_2 + w_3 &= 2\\ w_1\xi_1 + w_2\xi_2 + w_3\xi_3 &= 0\\ w_1\xi_1^2 + w_2\xi_2^2 + w_3\xi_3^2 &= \frac{2}{3}\\ w_1\xi_1^3 + w_2\xi_2^3 + w_3\xi_3^3 &= 0\\ w_1\xi_1^4 + w_2\xi_2^4 + w_3\xi_3^4 &= \frac{2}{5}\\ w_1\xi_1^5 + w_2\xi_2^5 + w_3\xi_3^5 &= 0\end{aligned}$$

By solving them simultaneously, we obtain the following:

$$w_1 = \frac{5}{9},\ w_2 = \frac{8}{9},\ w_3 = \frac{5}{9},\ \xi_1 = -\sqrt{3/5},\ \xi_2 = 0,\ \xi_3 = 1/\sqrt{3/5}$$

This leads to 3-point Gauss quadrature as

$$\int_{-1}^{1} f(\xi)d\xi \approx \sum_{i}^{3} f(\xi_i)w_i = \frac{5}{9}f(-\sqrt{3/5}) + \frac{8}{9}f(0) + \frac{5}{9}f(\sqrt{3/5}) \qquad (11.3)$$

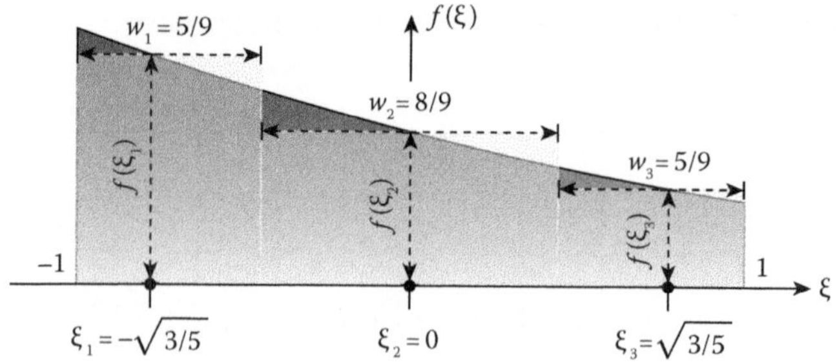

FIGURE 11.3
A 3-point Gauss quadrature.

Figure 11.3 illustrates the meaning of 3-point Gauss quadrature. The shaded area under the integrand curve is now approximated by three rectangles. Of these rectangles, the two side ones have a width (weight factor) of 5/9 and the middle one of 8/9. The sum of the three weight factors equals the width of the integration domain.

Example 11.1

Evaluate $I = \int_{-1}^{1} (\xi^2 - 5\xi + 9)d\xi$ by integration and by 1-point, 2-point, and 3-point Gauss quadrature.

Answer
We first integrate this expression directly to find the analytical answer:

$$I = \int_{-1}^{1} (\xi^2 - 5\xi + 9)d\xi = \left[\frac{\xi^3}{3} - \frac{5\xi^2}{2} + 9\xi\right]_{-1}^{1} = \frac{2}{3} + 9 = \frac{56}{3}$$

Next, we use Gauss quadrature to find approximate solutions.

For $n = 1$, we have $\xi_1 = 0, w_1 = 2$; thus,

$$I \approx w_1 f(\xi_1) = 2f(0) = 18$$

For $n = 2$, with $\xi_1 = -\frac{1}{\sqrt{3}}, \xi_2 = \frac{1}{\sqrt{3}}, w_1 = w_2 = 1$, we have

$$I \approx \sum_{i=1}^{2} w_i f(\xi_i) = (1)\left[\left(\frac{-1}{\sqrt{3}}\right)^2 - 5\left(\frac{-1}{\sqrt{3}}\right) + 9\right] + (1)\left[\left(\frac{1}{\sqrt{3}}\right)^2 - 5\left(\frac{1}{\sqrt{3}}\right) + 9\right] = \frac{56}{3}$$

For $n = 3$, we have

$$I \approx \sum_{i=1}^{3} w_i f(\xi_i) = \frac{5}{9}\left[\left(-\sqrt{\frac{3}{5}}\right)^2 - 5\left(-\sqrt{\frac{3}{5}}\right) + 9\right]$$

$$+ \frac{8}{9}[0 + 0 + 9] + \frac{5}{9}\left[\left(\sqrt{\frac{3}{5}}\right)^2 - 5\left(\sqrt{\frac{3}{5}}\right) + 9\right] = \frac{56}{3}$$

TABLE 11.1
Weights and locations of Gauss points

$$\int_{-1}^{1} f(\xi)d\xi \approx \sum_{i=1}^{n} f(\xi_i)w_i$$

Number of points, n	**Weights, w_i**	**Locations, ξ_i**
1	2.0	0.0
2	1.0	$\pm 1/\sqrt{3} \approx \pm 0.5773$
3	$8/9 \approx 0.8889$	0.0
	$5/9 \approx 0.5556$	$\pm\sqrt{3/5} \approx \pm 0.7746$
4	0.3479	± 0.8611
	0.6521	± 0.3399
5	0.5689	0.0
	0.2369	± 0.9062
	0.4786	± 0.5385
6	0.1713	± 0.9325
	0.3608	± 0.6612
	0.4679	± 0.2386

Clearly, for this second-degree integrand function, the solutions of 2-point and 3-point Gauss quadrature are exactly the same as the analytical answer, but that of 1-point Gauss quadrature is slightly less than the analytical answer.

11.1.4 Locations and weights of Gauss points

The procedure used to determine the locations and weights for the Gauss points can be extended to include more points. Table 11.1 lists the weights and locations of the Gauss points for the cases of 1- to 6-point Gauss quadrature. Note that in each case, the sum of the weight factors equals the width of the 1D isoparametric domain, which is 2.

11.2 Gauss Quadrature for 2D Quadrilateral Elements

The Gauss quadrature method discussed for 1D space can be extended to 2D space of quadrilateral shapes by adding a second dimension. The same sets of Gauss points and weights will be used. This statement can be expressed mathematically by

$$\iint_{-1}^{1} f(\xi,\eta)d\eta d\xi \approx \sum_{i=1,j=1}^{n} f(\xi_i,\eta_j)w_{\xi_i}w_{\eta_j}$$

where $f(\xi, \eta)$ is a 2D integrand function, and i, j are index numbers of Gauss points along the two axes in coordinates ξ and η. In a 2D situation, the location of a Gauss point is marked by the coordinates (ξ_i, η_j) and each point is associated with two weight factors (one for each coordinate), w_{ξ_i} and w_{η_j}.

11.2.1 A 2-point Gauss quadrature

Figure 11.4 shows how 2-point Gauss quadrature over the isoparametric square domain is determined. In this case, with two Gauss points along each coordinate direction, there are four Gauss points in total. We express the coordinates of these Gauss points and weights, in combination with the two locations and weights determined in 1D, as

$$\begin{aligned}
&\text{Gauss point 1: } \xi_1 = \sqrt{1/3}, \quad \eta_1 = \sqrt{1/3}, \quad w_{\xi_1} = w_{\eta_1} = 1\\
&\text{Gauss point 2: } \xi_2 = -\sqrt{1/3}, \quad \eta_2 = \sqrt{1/3}, \quad w_{\xi_2} = w_{\eta_2} = 1\\
&\text{Gauss point 3: } \xi_3 = -\sqrt{1/3}, \quad \eta_3 = -\sqrt{1/3}, \quad w_{\xi_3} = w_{\eta_3} = 1\\
&\text{Gauss point 4: } \xi_4 = \sqrt{1/3}, \quad \eta_4 = -\sqrt{1/3}, \quad w_{\xi_4} = w_{\eta_4} = 1
\end{aligned}$$

So, the 2-point Gauss quadrature in 2D approximates the volume under the curved surface, which is defined by the integrand function $(f(\xi, \eta))$, by the sum of the volume of four square blocks with heights of $f(\sqrt{1/3}, \sqrt{1/3})$, $f(-\sqrt{1/3}, \sqrt{1/3})$, $f(-\sqrt{1/3}, -\sqrt{1/3})$, and $f(\sqrt{1/3}, -\sqrt{1/3})$, respectively. The four quadrants on the base plane mark the bases of these square blocks, with a width equaling the weight factors (which is 1 for all cases). The sum of the four products of the two associated weight factors at each point equals the area of the base plane, which is 4.

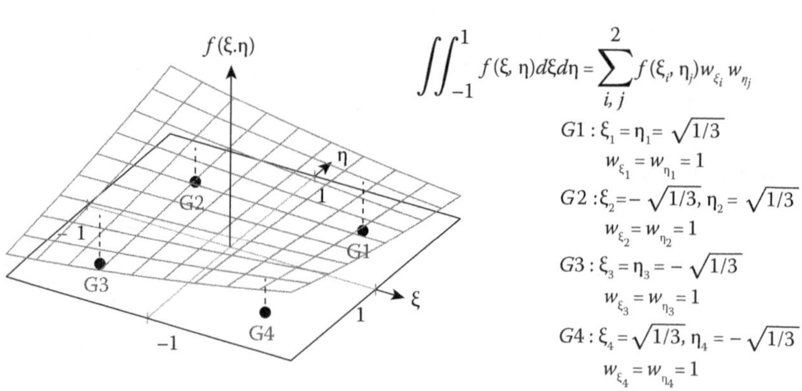

FIGURE 11.4
A 2-point Gauss quadrature extended to 2D.

$$\iint_{-1}^{1} f(\xi,\eta)d\xi d\eta = \sum_{i,j}^{2} f(\xi_i,\eta_j)w_{\xi i}w_{\eta j}$$

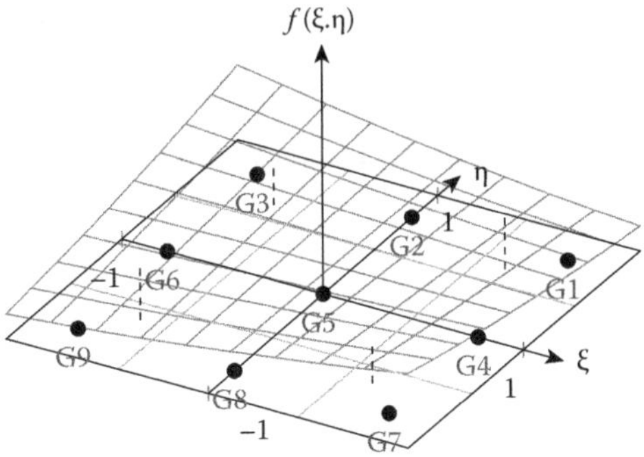

$G1: \xi_1 = \eta_1 = \sqrt{3/5}$
$w_{\xi_1} = w_{\eta_1} = 5/9$

$G2: \xi_2 = 0,\ \eta_2 = \sqrt{3/5}$
$w_{\xi_2} = 8/9,\ w_{\eta_2} = 5/9$

$G3: \xi_3 = -\sqrt{3/5},\ \eta_3 = \sqrt{3/5}$
$w_{\xi_3} = w_{\eta_3} = 5/9$

$G4: \xi_4 = \sqrt{3/5},\ \eta_4 = 0$
$w_{\xi_4} = 5/9,\ w_{\eta_4} = 8/9$

$G5: \xi_5 = \eta_5 = 0$
$w_{\xi_5} = w_{\eta_5} = 8/9$

$G6: \xi_6 = -\sqrt{3/5},\ \eta_6 = 0$
$w_{\xi_6} = 5/9,\ w_{\eta_6} = 8/9$

$G7: \xi_7 = \sqrt{3/5},\ \eta_7 = -\sqrt{3/5}$
$w_{\xi_7} = w_{\eta_7} = 5/9$

$G8: \xi_8 = 0,\ \eta_8 = -\sqrt{3/5}$
$w_{\xi_8} = 8/9,\ w_{\eta_8} = 5/9$

$G9: \xi_9 = \eta_9 = -\sqrt{3/5}$
$w_{\xi_9} = w_{\eta_9} = 5/9$

FIGURE 11.5
A 3-point Gaussian quadrature extended to 2D.

11.2.2 A 3-point Gauss quadrature

In a similar way, 3-point Gauss quadrature over the isoparametric square domain uses combinations of the three Gauss points and weight factors to produce nine Gauss points.

Figure 11.5 shows how 3-point Gauss quadrature is determined. It approximates the volume under the curved surface by the sum of the volume of nine blocks. The bases of these blocks are marked by the green lines on the base plane, and the heights are determined by the integrand function evaluated at these nine Gauss points, respectively. The sum of the nine products of the two associated weight factors at each point equals the area of the base plane.

Example 11.2

Evaluate $I = \iint_{-1}^{1}(4\xi^2\eta^2 - 15\xi\eta + 12)d\eta d\xi$ by integration and by 2-point and 3-point Gauss quadrature. We first integrate this expression directly to find the analytical answer:

$$I = \iint_{-1}^{1}(4\xi^2\eta^2 - 15\xi\eta + 12)d\eta d\xi = \int_{-1}^{1}\left(\frac{8\xi^2}{3} + 24\right)d\xi = \frac{448}{9}$$

Answer

For 2-point Gauss quadrature in 2D, referring to Figure 11.4, we evaluate the sum at four Gauss points:

$$
\begin{aligned}
I \approx & \sum_{i=1,j=1}^{2} f(\xi_i, \eta_j) w_{\xi_i} w_{\eta_j} \\
&= (1\times 1)\left[4\left(\frac{1}{\sqrt{3}}\right)^2\left(\frac{1}{\sqrt{3}}\right)^2 - 15\left(\frac{1}{\sqrt{3}}\right)\left(\frac{1}{\sqrt{3}}\right) + 12\right] \\
&\quad + (1\times 1)\left[4\left(\frac{-1}{\sqrt{3}}\right)^2\left(\frac{1}{\sqrt{3}}\right)^2 - 15\left(\frac{-1}{\sqrt{3}}\right)\left(\frac{1}{\sqrt{3}}\right) + 12\right] \\
&\quad + (1\times 1)\left[4\left(\frac{-1}{\sqrt{3}}\right)^2\left(\frac{-1}{\sqrt{3}}\right)^2 - 15\left(\frac{-1}{\sqrt{3}}\right)\left(\frac{-1}{\sqrt{3}}\right) + 12\right] \\
&\quad + (1\times 1)\left[4\left(\frac{1}{\sqrt{3}}\right)^2\left(\frac{-1}{\sqrt{3}}\right)^2 - 15\left(\frac{1}{\sqrt{3}}\right)\left(\frac{-1}{\sqrt{3}}\right) + 12\right] \\
&= \frac{448}{9}
\end{aligned}
$$

For 3-point Gauss quadrature, referring to Figure 11.5, we evaluate the sum at nine Gauss points:

$$
\begin{aligned}
I \approx & \sum_{i=1,j=1}^{3} f(\xi_i, \eta_j) w_{\xi_i} w_{\eta_j} \\
&= \left(\frac{5}{9}\times\frac{5}{9}\right)\left[4\left(\sqrt{\frac{3}{5}}\right)^2\left(\sqrt{\frac{3}{5}}\right)^2 - 15\left(\sqrt{\frac{3}{5}}\right)\left(\sqrt{\frac{3}{5}}\right) + 12\right] \\
&\quad + \left(\frac{8}{9}\times\frac{5}{9}\right)[0 - 0 + 12] \\
&\quad + \left(\frac{5}{9}\times\frac{5}{9}\right)\left[4\left(-\sqrt{\frac{3}{5}}\right)^2\left(\sqrt{\frac{3}{5}}\right)^2 - 15\left(-\sqrt{\frac{3}{5}}\right)\left(\sqrt{\frac{3}{5}}\right) + 12\right] \\
&\quad + \left(\frac{5}{9}\times\frac{8}{9}\right)[0 - 0 + 12] + \left(\frac{8}{9}\times\frac{8}{9}\right)[0 - 0 + 12] + \left(\frac{5}{9}\times\frac{8}{9}\right)[0 - 0 + 12] \\
&\quad + \left(\frac{5}{9}\times\frac{5}{9}\right)\left[4\left(\sqrt{\frac{3}{5}}\right)^2\left(-\sqrt{\frac{3}{5}}\right)^2 - 15\left(\sqrt{\frac{3}{5}}\right)\left(-\sqrt{\frac{3}{5}}\right) + 12\right] \\
&\quad + \left(\frac{8}{9}\times\frac{5}{9}\right)[0 - 0 + 12] \\
&\quad + \left(\frac{5}{9}\times\frac{5}{9}\right)\left[4\left(-\sqrt{\frac{3}{5}}\right)^2\left(-\sqrt{\frac{3}{5}}\right)^2 - 15\left(-\sqrt{\frac{3}{5}}\right)\left(-\sqrt{\frac{3}{5}}\right) + 12\right] \\
I &= 4\times\frac{25}{81}\left[\frac{36}{25} + 12\right] + 4\times\frac{40}{81}\times 12 + \frac{64}{81}\times 12 \\
&= \frac{1}{81}[4\times 36 + 48\times 25 + 40\times 48 + 64\times 12] = \frac{448}{9}
\end{aligned}
$$

Obviously, the results of both the 2-point and 3-point Gauss quadrature cases are the same as the analytical answer.

Like in 1D space, 2D Gauss quadrature may be evaluated with more points. To use more Gauss points, we just go down the list in Table 11.1 to find the values for the locations and weights of these points and extend the calculation to 2D in the same manner as in Example 11.1.

Example 11.3

Reevaluate the elementary $[K_e]$ matrix for the rectangular element in Example 9.3 of Chapter 9 and in Example 10.7 of Chapter 10.

Answer
Recall that in evaluating the elementary $[K_e]$ matrix for a rectangular element for axisymmetric solid mechanics problems (see Example 9.3 in Chapter 9), we noticed that the result had several terms of infinity due to division by zero in integration over the domain that includes the edge $r = 0$. In Example 10.7 of Chapter 10, we reexamined the same problem by using the isoparametric transformation method, but the result we got still contained the infinity terms. For comparison, we list the result obtained in these two examples here:

$$[K_e] = \int_{-1}^{1}\int_{-1}^{1} [[A_a]\,[\Gamma_{ea}]\,[\partial N_a]]^T\,[C]\,[[A_a]\,[\Gamma_{ea}]\,[\partial N_a]]\,\frac{(1+\xi)}{10}\det[J]d\eta d\xi$$

$$= 10^9 \times \begin{bmatrix} \infty & -0.64 & 2.56 & 0.64 & -2.56 & -3.21 & \infty & 3.21 \\ -0.64 & 10.26 & -1.28 & 7.69 & -6.41 & -9.62 & -3.21 & -8.33 \\ 2.56 & -1.28 & 20.51 & -10.26 & -1.28 & 5.13 & -2.56 & 6.41 \\ 0.64 & 7.69 & -10.26 & 28.21 & -5.13 & -26.28 & 3.21 & -9.62 \\ -2.56 & -6.41 & -1.28 & -5.13 & 20.51 & 10.26 & 2.56 & 1.28 \\ -3.21 & -9.62 & 5.13 & -26.28 & 10.26 & 28.21 & -0.64 & 7.69 \\ \infty & -3.21 & -2.56 & 3.21 & 2.56 & -0.64 & \infty & 0.64 \\ 3.21 & -8.33 & 6.41 & -9.62 & 1.28 & 7.69 & 0.64 & 10.26 \end{bmatrix}$$

We now use Gauss quadrature to evaluate the integration instead. With the following expressions obtained previously,

$$[A_a] = \begin{bmatrix} 1 & 0 & 0 & 0 & 0 \\ 0 & 1 & 0 & 0 & 0 \\ 0 & 0 & 0 & 0 & 1 \\ 0 & 0 & 1 & 1 & 0 \end{bmatrix}, \quad [C] = 10^{11} \times \begin{bmatrix} 2.69 & 1.15 & 1.15 & 0 \\ 1.15 & 2.69 & 1.15 & 0 \\ 1.15 & 1.15 & 2.69 & 0 \\ 0 & 0 & 0 & 0.77 \end{bmatrix}, \quad \det[J] = \frac{1}{200}$$

and

$$[\partial N_a] = \frac{1}{4}\begin{bmatrix} \eta-1 & 0 & 1-\eta & 0 & 1+\eta & 0 & -1-\eta & 0 \\ (1-\xi)(1-\eta) & 0 & (1+\xi)(1-\eta) & 0 & (1+\xi)(1+\eta) & 0 & (1-\xi)(1+\eta) & 0 \\ \xi-1 & 0 & -1-\xi & 0 & \xi+1 & 0 & 1-\xi & 0 \\ 0 & \eta-1 & 0 & 1-\eta & 0 & 1+\eta & 0 & -1-\eta \\ 0 & \xi-1 & 0 & -1-\xi & 0 & 1+\xi & 0 & 1-\xi \end{bmatrix}$$

we first express

$$f(\xi,\eta) = \left[[A_a]\,[\Gamma_{ea}]\,[\partial N_a]\right]^T [C]\left[[A_a]\,[\Gamma_{ea}]\,[\partial N_a]\right](1+\xi)\det[J]$$

Then, we evaluate $f(\xi,\eta)$ using 4-point Gauss quadrature using a computer program code (e.g., MATLAB) and obtain the following:

$$[K_e] = \int_{-1}^{1}\int_{-1}^{1} f(\xi,\eta)d\eta d\xi = \sum_{i=1,j=1}^{4} f(\xi_i,\eta_j)w_i w_j$$

$$= 10^9 \times \begin{bmatrix} 27.135 & -0.641 & 2.564 & 0.641 & -2.564 & -3.205 & 9.722 & 3.205 \\ -0.641 & 10.256 & -1.282 & 7.692 & -6.410 & -9.615 & -3.205 & -8.333 \\ 2.564 & -1.282 & 20.512 & -10.256 & -1.282 & 5.128 & -2.564 & 6.410 \\ 0.641 & 7.692 & -10.256 & 28.205 & -5.128 & -26.282 & 3.205 & -9.615 \\ -2.564 & -6.410 & -1.282 & -5.128 & 20.513 & 10.256 & 2.564 & 1.282 \\ -3.205 & -9.615 & 5.128 & -26.282 & 10.256 & 28.205 & -0.641 & 7.692 \\ 9.722 & -3.205 & -2.564 & 3.205 & 2.564 & -0.641 & 27.135 & 0.641 \\ 3.205 & -8.333 & 6.410 & -9.615 & 1.282 & 7.692 & 0.641 & 10.256 \end{bmatrix}$$

Clearly, the method of Gauss quadrature not only resolves finite values for these four previously unsolvable infinite terms but also provides the same corresponding values for the rest of the terms in the $[K_e]$ matrix.

11.3 Gauss Quadrature for 2D Triangular Elements

Since triangular elements are not in the same geometric group as the quadrilateral elements, as we noted during the development of the Lagrange interpolation formula, a different treatment is necessary to find the Gauss points and weights.

To evaluate a 2D function over the isoparametric triangle domain, we express the following approximation:

$$\int_0^1\int_0^{1-\xi} f(\xi,\eta)d\eta d\xi \approx \sum_{i=1}^{n} f(\xi_i,\eta_i)w_i$$

When using one Gauss point, we have

$$\int_0^1\int_0^{1-\xi} f(\xi,\eta)d\eta d\xi \approx w_1 f(\xi_1,\eta_1)$$

Since we have three parameters that need to be determined, namely, w_1, ξ_1, and η_1, we select a three-term polynomial function:

$$f(\xi,\eta) = a_0 + a_1\xi + a_2\eta$$

Plugging this function in to the above equation, we obtain

$$\int_0^1\int_0^{1-\xi} (a_0 + a_1\xi + a_2\eta)d\eta d\xi \approx w_1(a_0 + a_1\xi_1 + a_2\eta_1)$$

in which

$$\int_0^1 \int_0^{1-\xi} (a_0 + a_1\xi + a_2\eta) d\eta d\xi = \int_0^1 \left[(a_0(1-\xi) + a_1\xi(1-\xi) + \frac{a_2}{2}(1-\xi)^2 \right] d\xi$$
$$= \frac{a_0}{2} + \frac{a_1}{6} + \frac{a_2}{6}$$

Putting them together, we have

$$\begin{bmatrix} \frac{1}{2} & \frac{1}{6} & \frac{1}{6} \end{bmatrix} \begin{Bmatrix} a_0 \\ a_1 \\ a_2 \end{Bmatrix} = w_1 \begin{bmatrix} 1 & \xi_1 & \eta_1 \end{bmatrix} \begin{Bmatrix} a_0 \\ a_1 \\ a_2 \end{Bmatrix}$$

For this to be true for any arbitrary values of a_i, $i = 0, \ldots, 2$, we set

$$\begin{bmatrix} \frac{1}{2} & \frac{1}{6} & \frac{1}{6} \end{bmatrix} = w_1 \begin{bmatrix} 1 & \xi_1 & \eta_1 \end{bmatrix}$$

This leads to

$$w_1 = \frac{1}{2}, \quad \xi_1 = \frac{1}{3}, \quad \eta_1 = \frac{1}{3}$$

This procedure can be repeated for cases with more Gauss points.

11.3.1 Locations and weights of Gauss points

Table 11.2 lists the weights and locations of the Gauss points for the cases of 1-, 3-, and 4-point Gauss quadrature for triangles. Note that in each case, the sum of the weight factors equals the area of the triangle, which is 1/2.

Example 11.4

Evaluate $I = \int_0^1 \int_0^{1-\xi} (\xi^2 + 3\xi\eta + 4\eta^2 + 5\xi + 7\eta + 9) d\eta d\xi$ by direct integration and by 3-point Gauss quadrature for triangles.

Answer

By direct integration, we have

$$I \approx \int_0^1 \int_0^{1-\xi} (\xi^2 + 3\xi\eta + 4\eta^2 + 5\xi + 7\eta + 9) d\eta d\xi$$
$$= \int_0^1 \left[\xi^2\eta + \frac{3\xi\eta^2}{2} + \frac{4\eta^3}{3} + 5\xi\eta + \frac{7\eta^2}{2} + 9\eta \right]_0^{1-\xi} d\xi$$
$$= \int_0^1 \frac{(1-\xi)(5\xi^2 + 2\xi + 83)}{6} d\xi = \frac{169}{24}$$

For 3-point Gauss quadrature, referring to Figure 11.6, we notice that there are two sets of integration points and weights for the 3-point triangle Gauss quadrature. The first set (marked with hollow circles)

TABLE 11.2
Weights and locations of Gauss points for triangles

$$\int_0^1 \int_0^{1-\xi} f(\xi,\eta)d\eta d\xi \approx \sum_{i=1}^{n} f(\xi_i,\eta_i)w_i$$

Number of points, n	Weights, w_i	ξ_i	η_i	$1-\xi_i-\eta_i$
1	1/2	1/3	1/3	1/3
3	1/6	2/3	1/6	1/6
	1/6	1/6	2/3	1/6
	1/6	1/6	1/6	2/3
3	1/6	1/2	1/2	0
	1/6	0	1/2	1/2
	1/6	1/2	0	1/2
4	−9/32	1/3	1/3	1/3
	25/96	3/5	1/5	1/5
	25/96	1/5	3/5	1/5
	25/96	1/5	1/5	3/5

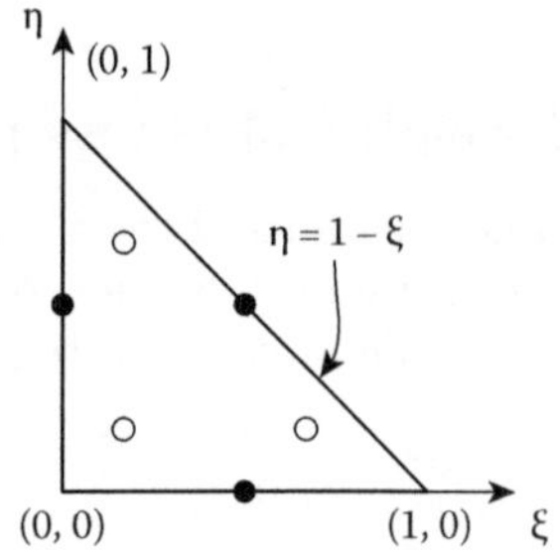

FIGURE 11.6
Gauss points in an isoparametric triangle.

has Gauss points at $\left(\frac{2}{3},\frac{1}{6}\right)$, $\left(\frac{1}{6},\frac{2}{3}\right)$, and $\left(\frac{1}{6},\frac{1}{6}\right)$, and the second set (marked by filled circles) has Gauss points at $\left(\frac{1}{2},\frac{1}{2}\right)$, $\left(0,\frac{1}{2}\right)$, and $\left(\frac{1}{2},0\right)$. In both sets, the weight factor is $\frac{1}{6}$ for all points. We will evaluate the integral for both cases.

A general expression for 3-point Gauss quadrature for triangles is expressed:

$$I = \int_0^1 \int_0^{1-\xi} (\xi^2 + 3\xi\eta + 4\eta^2 + 5\xi + 7\eta + 9)d\eta d\xi \approx \sum_{i=1}^{3} f(\xi_i,\eta_i)w_i$$

For the first case, we have

$$I \approx \sum_{i=1}^{3} f(\xi_i, \eta_i) w_i = \frac{1}{6}\left[\left(\frac{2}{3}\right)^2 + 3\left(\frac{2}{3}\right)\left(\frac{1}{6}\right) + 4\left(\frac{1}{6}\right)^2 + 5\left(\frac{2}{3}\right) + 7\left(\frac{1}{6}\right) + 9\right]$$
$$+ \frac{1}{6}\left[\left(\frac{1}{6}\right)^2 + 3\left(\frac{1}{6}\right)\left(\frac{2}{3}\right) + 4\left(\frac{2}{3}\right)^2 + 5\left(\frac{1}{6}\right) + 7\left(\frac{2}{3}\right) + 9\right]$$
$$+ \frac{1}{6}\left[\left(\frac{1}{6}\right)^2 + 3\left(\frac{1}{6}\right)\left(\frac{1}{6}\right) + 4\left(\frac{1}{6}\right)^2 + 5\left(\frac{1}{6}\right) + 7\left(\frac{1}{6}\right) + 9\right]$$
$$= \frac{169}{24}$$

For the second case, we have

$$I \approx \sum_{i=1}^{3} f(\xi_i, \eta_i) w_i = \frac{1}{6}\left[\left(\frac{1}{2}\right)^2 + 3\left(\frac{1}{2}\right)\left(\frac{1}{2}\right) + 4\left(\frac{1}{2}\right)^2 + 5\left(\frac{1}{2}\right) + 7\left(\frac{1}{2}\right) + 9\right]$$
$$+ \frac{1}{6}\left[4\left(\frac{1}{2}\right)^2 + 7\left(\frac{1}{2}\right) + 9\right] + \frac{1}{6}\left[\left(\frac{1}{2}\right)^2 + 5\left(\frac{1}{2}\right) + 9\right] = \frac{169}{24}$$

Obviously, the analytical solution and the quadrature results based on these two sets of Gauss points are exactly the same.

11.3.2 Integration in area coordinates

For the isoparametric triangular element in natural coordinates, ξ, η, its area coordinates are the same as the three shape functions of the 3-node triangular element (see Example 5.5 in Section 5.6.4); thus, we have

$$t_1 = 1 - \xi - \eta, \quad t_2 = \xi, \quad t_3 = \eta$$

With this information, it is now clear that the location coordinates of these Gauss points listed in Table 11.2 are actually expressed in area coordinates.

For a function expressed in terms of area coordinates t_1, t_2, or t_3, its integration can be calculated by using area coordinate integration formulas. For example, for an integrand expressed as $f(\xi, \eta) = t_1^a t_2^b$, in which a and b are positive-integer exponents (or power terms) of the area coordinates, its integration along a line with a length of l can be calculated as

$$\int_l t_1^a t_2^b ds = (l)\frac{a!\, b!}{(a+b+1)!} \tag{11.4}$$

where ! is the factorial symbol (e.g., $5! = 5 \times 4 \times 3 \times 2 \times 1 = 120$, and $0! = 1$). Moreover, for an integrand expressed as $f(\xi, \eta) = t_1^a t_2^b t_3^c$, in which $a, b,$ and c are exponents of the area coordinates, its integration over the domain of a triangle with an area of A can be calculated as

$$\iint_A t_1^a t_2^b t_3^c dA = (2A)\frac{a!\,b!\,c!}{(a+b+c+2)!} \tag{11.5}$$

Example 11.5

Use the area coordinate integration formula to calculate the elementary $[K_e]$ matrix for the triangular element in Example 10.5 in Section 10.2.2. Note that $k = 1000$.

Answer
For the triangular element, we know

$$[J] = \begin{bmatrix} 0.2 & 0 \\ 0.2 & 0.1 \end{bmatrix}, \quad \det[J] = \frac{1}{50}, \quad [\Gamma] = \begin{bmatrix} 5 & 0 \\ -10 & 10 \end{bmatrix}$$

and

$$\left[\frac{\partial N}{\partial \xi}\right] = \begin{bmatrix} -1 & 1 & 0 \end{bmatrix}, \quad \left[\frac{\partial N}{\partial \eta}\right] = \begin{bmatrix} -1 & 0 & 1 \end{bmatrix}, \quad r = \frac{\xi + \eta}{5}$$

Substituting them into Equation 10.21, we have

$$\begin{aligned} [K_e] &= \frac{1000 \times 25}{50 \times 5} \\ &\quad \times \iint_A \left[\begin{bmatrix} -1 \\ 1 \\ 0 \end{bmatrix} \begin{bmatrix} -1 & 1 & 0 \end{bmatrix} + 4 \left(\begin{bmatrix} -1 \\ 0 \\ 1 \end{bmatrix} - \begin{bmatrix} -1 \\ 1 \\ 0 \end{bmatrix} \right) \left(\begin{bmatrix} -1 & 0 & 1 \end{bmatrix} - \begin{bmatrix} -1 & 1 & 0 \end{bmatrix} \right) \right] \\ &\qquad \times (\xi + \eta) dA \\ &= 100 \begin{bmatrix} 1 & -1 & 0 \\ -1 & 5 & -4 \\ 0 & -4 & 4 \end{bmatrix} \iint_A (\xi + \eta) dA \end{aligned}$$

in which A is the area of the isoparametric triangle, $A = 1/2$. Using Equation 11.5, with $t_2 = \xi, t_3 = \eta$, we calculate

$$\begin{aligned} \iint_A (\xi + \eta) dA = \iint_A (t_2 + t_3) dA &= 2A \left[\frac{0!1!0!}{(0+1+0+2)!} + \frac{0!0!1!}{(0+0+1+2)!} \right] \\ &= \frac{2A}{3} = \frac{1}{3} \end{aligned}$$

Then, we have

$$[K_e] = \frac{100}{3} \begin{bmatrix} 1 & -1 & 0 \\ -1 & 5 & -4 \\ 0 & -4 & 4 \end{bmatrix} = \begin{bmatrix} 33.33 & -33.33 & 0 \\ -33.33 & 166.67 & -133.33 \\ 0 & -133.33 & 133.33 \end{bmatrix}$$

Obviously, this result is the same as that in Example 10.5 in Section 10.2.2.

11.4 Gauss Quadrature for 3D Hexahedral Elements

In a similar way, Gauss quadrature can be further extended to the 3D space of hexahedral shapes by adding a third dimension. The same sets of Gauss points and weights will be used. In mathematical expression, we write

$$\iiint_{-1}^{1} f(\xi,\eta,\zeta)d\zeta d\eta d\xi \approx \sum_{i=1,j=1,k=1}^{n} f(\xi_i,\eta_j,\zeta_k)w_{\xi_i}w_{\eta_j}w_{\zeta_k}$$

where $f(\xi,\eta,\zeta)$ is a 3D integrand function, and i,j,k are index numbers of Gauss points along the three axes in coordinates ξ, η, and ζ. In a 3D situation, the location of a Gauss point is marked by (ξ_i,η_j,ζ_k) and each point is associated with three weight factors (one for each coordinate), w_{ξ_i}, w_{η_j}, and w_{ζ_j}.

Example 11.6

Evaluate $I = \iiint_{-1}^{1}(7\xi^2\eta^2\zeta^2 - 25\xi\eta\zeta + 23)d\zeta d\eta d\xi$ by integration and by 2-point Gauss quadrature.

Answer

We first integrate this expression directly to find the analytical answer:

$$I = \iiint_{-1}^{1}(7\xi^2\eta^2\zeta^2 - 25\xi\eta\zeta + 23)d\zeta d\eta d\xi = \iint_{-1}^{1}\left(\frac{14\xi^2\eta^2}{3} + 46\right)d\eta d\xi$$
$$= \int_{-1}^{1}\left(\frac{28\xi^2}{9} + 92\right)d\xi = \frac{5024}{27}$$

To evaluate 2-point Gauss quadrature over the isoparametric cubic domain, referring to Table 11.1, we have two Gauss points, $\xi = \pm\frac{1}{\sqrt{3}}$, $\eta = \pm\frac{1}{\sqrt{3}}$, and $\zeta = \pm\frac{1}{\sqrt{3}}$, along each of the three axis directions, with weight factors of 1 for all, making a total of eight Gauss points. Then, we calculate the following sum at these eight Gauss points:

$$I \approx \sum_{i=1,j=1,k=1}^{2} f(\xi_i,\eta_j,\zeta_k)w_{\xi_i}w_{\eta_j}w_{\zeta_k}$$
$$= (1\times1\times1)\left[7\left(\frac{1}{\sqrt{3}}\right)^2\left(\frac{1}{\sqrt{3}}\right)^2\left(\frac{1}{\sqrt{3}}\right)^2 - 25\left(\frac{1}{\sqrt{3}}\right)\left(\frac{1}{\sqrt{3}}\right)\left(\frac{1}{\sqrt{3}}\right) + 23\right]$$
$$+ (1\times1\times1)\left[7\left(\frac{-1}{\sqrt{3}}\right)^2\left(\frac{1}{\sqrt{3}}\right)^2\left(\frac{1}{\sqrt{3}}\right)^2 - 25\left(\frac{-1}{\sqrt{3}}\right)\left(\frac{1}{\sqrt{3}}\right)\left(\frac{1}{\sqrt{3}}\right) + 23\right]$$
$$+ (1\times1\times1)\left[7\left(\frac{-1}{\sqrt{3}}\right)^2\left(\frac{-1}{\sqrt{3}}\right)^2\left(\frac{1}{\sqrt{3}}\right)^2 - 25\left(\frac{-1}{\sqrt{3}}\right)\left(\frac{-1}{\sqrt{3}}\right)\left(\frac{1}{\sqrt{3}}\right) + 23\right]$$

$$+(1\times1\times1)\left[7\left(\frac{1}{\sqrt{3}}\right)^2\left(\frac{-1}{\sqrt{3}}\right)^2\left(\frac{1}{\sqrt{3}}\right)^2-25\left(\frac{1}{\sqrt{3}}\right)\left(\frac{-1}{\sqrt{3}}\right)\left(\frac{1}{\sqrt{3}}\right)+23\right]$$
$$+(1\times1\times1)\left[7\left(\frac{1}{\sqrt{3}}\right)^2\left(\frac{1}{\sqrt{3}}\right)^2\left(\frac{-1}{\sqrt{3}}\right)^2-25\left(\frac{1}{\sqrt{3}}\right)\left(\frac{1}{\sqrt{3}}\right)\left(\frac{-1}{\sqrt{3}}\right)+23\right]$$
$$+(1\times1\times1)\left[7\left(\frac{-1}{\sqrt{3}}\right)^2\left(\frac{1}{\sqrt{3}}\right)^2\left(\frac{-1}{\sqrt{3}}\right)^2-25\left(\frac{-1}{\sqrt{3}}\right)\left(\frac{1}{\sqrt{3}}\right)\left(\frac{-1}{\sqrt{3}}\right)+23\right]$$
$$+(1\times1\times1)\left[7\left(\frac{-1}{\sqrt{3}}\right)^2\left(\frac{-1}{\sqrt{3}}\right)^2\left(\frac{-1}{\sqrt{3}}\right)^2-25\left(\frac{-1}{\sqrt{3}}\right)\left(\frac{-1}{\sqrt{3}}\right)\left(\frac{-1}{\sqrt{3}}\right)+23\right]$$
$$+(1\times1\times1)\left[7\left(\frac{1}{\sqrt{3}}\right)^2\left(\frac{-1}{\sqrt{3}}\right)^2\left(\frac{-1}{\sqrt{3}}\right)^2-25\left(\frac{1}{\sqrt{3}}\right)\left(\frac{-1}{\sqrt{3}}\right)\left(\frac{-1}{\sqrt{3}}\right)+23\right]$$
$$=8\left(\frac{7}{27}+23\right)=\frac{5024}{27}$$

Obviously, the result is the same as the analytical answer.

11.5 Gauss Quadrature for 3D Tetrahedral Elements

For 3D tetrahedral shapes, Gauss quadrature can be expressed as

$$\int_0^1\int_0^{1-\xi}\int_0^{1-\xi-\eta} f(\xi,\eta,\zeta)d\zeta d\eta d\xi \approx \sum_{i=1}^{n} f(\xi_i,\eta_i,\zeta_i)w_i$$

where $f(\xi,\eta,\zeta)$ is a 3D integrand function. In this case, the location of a Gauss point is marked by (ξ_i,η_i,ζ_i) and each point is associated with one weight factor w_i. Table 11.3 lists the weights and locations of the Gauss points for the cases of 1-, 4-, and 5-point Gauss quadrature for tetrahedral elements. Note that in each case, the sum of the weight factors equals the volume of the tetrahedron, which is 1/6.

Example 11.7

Evaluate $I=\int_0^1\int_0^{1-\xi}\int_0^{1-\xi-\eta}(\xi^3+4\eta^3+9\zeta^3+5\xi\eta\zeta+45)d\zeta d\eta d\xi$ by integration and by 5-point Gauss quadrature for tetrahedrons.

Answer

We first evaluate this expression by integrating with respect to each independent variable in a reversing order, ζ,η,ξ, to find the analytical answer:

$$I=\int_0^1\int_0^{1-\xi}(1-\xi-\eta)\left(\xi^3+\frac{9(1-\xi-\eta)^3}{4}+4\eta^3+\frac{5\xi\eta(1-\xi-\eta)}{2}+45\right)d\eta d\xi$$
$$+\int_0^1\frac{(1-\xi)^2(7\xi^3+184\xi^2-209\xi+2778)}{120}d\xi=\frac{5489}{720}$$

TABLE 11.3
Weights and locations of Gauss points for tetrahedrons

$$\int_0^1 \int_0^{1-\xi} \int_0^{1-\xi-\eta} f(\xi,\eta,\zeta)d\zeta d\eta d\xi \approx \sum_{i=1}^{n} f(\xi_i,\eta_i,\zeta_i)w_i$$

Number of points, n	Weights, w_i	ξ_i	η_i	ζ_i	$1-\xi_i-\eta_i-\zeta_i$
1	1/6	1/4	1/4	1/4	1/4
4	1/24	0.5854	0.1382	0.1382	0.1382
	1/24	0.1382	0.5854	0.1382	0.1382
	1/24	0.1382	0.1382	0.5854	0.1382
	1/24	0.1382	0.1382	0.1382	0.5854
5	−2/15	1/4	1/4	1/4	1/4
	3/40	1/2	1/6	1/6	1/6
	3/40	1/6	1/2	1/6	1/6
	3/40	1/6	1/6	1/2	1/6
	3/40	1/6	1/6	1/6	1/2

Note: $\dfrac{5+3\sqrt{5}}{20} = 0.5854$ and $\dfrac{5-\sqrt{5}}{20} = 0.1382$

For 5-point Gauss quadrature over a tetrahedron domain, referring to Table 11.3, we evaluate the sum at five Gauss points:

$$\begin{aligned}
I &\approx \sum_{i=1}^{5} f(\xi_i,\eta_i,\zeta_i)w_i \\
&= \frac{-2}{15}\left[\left(\frac{1}{4}\right)^3 + 4\left(\frac{1}{4}\right)^3 + 9\left(\frac{1}{4}\right)^3 + 5\left(\frac{1}{4}\right)\left(\frac{1}{4}\right)\left(\frac{1}{4}\right) + 45\right] \\
&+ \frac{3}{40}\left[\left(\frac{1}{2}\right)^3 + 4\left(\frac{1}{6}\right)^3 + 9\left(\frac{1}{6}\right)^3 + 5\left(\frac{1}{2}\right)\left(\frac{1}{6}\right)\left(\frac{1}{6}\right) + 45\right] \\
&+ \frac{3}{40}\left[\left(\frac{1}{6}\right)^3 + 4\left(\frac{1}{2}\right)^3 + 9\left(\frac{1}{6}\right)^3 + 5\left(\frac{1}{6}\right)\left(\frac{1}{2}\right)\left(\frac{1}{6}\right) + 45\right] \\
&+ \frac{3}{40}\left[\left(\frac{1}{6}\right)^3 + 4\left(\frac{1}{6}\right)^3 + 9\left(\frac{1}{2}\right)^3 + 5\left(\frac{1}{6}\right)\left(\frac{1}{6}\right)\left(\frac{1}{2}\right) + 45\right] \\
&+ \frac{3}{40}\left[\left(\frac{1}{6}\right)^3 + 4\left(\frac{1}{6}\right)^3 + 9\left(\frac{1}{6}\right)^3 + 5\left(\frac{1}{6}\right)\left(\frac{1}{6}\right)\left(\frac{1}{6}\right) + 45\right] = \frac{5489}{720}
\end{aligned}$$

Obviously, the result is the same as the analytical answer.

11.5.1 Integration in volume coordinates

For the isoparametric tetrahedral element in natural coordinates, ξ, η, ζ, its volume coordinates are the same as the four shape functions of the 4-node tetrahedral element (see Example 5.7 in Section 5.6.6); thus, we have the following four volume coordinates:

$$t_1 = 1 - \xi - \eta - \zeta, \quad t_2 = \xi, \quad t_3 = \eta, \quad t_4 = \zeta$$

Referring to Table 11.3, it is obvious that the location coordinates of these Gauss points are expressed in volume coordinates.

For a function expressed in terms of volume coordinates t_1, t_2, t_3, and t_4, for example, $f(\xi, \eta, \zeta) = t_1^a t_2^b t_3^c t_4^d$, in which a, b, c, and d are exponents of the volume coordinates, its integration over the domain of a tetrahedral element with a volume of V can be calculated by using the following volume coordinate integration formula:

$$\iiint_V t_1^a t_2^b t_3^c t_4^d dV = (6V)\frac{a!\,b!\,c!\,d!}{(a+b+c+d+3)!} \tag{11.6}$$

For integrations over a side surface or along an edge, the formulas given in Equations 11.4 and 11.5 can be used (with the volume coordinates replacing the area coordinates, of course).

Example 11.8

Use the volume coordinate integration formula to calculate the elementary $[K_e]$ matrix for the tetrahedral element in Example 10.8 in Section 10.3.2. Note that $k = 1000$.

Answer

For the tetrahedral element, we know

$$[J] = \begin{bmatrix} 1 & 0 & 0 \\ 0 & 2 & 0 \\ 0 & 0 & 1 \end{bmatrix}, \quad \det[J] = 2, \quad [\Gamma] = \begin{bmatrix} 1 & 0 & 0 \\ 0 & 0.5 & 0 \\ 0 & 0 & 1 \end{bmatrix}$$

and

$$\left[\frac{\partial N}{\partial \xi}\right] = \begin{bmatrix} -1 & 1 & 0 & 0 \end{bmatrix}, \quad \left[\frac{\partial N}{\partial \eta}\right] = \begin{bmatrix} -1 & 0 & 1 & 0 \end{bmatrix}, \quad \left[\frac{\partial N}{\partial \zeta}\right] = \begin{bmatrix} -1 & 0 & 0 & 1 \end{bmatrix}$$

Substituting them into Equation 10.36, we have

$$\begin{aligned}[K_e] &= 2000 \\ &\times \iiint_V \left(\begin{bmatrix} -1 \\ 1 \\ 0 \\ 0 \end{bmatrix} \begin{bmatrix} -1 & 1 & 0 & 0 \end{bmatrix} + 0.25 \begin{bmatrix} -1 \\ 0 \\ 1 \\ 0 \end{bmatrix} \begin{bmatrix} -1 & 0 & 1 & 0 \end{bmatrix} \right. \\ &\quad \left. + \begin{bmatrix} -1 \\ 0 \\ 0 \\ 1 \end{bmatrix} \begin{bmatrix} -1 & 0 & 0 & 1 \end{bmatrix} \right) dV\end{aligned}$$

$$= 2000 \begin{bmatrix} 2.25 & -1 & -0.25 & -1 \\ -1 & 1 & 0 & 0 \\ -0.25 & 0 & 0.25 & 0 \\ -1 & 0 & 0 & 1 \end{bmatrix} \iiint_V dV$$

$$= \begin{bmatrix} 750.00 & -333.33 & -83.33 & -333.33 \\ -333.33 & 333.33 & 0 & 0 \\ -83.33 & 0 & 83.33 & 0 \\ -333.33 & 0 & 0 & 333.33 \end{bmatrix}$$

in which $\iiint_V dV$ is evaluated using Equation 11.6, with V being the volume of the isoparametric tetrahedron ($V = 1/6$):

$$\iiint_V dV = 6V \frac{0!0!0!0!}{(0+0+0+0+3)!} = V = \frac{1}{6}$$

Obviously, this result is the same as in Example 10.8 in Section 10.3.2.

Note that in this case, it is not necessary to use the volume coordinate integration formula (Equation 11.6) because when the integrand is 1, we know $\iiint_V dV = V$. Nevertheless, using it allows us to deal with situations when the integrand is a function of the volume coordinates t_1, t_2, t_3, and t_4, which are subsequently functions of the independent variables ξ, η, and ζ.

11.6 Exercises

1. Evaluate the following integral by direct integration and by 1-point, 2-point, 3-point, and 4-point Gauss quadrature.

$$I = \int_{-1}^{1} (5r^2 + 27r - 67)dr$$

2. Evaluate the following integral by direct integration and by 1-point, 2-point, 3-point, and 4-point Gauss quadrature.

$$I = \int_{-1}^{1} (r^3 + 9r^2 - 21r + 99)dr$$

3. Evaluate the following integral by direct integration and by 1-point, 2-point, 3-point, and 4-point Gauss quadrature.

$$I = \int_{-1}^{1} (3r^4 + 29r^3 - 2r^2 + 9r - 19)dr$$

4. Evaluate the following integral by direct integration and by 1-point, 2-point, 3-point, and 4-point Gauss quadrature.

$$I = \int_{-1}^{1}\int_{-1}^{1} (7r^2 + 5rs + 6s^2)drds$$

5. Evaluate the following integral by direct integration and by 1-point, 2-point, 3-point, and 4-point Gauss quadrature.

$$I = \int_{-1}^{1}\int_{-1}^{1} (r^3 + 25r^2s - 23rs^2 + 63s^3)drds$$

6. Evaluate the following integral by direct integration and by 2-point and 3-point Gauss quadrature.

$$I = \int_{-1}^{1}\int_{-1}^{1}\int_{-1}^{1} \left[(x-2)^2(y^2-1)z^2 + xyz\right] dxdydz$$

7. Evaluate the following integral by direct integration and by 3-point Gauss quadrature for triangles.

$$I = \int_{0}^{1}\int_{0}^{1-r} (7r^2 + 127rs + 44s^2 + 15r + 37s - 29)drds$$

8. Evaluate the following integral by direct integration and by 3-point Gauss quadrature for triangles.

$$I = \int_{0}^{1}\int_{0}^{1-r} (r^3 + 12r^2s + 35rs^2 + s^3 + 6r^2 + 56s^2 - 5rs + 7r + 3s + 78)drds$$

9. Evaluate the following integral by direct integration and by 4-point Gauss quadrature for tetrahedrons.

$$I = \int_{0}^{1}\int_{0}^{1-r}\int_{0}^{1-r-s} (3r^2 + 4s^2 + 7t^2 + 15rs + 4st + 23rt + 17rst + 50)drdsdt$$

10. Evaluate the following integral by direct integration and by 4-point Gauss quadrature for tetrahedrons.

$$I = \int_{0}^{1}\int_{0}^{1-r}\int_{0}^{1-r-s} (3r^3 + 34s^3 + 19t^3 + 25r^2s + 4rs^2 + 7rst + 5)drdsdt$$

11. Use 4-point Gauss quadrature to evaluate the $[K_e]$ matrix for the two 3-node bar elements shown in Figure 11.7 having $l = 1$ m, $A = 1$ m^2, and $E = 1$ N/m^2.

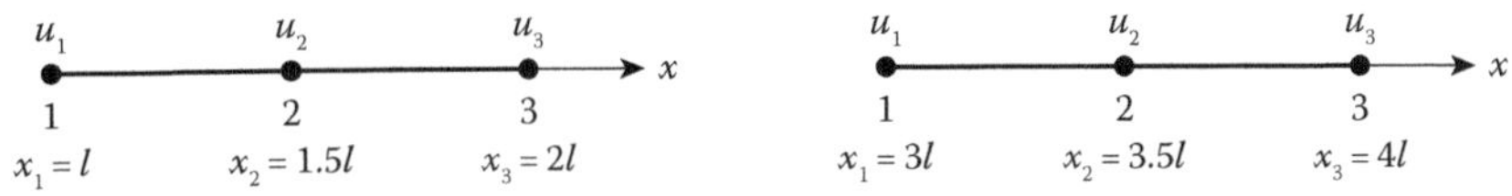

FIGURE 11.7
Two 1D 3-node elements located at different positions.

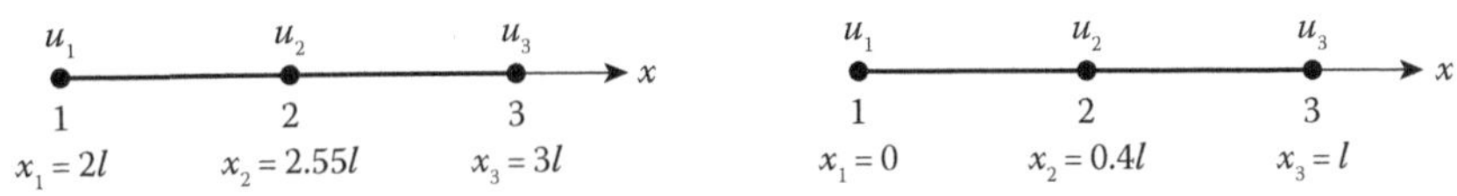

FIGURE 11.8
Two 1D 3-node elements located at different positions.

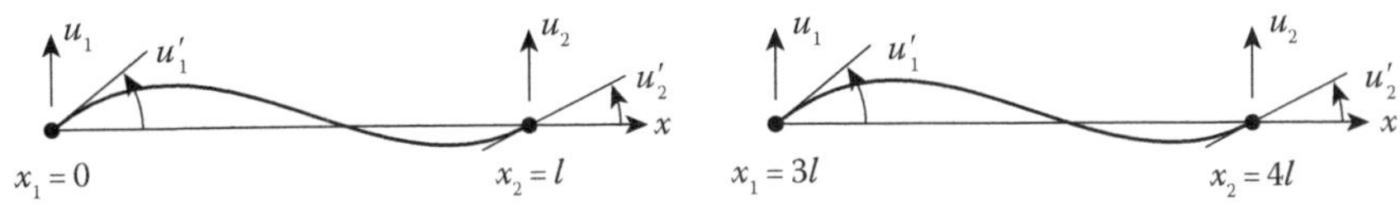

FIGURE 11.9
Two 2-node beam elements at different locations.

12. Use 4-point Gauss quadrature to evaluate the $[K_e]$ matrix for the two 3-node bar elements shown in Figure 11.8 having $l = 1$ m, $A = 1$ m^2, and $E = 1$ N/m^2.

13. Use 4-point Gauss quadrature to evaluate the $[K_e]$ matrix for the two 2-node beam elements shown in Figure 11.9 having $l = 1$ m, $I = 1$ m^4, and $E = 1$ N/m^2.

14. For the 2D quadrilateral element shown in Figure 11.10 to be used for 2D scalar problems, use 4-point Gauss quadrature to evaluate its $[K_e]$ matrix. Assume that the element has a constant property of $kt = 4$ (ignore the units).

15. For the 2D square and rectangular elements shown in Figure 11.11 to be used for 2D scalar problems, use 4-point Gauss quadrature to evaluate their $[K_e]$ matrices. Assume that the elements have a constant property of $kt = 4$ (ignore the units).

16. For the two 2D triangular elements shown in Figure 11.12 to be used for 2D scalar problems, use 4-point Gauss quadrature to evaluate their $[K_e]$ matrices. Assume that the elements have a constant property of $kt = 4$ (ignore the units).

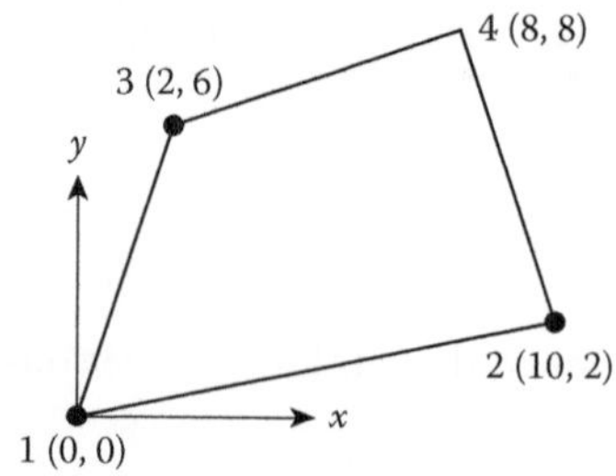

FIGURE 11.10
A 2D 4-node quadrilateral element.

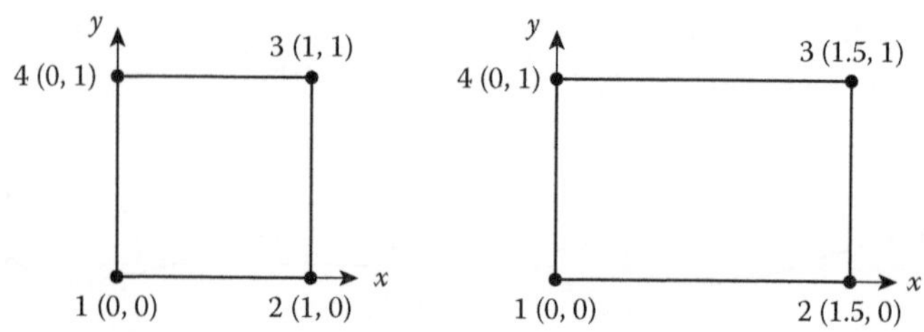

FIGURE 11.11
Two 2D rectangular elements with a uniform thickness.

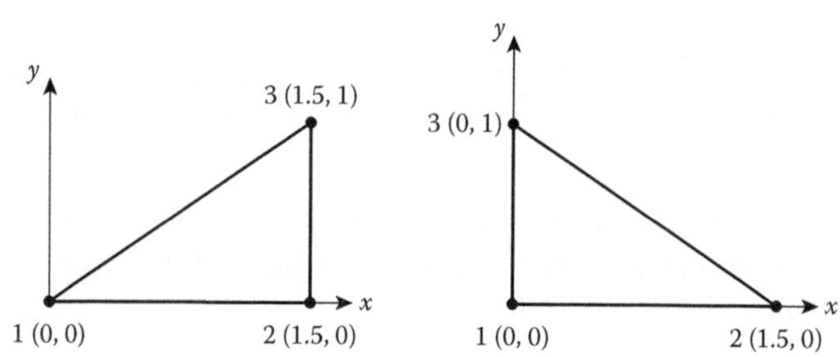

FIGURE 11.12
Two 2D triangular elements with a uniform thickness.

17. For the two 2D rectangular elements shown in Figure 11.13 to be used for scalar axisymmetric problems, use 4-point Gauss quadrature to evaluate their $[K_e]$ matrices. Assume that the elements have a constant property of $k = 500$ (ignore the units).
18. For the two 2D triangular elements shown in Figure 11.14 to be used for scalar axisymmetric problems, use 4-point Gauss quadrature to evaluate their $[K_e]$ matrices. Assume that the elements have a constant property of $k = 500$ (ignore the units).

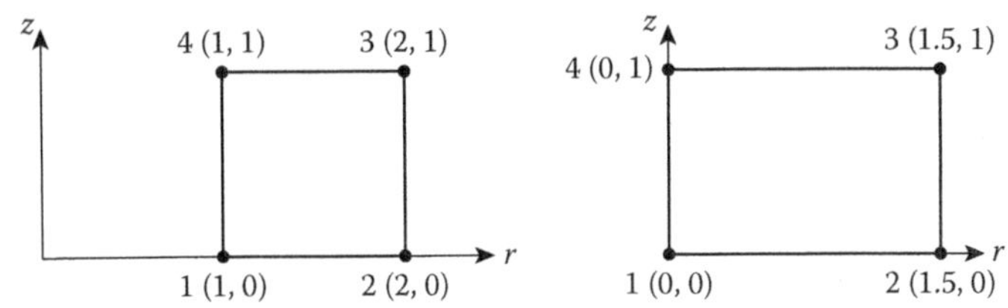

FIGURE 11.13
Two 2D rectangular elements with a uniform thickness.

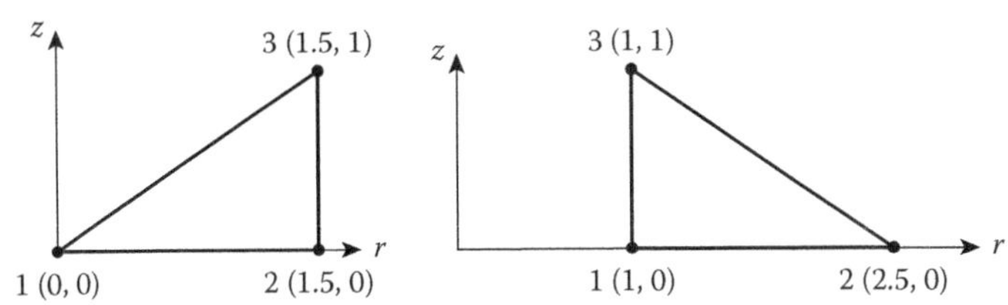

FIGURE 11.14
Two 2D triangular elements with a uniform thickness.

19. For the 2D square and rectangular elements shown in Figure 11.11 to be used for 2D solid mechanics problems, use 4-point Gauss quadrature to evaluate their $[K_e]$ matrices. Assume that the elements are made of an isotropic material with $E = 200$ GPa and $\nu = 0.3$. Consider both the plane stress and plane strain situations.
20. For the two 2D triangular elements shown in Figure 11.12 to be used for 2D solid mechanics problems, use 4-point Gauss quadrature to evaluate their $[K_e]$ matrices. Assume that the elements are made of an isotropic material with $E = 200$ GPa and $\nu = 0.3$. Consider both the plane stress and plane strain situations.
21. For the two 2D rectangular elements shown in Figure 11.13 to be used for axisymmetric solid mechanics problems, use 4-point Gauss quadrature to evaluate their $[K_e]$ matrices. Assume that the elements are made of an isotropic material with $E = 200$ GPa and $\nu = 0.3$.
22. For the two 2D triangular elements shown in Figure 11.14 to be used for axisymmetric solid mechanics problems, use 4-point Gauss quadrature to evaluate their $[K_e]$ matrices. Assume that the elements are made of an isotropic material with $E = 200$ GPa and $\nu = 0.3$.
23. Use the area coordinate integration formula to solve Exercise 16.
24. Use the area coordinate integration formula to solve Exercise 18.

25. For the 3D tetrahedral element shown in Figure 11.15 to be used for 3D scalar problems, use the volume coordinate integration formula to determine its elementary $[K_e]$ matrix. Assume that the element has a constant $k = 1000$ (ignore the units).

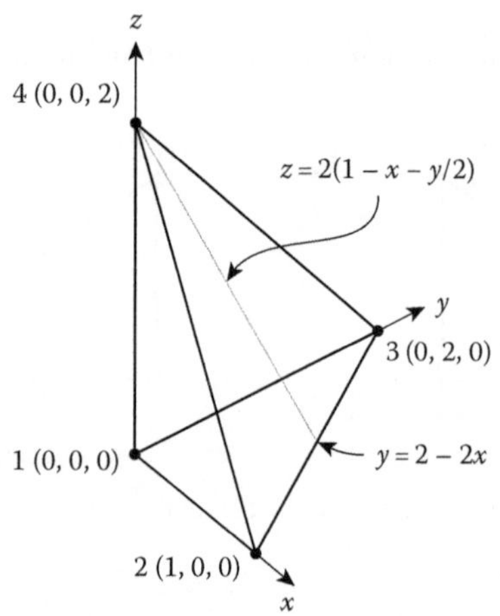

FIGURE 11.15
A 3D tetrahedral element.

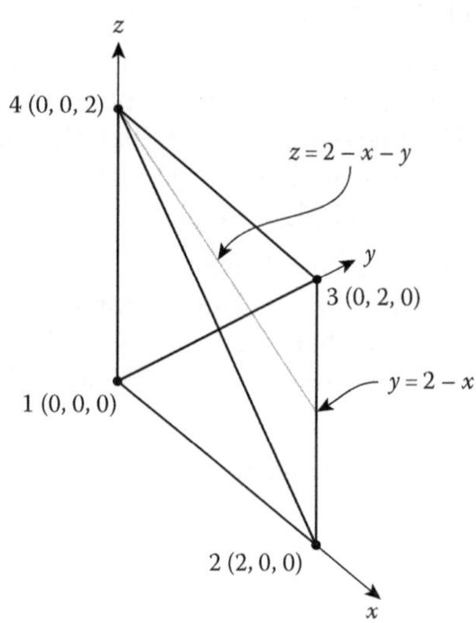

FIGURE 11.16
A 3D tetrahedral element.

26. For the 3D tetrahedral element shown in Figure 11.15 to be used for 3D solid mechanics problems, use the volume coordinate integration formula to determine its elementary $[K_e]$ matrix. Assume that the element is made of an isotropic material with $E = 200$ GPa and $\nu = 0.3$.
27. For the 3D tetrahedral element shown in Figure 11.16 to be used for 3D scalar problems, use the volume coordinate integration formula to determine its elementary $[K_e]$ matrix. Assume that the element has a constant $k = 1500$ (ignore the units).
28. For the 3D tetrahedral element shown in Figure 11.16 to be used for 3D solid mechanics problems, use the volume coordinate integration formula to determine its elementary $[K_e]$ matrix. Assume that the element is made of an isotropic material with $E = 210$ GPa and $\nu = 0.33$.

Recommended Readings

1. J. N. Reddy. 1993. *An Introduction to the Finite Element Method.* 2nd ed. Boston: McGraw-Hill.
2. David V. Hutton. 2004. *Fundamentals of Finite Element Analysis.* Boston: McGraw-Hill.
3. Tirupathi R. Chandrupatla and Ashok D. Belegundu. 2002. *Introduction to Finite Elements in Engineering.* 3rd ed. Upper Saddle River, NJ: Prentice Hall.
4. Jacob Fish and Ted Belytschko. 2007. *A First Course in Finite Elements.* Hoboken, NJ: John Wiley & Sons.

[illegible] For the 3D [illegible] element shown in Figure [illegible] [illegible] [illegible] [illegible]

[illegible] For the [illegible] element shown in Figure [illegible] [illegible] integration formula [illegible]

[illegible] For the [illegible] [illegible] integration formula [illegible]

Recommended Readings

[illegible] N. Reddy. 1993. *An Introduction to the Finite Element Method*. 2nd ed. Boston: McGraw-Hill.

[illegible] 2011. [illegible] Boston: McGraw-Hill.

[illegible]

[illegible]

12

Dealing with Generalized PDEs

The partial differential equations (PDEs) we solved in Chapters 6 and 7 are simplified ones, containing only a second derivative (the Laplacian) term (or a fourth derivative term for a beam structure) and a constant term (see Equation 6.1). The finite element method (FEM) formulation for solving these simple PDEs results in the following matrix form algebraic equations at the elementary and global levels, respectively:

$$[K_e]\{d_0\} = \{P_e\} \quad \text{and} \quad [K]\{D\} = \{P\}$$

The FEM formulation for the solid mechanics problems discussed in Chapter 8 also results in the same matrix equations, respectively, although the governing PDEs are different from those presented in Chapters 6 and 7. In a real world, however, we may encounter very complicated PDEs containing many more terms than the ones we have seen thus far. For example, of these other terms, one that we have encountered several times but have repeatedly ignored is the time-dependent term ($\partial^2 u/\partial t^2$). In this chapter, we discuss how these other terms are handled.

12.1 A General Form PDE and Its Matrix Equation

In a general form, a PDE may be expressed:

$$\rho\frac{\partial^2 u}{\partial t^2} + \chi\frac{\partial u}{\partial t} + \nabla\cdot(k\nabla u) + \alpha\nabla u + \beta u + f = 0 \tag{12.1}$$

where the first term represents acceleration, the second damping, the third the Laplacian term, the fourth convection, the fifth absorption, and the last the volume source.

Referring to the discussion in Section 5.8, we approximate the field quantity in a matrix form expression as

$$u = \{d\} = [N]\{d_0\}$$

Since the shape function matrix is only a function of spacial coordinates, independent of time, we calculate the first and second derivatives of the field quantity with respect to time as

$$\ddot{u} = [N]\{\ddot{d}_0\}, \quad \dot{u} = [N]\{\dot{d}_0\}$$

where $\{\ddot{d}_0\}$ and $\{\dot{d}_0\}$ are the second and first derivatives of the degrees of freedom (DOF) vector, $\{d_0\}$, with respect to time. By going through the same FEM formulation procedure, we arrive at the following general matrix equation:

$$[M_e]\{\ddot{d}_0\} + [G_e^d]\{\dot{d}_0\} + [K_e]\{d_0\} + [G_e^c]\{d_0\} + [G_e^a]\{d_0\} = \{P_e\} \tag{12.2}$$

where other than the two familiar matrices ($[K_e]$ and $[P_e]$), $[M_e]$, $[G_e^d]$, $[G_e^c]$, and $[G_e^a]$ are the elementary mass, damping, convection, and absorption matrices, respectively.

So, to a general form PDE we still solve a linearized matrix form algebraic equation. The difference is that the matrix equation now has more terms: it may include time-dependent DOF vectors like the $\{\ddot{d}_0\}$ and $\{\dot{d}_0\}$, as well as convection and adsorption terms, among others. In the following sections, we evaluate these matrix terms and learn some basics about how to deal with time-dependent DOF vectors.

12.1.1 Elementary mass matrix: consistent and lumped

First, let us examine the elementary mass matrix, $[M_e]$, by isolating the acceleration term $\left(\rho\frac{\partial^2 u}{\partial t^2}\right)$ in Equation 12.1 and calculating the residual of its weighted integral as follows:

$$\iiint_V w_m \rho \frac{\partial^2 u}{\partial t^2} dV$$

By using the matrix form field quantity interpolation and applying the Galerkin method (i.e., replacing the weight functions with shape functions), we have

$$\{u\} = [N]\{d_0\}, \quad w_m = N_m, m = 1, \ldots, n_e$$

Substituting these expressions into the above equation and summing all n_e terms, we obtain

$$\iiint_V \sum_{m=1}^{n_e} w_m \rho \frac{\partial^2 u}{\partial t^2} dV = \iiint_V [N]^T \rho [N] dV \{\ddot{d}_0\}$$

The coefficient of the second derivative of the DOF vector, $\{\ddot{d}_0\}$, is called the elementary mass matrix, that is,

$$[M_e] = \iiint_V [N]^T \rho [N] dV \tag{12.3}$$

Example 12.1

Determine the elementary mass matrix, $[M_e]$, for a 2-node and a 3-node bar element located between $x_1 = l$ and $x_2 = 2l$ having a length of l, a uniform cross section area of A, and a constant density of ρ.

Answer
For the 2-node bar element, using Equation 12.3 along with the shape functions expressed in an isoparametric form (see Section 10.1.1), we write

$$[M_e] = \rho A \int_{x_1}^{x_2} [N]^T [N] dx = \rho A \int_{-1}^{1} [N]^T [N] J d\xi$$

where $J = l/2$, $N_1 = \frac{1}{2}(1-\xi)$, and $N_2 = \frac{1}{2}(1+\xi)$. With substitution, we obtain the following mass matrix for the 2-node bar element:

$$[M_e] = \frac{\rho A l}{2} \int_{-1}^{1} \frac{1}{2} \begin{bmatrix} (1-\xi) \\ (1+\xi) \end{bmatrix} \frac{1}{2} \begin{bmatrix} (1-\xi) & (1+\xi) \end{bmatrix} d\xi$$
$$= \frac{\rho A l}{8} \int_{-1}^{1} \begin{bmatrix} (1-\xi)^2 & 1-\xi^2 \\ 1-\xi^2 & (1+\xi)^2 \end{bmatrix} d\xi = \frac{\rho A l}{8} \begin{bmatrix} 8/3 & 4/3 \\ 4/3 & 8/3 \end{bmatrix} = \frac{\rho A l}{6} \begin{bmatrix} 2 & 1 \\ 1 & 2 \end{bmatrix}$$

Similarly, for the 3-node bar element, with $J = l/2$, $N_1 = \frac{1}{2}(-\xi + \xi^2)$, $N_2 = 1 - \xi^2$, and $N_3 = \frac{1}{2}(\xi + \xi^2)$ we calculate

$$[M_e] = \frac{\rho A l}{2} \int_{-1}^{1} \begin{bmatrix} \frac{1}{2}(-\xi+\xi^2) \\ 1-\xi^2 \\ \frac{1}{2}(\xi+\xi^2) \end{bmatrix} \begin{bmatrix} \frac{1}{2}(-\xi+\xi^2) & 1-\xi^2 & \frac{1}{2}(\xi+\xi^2) \end{bmatrix} d\xi$$
$$= \frac{\rho A l}{30} \begin{bmatrix} 4 & 2 & -1 \\ 2 & 16 & 2 \\ -1 & 2 & 4 \end{bmatrix}$$

This is the mass matrix for the 3-node bar element.

Example 12.2

Determine the elementary mass matrix, $[M_e]$, for the 3-node isoparametric triangular element and the 4-node isoparametric square element by assuming that the elements have a thickness of t_e, area of A_e, and a constant material density of ρ.

Answer
For 2D elements, we will first use the shape functions defined in Section 10.2.1 to build the corresponding $[N]$ matrix according to Equation 5.34 (note that when considering mass, we often deal with motion—hence a vector problem).

So for the 3-node isoparametric triangular element, with $N_1 = 1-\xi-\eta$, $N_2 = \xi$, and $N_3 = \eta$, we write

$$[N] = \begin{bmatrix} 1-\xi-\eta & 0 & \xi & 0 & \eta & 0 \\ 0 & 1-\xi-\eta & 0 & \xi & 0 & \eta \end{bmatrix}$$

Substituting this $[N]$ matrix into Equation 12.3, along with $A_e = 1/2$, we obtain

$$[M_e] = \rho t_e \int_0^1 \int_0^{1-\xi} [N]^T [N] d\xi d\eta = \frac{\rho t_e A_e}{12} \begin{bmatrix} 2 & 0 & 1 & 0 & 1 & 0 \\ 0 & 2 & 0 & 1 & 0 & 1 \\ 1 & 0 & 2 & 0 & 1 & 0 \\ 0 & 1 & 0 & 2 & 0 & 1 \\ 1 & 0 & 1 & 0 & 2 & 0 \\ 0 & 1 & 0 & 1 & 0 & 2 \end{bmatrix}$$

Similarly for the 4-node isoparametric square element, with $N_1 = \frac{(1-\xi)(1-\eta)}{4}$, $N_2 = \frac{(1+\xi)(1-\eta)}{4}$, $N_3 = \frac{(1+\xi)(1+\eta)}{4}$, and $N_4 = \frac{(1-\xi)(1+\eta)}{4}$ we first build the following $[N]$ matrix:

$$[N] = \begin{bmatrix} N_1 & 0 & N_2 & 0 & N_3 & 0 & N_4 & 0 \\ 0 & N_1 & 0 & N_2 & 0 & N_3 & 0 & N_4 \end{bmatrix}$$

Then, by substituting this $[N]$ matrix into Equation 12.3, along with $A_e = 4$, we obtain

$$[M_e] = \rho t_e \int_{-1}^1 \int_{-1}^1 [N]^T [N] d\xi d\eta = \frac{\rho t_e A_e}{36} \begin{bmatrix} 4 & 0 & 2 & 0 & 1 & 0 & 2 & 0 \\ 0 & 4 & 0 & 2 & 0 & 1 & 0 & 2 \\ 2 & 0 & 4 & 0 & 2 & 0 & 1 & 0 \\ 0 & 2 & 0 & 4 & 0 & 2 & 0 & 1 \\ 1 & 0 & 2 & 0 & 4 & 0 & 2 & 0 \\ 0 & 1 & 0 & 2 & 0 & 4 & 0 & 2 \\ 2 & 0 & 1 & 0 & 2 & 0 & 4 & 0 \\ 0 & 2 & 0 & 1 & 0 & 2 & 0 & 4 \end{bmatrix}$$

Example 12.3

Determine the elementary mass matrix, $[M_e]$, for a 2-node beam element located between $x_1 = 0$ and $x_2 = l$ having a length of l, a uniform cross section area of A, and a constant density of ρ.

Answer

By referring to the discussion in Section 10.1.3, we copy the shape function matrix in an isoparametric form as given in Equation 10.9 here:

$$[N] = \left[\frac{(1-\xi)^2(\xi+2)}{4} \quad \frac{(1-\xi)^2(1+\xi)l}{8} \quad \frac{(1+\xi)^2(2-\xi)}{4} \quad \frac{(\xi-1)(1+\xi)^2 l}{8} \right]$$

By substituting the above shape function matrix into Equation 12.3, along with $J = l/2$, we arrive at

$$[M_e] = \rho A \int_{x_1}^{x_2} [N]^T [N] dx = \rho A \int_{-1}^{1} [N]^T [N] J d\xi$$

$$= \frac{\rho A l}{2} \int_{-1}^{1} \begin{bmatrix} \frac{(1-\xi)^2(\xi+2)}{4} \\ \frac{(1-\xi)^2(1+\xi)l}{8} \\ \frac{(1+\xi)^2(2-\xi)}{4} \\ \frac{(\xi-1)(1+\xi)^2 l}{8} \end{bmatrix} \begin{bmatrix} \frac{(1-\xi)^2(\xi+2)}{4} & \frac{(1-\xi)^2(1+\xi)l}{8} & \frac{(1+\xi)^2(2-\xi)}{4} & \frac{(\xi-1)(1+\xi)^2 l}{8} \end{bmatrix} d\xi$$

$$= \frac{\rho A l}{420} \begin{bmatrix} 156 & 22l & 54 & -13l \\ 22l & 4l^2 & 13l & -3l^2 \\ 54 & 13l & 156 & -22l \\ -13l & -3l^2 & -22l & 4l^2 \end{bmatrix}$$

These elementary mass matrices are sometimes called the *consistent mass matrices* because they are obtained using the shape functions in a way that is *consistent* with the elementary $[K_e]$ matrix. Calling them consistent is also for distinguishing them from *lumped mass matrices*, which have the same number of rows and columns as the consistent matrices but with only nonzero diagonal terms as a direct result of distributing the mass of a structure evenly to the nodes. For example, the lumped mass matrix for a 2-node bar element is

$$[M_e] = \frac{\rho A l}{2} \begin{bmatrix} 1 & 0 \\ 0 & 1 \end{bmatrix}$$

and the lumped mass matrix for a 3-node bar element is

$$[M_e] = \frac{\rho A l}{3} \begin{bmatrix} 1 & 0 & 0 \\ 0 & 1 & 0 \\ 0 & 0 & 1 \end{bmatrix}$$

Similarly, the lumped mass matrices for the isoparametric triangular and square elements are as follows, respectively,

$$[M_e]^{\text{iso-triangle}} = \frac{\rho t_e A_e}{3} \begin{bmatrix} 1 & 0 & 0 & 0 & 0 & 0 \\ 0 & 1 & 0 & 0 & 0 & 0 \\ 0 & 0 & 1 & 0 & 0 & 0 \\ 0 & 0 & 0 & 1 & 0 & 0 \\ 0 & 0 & 0 & 0 & 1 & 0 \\ 0 & 0 & 0 & 0 & 0 & 1 \end{bmatrix}$$

$$[M_e]^{\text{iso-square}} = \frac{\rho t_e A_e}{4}\begin{bmatrix} 1 & 0 & 0 & 0 & 0 & 0 & 0 & 0 \\ 0 & 1 & 0 & 0 & 0 & 0 & 0 & 0 \\ 0 & 0 & 1 & 0 & 0 & 0 & 0 & 0 \\ 0 & 0 & 0 & 1 & 0 & 0 & 0 & 0 \\ 0 & 0 & 0 & 0 & 1 & 0 & 0 & 0 \\ 0 & 0 & 0 & 0 & 0 & 1 & 0 & 0 \\ 0 & 0 & 0 & 0 & 0 & 0 & 1 & 0 \\ 0 & 0 & 0 & 0 & 0 & 0 & 0 & 1 \end{bmatrix}$$

12.1.2 Elementary damping matrix

In a similar way, we can find the elementary damping matrix $[G_e^d]$ by isolating the damping term $\left(\chi\frac{\partial u}{\partial t}\right)$ in Equation 12.1 and calculating the residual of its weighted integral, as follows:

$$\iiint_V w_m \chi \frac{\partial u}{\partial t} dV$$

After substituting the matrix form field quantity interpolation, replacing the weight functions with shape functions (per the Galerkin method), and summing all n_e terms, we obtain

$$\iiint_V \sum_{m=1}^{n_e} w_m \chi \frac{\partial u}{\partial t} dV = \iiint_V [N]^T \chi [N] dV \{\dot{d}_0\}$$

The coefficient of the first derivative of the DOF vector, $\{\dot{d}_0\}$, is called the damping matrix, that is,

$$[G_e^d] = \iiint_V [N]^T \chi [N] dV \tag{12.4}$$

It is clear from Equations 12.3 and 12.4 that by replacing ρ (density) with χ (damping coefficient) in the above mass matrices, we can obtain the corresponding damping matrices. For example, the damping matrix for a 2-node and a 3-node bar element having a constant damping coefficient is, respectively,

$$[G_e^d]^{\text{2-node}} = \frac{\chi A l}{6}\begin{bmatrix} 2 & 1 \\ 1 & 2 \end{bmatrix}, \quad [G_e^d]^{\text{3-node}} = \frac{\chi A l}{30}\begin{bmatrix} 4 & 2 & -1 \\ 2 & 16 & 2 \\ -1 & 2 & 4 \end{bmatrix}$$

A situation in which the damping matrix is proportional to the mass matrix is sometimes called mass proportional damping. In practice, there are several ways to determine the damping of a system. For example, in addition to this mass proportional damping, Rayleigh damping defines the elementary damping matrix in a linear sum of the $[M]$ matrix and $[K]$ matrix as

$$[G_e^d] = \alpha[M] + \beta[K]$$

where α and β are constants.

12.1.3 Elementary absorption matrix

By applying the same procedure to the absorption term, βu, in Equation 12.1, we have

$$\iiint_V \sum_{m=1}^{n_e} w_m \beta u dV = \iiint_V [N]^T \beta [N] dV \{d_0\}$$

From this, we find the absorption matrix:

$$[G_e^a] = \iiint_V [N]^T \beta [N] dV \tag{12.5}$$

Comparing Equations 12.3 and 12.5, we can see that by replacing ρ with β (absorption coefficient) in the mass matrices, we can obtain the corresponding absorption matrices. For example, the absorption matrix for the isoparametric triangle and square element having a constant absorption coefficient is, respectively,

$$[G_e^a]^{\text{iso-triangle}} = \frac{\beta t_e A_e}{12}\begin{bmatrix} 2 & 0 & 1 & 0 & 1 & 0 \\ 0 & 2 & 0 & 1 & 0 & 1 \\ 1 & 0 & 2 & 0 & 1 & 0 \\ 0 & 1 & 0 & 2 & 0 & 1 \\ 1 & 0 & 1 & 0 & 2 & 0 \\ 0 & 1 & 0 & 1 & 0 & 2 \end{bmatrix}$$

$$[G_e^a]^{\text{iso-square}} = \frac{\beta t_e A_e}{36}\begin{bmatrix} 4 & 0 & 2 & 0 & 1 & 0 & 2 & 0 \\ 0 & 4 & 0 & 2 & 0 & 1 & 0 & 2 \\ 2 & 0 & 4 & 0 & 2 & 0 & 1 & 0 \\ 0 & 2 & 0 & 4 & 0 & 2 & 0 & 1 \\ 1 & 0 & 2 & 0 & 4 & 0 & 2 & 0 \\ 0 & 1 & 0 & 2 & 0 & 4 & 0 & 2 \\ 2 & 0 & 1 & 0 & 2 & 0 & 4 & 0 \\ 0 & 2 & 0 & 1 & 0 & 2 & 0 & 4 \end{bmatrix}$$

12.1.4 Elementary convection matrix

For the convection term, $\alpha\nabla u$, in Equation 12.1, we can apply the same weak-form FEM formulation procedure by calculating the residual of its weighted integral,

$$\iiint_V w_m \alpha \nabla \cdot u dV$$

along with

$$\{u\} = [N]\{d_0\}, \quad w_m = N_m, m = 1, \ldots, n_e$$

With substitution, we obtain

$$\iiint_V \sum_{m=1}^{n_e} w_m \alpha \nabla u dV = \iiint_V [N]^T \alpha [\nabla N]\{d_0\} dV$$

From this expression, we find the convection matrix as

$$[G_e^c] = \iiint_V [N]^T \alpha [\nabla N] dV \tag{12.6}$$

Example 12.4

Determine the convection matrix for a 3-node bar element located between $x_1 = -l/2$ and $x_3 = l/2$ having a length of l, a uniform cross section area of A, and a constant convective coefficient of α.

Answer

By using the Lagrange formula for one-dimensional (1D) elements given in Equation 5.13, we first find the shape functions for the element. For conveniences sake, by referring to Example 5.1b in Section 5.6.1, along with $x_1 = l/2, x_2 = 0$, and $x_3 = l/2$, we obtain

$$[N] = \begin{bmatrix} \frac{2x^2 - xl}{l^2} & \frac{l^2 - 4x^2}{l^2} & \frac{2x^2 + xl}{l^2} \end{bmatrix}$$

and

$$[\nabla N] = \begin{bmatrix} \frac{dN}{dx} \end{bmatrix} = \begin{bmatrix} \frac{4x - l}{l^2} & \frac{-8x}{l^2} & \frac{4x + l}{l^2} \end{bmatrix}$$

By substituting these expressions into Equation 12.6, we obtain

$$[G_e^c] = \alpha A \int_{-l/2}^{l/2} \begin{bmatrix} \frac{2x^2 - xl}{l^2} \\ \frac{l^2 - 4x^2}{l^2} \\ \frac{2x^2 + xl}{l^2} \end{bmatrix} \begin{bmatrix} \frac{4x - l}{l^2} & \frac{-8x}{l^2} & \frac{4x + l}{l^2} \end{bmatrix} dx = \alpha A \begin{bmatrix} -3 & 4 & -1 \\ -4 & 0 & 4 \\ 1 & -4 & 3 \end{bmatrix}$$

12.2 Solving the General Matrix Equation

For the absorption and convection matrices, when they are plugged back into the general matrix equation (Equation 12.2), they are associated directly with the DOF vector, $\{d_0\}$. This is the same as the elementary $[K]$ matrix. Thus, in solving the matrix equation, these terms can be summed together to form an expanded $[K']$ matrix. In this way, the general form matrix equation given in Equation 12.2 can be condensed to

$$[M_e]\{\ddot{d}_0\} + [G_e^d]\{\dot{d}_0\} + [K_e']\{d_0\} = \{P_e\} \tag{12.7}$$

For the mass and damping matrices, when substituting them back into the general matrix equation (Equation 12.2), the mass matrix is associated with the second derivative of the DOF vector, $\{\ddot{d}_0\}$, and the damping matrix with the first derivative of the DOF vector, $\{\dot{d}_0\}$. These are time-dependent terms, and they are handled differently, as we will see in Section 12.3.

12.3 Eigenvalues, Eigenvectors, and Free Vibration

12.3.1 Eigenvalues and eigenvectors

Before we discuss solving PDEs with time-dependent terms, let us first review the two relevant concepts, eigenvalues and eigenvectors. Eigenvalues are a special set of scalars that are associated with a matrix equation, and they are sometimes known as characteristic values. Similarly, eigenvectors are a special set of vectors associated with a matrix equation, and they are sometimes referred to as characteristic vectors. In daily life, the determination of the eigenvalues and eigenvectors of a physical or engineering system is extremely important in situations such as stability analysis, rotating bodies, and free vibration. Each eigenvalue is associated with a corresponding eigenvector.

Mathematically, an eigenvector of a square matrix $[A]$ is a nonzero vector $\{v\}$, which when multiplied with the matrix yields a constant multiple of $\{v\}$ as follows:

$$[A]\{v\} = \lambda\{v\}$$

where λ, the constant multiplier, is the eigenvalue of $[A]$ corresponding to the eigenvector vector $\{v\}$. The above equation can also be expressed equivalently as

$$([A] - \lambda[I])\{v\} = \{0\} \tag{12.8}$$

where $[I]$ is the identity matrix.

To find the eigenvalues, one just solves the following equation,

$$det([A] - \lambda[I]) = 0 \tag{12.9}$$

and to find the eigenvectors, one just substitutes the eigenvalues into the following equation and solves for $\{v\}$:

$$([A] - \lambda[I])\{v\} = \{0\} \tag{12.10}$$

Example 12.5

Find the eigenvalues and eigenvectors of square matrix $[A]$:

$$[A] = \begin{bmatrix} 2 & -4 \\ -3 & 3 \end{bmatrix}$$

Answer
Using Equation 12.9, we calculate

$$det\left(\begin{bmatrix} 2 & -4 \\ -3 & 3 \end{bmatrix} - \begin{bmatrix} \lambda & 0 \\ 0 & \lambda \end{bmatrix}\right) = \lambda^2 - 5\lambda - 6 = 0 = (\lambda - 6)(\lambda + 1) = 0$$

From this equation, we obtain two roots as the two eigenvalues:

$$\lambda_1 = 6, \quad \lambda_2 = -1$$

For the eigenvectors, we substitute these eigenvalues, one at a time, into Equation 12.10. When $\lambda_1 = 6$, we have

$$\left(\begin{bmatrix} 2 & -4 \\ -3 & 3 \end{bmatrix} - \begin{bmatrix} 6 & 0 \\ 0 & 6 \end{bmatrix}\right)\{v\} = \begin{bmatrix} -4 & -4 \\ -3 & -3 \end{bmatrix}\{v\} = \{0\}$$

Solving this equation, we find the first eigenvector, after normalization, as

$$\{v\}_1 = \begin{Bmatrix} 0.707 \\ -0.707 \end{Bmatrix}$$

Note that a normalized vector is one having unity (1) length, that is, $\{v\}^T\{v\} = 1$. When $\lambda_2 = -1$, we have

$$\left(\begin{bmatrix} 2 & -4 \\ -3 & 3 \end{bmatrix} - \begin{bmatrix} -1 & 0 \\ 0 & -1 \end{bmatrix}\right)\{v\} = \begin{bmatrix} 3 & -4 \\ -3 & 4 \end{bmatrix}\{v\} = \{0\}$$

Solving this equation, we have the second eigenvector (after normalization) as

$$\{v\}_2 = \begin{Bmatrix} 0.800 \\ 0.600 \end{Bmatrix}$$

12.3.2 Free vibration

Free vibration describes a situation in which a mechanical system is activated with a brief input and is allowed to deform (or more precisely, vibrate) freely afterwards. The motion of a tuning fork is a typical example of free vibration. In free vibration, the frequencies at which the system oscillates are called natural frequencies and the profiles of oscillation are called vibration modes. Usually, a system possesses a number of natural frequencies, with the lowest frequency associated with the simplest vibration mode permissible and higher natural frequencies associated with higher-order vibration modes. The lowest

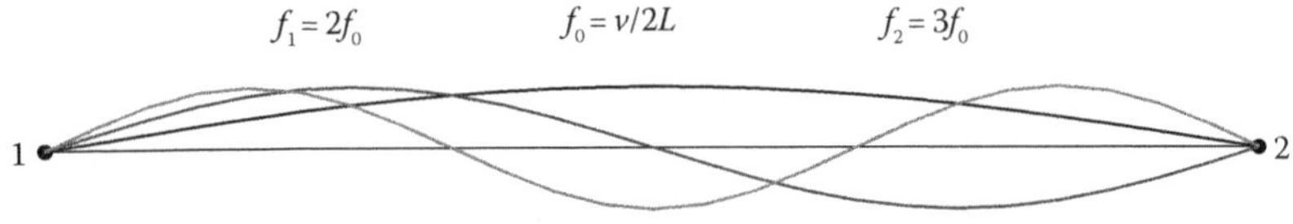

FIGURE 12.1
Vibration modes of a string.

natural frequency is often termed the fundamental frequency. To visualize this, we can picture a tensioned string pinned at the two ends, as shown in Figure 12.1. The profiles of free vibration of this string can be represented by a series of sinusoidal wave functions. The fundamental vibration mode takes the shape of a sinusoid passing through the two end points with $2L$ as its period, where L is the length of the string, and the fundamental frequency is $f_0 = v/2L$, where v is the speed of the wave. Higher-order vibrational modes take the shapes of sinusoids with periods of $2L/i$ and frequencies of $f_{i-1} = if_0$, where i is an integer, $i = 2, 3$, and so on.

The PDE for free vibration can be obtained by eliminating the damping and force terms in Equation 12.7 as follows:

$$[M]\{\ddot{d}_0\} + [K]\{d_0\} = \{0\} \tag{12.11}$$

In free vibration, the DOF vector $\{d_0\}$ can be represented by a sinusoidal wave function $\{d_0\} = \{\bar{d}\} \sin \omega t$, where $\{d_0\} = \{\bar{d}\}$ is the magnitude of the wave function and ω is the angular frequency ($\omega = 2\pi f$; f is the natural frequency). With this, we derive the acceleration vector as $\{\ddot{d}_0\} = -\omega^2\{\bar{d}\} \sin \omega t$. After substituting the DOF and acceleration vectors into Equation 12.11, we obtain

$$\left([K] - \omega^2[M]\right)\{\bar{d}\} = \{0\} \tag{12.12}$$

Here, the matrix term $[K] - \omega^2[M]$ is often referred to as the dynamic stiffness matrix of a mechanical system undergoing free vibration.

In comparing with Equation 12.8, we can see that Equation 12.12 represents a generalized eigenvalue and eigenvector problem, with ω^2 being the eigenvalues and the corresponding vibration modes being the eigenvectors. In other words, in free vibration the natural frequencies of a mechanical system are its eigenfrequencies (which are related to the eigenvalues by the relationship of $f = \omega/2\pi$) and the vibration modes are its eigenvectors.

Example 12.6

Find the first two natural frequencies and vibration modes for the standing post undergoing free vibration. As shown in Figure 12.2, the post has a length of l and its bottom end fixed to the ground.

Answer
We solve this free vibration problem as an eigenvalue problem. Since this standing post with a fixed end will vibrate with flexural deformation,

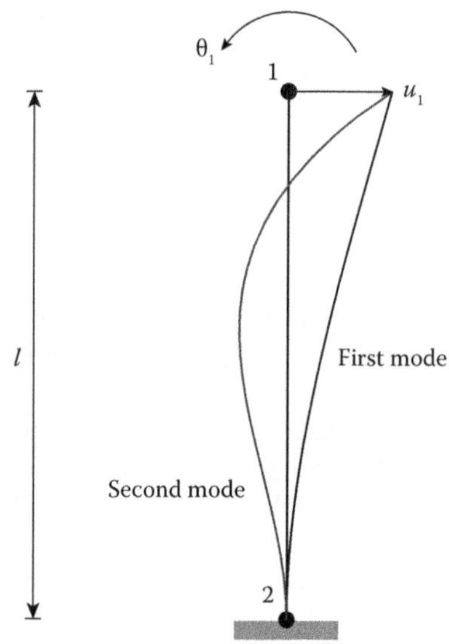

FIGURE 12.2
Standing post and its first two vibration modes.

it should be treated as a beam structure. Thus, we will use the Hermite elements for its discretization. To simplify matters, we will represent the post with a single beam element, with nodal assignment shown in Figure 12.2. For the $[K]$ matrix, referring to Equation 6.24 we write

$$[K] = \frac{EI}{l^3}\begin{bmatrix} 12 & 6l & -12 & 6l \\ 6l & 4l^2 & -6l & 2l^2 \\ -12 & -6l & 12 & -6l \\ 6l & 2l^2 & -6l & 4l^2 \end{bmatrix}$$

For the $[M]$ matrix, we will use the consistent mass matrix. Thus, from Example 12.3 discussed earlier, we have

$$[M] = \frac{\rho Al}{420}\begin{bmatrix} 156 & 22l & 54 & -13l \\ 22l & 4l^2 & 13l & -3l^2 \\ 54 & 13l & 156 & -22l \\ -13l & -3l^2 & -22l & 4l^2 \end{bmatrix}$$

By substituting the $[K]$ and $[M]$ matrices into Equation 12.12, we have

$$\left(\frac{EI}{l^3}\begin{bmatrix} 12 & 6l & -12 & 6l \\ 6l & 4l^2 & -6l & 2l^2 \\ -12 & -6l & 12 & -6l \\ 6l & 2l^2 & -6l & 4l^2 \end{bmatrix} - \frac{\omega^2\rho Al}{420}\begin{bmatrix} 156 & 22l & 54 & -13l \\ 22l & 4l^2 & 13l & -3l^2 \\ 54 & 13l & 156 & -22l \\ -13l & -3l^2 & -22l & 4l^2 \end{bmatrix}\right)\begin{Bmatrix} v_1 \\ \theta_1 \\ v_2 \\ \theta_2 \end{Bmatrix} = \begin{Bmatrix} 0 \\ 0 \\ 0 \\ 0 \end{Bmatrix}$$

Since node 2 is fixed, we have $v_2 = 0$ and $\theta_2 = 0$. Thus, we strike out the corresponding rows and columns and obtain

$$\left(\frac{EI}{l^3}\begin{bmatrix}12 & 6l\\ 6l & 4l^2\end{bmatrix} - \frac{\omega^2\rho Al}{420}\begin{bmatrix}156 & 22l\\ 22l & 4l^2\end{bmatrix}\right)\begin{Bmatrix}v_1\\ \theta_1\end{Bmatrix} = \begin{Bmatrix}0\\ 0\end{Bmatrix} \tag{12.13}$$

From this equation, we can find the eigenvalues, ω^2, by solving

$$det\left(\frac{EI}{l^3}\begin{bmatrix}12 & 6l\\ 6l & 4l^2\end{bmatrix} - \frac{\omega^2\rho Al}{420}\begin{bmatrix}156 & 22l\\ 22l & 4l^2\end{bmatrix}\right) = 0$$

To do that, we first simplify it to

$$det\left(\begin{bmatrix}12-156c & 6l-22lc\\ 6l-22lc & 4l^2-4l^2c\end{bmatrix}\right) = 0 \tag{12.14}$$

where

$$c = \frac{\omega^2\rho Al^4}{420EI}$$

Solving Equation 12.14, we obtain $c_1 = 0.0297$ and $c_2 = 2.8846$. With that, we further find the first two eigenvalues as

$$\omega_1 = 3.5327\sqrt{\frac{EI}{\rho Al^4}}, \quad \omega_2 = 34.8069\sqrt{\frac{EI}{\rho Al^4}}$$

From the vibration theory of beams, one can find that the exact solution has a coefficient of 3.5156 for the first eigenvalue and 22.0336 for the second eigenvalue. Clearly, the first eigenvalue obtained from our single-beam discretization approximation is much closer to the exact solution than the second eigenvalue. The errors can be reduced by using more elements or different types of mass matrices.

To find the eigenvectors, or the vibration modes, we just solve Equation 12.13 with the above eigenvalues substituted.

For the first eigenvalue (ω_1), we obtain

$$\frac{EI}{l^3}\left(\begin{bmatrix}12 & 6l\\ 6l & 4l^2\end{bmatrix} - 0.0297\begin{bmatrix}156 & 22l\\ 22l & 4l^2\end{bmatrix}\right)\begin{Bmatrix}v_1\\ \theta_1\end{Bmatrix} = \begin{Bmatrix}0\\ 0\end{Bmatrix} \tag{12.15}$$

This leads to the two following equations:

$$7.3668v_1 + 5.3466l\theta_1 = 0 \quad \text{and} \quad 5.3466V_1 + 3.8812l\theta_1 = 0$$

From these equations, by setting $v_1 = 1$, we obtain the first eigenvector as

$$\begin{Bmatrix}v_1\\ \theta_1\end{Bmatrix} = \begin{Bmatrix}1\\ -1.3778/l\end{Bmatrix}$$

Similarly, we find the second eigenvector corresponding to ω_2 as

$$\begin{Bmatrix}v_1\\ \theta_1\end{Bmatrix} = \begin{Bmatrix}1\\ -7.6225/l\end{Bmatrix}$$

Plotting these two eigenvectors in position with the standing post, as shown in Figure 12.2, we can see the corresponding vibration modes.

12.4 Exercises

1. Determine the elementary mass matrix, $[M_e]$, for the two 2-node bar elements shown in Figure 12.3 in terms of length l, cross section area A, and density of ρ.
2. Determine the elementary mass matrix, $[M_e]$, for the two 3-node bar elements shown in Figure 12.4 in terms of length l, cross section area A, and density ρ.
3. Determine the convection matrix $[G_e^c]$ for the two 2-node bar elements shown in Figure 12.3 in terms of length l, cross section area A, and convective coefficient α.
4. Determine the convection matrix $[G_e^c]$ for the two 3-node bar elements shown in Figure 12.4 in terms of length l, cross section area A, and convective coefficient α.
5. Determine the elementary mass matrix, $[M_e]$, for the two 2-node beam elements shown in Figure 12.5 in terms of length l, cross section area A, and density ρ.
6. For the 2D square and rectangular elements shown in Figure 12.6, determine their elementary mass matrix, $[M_e]$, in terms of thickness t_e, area A_e, and material density ρ.

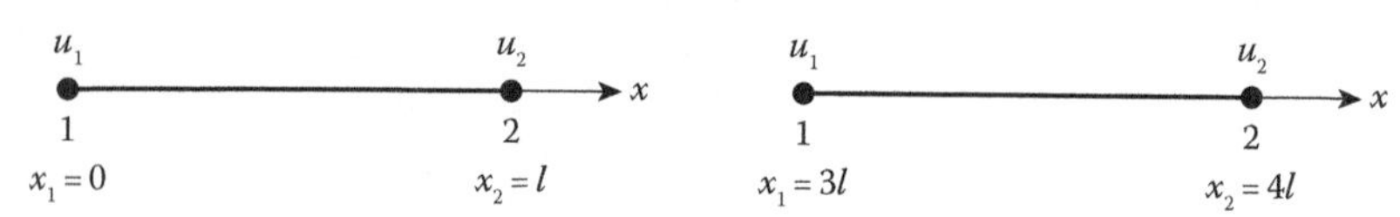

FIGURE 12.3
Two 1D 2-node elements located at different positions.

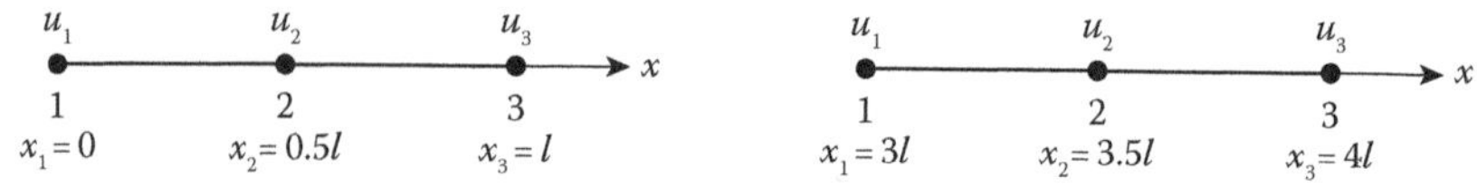

FIGURE 12.4
Two 1D 3-node elements located at different positions.

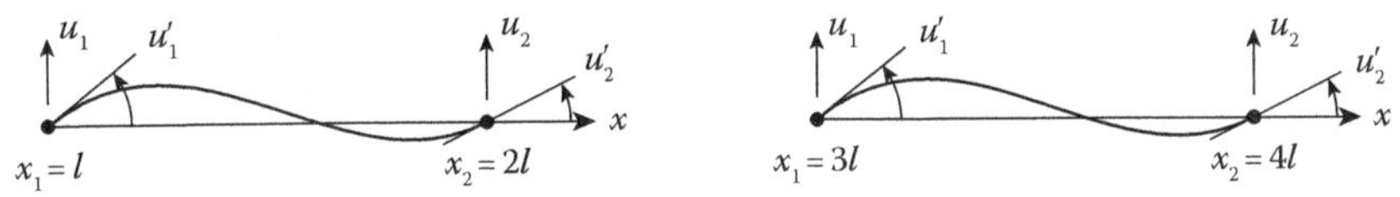

FIGURE 12.5
Two 2-node beam elements at different locations.

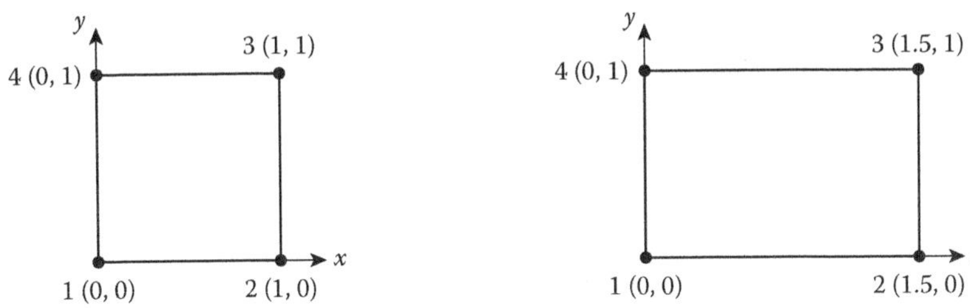

FIGURE 12.6
Two 2D rectangular elements with a uniform thickness.

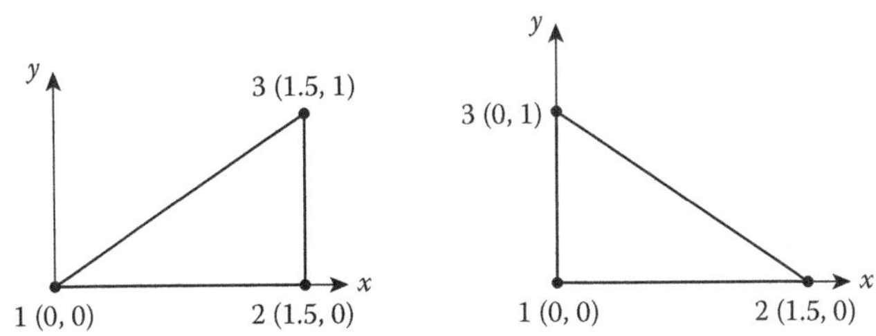

FIGURE 12.7
Two 2D triangular elements with a uniform thickness.

7. Determine the convection matrix $[G_e^c]$ for the two square and rectangular elements shown in Figure 12.6 in terms of thickness t_e, area A_e, and convective coefficient α.

8. For the two 2D triangular elements shown in Figure 12.7, determine their elementary mass matrix, $[M_e]$, in terms of thickness t_e, area A_e, and material density ρ.

9. Determine the convection matrix $[G_e^c]$ for the two 2D triangular elements shown in Figure 12.7 in terms of thickness t_e, area A_e, and convective coefficient α.

10. Solve the problem discussed in Example 12.6 by using two beam elements, as illustrated in Figure 12.8.

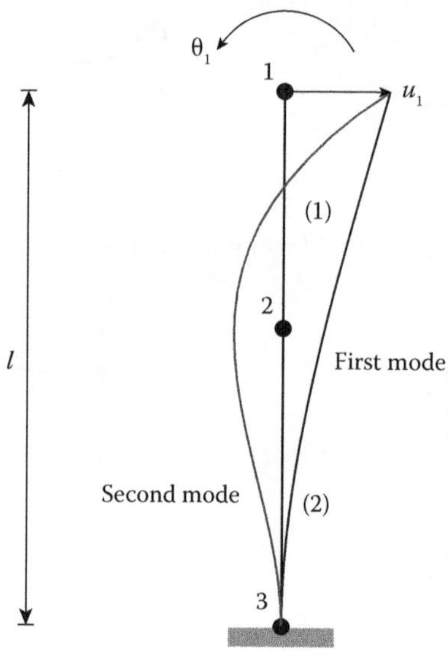

FIGURE 12.8
Standing post and its first two vibration modes.

Recommended Readings

1. Robert D. Cook, David S. Malkus, Michael E. Plesha, and Robert J. Witt. 2002. *Concepts and Applications of Finite Element Analysis*. 4th ed. Hoboken, NJ: John Wiley & Sons.
2. David V. Hutton. 2004. *Fundamentals of Finite Element Analysis*. Boston: McGraw-Hill.

13

Errors in FEM Results

The finite element method (FEM) is a computer-based approximate way of finding solutions to differential equations. As we learned in Chapter 4, an approximate way of seeking solutions to partial differential equations (PDEs) and ordinary differential equations (ODEs) will inherently introduce errors. Thus, FEM results will always contain errors. There are several different types of errors in FEM, such as modeling error, user error, and program error. Of all the possible errors, modeling errors are the most common ones, and they are discussed in detail in this chapter. On the other end of the spectrum, the most challenging cause for errors is when framing the problem becomes difficult. This type of error is often categorized as the *problem-framing error*, and it occurs when the PDE or the constraining conditions do not capture the actual situation of the problem at hand due to required simplifications in formulating the problem. This type of error may not be avoidable, especially when the underlying physics of the problem is complicated or not fully known. In this situation, the best thing one can do is to be fully aware of the limitation of the framed problem and the results.

For other errors, especially those caused by human mistakes, they can be further categorized as user error and programmer error, or simply program error. If a user makes a mistake in building the model, selecting appropriate elements, or assigning incorrect material properties, or even loading and constraining boundary conditions, and so forth, the results the user obtains will surely not be correct. This type of error is *user error*, and it could be avoided as the user becomes more knowledgeable of the FEM modeling technique and the underlying science and engineering principles. If a programming engineer makes a mistake causing some programming bugs in the software, this type of error is *program error*, which is sometimes very hard to identify. In the case of a commercial software package, because the developers and users are often not the same group of people, any program bugs, when they go undetected during the debugging stage, will be embedded in the package to introduce calculation errors to the FEM results. This type of error, however, can be identified by comparing some selected results either with known theoretical values or with FEM results from a different software package. It is therefore very important to develop a habit of validating FEM results in as many ways as possible.

13.1 Modeling Errors

Even when the software is free of bugs and when everything is done right by an engineer, the FEM results will still possess errors. These are often regarded as *modeling errors*. Modeling errors can come from three main sources:

1. *Domain approximation error.* This is caused by the elements used for domain discretization not fully representing the actual domain, leading an engineer to solve PDEs on a modified domain.

2. *Field variable approximation error.* This is inherent to any numerical solutions, and it is generated from the approximation of a field variable using polynomial interpretation functions.

3. *Quadrature and arithmetic error.* This is the round-off error in the computation of values, numerical evaluation of integrals, and so forth.

13.1.1 Domain approximation error

Since the various types of elements we have discussed in previous chapters have either straight shapes (e.g., one-dimensional [1D] elements), straight edges (e.g., two-dimensional [2D] elements), or straight edges and flat surfaces (e.g., three-dimensional [3D] elements), for physical domains with straight shapes and straight boundaries, domain approximation may be less a problem. However, for physical domains possessing curved shapes, edges, or surfaces, domain approximation will become inevitable, leading to domain approximation error. To minimize this type of errors, one could reduce the size of elements (i.e., refine the mesh) such that the domain is more accurately represented by smaller elements.

13.1.2 Field variable approximation error

Field variable approximation error is likely caused by the selected polynomial interpretation functions not capturing the actual variation of the field variable (the primary variable), or lacking the degree of continuity to represent truthfully various secondary variables (i.e., various derivatives of the primary variable). As we discussed in Chapter 5, the order of element discretization can be linear, quadratic, cubic, quartic, and so on, and these discretization orders are directly linked to the degrees of polynomial functions used for field variable approximation. With Lagrange elements (see Section 5.6), increasing the order of element discretization can be implemented by using elements with midside nodes. Thus, even with elements of the same shapes as linear elements, by selecting a higher discretization order, we may reduce the field variable approximation error.

13.1.3 Quadrature and arithmetic error

As discussed in Chapter 11, in FEM most operations for numerical computation and integral evaluation are done using quadrature techniques. Thus, the accuracy of these numerical operations may rely on the number of points used in the quadrature (see Tables 11.1 through 11.3). In this regard, adjusting the number of quadrature points may help reduce the numerical error.

13.2 Convergence of FEM Solutions

Since errors in FEM results are inevitable, one of the most important things an engineer must do is to ensure that the error is small or negligible, such that the FEM solutions are reasonably close to the true solutions. This statement can be conveyed by mathematical expressions. For example, let u be the true solution to a given PDE, $\tilde{u}$ the FEM solution, and e_0 a preset small error tolerance value; when the difference of these two solutions satisfies the following relationship,

$$|u - \tilde{u}| \leq e_0$$

the FEM solution will be regarded as an acceptable solution because the error associated with it is considered tolerable or negligible.

Let us now add some practical meaning to this mathematical expression by using a 2-node bar element of length l to solve the second-order ODE given in Equation 6.1.

By Equation 5.6, we express the FEM solution in terms of the shape functions and nodal degrees of freedom (DOF) as

$$\tilde{u} = N_i u_1 + N_2 u_2$$

where the two shape functions (see Section 5.5) are

$$N_1 = \frac{l-x}{l} \text{ and } N_2 = \frac{x}{l}, \quad \text{in which } 0 \leq x \leq l$$

We now introduce a fractional variable, s, such that

$$s = \frac{x}{l} \text{ with } 0 \leq s \leq 1$$

With this new variable, we then express the FEM solution as a function of s:

$$\tilde{u} = (1-s)u_1 + su_2 \tag{13.1}$$

For the sake of facilitating convenient comparison, we need to express the true solution also in terms of s as $u(s)$. So by using the Taylor series (see Appendix B), we expand $u(s)$ in term of a as

$$u(s) = u(a) + u'(a)(s-a) + \frac{u''(a)}{2!}(s-a)^2 + \cdots$$

in which a represents an arbitrary point within the elementary domain $(0 \leq a \leq 1)$. When $a = 0$, we are at node 1; therefore, we have $u(0) = u_1, u'(0) = u'_1, \ldots$. With these values, we express $u(s)$ in terms of the first nodal DOF (u_1) as

$$u(s) = u_1 + u'_1 s + \frac{u''_1}{2} s^2 + \cdots \tag{13.2}$$

This equation means that the true solution is now expressed as a function variable s along with known values of $u_1, u'_1, \ldots$ at node 1 as constant coefficients.

Letting $s = 1$ in Equation 13.2, we reach node 2 with associated second nodal DOF (u_2). In other words, u_2 can be expressed in terms of $u_1, u'_1, \ldots$ as

$$u_2 = u_1 + u'_1 + \frac{u''_1}{2!} + \cdots \tag{13.3}$$

Substituting Equation 13.3 into Equation 13.1, we obtain

$$\tilde{u}(s) = (1-s)u_1 + s\left(u_1 + u'_1 + \frac{u''_1}{2} + \cdots\right) = u_1 + u'_1 s + \frac{u''_1}{2} s + \cdots \tag{13.4}$$

From Equations 13.2 and 13.4, we calculate

$$|u - \tilde{u}| = \left| \frac{u''_1}{2}(s - s^2) + \cdots \right|$$

By taking the maximum value for u''_1 along the entire element, we express the above equation as the following inequity:

$$|u - \tilde{u}| \leq \frac{(s-s^2)}{2} \max_{0 \leq s \leq 1} \left| \frac{d^2u}{ds^2} \right|$$

Since $s = x/l$, we have $ds = dx/l$ and

$$\max_{0 \leq s \leq 1} \left| \frac{d^2u}{ds^2} \right| = \max_{0 \leq s \leq 1} \left| \frac{d^2u}{dx^2} \left(\frac{dx}{ds} \right)^2 \right| = l^2 \max_{0 \leq s \leq 1} \left| \frac{d^2u}{dx^2} \right|$$

With this relationship, we write

$$|u - \tilde{u}| \leq \frac{(s-s^2)}{2} \max_{0 \leq s \leq 1} \left| \frac{d^2u}{dx^2} \right| l^2 \tag{13.5}$$

Because $0 \leq s \leq 1$, we can regard $(s - s^2) \leq 1$; then we further simplify Equation 13.5 to

$$|u - \tilde{u}| \leq \frac{1}{2} \max_{0 \leq s \leq 1} \left| \frac{d^2u}{dx^2} \right| l^2 = c_1 l^2 \tag{13.6}$$

where c_1 represents $\frac{1}{2}\max_{0\leq s\leq 1}\left|\frac{d^2u}{dx^2}\right|$, which is a constant. By taking the first derivative of Equation 13.5 with respect to x, we obtain

$$\frac{d}{dx}|(u-\tilde{u})| \leq \frac{(1-2s)}{2}(\frac{ds}{dx})\max_{0\leq s\leq 1}\left|\frac{d^2u}{dx^2}\right|l^2 \leq \frac{1}{2}\max_{0\leq s\leq 1}\left|\frac{d^2u}{dx^2}\right|l = c_2 l \quad (13.7)$$

in which c_2 is a also constant.

Equations 13.6 and 13.7 show that by selecting a 2-node bar element of length l, we can express the possible errors as

$$|u-\tilde{u}| \leq c_1 l^2 \quad \text{and} \quad |u-\tilde{u}|_1 \leq c_2 l \quad (13.8)$$

where $|u-\tilde{u}|_1$ denotes the first derivative of $|u-\tilde{u}|$ with respect to x. Clearly, when the length of the element becomes small, the values of c_1l^2 and c_2l will be small.

The inequalities given in Equation 13.8 can be expressed in a general form as follows:

$$|u-\tilde{u}|_m \leq ch^p, \quad p = k+1-m \quad (13.9)$$

where c is a constant, h is the characteristic length of an element, and p is the power term with a positive value, often referred to as the *rate of convergence.* The p value is determined as $p = k+1-m$, in which k represents the degree of polynomials associated with the selected element, and m is related to the order of the differential equation (with $2m$ equal to the order).

For a FEM solution that satisfies Equation 13.9, it is said that as the characteristic length (h) decreases or as the rate of convergence (p) increases, the error in the FEM solution will become negligibly small, leading to the convergence of the FEM solution to the true solution.

So for the case discussed earlier in which we use a 2-node bar element (with first-order linear interpolation polynomials) of length l to solve a second-order ODE, we have $2m = 2$, or $m = 1$ and $k = 1$, along with $h = l$. Then, we calculate $p = 1+1-1 = 1$. With these values, Equation 13.9 reduces to Equation 13.7. This fact suggests that the FEM solution provided by the 2-node element will converge to the true solution for the second-order ODE as the length of the elements decreases.

According to Equation 13.9, the error in the FEM approximation can be reduced by either reducing the size of the elements or increasing the degree of polynomial interpretation. So when a FEM solution satisfies Equation 13.9, the solution will converge to the true solution as the size of elements decreases or the degree of the polynomial interpretation increases. Convergence of the FEM solutions by decreasing the size of the elements with more of the same kind of elements, which is often referred to as mesh refinement, is termed *h-convergence.* Convergence with increasing the degree of polynomials is called *p-convergence.*

Example 13.1

Referring to Equation 13.9 show that a 3-node bar element used for solving a second-order PDE or ODE will meet the convergence requirement.

Answer
Since $2m = 2$ and $k = 2$, we have $p = k + 1 - m = 2 + 1 - 1 = 2$; thus, if the element meets the convergence requirement, by referring to Equation 13.9, we need to establish the following relationship:

$$|u - \tilde{u}|_1 \leq cl^2$$

By introducing a fractional variable s as $s = x/l$, along with the three shape functions for a 3-node bar element (see Section 5.6), we express the FEM solution as

$$\tilde{u}(s) = (1 - 3s + 2s^2)u_1 + (4s - 4s^2)u_2 + (2s^2 - s)u_3 \tag{13.10}$$

Using the Taylor series (see Appendix B), we expand $u(s)$ at $s = 0$ to express $u(s)$ in terms of the first nodal DOF, u_1:

$$u(s) = u_1 + u_1' s + \frac{u_1''}{2} s^2 + \frac{u_1^{(3)}}{3!} s^3 + \cdots \tag{13.11}$$

By letting $s = 1/2$ in Equation 13.11, we express the second nodal DOF (u_2) in terms of u_1 as

$$u_2 = u_1 + u_1' \frac{1}{2} + \frac{u_1''}{2} \frac{1}{4} + \frac{u_1^{(3)}}{6} \frac{1}{8} + \cdots \tag{13.12}$$

and by letting $s = 1$ in Equation 13.11, we express the third nodal DOF (u_3) in terms of u_1 as

$$u_3 = u_1 + u_1' + \frac{u_1''}{2} + \frac{u_1^{(3)}}{6} + \cdots \tag{13.13}$$

Substituting Equations 13.12 and 13.13 into Equation 13.10, we obtain

$$\tilde{u}(s) = (1 - 3s + 2s^2)u_1 + (4s - 4s^2)\left(u_1 + u_1' \frac{1}{2} + \frac{u_1''}{2} \frac{1}{4} + \frac{u_1^{(3)}}{6} \frac{1}{8} + \cdots\right)$$
$$+ (2s^2 - s)\left(u_1 + u_1' + \frac{u_1''}{2} + \frac{u_1^{(3)}}{6} + \cdots\right)$$

With simplification, we have

$$\tilde{u}(s) = u_1 + u_1' s + \frac{u_1''}{2} s^2 + \frac{u_1^{(3)}}{6} \frac{(3s^2 - s)}{2} + \cdots \tag{13.14}$$

From Equations 13.11 and 13.14, we calculate

$$|u - \tilde{u}| = \left| \frac{u_1^{(3)}}{6} \left(s^3 - \frac{3s^2 - s}{2} \right) + \cdots \right| = \left| \frac{1}{12} (s - 3s^2 + 2s^3) u_1^{(3)} + \cdots \right|$$

Since $s = x/l$ and $s \leq 1$, we have $ds = dx/l$ and

$$|u - \tilde{u}| \leq \frac{1}{12}(s - 3s^2 + 2s^3) \max_{0 \leq s \leq 1} \left| \frac{d^3u}{ds^3} \right| = \frac{1}{12} \max_{0 \leq s \leq 1} \left| \frac{d^3u}{dx^3} \right| l^3 = c_3 l^3$$

where c_3 is a constant related to the length of the element.

Similarly, we have

$$\frac{d}{dx} |(u - \tilde{u})| = |u - \tilde{u}|_1 \leq \frac{1}{12}(1 - 6s + 6s^2) \max_{0 \leq s \leq 1} \left| \frac{d^3u}{dx^3} \right| l^2 \leq \frac{1}{12} \max_{0 \leq s \leq 1} \left| \frac{d^3u}{dx^3} \right| l^2$$

that is,

$$|u - \tilde{u}|_1 \leq c_4 l^2 \tag{13.15}$$

in which c_4 is a also constant related to the length of the element.

Equation 13.15 is exactly the relationship we set out to establish. This result thus confirms that the convergence requirement is met when a 3-node bar element is used for solving a second-order PDE or ODE.

13.2.1 Effect of mesh refinement: *h*-convergence

In this section, we use a quantitative example to illustrate the effect of mesh refinement on the convergence of FEM solutions, or the h-convergence.

For many structures, either due to some specific design requirements or as a result of processing flaws, they may possess geometric features such as holes or notches. These features will cause elevated stresses in the surrounding region. This phenomenon is commonly known as *stress concentration.*

Stress concentration is often characterized by the ratio of the maximum stress (σ_{max}) in the region to the nominal stress (σ_{nom}), and this ratio is called the stress concentration factor (K_t). As shown in Figure 13.1, the stress concentration factor in a rectangular plate with an elliptic hole is found to be

$$K_t = C_1 + C_2 \left(\frac{2a}{D}\right) + C_3 \left(\frac{2a}{D}\right)^2 + C_4 \left(\frac{2a}{D}\right)^3 \tag{13.16}$$

where for $0.5 \leq a/b \leq 10$, $C_1 = 1 + 2a/b$, $C_2 = -0.351 - 0.021\sqrt{a/b} - 2.483a/b$, $C_3 = 3.621 - 5.183\sqrt{a/b} + 4.494a/b$, $C_4 = -2.27 + 5.204\sqrt{a/b} - 4.011a/b$, D is the width of the plate, and a and b are the lengths of the semimajor and semiminor axises of the ellipse, respectively.

Figure 13.1 also shows the curve for the case of $a/d = 1.5$ based on the analytical expression K_t as a function of $2a/D$. We will now use FEM to solve this problem by using different mesh densities to examine the differences of the FEM solutions to the analytical solution. We use four different meshes for domain discretization, as shown in Figure 13.2. Among the four meshes, Mesh 1 and Mesh 2 are very coarse, Mesh 3 is fine, and Mesh 4 is extrafine.

Clearly, the two coarse meshes introduce domain discretization errors by shaping the elliptic hole into polygonal ones. In the two refined meshes, Mesh 3

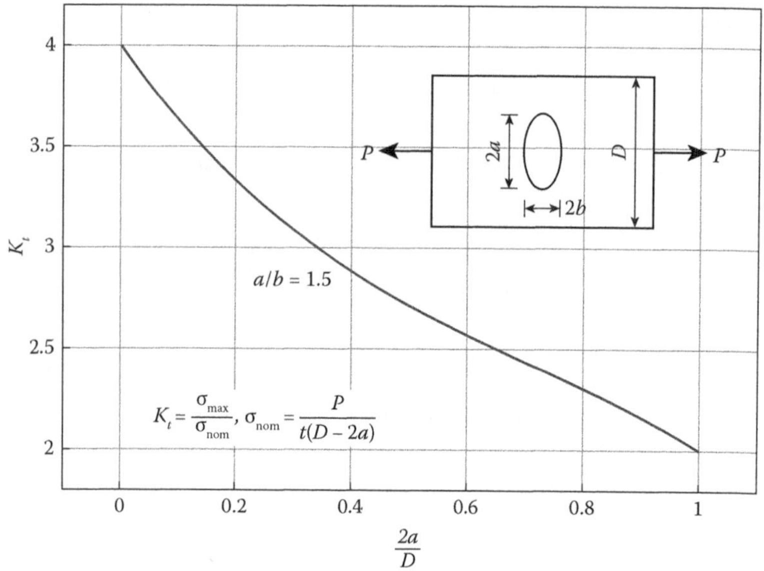

FIGURE 13.1
Stress concentration in a rectangular plate around an elliptic hole.

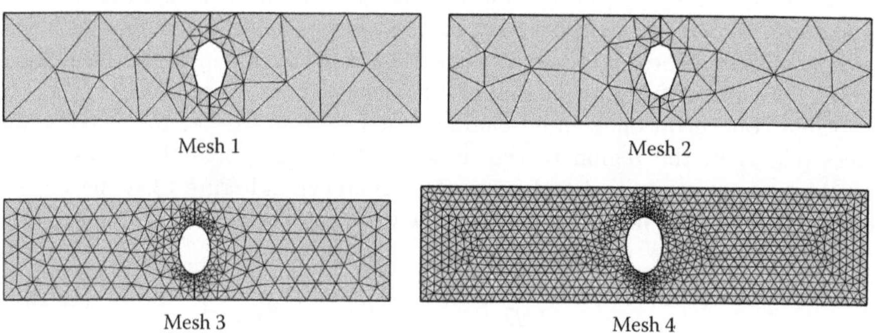

FIGURE 13.2
Mesh refinement using more elements of smaller sizes.

and Mesh 4, such domain discretization error is reduced and the resulting meshes provide much better geometrical representation of the domain.

Now let us look at the FEM results obtained from the four cases. As shown in Figure 13.3, comparing with the analytical solution (the red solid curve), the FEM solutions for Mesh 1 and Mesh 2 are scattered far away from the analytic curve in regions below the curve, suggesting that the solutions from Mesh 1 and Mesh 2 are less than the analytical solution. The results of Mesh 3 and Mesh 4 fare much better. While Mesh 4 provides slightly better results

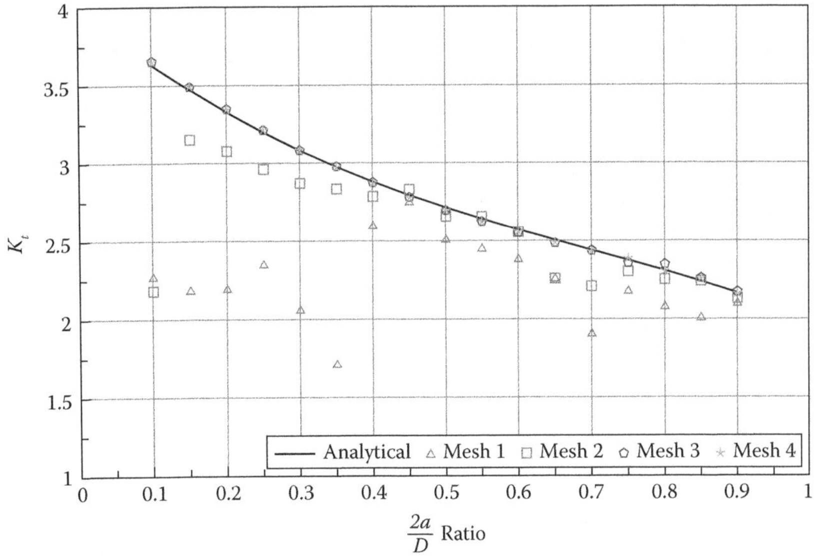

FIGURE 13.3
Convergence of FEM solutions with mesh refinement.

than Mesh 3, both results are overall very close to the analytical curve. This example shows that with mesh refinement, one can reduce errors in FEM solutions.

As we know, in pretty much all real-world situations we will not have the analytical solution to make any comparisons with. However, as this example shows, even without the analytical curve, we can make the following observations: (1) Mesh 2 solution differs from Mesh 1 solution quite significantly; (2) Mesh 3 solution also differs from Mesh 2 solution, but with much reduced differences; and (3) Mesh 4 solution almost overlaps that of Mesh 3. In other worlds, from the solutions of Mesh 3 and Mesh 4, we can say that there is a trend of convergence in the FEM solution with mesh refinement. With such outcomes of a mesh refinement study, we can be confident that Mesh 4 will produce reasonably converged solution. With this properly refined mesh (e.g., Mesh 4), we can go on to perform further analyses to obtain the physical quantities of interest, such as tensile stresses, as shown in Figure 13.4. From Figure 13.4, we can see that the maximum tensile stress increases as the size of the elliptic hole increases. But as the elliptic hole becomes larger, the nominal stress ($\sigma_{\text{nom}} = P/(D - 2a)/t$) also increases, albeit at a slower rate, thus leading to a decrease in the stress concentration factor (K_t) with increasing $2a/D$ ratio.

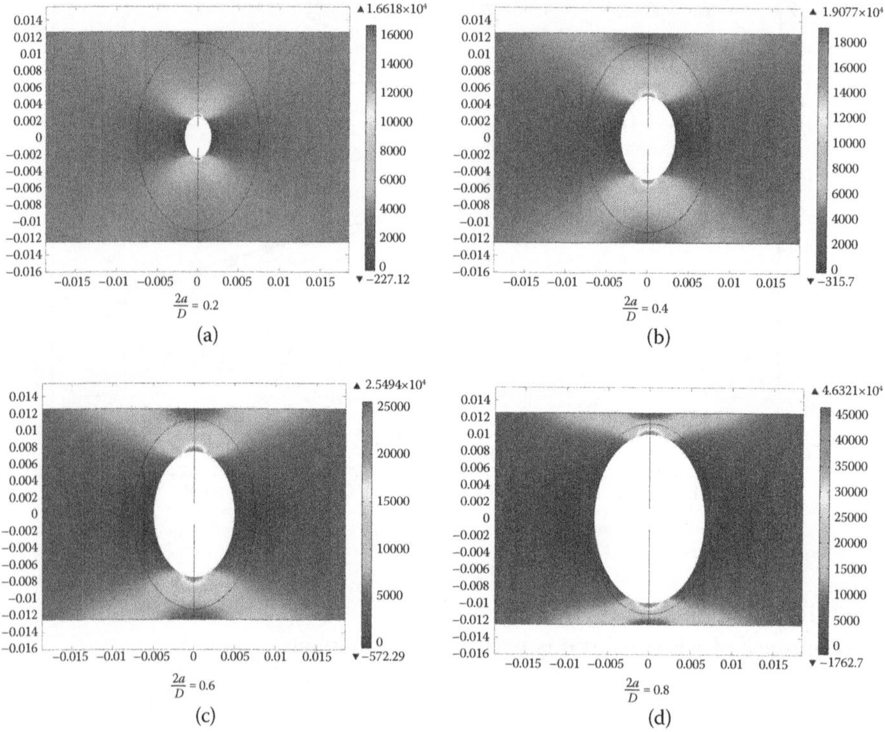

FIGURE 13.4
Stress distribution around an elliptic hole with different sizes.

13.2.2 Effect of element discretization order: *p*-convergence

In the above example, one reason the FEM solutions converge quickly to the analytical solution with the use of slightly finer meshes is that the elements used in those cases are of quadratic order; that is, the elements use quadratic interpretation functions for field variable approximation. As we discussed in Chapter 5, for elements of a common shape, the order of discretization (i.e., the degree of polynomial interpretation functions) can be increased by introducing side nodes.

To see the effect of changing the order of element discretization or the order of polynomial interpretation functions on the convergence of FEM solutions (i.e., the *p*-convergence), we examine the outcomes when using elements of linear, quadratic, and cubic orders for the case of Mesh 4, the finest mesh case in the previous example.

Figure 13.5 shows the results for the variation of K_t as a function of $2a/D$ when the case of Mesh 4 is reanalyzed by using linear, quadratic, and

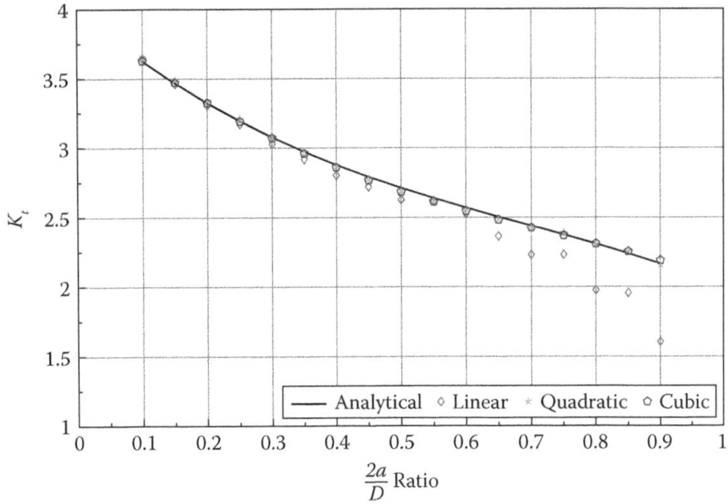

FIGURE 13.5
FEM solutions with increasing order of discretization.

cubic element discretization, respectively. Clearly, even with the extrafine mesh (Mesh 4), the case of linear element discretization exhibits poor results, especially when the $2a/D$ ratio is large: the solutions deviate farther away from the analytical curve as the $2a/D$ ratio increases. Of the quadratic and cubic cases, although both results are very close to the analytic curve, the quadratic case seems to have slightly better solutions than the cubic one. Recall that the governing equation for this mechanical problem is a second-order PDE (see Chapter 8); the fact that cubic elements do not provide any significant benefits over quadratic elements may suggest that an element discretization order higher than the order of the governing PDE may not necessarily provide better FEM solutions.

13.2.3 Effect of quadrature points

Aside from the domain and discretization-related errors, errors in numerical computation and integral evaluation are also common due to the use of quadrature techniques (see Chapter 11). Therefore, to have a complete discussion of the possible sources of errors in FEM solutions, we now examine the effect of changing the number of quadrature points. Note that due to the use of a commercial FEM software program for this evaluation, the quadrature points used to evaluate the $[K]$ matrix, the load vector $[P]$, and so forth, are not accessible for making changes; thus, we just limit the change in the number of quadrature points to the evaluation of the $\sigma_{\max}$. With $\sigma_{\max}$ calculated

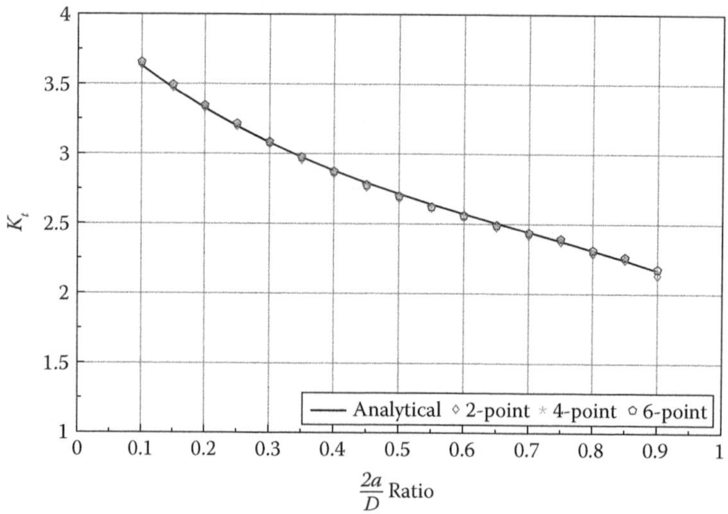

FIGURE 13.6
FEM solutions with increasing number of integration points.

with different quadrature points, we then determine the stress concentration factor (K_t) and make comparisons among the different cases.

Figure 13.6 shows the results of changing the number of quadrature points from 2 to 6 in evaluating $\sigma_{\max}$. While the results for all three cases are very close to the analytic curve and differ only slightly among themselves, the cases of 4-point and 6-point seem to provide better results than the case of 2-point. It is worth noting that because the change of quadrature points is limited to the evaluation of the maximum stress only, the actual difference could have been larger than what we see here if we had a way to change the quadrature points for all numerical evaluations. Nevertheless, this example suggests that increasing the number of quadrature points beyond 4 may provide little benefit.

13.3 Exercises

1. What are the three main modeling errors and how can one avoid them?

2. Based on the definitions of *p-convenience* and *h-convergence*, describe what one can do to ensure the convergence of FEM solutions.

3. According to Equation 13.9, what types of bar elements are required in order to ensure that the FEM solution for a fourth-order PDE will meet the converge requirements.

4. Follow the steps and discussion given in Example 13.1 to show whether a 2-node, a 3-node, or even a 4-node bar element will be needed for solving a fourth-order PDE in order for the FEM solutions to meet the convergence requirements.

5. For the stress distribution around a circular hole centered in a rectangular plate, as shown in Figure 13.7, the stress concentration factor can be expressed as a function of $2r/D$ as follows:

$$K_t = 3.00 - 3.13\left(\frac{2r}{D}\right) + 3.66\left(\frac{2r}{D}\right)^2 - 1.53\left(\frac{2r}{D}\right)^3$$

   where r is the radius of the circular hole and D is the width of the rectangular plate. Use a FEM program to show the effect of mesh refinement using meshes with different densities (similar to the ones used in this chapter). Plot your FEM solutions together with the analytical solution and comment on them. If necessary, refer to Part III for modeling help.

6. Use a coarse mesh with different discretization orders, that is, linear, quadratic, cubic, and aquatic, to reexamine the stress concentration problem shown in Figure 13.7. Plot your FEM solutions together with the analytical solution. If necessary, refer to Part III for modeling help.

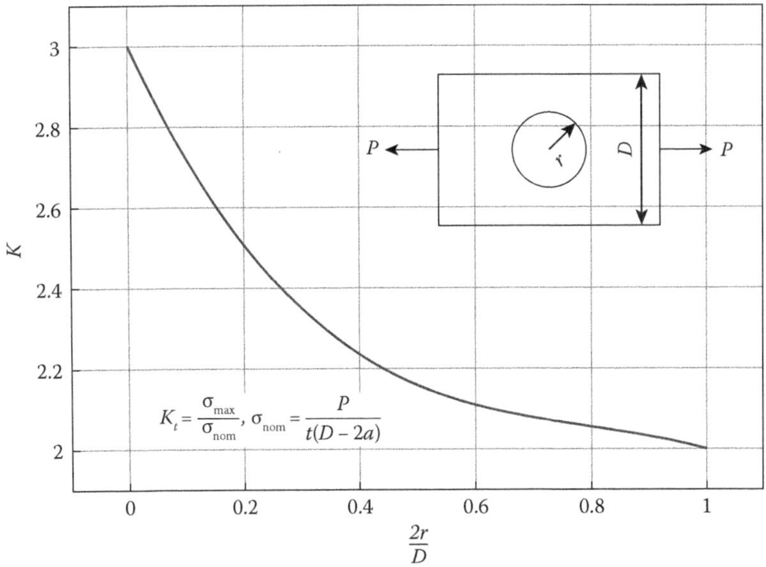

FIGURE 13.7
Stress concentration in a rectangular plate around a circular hole.

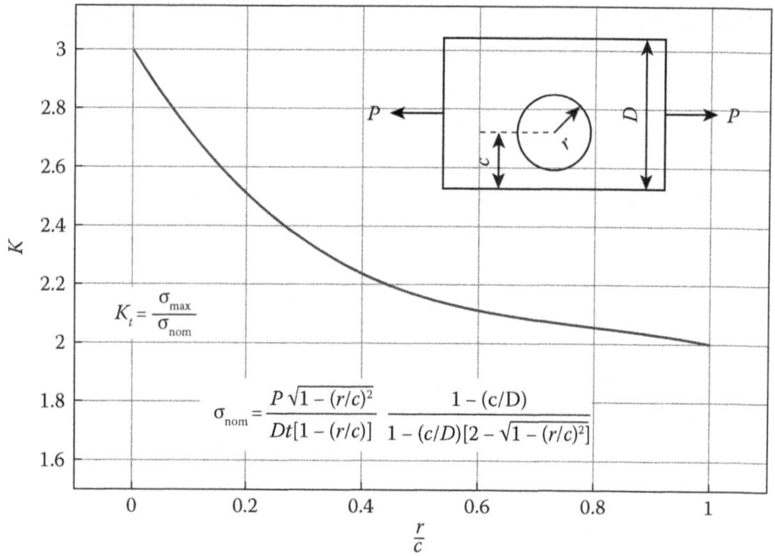

FIGURE 13.8
Stress concentration in a rectangular plate around a circular hole.

7. For the stress distribution around an off-center circular hole in a rectangular plate, as shown in Figure 13.8, the stress concentration factor can be expressed as a function of r/c as follows:

$$K_t = 3.00 - 3.13\left(\frac{r}{c}\right) + 3.66\left(\frac{r}{c}\right)^2 - 1.53\left(\frac{r}{c}\right)^3$$

where r is the radius of the circular hole, c is the off-center location of the hole, and D is the width of the rectangular plate. Use a FEM program to show the effect of mesh refinement using meshes with different densities (similar to the ones used in this chapter). Plot your FEM solutions together with the analytical solution and comment on them. If necessary, refer to Part III for modeling help.

8. Use a coarse mesh with different discretization orders, that is, linear, quadratic, cubic, and aquatic, to reexamine the stress concentration problem shown in Figure 13.8. Plot your FEM solutions together with the analytical solution. If necessary, refer to Part III for modeling help.

Recommended Reading

1. J. N. Reddy. 1993. *An Introduction to the Finite Element Method.* 2nd ed. Boston: McGraw-Hill.

Part III

Developing Hands-On Modeling Skills

14

A Quick Tour of the COMSOL Modeling Environment

The discussions in Part II apply to any finite element method (FEM) modeling software, such as COMSOL, ABAQUS, and ANSYS, as well as free-ware packages. In this chapter, we briefly introduce the COMSOL platform and highlight some of the connections between software settings and the FEM fundamentals.

In a nutshell, a simple way to understand how a computer model based on FEM should be developed is to keep in mind how a differential equation is defined and solved. Based on the discussions in Part II, we can list a partial differential equation (PDE)–solving procedure as follows:

1. Define the physics: the underlying governing PDE(s).
2. Specify the spacial dimension: the number of independent spacial variables in the PDE(s).
3. Specify time dependency: whether the PDE(s) is time dependent.
4. Define the domain: the geometric construct or space over which the PDE(s) is solved.
5. Define the coefficients: the material or other related properties for the domain.
6. Set the study: the type of phenomena one seeks to investigate, such as static or steady state, dynamic, and eigenvalues.
7. Apply boundary and initial conditions: the constraints at the boundaries and at the beginning of an event if time dependent.
8. Apply loading conditions: internal and external sources of loads or other forms of energy, and so forth.
9. Choose elements and their discretization order: the type of elements and the order of discretization.

14.1 COMSOL Starting Screen

Now let us have a look at the COMSOL interface to familiarize ourselves with some of the key attributes, features, and functions of COMSOL and relate them to the items in the procedural list above.

Figure 14.1 shows the screen image of COMSOL at the launch of the software. At this stage, we can select either Model Wizard to take a step-by-step approach to build models or Blank Model to build models at will. An easy way to start a new model is to take the Model Wizard step-by-step route (see Figure 14.2a), while the at-will Blank Model route is suited for more experienced users or for accessing existing models. For example, clicking Blank Model will send us directly to the COMSOL working environment, as shown in Figure 14.2b where we can work on all aspects of modeling at will.

14.2 Making Initial Selections Step-By-Step

We now take a step-by-step approach to see what are the main selections we have to make before reaching the COMSOL modeling working environment.

14.2.1 Selecting spacial dimension

After clicking the Model Wizard button, the first step is to Select Space Dimension, as shown in Figure 14.3. This is where we decide the spacial

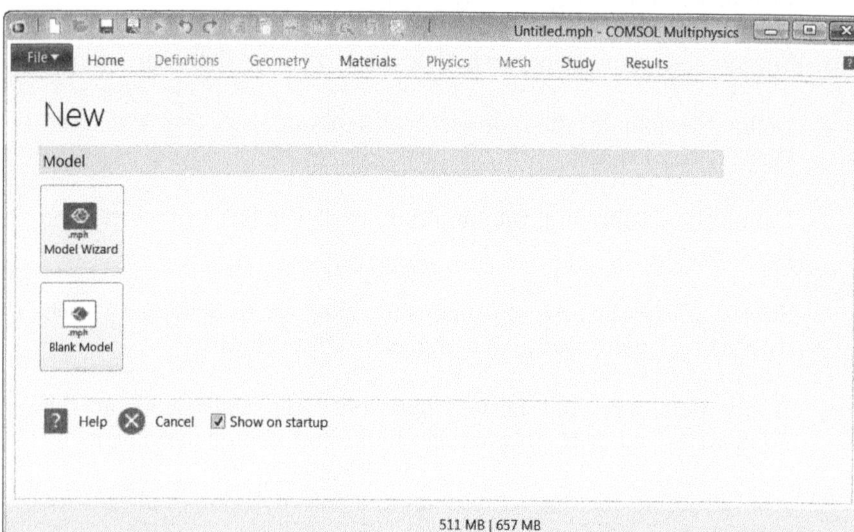

FIGURE 14.1
COMSOL starting screen.

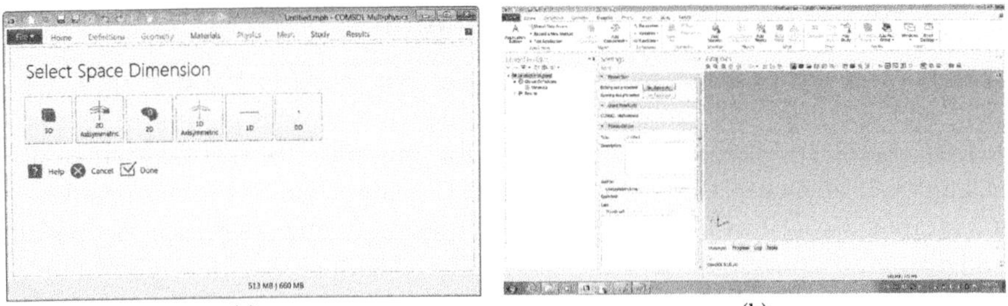

(a) (b)

FIGURE 14.2
COMSOL user interfaces showing two possible ways to start modeling: (a) through the Model Wizard route and (b) through the Blank Model route.

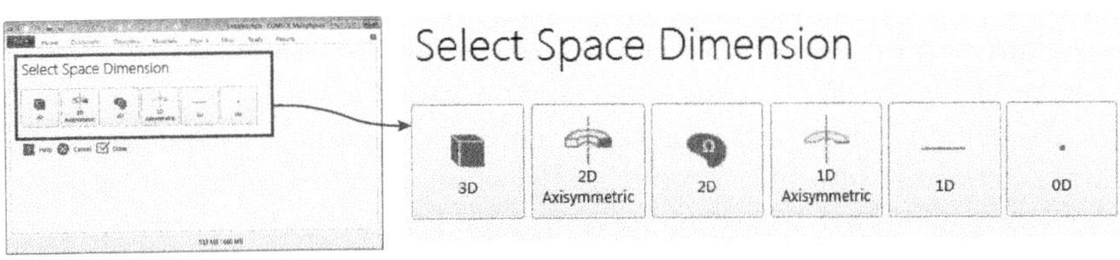

FIGURE 14.3
Determining the spacial dimension for the model.

dimension in which the PDE is to be solved. The choices we have are 3D, 2D Axisymmetric, 2D, 1D Axisymmetric, 1D, and 0D. Recall the discussions in Chapter 2; the selection should be as follows:

- If the problem we intend to solve, or the governing PDE of the problem, has three spacial independent variables (e.g., x, y, and z), select 3D.
- If the 3D problem has the rotational features discussed in Chapter 9, select 2D Axisymmetric.
- If the governing PDE of the problem has two spacial variables, select 2D.
- If the 2D problem has the rotational features as discussed in Chapter 9, select 1D Axisymmetric.
- If the governing PDE of the problem has one spacial variable, select 1D.
- If the governing PDE of the problem has no spacial variable, select 0D. In this case, the PDE is likely a time-dependent equation with no reference to spacial dimensions. Thus, this type of PDE is sometimes called a point equation—hence 0D.

14.2.2 Selecting proper physics modules

After choosing a spacial dimension, the next step is to Select Physics, as shown in Figure 14.4. This is where we need to decide what physics module(s) will be needed to solve the PDE from a list of available modules. Recall the discussions in Chapter 3; in each of these modules, a PDE of a particular physics problem, for example, structural mechanics, mass diffusion, heat transfer, or electrical problems, is to be solved.

If the problem to be solved is governed by a single physics principle, a single module is sufficient, but if the problem is governed by a set of multiple physics principles, all relevant modules will need to be selected. Aside from picking the right module(s), this is also the moment we have the opportunity to review the physics interface to make proper changes if desirable. For example, we may give the dependent variables specific names, or add more dependent variables in situations where the diffusion of multiple species is considered. If we were to solve a problem of mass transport of chemical species, we would click and expand Chemical Species Transport to select Transport of Diluted Species. If we were dealing with the diffusion of five chemical species, we would enter 5 to replace the default value of 1 as the number of dependent variables. Once all is set, we then click the Add button to load the selected module to the Added Physics Interfaces box, as shown in Figure 14.4, to activate the module(s).

14.2.3 Selecting a proper type of study

The next step is to Select Study. To do that, we just click the Study arrow button, which will lead us to the interface shown in Figure 14.5. This is where we tell the software if the problem, or the PDE(s), we intend to solve is time dependent or independent, or if the problem is an eigenvalue problem (e.g., linear buckling or modal analysis) or an eigenfrequency problem

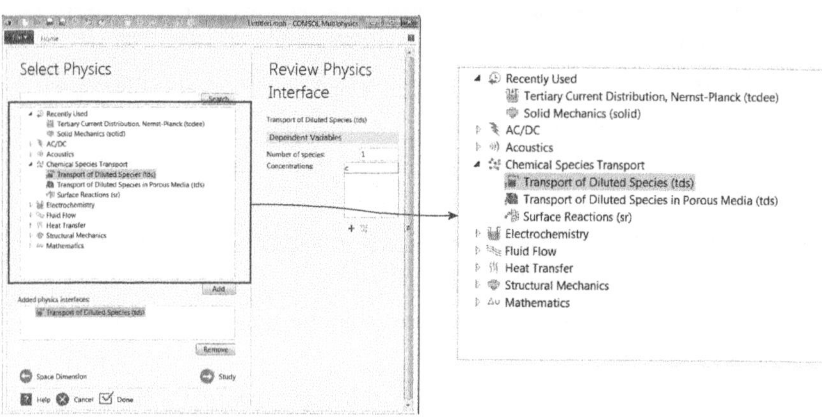

FIGURE 14.4
Selecting the right physics module(s) for the model.

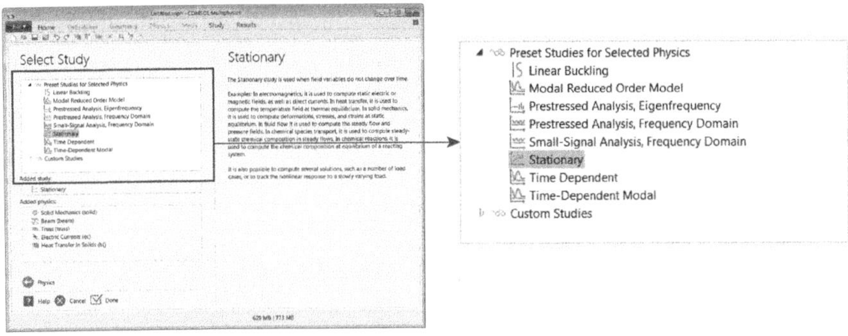

FIGURE 14.5
Selecting the right study for the model.

(e.g., resonant frequency), from a list of Preset Studies or Custom Studies if we have a different need.

14.3 Getting Familiar with the Modeling Environment

Once these three main selections are made, we just click the Done check box to go to the modeling working environment, as shown in Figure 14.6, where we will deal with the rest of the modeling issues. Note that the working environments shown in Figures 14.2b and 14.6 are almost identical except that

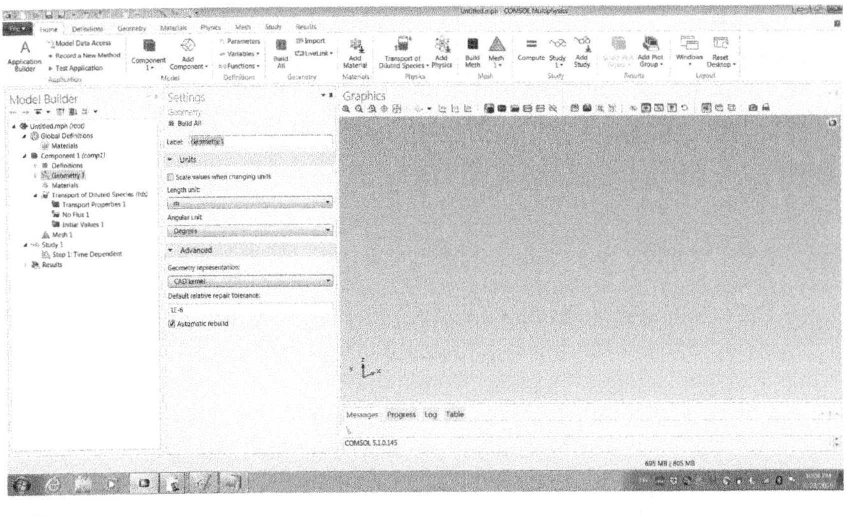

FIGURE 14.6
COMSOL modeling environment.

in the former, the three selections, namely, dimension, physics, and study, have not been made. Of course, for an experienced modeler, making these selections at this stage is an easy task.

In a close look at the COMSOL modeling environment shown in Figure 14.6, we note that it is further grouped into three main windows: (1) Model Builder, (2) Settings, and (3) Graphics. Let us now discuss what each of the components does.

14.3.1 Model Builder window

As highlighted in Figures 14.7 and 14.8, the Model Builder window is like a model building tree, listing all attributes of the model under development (see Figure 14.7a), including defining parameters and variables to be used in the model (Figure 14.7b), building geometry for the domain over which the governing PDE(s) is solved (Figure 14.7c), and selecting materials (Figure 14.7d). Note that there are two levels of definitions, one at the global level (Global Definitions) and the other at the component level (Component → Definitions). Under the Component Definition tab, we can further define variables, functions, component couplings, and so forth. For example, integration coupling can be added here to perform numerical integration of variables of interest.

Moreover, we can also set boundary and initial conditions, as well as other constraints for the PDE(s) (Figure 14.8a), and mesh the geometry for domain discretization, as well as further tune the study (Figure 14.8b). Finally, we can access the results for reviewing and analyzing (Figure 14.8a).

This tree type listing of all modeling attributes provides a quick overall view, as well as easy access to all the modeling setups for modifications, additions or deletions, enabling or disabling, and many more. Each of the tabs in the Model Builder trees can be expanded through right-clicking for viewing and accessing many more attributes and functionalities. These illustrations highlight just some of these functionalities.

14.3.2 Settings window

The Settings window shown in Figures 14.9 and 14.10 is where all the data entry and selection of units, among others, take place. For example, by highlighting the Geometry tab in the Model Builder window, we can select a proper units system for both the linear and angular dimensions of the model in the Settings window (see Figure 14.9a) from a list of built-in unit systems, and by adding a block feature to the geometry tab to build the geometry for a cubic domain, we will enter the size, position, rotation angle, and other geometric information for the block here (see Figure 14.9b). If an integration coupling function is defined in the component definitions, we can select the domain, boundary, edge, or point where the integration is to be performed in the corresponding Settings window, as well as the integration order (i.e., the number

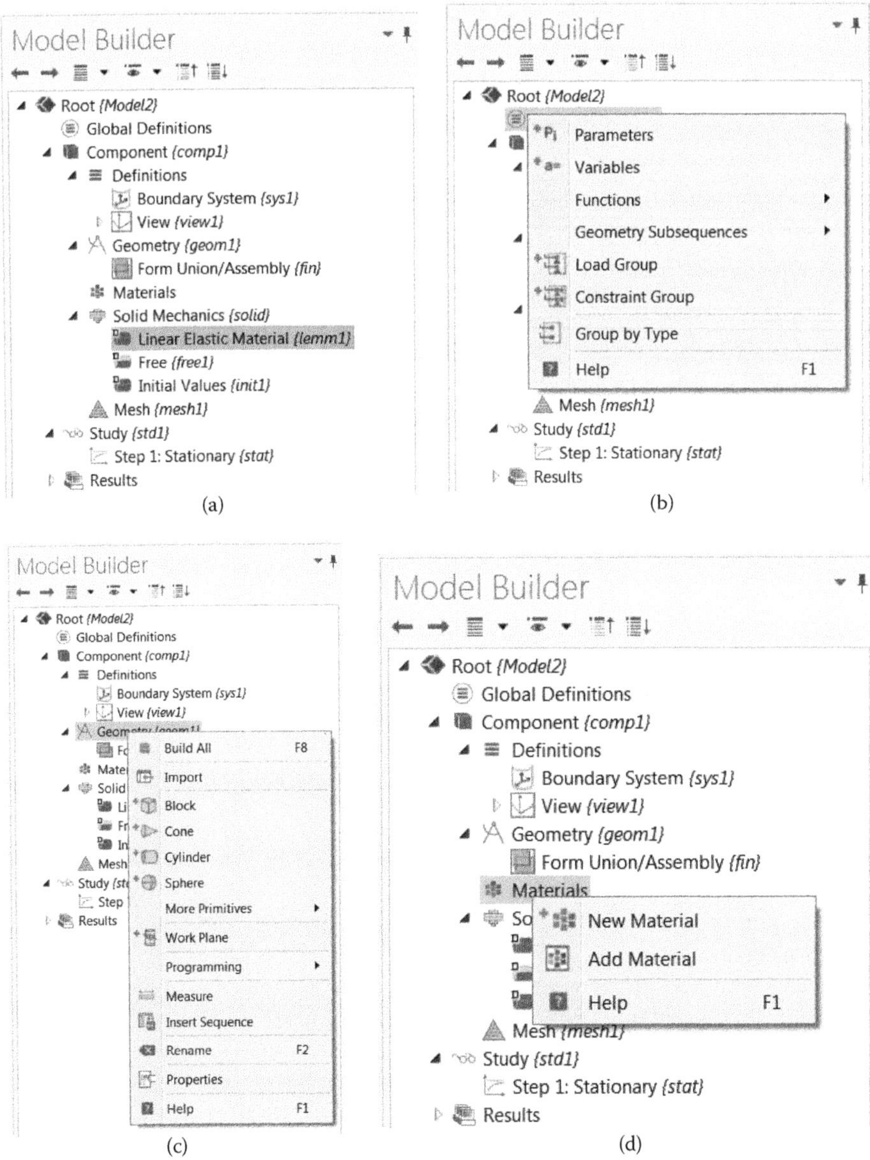

FIGURE 14.7
Close look at the Model Builder window. An overall view of the Model Builder node (a) and expanded views of the settings under global definitions (b), geometry (c), and materials (d).

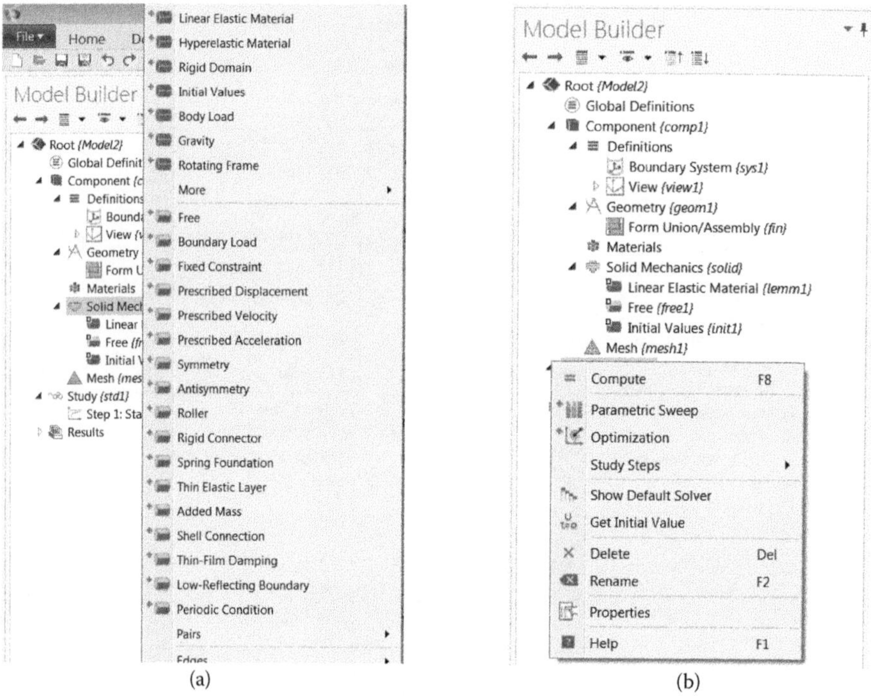

FIGURE 14.8
Close look at the Model Builder window. Expanded views of the Solid Mechanics node (a) and Study node (b).

of Gauss points to be used to calculate the integration; see Chapter 11 for more discussion).

We can view the underlying PDE(s) and change the order of element discretization in the Settings window, as shown in Figure 14.10a from a list of Linear, Quadratic, Cubic, Quartic, and so forth. Note that in many other software packages, selection of the order of element discretization is taken care of together with the selection of element types. In COMSOL, these two choices are made in separate places. Moreover, in COMSOL's default setting, the Discretization box may not be visible. If so, one can activate it by expanding the "eye icon" at the top of the Model Builder window (Figure 14.7a) to check it out.

We can also modify a material's properties (Figure 14.10b), change the type of mesh density (Figure 14.10c) to be used for the model, and tune the study settings (Figure 14.10d), such as deciding how the selected physics modules are combined, or not, and whether the Include geometric nonlinearity box should be checked. These are just a few highlights of the many setting functionalities available in the software.

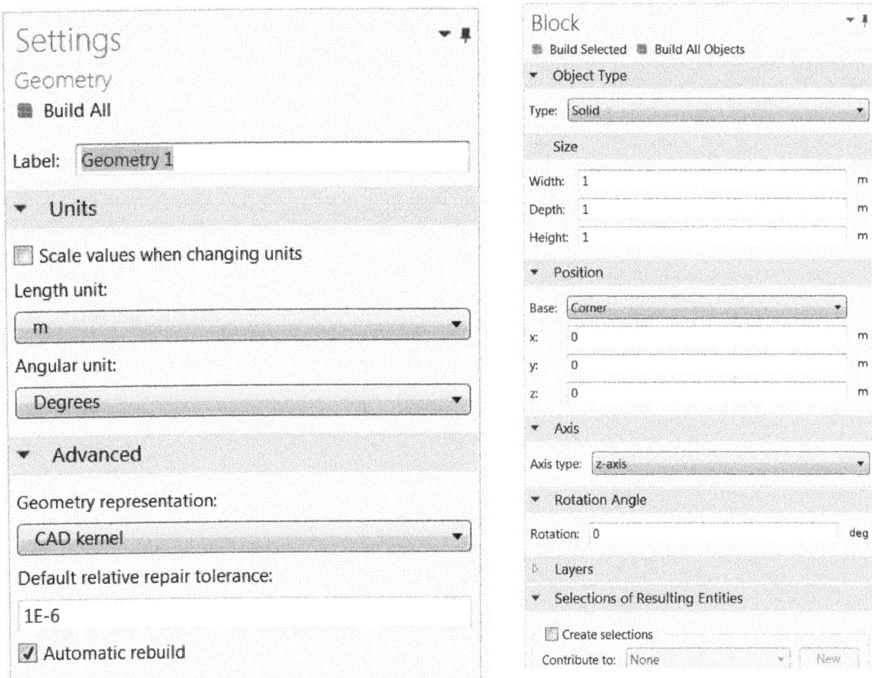

FIGURE 14.9
Close look at the Settings window. Expanded views of the Setting node (a) and Block node (b).

14.3.3 Graphics window

The Graphics window shown in Figure 14.11 is where the geometry of the model, meshing outcome, results, and so forth. are presented for real-time visualization and other postprocessing purposes. Zooming and panning functions, as well as various surface rendering tools, are available at the top. Moreover, output functions in the form of snapshot images and data can be made to files and other formats.

14.4 A Practical Sense of Building Proper Models

It is now clear that all the selection entries in the preceding sections are for providing the necessary information for solving PDE(s). Thus, another way to get a sense of whether one has done all that is required to build a proper computational model is to check if all the items listed in the procedural list at the beginning of this chapter have been taken care of.

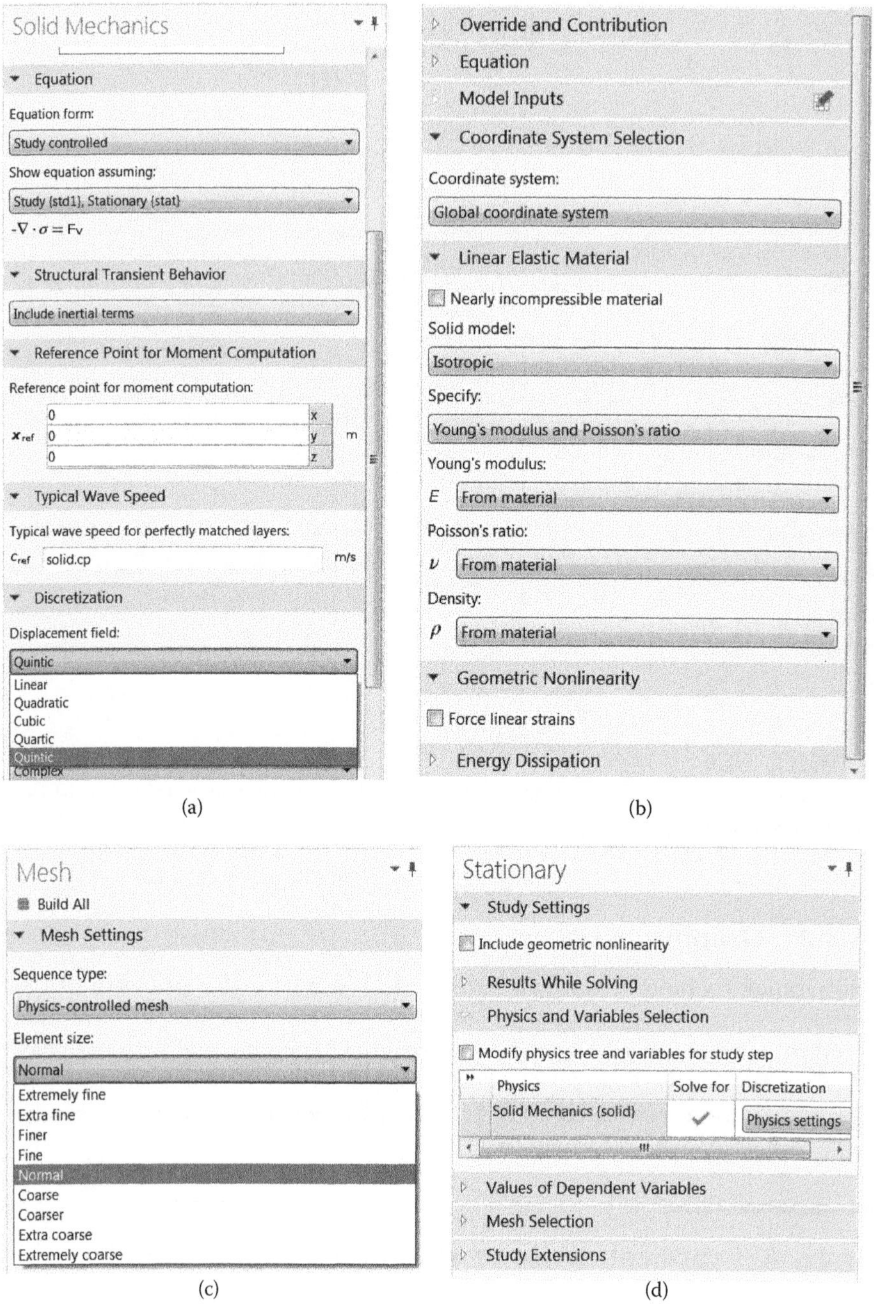

FIGURE 14.10
Close look at the Settings window. Expanded views of the Solid Mechanics node with the types of discretization highlighted (a), material property setting (b), mesh setting (c), and stationary study settings (d).

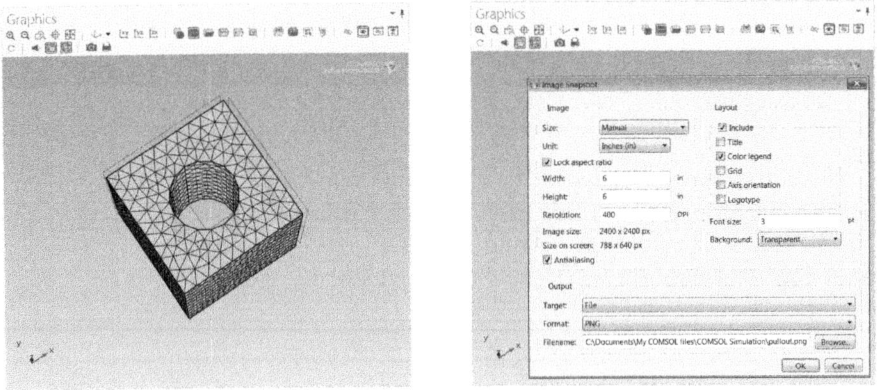

(a) (b)

FIGURE 14.11
Close look at the Graphics window. A 3D object (a) and graphics output window (b) are shown.

14.5 Modeling Example: Tuning the Sound of Music

In Section 3.2, we developed the PDE for a vibrating string of length L fixed at its two ends, A and B, as depicted in Figure 14.12 (see Equation 3.3):

$$\rho_l \frac{\partial^2 u}{\partial t^2}(x,t) = T\frac{\partial^2 u}{\partial x^2}(x,t)$$

where u is the transverse vibrational displacement, ρ_l is the linear density (i.e., mass per unit length) of the string material, and T is the tension force in the string. In this section, we relate this physics phenomenon and mathematic equation to our daily life—the tuning of strings in string instruments—to highlight some connections between modeling settings and the FEM fundamentals discussed in Part II.

Consider the string shown in Figure 14.12 as a string in a violin or gaiter, or any other kind of string instrument. With the above PDE, we can express

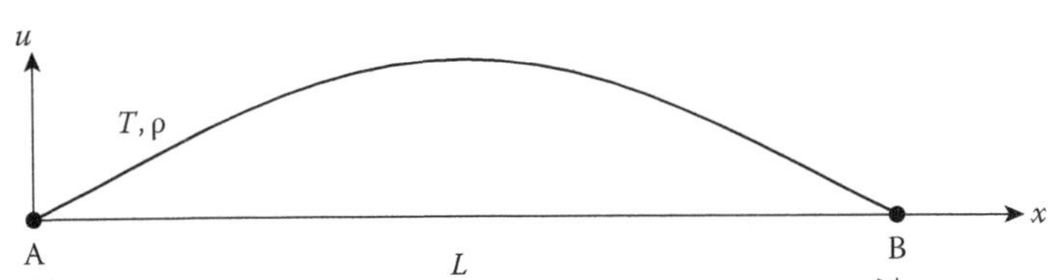

FIGURE 14.12
Vibrating string in a string instrument.

the propagation speed of sound waves in the string as

$$v = \sqrt{\frac{T}{\rho_l}} = \lambda f$$

in which λ is the wavelength ($\lambda = 2L$) and f is the resonant frequency, or the first eigenfrequency in this case (see more discussion in Chapter 12). Let ρ be the mass density of the string material and A the cross section area of the string; we then express the resonant frequency as

$$f = \frac{1}{2L}\sqrt{\frac{T}{\rho A}} \tag{14.1}$$

Clearly, even with a fixed length, the resonant frequency of the string changes as the tension in the string and the diameter of the string change. This is the principle guiding the tuning of string instruments like violins and gaiters.

14.5.1 Tuning a string by adjusting string tension

We now use this fun phenomenon to learning some hands-on modeling skills to do some tuning of the string, namely, to determine the first eigenfrequency of the string as a function of the string tension. Considering a string of 50 cm in length and 1 mm in diameter made of nylon, we will use COMSOL to adjust the tension from 100 to 250 N, and determine the value for the eigenfrequency at each string tension. As a way to validate the modeling results, we will compare the COMSOL results with the predictions based on the analytical solution given in Equation 14.1. Below are the procedural steps to perform this modeling analysis.

Step-by-Step Modeling Procedures

Launch COMSOL; if already in, from the **File** menu, choose **New**.

Click the **Model Wizard** button.

1. In the **Model Wizard** window, click the **2D** button. Note that the eigenfrequency module is available only to dimensions of 2D and above in COMSOL.
2. In the **Select Physics** window, select **Structural Mechanics** → **Truss (truss)**, and then click the **Add** button. Here, we consider the string as a truss structure instead of a beam structure by ignoring the rotational constraints (see discussion in Section 5.7.2).

3. Click the **Study** button, select **Preset Studies** → **Eigenfrequency**, and then click the **Done** button.

Global Definitions → Parameters

1. In the **Parameters** settings window, enter the following (note that the value column will be resolved by the program) to define three parameters for the tension, diameter, and length of the string and assign some initial values. Note that parameters defined here will be available for parametric studies later on.

Name	**Expression**	**Value**	**Description**
T	100 (N)	—	String tension
d	1 (mm)	—	String diameter
L	50 (cm)	—	String length

Component → Definitions → Variables

1. In the **Variables** settings window, enter the following (note that the Units column will be resolved by the program) to define three variables, namely, the resonant frequency calculated using Equation 14.1 to be used for results comparison, the cross section area of the string calculated using the string diameter, and the tension stress calculated based on the definition of stress, that is, tension force divided by cross section area.

Name	**Expression**	**Units**	**Description**
f0	sqrt(T/truss.rho*A)/(2*L)	—	String resonant frequency
A	pi*d^2/4	—	String cross section area
sigma	T/A	—	Initial stress in string

Geometry → Bezier Polygon

1. In the **Bezier Polygon** settings window, click **Add Linear** and enter the following:

	x	y
1	L	0
2	0	0

Material → Add Material → Built In → Nylon

1. In the **Add Material** window, click **Add to Component** to upload the material data.

Truss → Linear Elastic Material

1. Right-click **Linear Elastic Material** and select **Initial Stress and Strain.**
2. In the **Initial Stress and Strain** settings window, enter **sigma** in the **Initial axial stress** box.
3. Click **Cross Section Data** and in the **Boundary Selection** settings window, enter **A** in the **Area** box.
4. Disable the **Straight Edge Constraint** to allow transverse displacements.
5. Right-click **Truss** and add a **Pinned** boundary condition.
6. Click **Pinned** and in the **Point Selection** settings window, and select **All points** in the selection box.

Mesh

1. In the **Mesh** settings window, select **Physics-controlled mesh** for the sequence type and **Fine** for the element size; then click **Build All.**

Study → Step 1: Eigenfrequency

1. In the **Eigenfrequency** settings window, enter **1** for the Desired number of eigenfrequencies, **300** for the Search for eigenfrequency around, and make sure the **Include geometric nonlinearity** box is checked to allow large transverse deformation (see discussion in Appendix A).

2. Right-click **Study** and select **Parametric Sweep**.
3. In the **Parametric Sweep** settings window, click the + button in the Study Settings section to add a parameter to the list.
4. In the table, enter the following settings:

Parameter names	Parameter value list
T	range(100[N],10[N],250[N])

5. In the **Eigenvalue Solver** settings window, enter **1e-3** in the Relative tolerance in the General section near the top.
6. Click **Study**, and in the **Study** settings window click = **Compute** to perform the analysis.

Figure 14.13 shows the outcome after the analysis is completed.

Results → Derived Values → Global Evaluation

1. In the **Global Evaluation** settings window, locate the Data section and choose **Solution 2** from the Data set list, choose **All** from the Parameter selection list, select **First** from the Eigenfrequency selection list, and **Inner Solutions** from the Table column list.

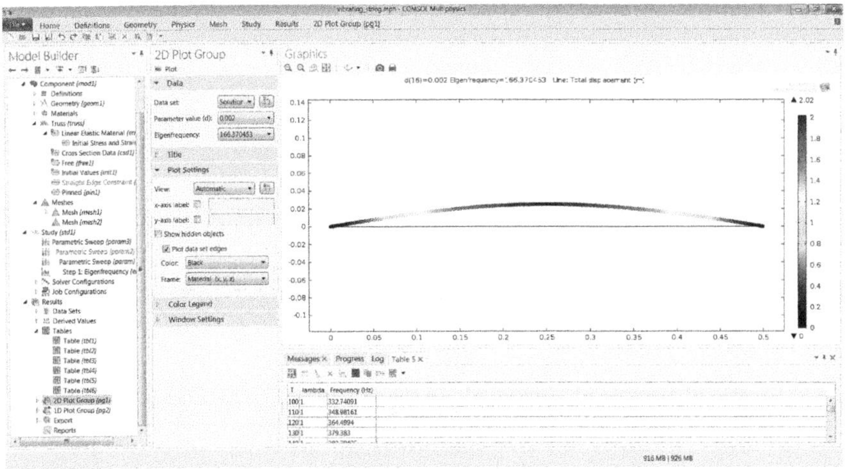

FIGURE 14.13
First eigenmode of the vibrating string.

2. Click Replace Expression → Truss → Frequency (truss.freq).

3. Right-click Global Evaluation and choose **Evaluate → New Table**.

After copying the data in the table to a spreadsheet, we plot the variation of string resonant frequency as a function of string tension, as shown in Figure 14.14. As a means to validate the modeling results, we also plot the analytical solution based on Equation 14.1. Clearly, the COMSOL results overlap with the analytical solution exactly, suggesting the validity of the modeling results.

From Figure 14.14, we can see that the string resonant frequency increases with the increase in string tension in a slightly nonlinear manner. Intuitively, the results make sense, as we all know that the greater one tightens the string tension, the higher pitch the string becomes—hence higher frequency. However, if we pay attention to the value of the induced frequency, we note that such a drastic increase in the string tension from 100 to 250 N has only caused it to increase from approximately 330–530 Hz. Knowing that the string could easily break under a high tension, we may conclude that varying the pitch of the string by tightening the string does not provide much flexibility.

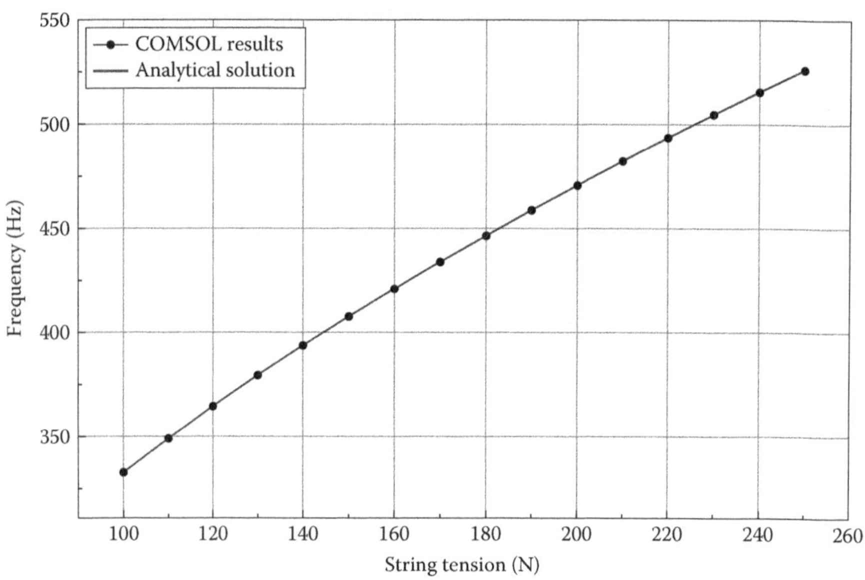

FIGURE 14.14
Variation of string resonant frequency with tension.

14.5.2 Changing pitches using strings of different sizes

Now let us consider the same string to see if using strings of different sizes will fare better in terms of proving more flexibility to having a wider range of frequencies. So by fixing the string tension at 100 N, we will determine the string resonant frequency as a function of the string diameter varying from 0.5 to 2 mm.

To model this problem, all we need to do is to set up another parametric sweep. An easy way to do this without increasing the file size significantly is to disable the previous sweep and enable the newly added parametric sweep as follows.

Modeling Procedures

1. Right-click **Parametric Sweep(param)** and select **Disable**.
2. Right-click **Study** and select **Parametric Sweep** to add a new parametric sweep **Parametric Sweep(param2)**.
3. In the **Parametric Sweep(param2)** settings window, click the + button in the Study Settings section to add a parameter to the list

Parameter names	Parameter value list
d	range(0.5[mm],0.1[mm],2.0[mm])

4. Click **Study**, and in the **Study** settings window click = **Compute** to perform the analysis.

Again, after exporting the data in the table to a spreadsheet using the same steps discussed earlier, we plot the variation of string resonant frequency as a function of string diameter, as shown in Figure 14.15. As validation, the analytical solution is also plotted. The COMSOL results overlap exactly with the analytical solution, suggesting the validity of the modeling results.

From Figure 14.15, we can see that the string resonant frequency decreases with the increase in string diameter in a nonlinear manner. Intuitively, the results make sense, as we all know that the thicker the string is, the lower pitch the string becomes (or lower frequency). With a close look at the value of the induced frequency, we note that this time the range of frequency is much wider, from approximately 660 to 170 Hz as the string diameter increases

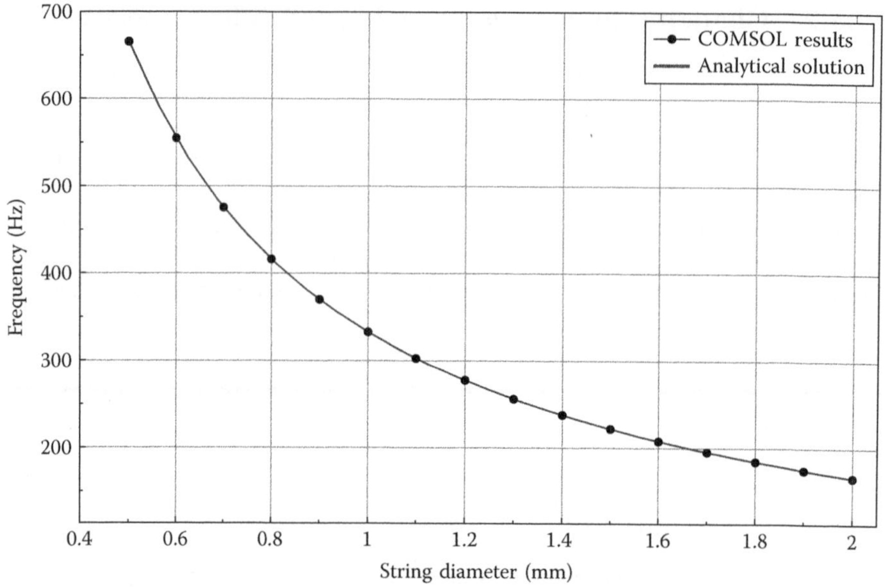

FIGURE 14.15
Variation of string resonant frequency with diameter.

from 0.5 to 2.0 mm. Knowing this fact, it is logical to use strings of several different diameters to achieve a wider range of pitches in a string instrument.

14.5.3 Taking advantage of COMSOL tutorials

The COMSOL software package comes with numerous tutorials showing step-by-step instructions for the modeler to gain hands-on skills and technical proficiency. Some of these tutorials are examples that highlight the coupling of multiple modules and will help set the reader on a path to integrative engineering problem solving.

1. Fluid-Structure Interaction
2. Fluid-Structure Interaction in a Network of Blood Vessels
3. SAW Gas Sensor
4. Convective Cooling of a Busbar
5. Electrical Heating in a Busbar
6. Joule Heating of a Microactuator

Besides these examples, the reader is encouraged to go through other exercises as well (the more the better) to become well versed with COMSOL terminologies, interfaces, attributes, and so on.

14.6 Taking Advantage of COMSOL's Geometric Parameterization Capability

In many design, analysis, and optimization practices, it is ideal to have a means to quickly adjust the geometric domains so that different concepts and designs can be tested and optimized. To meet this need, COMSOL software has provided a useful feature allowing geometric parameterization. With this capability, the modeler can define geometric dimensions in the forms of parameters that can be easily adjusted for the purpose of modifying the shape of the geometric domains without going back to the geometry creation step. This change of the value of the geometric parameters can be done either discretely, one value at a time, or continuously in a parametric sweep manner.

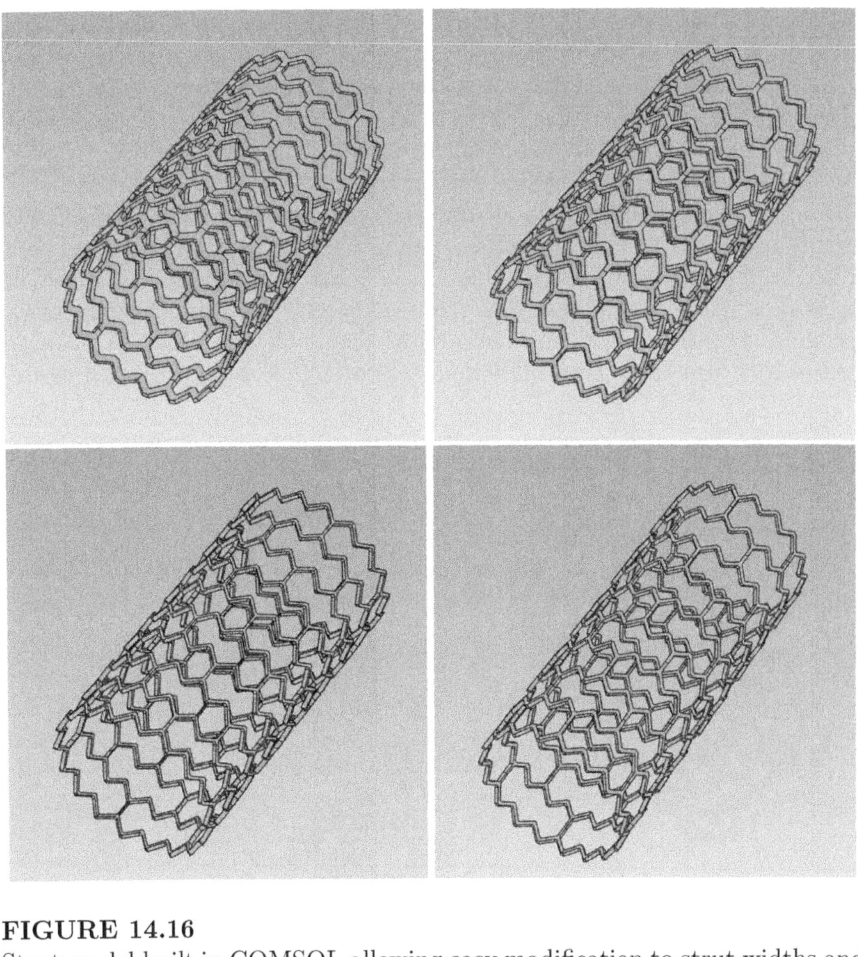

FIGURE 14.16
Stent model built in COMSOL allowing easy modification to strut widths and gaps.

Here, let us have a look at an example to see how useful this geometric parameterization capability is. Figure 14.16 shows an example in which a model of a coronary stent is built in COMSOL. Note that a coronary stent is a tube-shaped wire-mesh device (often made of memory alloy) used in the coronary arteries to keep the arteries open for the blood flow to the heart in the treatment of coronary heart disease.

With COMSOL's geometric parameterization capability, the design of the stent in terms of cylindrical dimensions, strut patterns, and dimensions, including strut width and gap, can be easily adjusted by simply assigning different values to these parameters after the model is built. As shown in Figure 14.16, the strut widths and gaps can be modified easily by assigning different values for these strut parameters. Figure 14.17 shows the stent model after the meshing step in COMSOL, in which fine tetrahedral elements are used for domain discretization.

Figure 14.18a shows the distribution of the obtained von Mises stress in the stent, and Figure 14.18b shows the distribution of the first principal stress in the stent. From these stresses, two interesting observations can be made. On the one hand, the von Mises stress is high along all the circumference rings of struts. This is true throughout the stent, as the high stresses are visible from both the inside and outside surfaces of the stent. On the other hand, the first principal stress is high at different regions on the inside and outside surfaces of the stent. On the inside surface, the first principal stress is high on the bridges of struts, and on the outside surface, it is high at the feet of the bridges. Referring to the discussions in Section A.7, we know that the mechanical stress states in the stent are quite complicated. Due to the phase transition nature of memory alloy materials of which stents are often made,

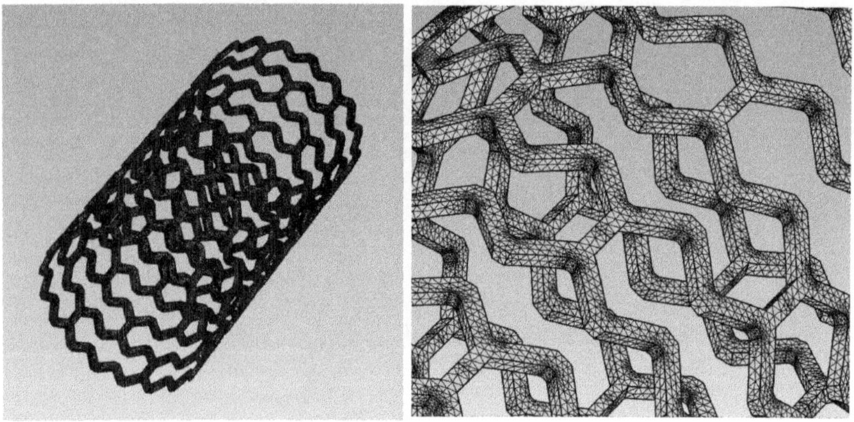

(a) (b)

FIGURE 14.17
Stent model after meshing in an overall view (a) and a close-up view (b).

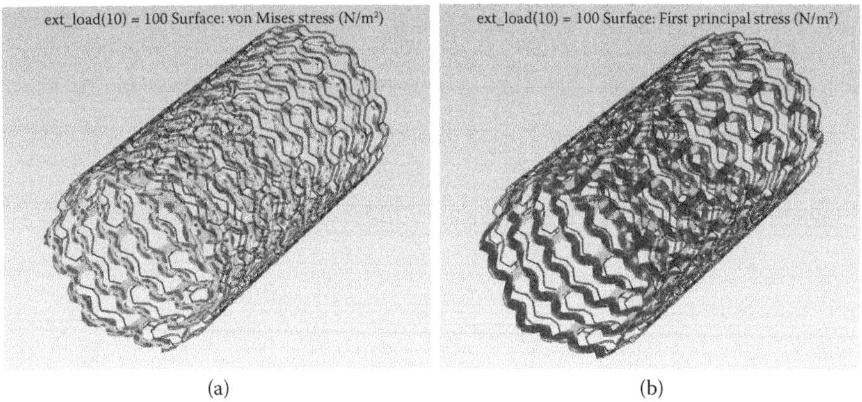

FIGURE 14.18
(a) Induced von Mises and (b) first principal stresses in the stent subjected to a radially inward pressure loading condition.

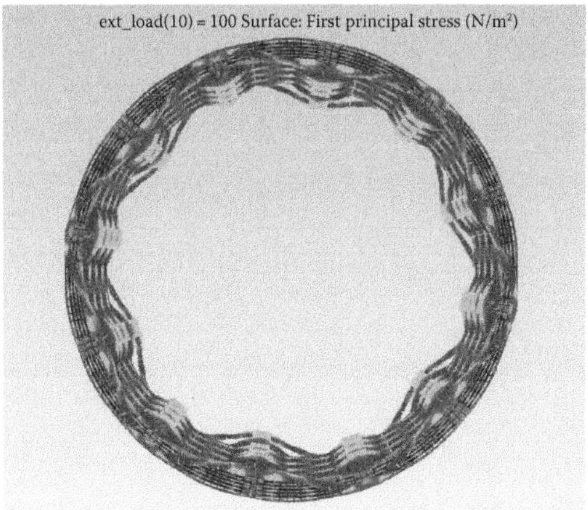

FIGURE 14.19
Longitudinal view of the induced deformation, along with the first principal stresses in the stent.

all these regions of high von Mises and first principal stresses are of concern in terms of failure analysis and prediction.

Figure 14.19 shows a longitudinal view of the induced deformation in the stent, along with the first principal stress. Although the induced deformation is exaggerated, it nevertheless indicates that all the high tensile stress (the first principal stress) in this case is due to the inward bending of the strut bridges caused by the inward pressure loading on the outer surface of the stent. Note that because the actual in vitro loading conditions may different from those applied in this study, the results presented here may not represent an actual situation.

15

A Glimpse of the ABAQUS and ANSYS User Interfaces

We now take a look at the ABAQUS and ANSYS modeling environments to gain a sense of how items such as physics, spacial dimension, time dependency, model domain, coefficients, type of study, boundary and initial conditions, and loading conditions, as well as type of elements and order of discretization, as discussed in the procedural list in Chapter 14, are taken care of in these software packages.

15.1 ABAQUS Modeling Environment

As shown in Figures 15.1 and 15.2, in a glance, the ABAQUS modeling environment has a familiar look. It consists of a pull-down menu at the top for handling File, Model, View, Part, and so forth, of the modeling needs; a Model building tree on the left for accessing all the modeling features; a Results tree that can be toggled back and forth with the Model tree; and a large Graphics window in the center to the lower right for visualization purposes.

15.1.1 Model tree in ABAQUS

Figure 15.3 shows a close view of the ABAQUS Model building tree on the left. The Model tree provides a visual description of the hierarchy of items in a model, including, categorically, Part, Materials, Assembly, Steps, and Fields. In parallel with the Model tree, an Annotations tab and an Analysis tab are also provided at the bottom.

The items in the Model tree are also called containers. Obviously, the Part container is where we define the spacial dimension and build (or import) the geometry for the model domain of the underlying problem, and the Materials container is where we assign proper material properties to the model domain. Moreover, the Assembly container is for dealing with how multiple parts, if any, in the model will be assembled, and the Step container is for defining how the model will be analyzed, and so on. The arrangement of the items in the Model tree reflects the order in which the modeler is expected to create the model.

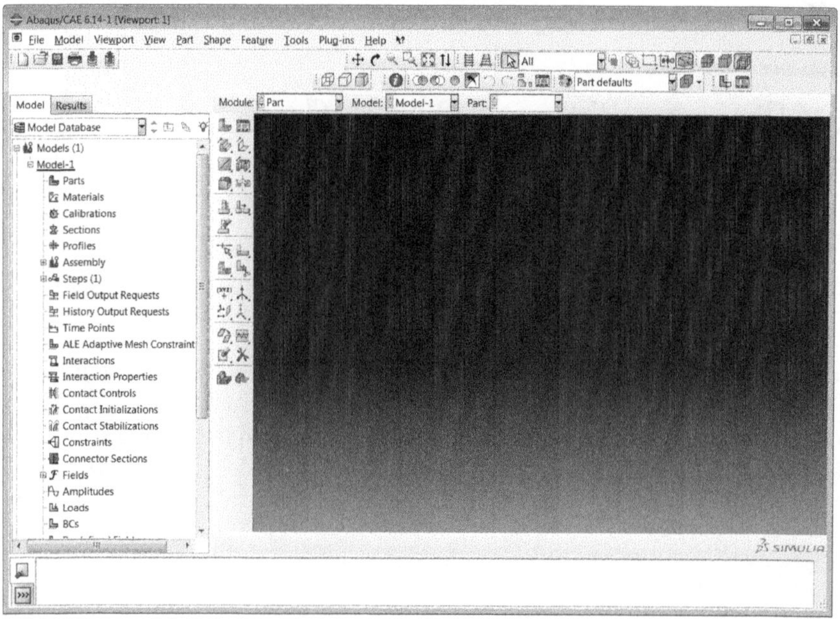

FIGURE 15.1
ABAQUS modeling environment.

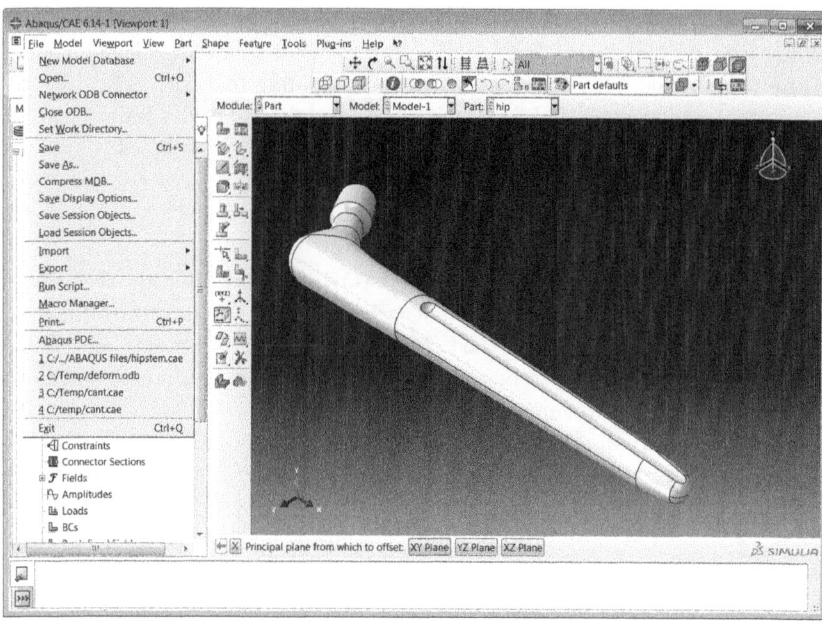

FIGURE 15.2
ABAQUS modeling environment.

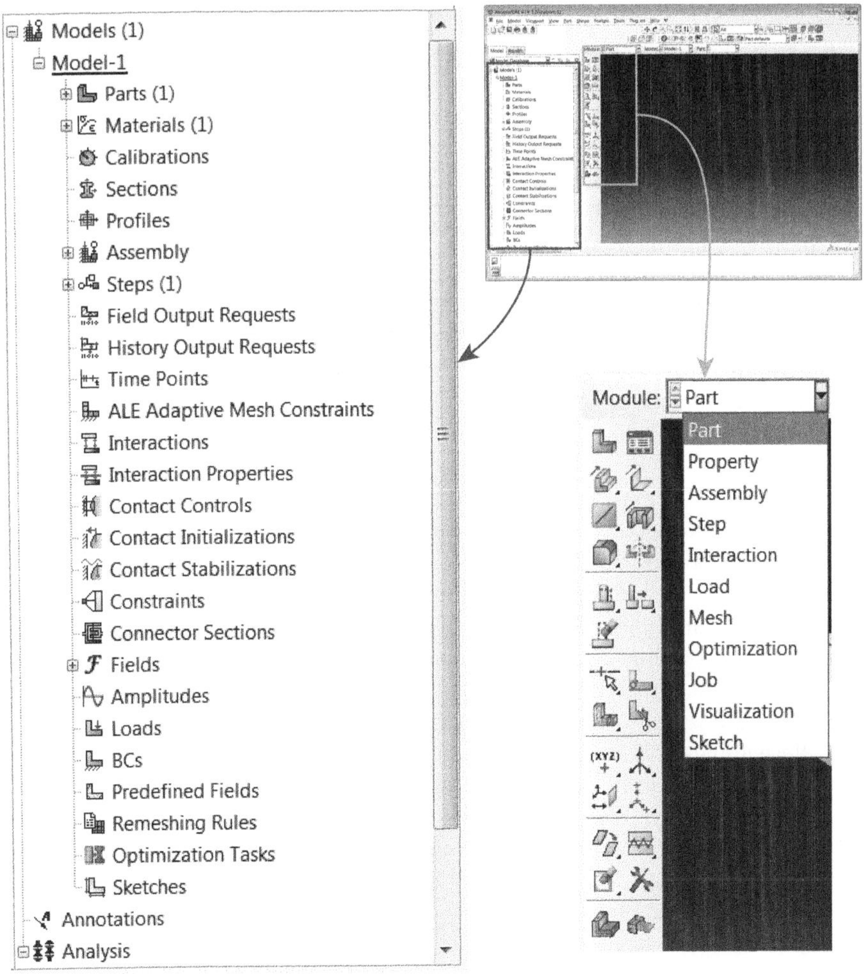

FIGURE 15.3
Close look at the ABAQUS modeling building tree.

15.1.2 Module in ABAQUS

While the Model tree provides most of the functions we would need to build a model, there is another list tab in the upper middle part of the user interface called Module, as also shown in Figure 15.3. In the Module list, we can select from an assortment of Part, Property, Assembly, Step, Interactions, Load, Mesh, Optimization, Job, Visualization, and Sketch. Note that ABAQUS's module is a different concept from that of COMSOL, where in the former, various modules refer to the various modeling components, and in the latter, various modules refer to different subphysics engines for solving different underlying differential equations.

The Module list in ABAQUS provides not only quick access to various model-building components but also lists of icons for the modeling functions corresponding to each item on the Module list. For example, by selecting Part, all the functions available for building a part will be shown in a list of icons on the left, and by selecting Property, all functions for defining the material and other related physical properties will be listed. Once an icon is clicked, more pop-up windows and dialog boxes will show up for further selections or data entry. For example, Figure 15.4 shows a pop-up window listing the choices of different types of materials for mechanical, thermal, and electrical or magnetic applications once the Create Material icon under Property is clicked. So for building a model, we can either use the Model tree to add necessary components to each container or go through the Module list.

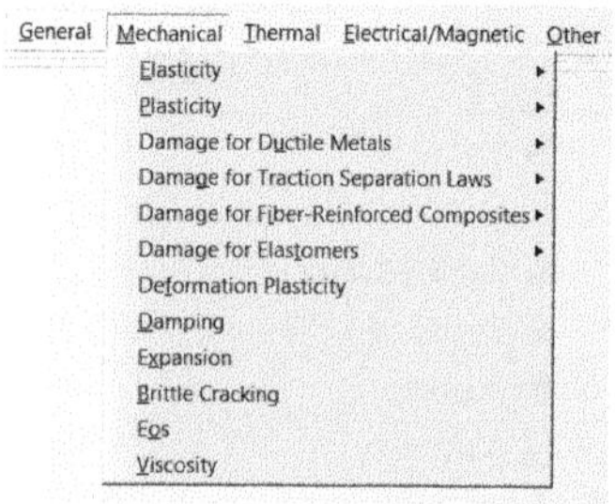

FIGURE 15.4
ABAQUS material selection window.

Aside from building the geometry from **Part**, defining the materials from **Property**, assembling parts from **Assembly**, and defining type of studies and setup analysis procedures and output requests from **Step**, other functions are also handily available here. For example, through **Interaction** we define how different parts, if any, will interact in a multiple-part assembled model; through **Load** we apply loads and boundary conditions; through **Mesh** we select proper types of elements and orders of discretization for meshing the geometric domain; through **Job** we create a job sequence for submission and analysis; and through **Visualization** we perform postanalysis. Figure 15.5 shows a close view of the Graphics window, along with rendering tool tabs at the top.

15.2 ANSYS Modeling Environment

Let us now move on to ANSYS user interfaces. As shown in Figure 15.6a and b, the ANSYS modeling environment also has a familiar look, consisting of a pull-down menu (or Utility Menu) at the top, a main menu on the left, and a graphics window in the center region. Exceptions include an Input Field allowing the user to enter programming commands directly and a Toolbar section allowing quick access of some frequent file handling functions.

In the utility pull-down menu list, there are tabs for file handling; for selection of entities, components, assembly, and so forth; and others. Each of these pull-down menus has more functions built with it. In the Toolbar, buttons for saving the file (or database [DB] in ANSYS's term inology), resuming,

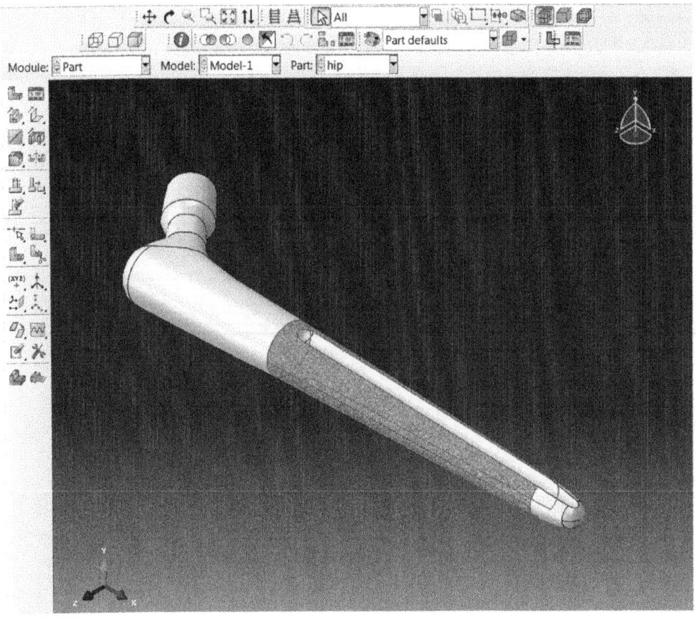

FIGURE 15.5
ABAQUS graphics window.

quitting, and so forth, are provided. In the Main Menu, there is a model building tree with key modeling components listed, including Preferences, Preprocessor, Solution, General Postproc, and TimeHist Postpro. In the Graphics window, we can see the model in development and visualize results during postprocessing.

15.2.1 Main Menu in ANSYS

We now take a close look at the Main Menu in ANSYS.

As shown in Figure 15.7a, once the **Preferences** tab in the Main Menu is clicked, a pop-up dialog box appears where we need to decide which type of physical problems to be solved among a set of choices of Structure, Thermal, ANSYS Fluid, Magnetic-Nodal, Magnetic Edge, High Frequency, and Electric. This is a like picking a physics module in COMSOL, except the choices are fewer.

By expanding the **Preprocessor** tab, we will see many more functions, as highlighted in Figure 15.7b–e. Here, we can pick the right type of elements and discretization order through **Element Type**. Figure 15.8 shows the pop-up window for selecting the type of elements. Moreover, we can apply boundary conditions using **Real Constraints**, and select the right materials through **Material Props**. Figure 15.7b shows some further choices once **Material Props** is expanded.

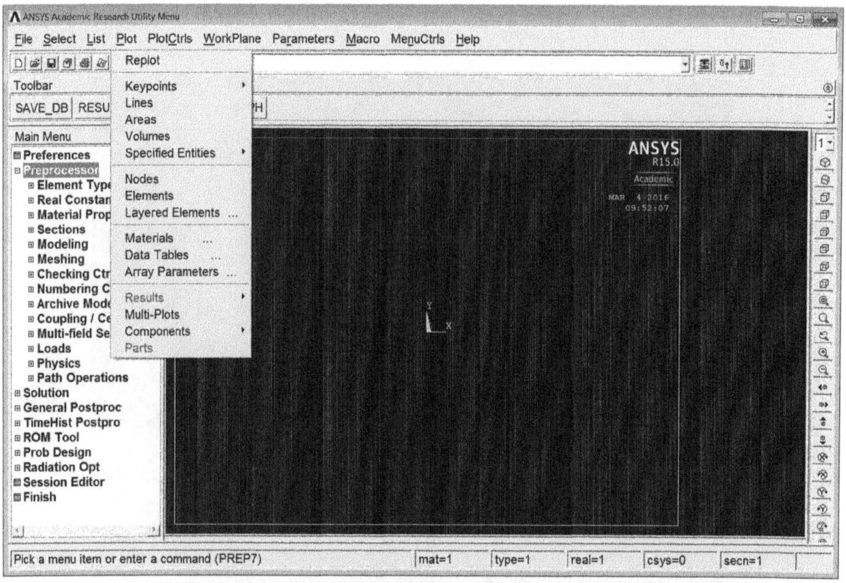

(a)

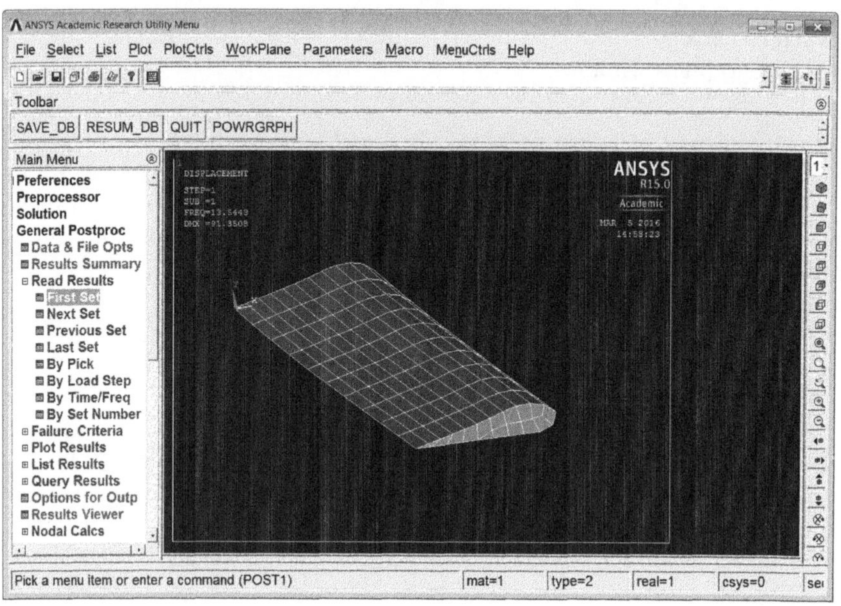

(b)

FIGURE 15.6
ANSYS modeling environment. An expanded view of the Plot function (a) and an example model (b).

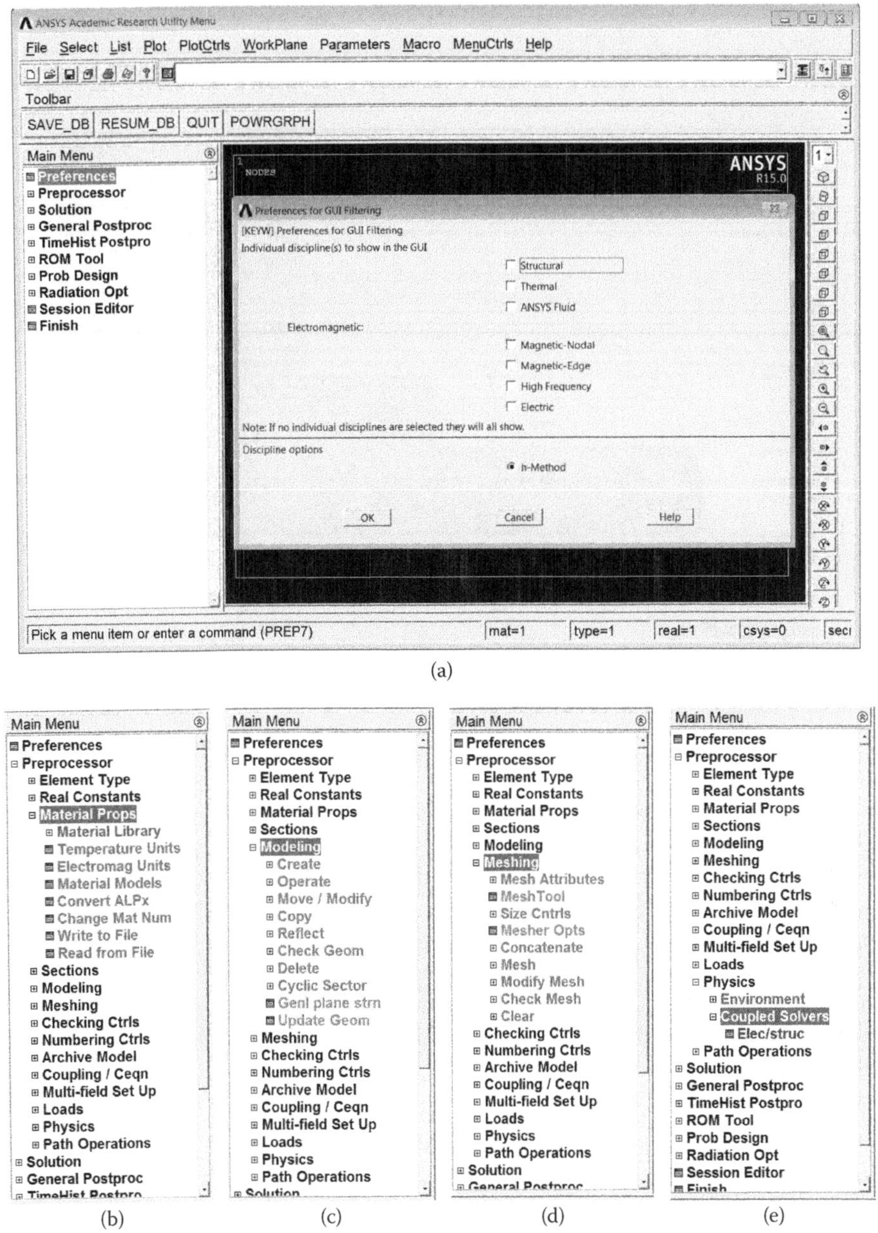

FIGURE 15.7
Close look at the ANSYS main menu. Expanded views of the Preferences setting window (a), the Material properties setting (b), the Modeling setting (c), the Meshing setting (d), and the Physics setting (e).

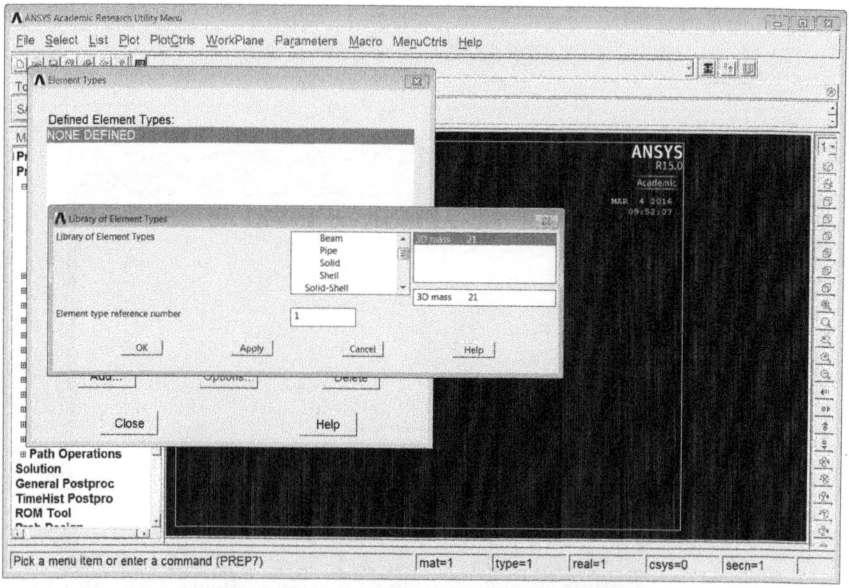

FIGURE 15.8
ANSYS element selection window.

As shown in Figure 15.7c, once **Preprocessor** → **Modeling** is expanded, we will have access to tools to create the geometry for the model, along with other necessary capabilities. As shown in Figure 15.7d, once **Preprocessor** → **Meshing** is expanded, we will have access to tools to create and modify mesh for the geometry. The **Load** tab down the list will allow us to apply load and other constraints to the model. So to build a model, we just keep moving down the list until all necessary steps are taken care of.

Figure 15.7e shows the choices once the **Physics** tab is expanded, where we can activate the coupled solver for coupled physics problems, if necessary. Of course, the choice available is the coupling of electric and structural phenomena.

15.3 Practice, Practice, Practice

As we see from the discussions in the preceding sections, all the modeling procedural items, including physics, spacial dimension, time dependency, model domain, coefficients, type of study, boundary and initial conditions, and loading conditions, as well as type of elements and order of discretization, are taken care of by going through the items in the Module list in ABAQUS and in the Main Menu in ANSYS.

While all three software packages can deal with problems governed by multiple equations, one thing we may note is that the way they handle the issue of multiple governing physics is different. While COMSOL explicitly use numerous different modules in various combinations to model such problems, ABAQUS and ANSYS take a rather inexplicit approach, albeit to a lesser extent. In the future, as the needs for integrative engineering expand, I am hopeful that we will see further developments and expansions of all finite element–based modeling software to allow modelers to couple all relevant physical phenomena as situations demand in a single package such that all real-world problems can be examined in a holistic manner.

Although it was argued in Chapter 1 that knowing the difference between *learning that* and *learning how* may help us to speed up our learning curve, when it comes to gaining hands-on skills, even after you know how, practice still makes perfect. Thus, it is highly recommended that the reader go through more tutorials that come with these software packages to gain hands-on experiences and develop technical proficiency. It is also hoped that by keeping in mind the list of model development procedural items discussed in the beginning of Chapter 14, the modeler will not only know the purpose of each modeling step, but also have a sense whether one has done all that is required to build a proper computational model. Furthermore, with the knowledge (including that and how) learned in Part II put in use, it is believed that the modeler will be more capable of doing computational modeling the right way and obtaining valid results.

16

Dealing with Problems of Biomedical and Regulatory Interest

As discussed in Chapter 1, bioengineering is a field in which biomedical problems are solved based on myriad laws of physics, thermodynamics, biochemistry, and biology, as well as probabilistic rules of statistics. A computational modeling approach is well suited to dealing with such problems, in which phenomena of mechanical, electrical, electrostatic, electrochemical, chemical, biochemical, biological, thermal, and electromagnetic natures, as well as mass, momentum, and energy concerns, either individually or combined, under the governing laws of physics, thermodynamics, and biology, are dealt with in an integrative way.

16.1 Computational Bioengineering

As we learned in Part II, in most deterministic problems, the physical phenomena encountered can be described by partial differential equations (PDEs) because these phenomena follow the laws of thermodynamics in terms of mass, momentum, and energy conservation. Solutions to these partial differential equations under certain initial and boundary conditions can shed in-depth and systemic insights into the underlying mechanisms governing these physical phenomena. So solving a problem governed by multidisciplinary principles is to solve a set of coupled PDEs simultaneously. Doing so can provide valuable information toward the analysis of real-world problems, as well as the design of engineering solutions to address the real-world problems. As we learned in Chapters 14 and 15, solving coupled PDEs using a computational modeling approach is relatively easy to implement with today's finite element method (FEM) software.

In a recent book entitled *Computational Bioengineering* published by CRC Press/Taylor & Francis Group, I highlighted the capabilities of computational bioengineering through discussions of a variety of bioengineering problems, including orthopedic joint prostheses, bone remodeling, fixation devices, degeneration of load-bearing soft connective tissues and intervertebral discs (IVDs), blood flow in the cardiovascular system and treatment of heart valve disease, cancer metastases and photodynamic cancer therapy, cellular and ionic activities at solid–liquid interfaces, and operations of fluidic biosensors. The following are some recaps of these biomedical problems that are solved by a computational modeling approach.

16.1.1 Problems of musculoskeletal concerns

Although joint replacement is a common treatment for arthritis, a significant number of total joint (hip and knee) replacement patients remain dissatisfied with the outcome of their procedure. To change this, premarketing assessment tools capable of predicting performance outcomes of joint prostheses, especially in younger and physically active patients, are needed. A computational framework that combines both experimental and computational approaches, describing subject-specific deterministic and probabilistic factors, has been developed to generate functional performance assessments of joint prostheses.

Human bones constantly remodel. But when there is an imbalance between bone resorption and bone formation within basic multicellular units (BMUs), bone disorders such as osteoporosis and osteopetrosis can develop. While coupling between osteoclasts and osteoblasts is known to occur, the mechanisms of action for the involved molecules between spatially segregated populations of osteoclasts and osteoblasts within BMUs are by no means clear. A computational model has been developed to examine the functionalities of BMUs and their roles in bone remodeling.

External fixation is useful for the treatment of unstable fractures, limb lengthening, and congenital and pathological orthopedic deformities. The functionality of an external fixation device relies mainly on the use of tensioned wires to support bone fragments. One major problem with these wires is their yielding. Once the wires yield, the fracture healing process will be compromised. Computational models have been developed to examine the cause of the nonlinear behavior observed in these tensioned wires and illustrate how material yielding can be minimized to enhance the functionality of such a fixation device.

Soft tissue instability can cause and accelerate joint tissue degeneration, especially in situations during accidental fall, high-speed sports, or traumatic events. Understanding the viscoelastic mechanical behavior of connective tissues is a crucial first step in developing treatment modalities for joint instability. To address the limitations in current soft tissue viscoelastic characterization paradigms, enhance our ability to predict the functional role of soft connective tissues in whole joint mechanics, and develop future treatment options, computational models have been developed to investigate the nonlinear viscoelastic behavior of load-bearing soft tissues based on a constitutive formulation along with a corresponding experimental characterization technique.

Back pain is a major public health problem, and more than 70% of people will have back pain at some time in their life. Back pain is strongly associated with the degeneration of IVDs, which in the long run can lead to spinal stenosis. To help elucidate the etiology of human disc degeneration and develop strategies for restoring tissue function or retarding further disc degeneration, a three-dimensional (3D) computational model has been developed to analyze the mechanical, chemical, and electrical signals within the IVD during axial unconfined compression and physiological loading conditions. By considering the human IVD as an inhomogeneous composite consisting of a charged elastic solid, water, ions (Na^+ and Cl^-), and nutrient solute (oxygen, glucose, and lactate), and by accounting for the effects of the end-plate calcification and cell injection, this model sheds many valuable insights into the interplay among fluid pressurization, effective solid stress, and charge density, as well as some new understanding toward disc biomechanics, pathology of IVD degeneration, and possible cell-based therapies for low back pain.

16.1.2 Problems of circulatory concerns

Modeling of blood flow in the cardiovascular system offers investigative and predictive capabilities to augment current clinical tools. Image-based patient-specific 3D anatomical models coupled with associated hemodynamic and electrodynamic behavior of the circulatory system have been developed to demonstrate that relevant physiological parameters such as wall shear stress and particle residence times can be estimated and correlated with clinical data for treatment planning and device evaluation.

Computational fluid dynamics–based models have been developed to elucidate the complex hemodynamics in the vicinity of the heart valve and the time-varying stresses on the leaflets, and provide valuable information in treating heart valve disease, as well as surgical planning and preoperative, postoperative, and temporal longitudinal functional assessment.

16.1.3 Problems of cancer development and treatment

Most cancer types develop the ability to metastasize, leading to death among most cancer patients. There is an immense clinical interest and societal value to understand the underlying biological mechanisms and develop preventive and therapeutic measures. Computational models can be developed to address such important challenges for the study of cancer and cancer metastases. Moreover, numerous photochemical-based computational models have been developed to simulate the transport of light, photosensitizer drug, and oxygen through vasculature in human tissues, as well as interactions among them during photodynamic therapy with visible light.

16.1.4 Other types of bioengineering problems

In addition to addressing problems directly related to the hard and soft tissues of the human musculoskeletal system, the flow dynamics and valves of the circulatory system, and cancer development and treatment, computational models have also been developed to address issues such as cell phenotyping, electrical double layer at a solid–liquid interface, biosensors, and rapid alignment and patterning of particles and cells.

In the case of cell phenotyping, modeling can help scientists to characterize and transform biological systems in various laboratory, industrial plant, and clinic settings with impressive quantitative precision. At a solid–liquid interface, the ubiquitous electrical double layer plays an important role in affecting how the solid will interact with the surrounding liquid environment. Modeling can provide an in-depth understanding of the structure, which is important to many bioengineering problems, including implant–tissue interactions, ion transport through charged channels of biological membranes, colloid stability on the surface of a biomaterial, electrochemical processes (e.g., corrosion) of a metallic implant, and electrokinetic phenomena within a biosensor channel, to name just a few.

Development of biosensors is another active area of bioengineering. Solid-state nanopore devices are regarded as one promising platform for future biosensors. Computational models can be used to understand the inherent complexity in the operations of a nanopore device. Moreover, computational modeling of a nanopore-based DNA sequencing technique based on the change in the recorded ionic current flowing through the nanopore has been performed.

Dielectrophoresis (DEP) has been widely used in micro- and nanofluidic systems for positioning, sorting, and separation of particles involved in medical diagnostics, drug discovery, cell therapeutics, and biosensor development. Computational models have been developed to reexamine the dielectrophoretic phenomenon and address some of the problems in current prevailing DEP theory.

The reader is encouraged to consult *Computational Bioengineering* for further learning. It is believed that a systematic use of a computational modeling approach to solve engineering and bioengineering problems will help address many critical challenges facing the engineering fields in general and bioengineering in particular, and set a new direction for advancing the fields. In the following sections, we discuss some of the other practical issues encountered in computational modeling of bioengineering interest that are not addressed in the aforementioned book.

16.2 Some Practical Issues in Image-Based Modeling

Dealing with bioengineering problems is not like dealing with conventional engineering problems. In some situations, patient-specific models of organs or constructs are needed, and in others, design data from manufacturers, such as in the cases of biomedical implant devices, are required. Patient-specific models are often obtained from volumetric images like computer tomographic (CT) scans. Here, we discuss a case of how a computational modeling approach can be used to develop strategies to strengthen complete dentures.

Dentures, either partial or complete, are removable appliances that serve to fulfill the functionality of missing teeth. Common materials used for the base of complete dentures are acrylic resins. Complete dentures made of these materials are prone to breakage or fracture due to the brittle nature and low strength of the materials. For this reason, denture damage is common in maxillary complete dentures with a typical midline fracture.

To change this situation, reinforcements with wires or fibers are sometimes used to strengthen the acrylic resin materials by taking advantage of the concept of fiber-reinforced composites for structural strengthening. Since acrylic materials under a rapid loading condition, such as during mastication, exhibit brittle behavior, fracture under tension is of a greater concern than shearing or other types of failure (see discussions in Section A.6 in Appendix A). Thus, placement of wire or fibers should achieve the purpose of reducing tensile stresses in dentures during mastication. A computational modeling approach is well suited for developing a proper strategy on where to place the reinforcing wires and fibers in order to achieve the denture strengthening purpose. Here, we describe some crucial steps to demonstrate how such a modeling study can be performed.

16.2.1 Image scanning and segmentation

Image-based modeling allows us to deal with highly complex geometry of anatomic components. For example, by treating the denture shown in Figure 16.1 as an anatomic part, we can use X-ray CT to scan the denture and reconstruct it in a FEM software for further modeling analysis.

In this case, we consider the maxillary complete denture (i.e., the upper part) shown in Figure 16.1b. Figure 16.2 shows some selected two-dimensional (2D) slices, from bottom to top, of the scanned images of the maxillary denture using an X-ray CT machine.

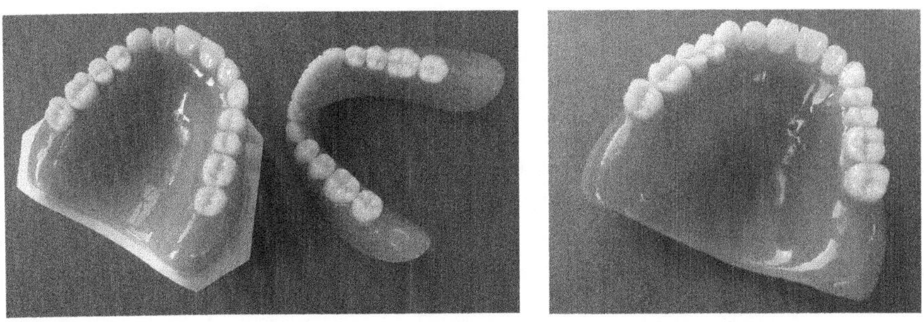

(a) (b)

FIGURE 16.1
(a) Set of complete dentures and (b) the maxillary part.

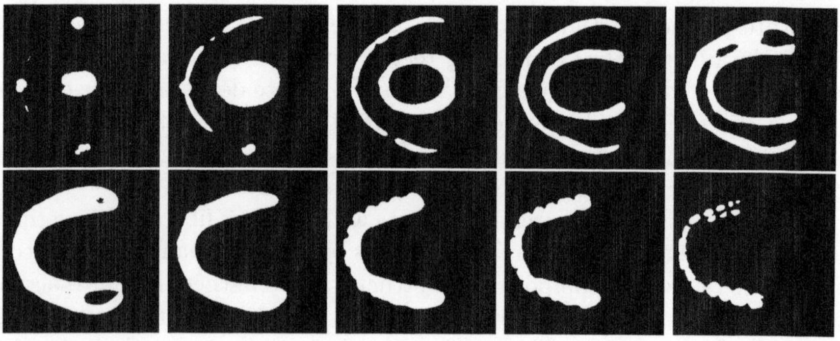

FIGURE 16.2
Series of selected slices, from bottom to top, of CT scanned images of the maxillary denture.

These slices of pixel images are subsequently converted to 3D volumetric arrangements of voxels representing the geometric domain of the maxillary denture after removing unwanted pixels in a process commonly known as segmentation. Note that in the case of this denture, although it contains the tooth and supporting soft tissue components, the same acrylic material is used for both. Therefore, there is no material density difference between the tooth and soft tissue components for the X-ray CT to discern in terms of image intensity. For this reason, the segmentation process is simply to remove the surrounding air space to extract the denture object.

The volumetric arrangement of voxels is further processed, rendered, and exported as 3D geometry in various computer-aided design (CAD) file formats. For example, the STL (Stereo Lithography) format is widely used to describe arbitrarily complex surfaces and the IGES (Initial Graphics Exchange Specification) format is exchangeable among various CAD software platforms. In our case, the volumetric data are exported as a CAD file in STL format.

16.2.2 Importing and meshing the CAD geometry

As shown in Figure 16.3, by right-clicking the **Geometry** tab in COMSOL, we can add an **Import** tab, and in the corresponding Settings window, we can then import STL files by selecting **STL/VRML file** from the list in the **Geometry import** box. Note that selecting **Any importable file** or **3D CAD file** will allow us to import files in IGES and X_T formats, as well as many others; here, the X_T format is a parasolid CAD file format.

After locating the desired CAD file and clicking the **Import** button, we bring the geometry of the maxillary denture into COMSOL for modeling processes. Figure 16.4a shows the imported denture geometry in COMSOL, and Figure 16.4b shows the denture after applying the meshing step with tetrahedral elements.

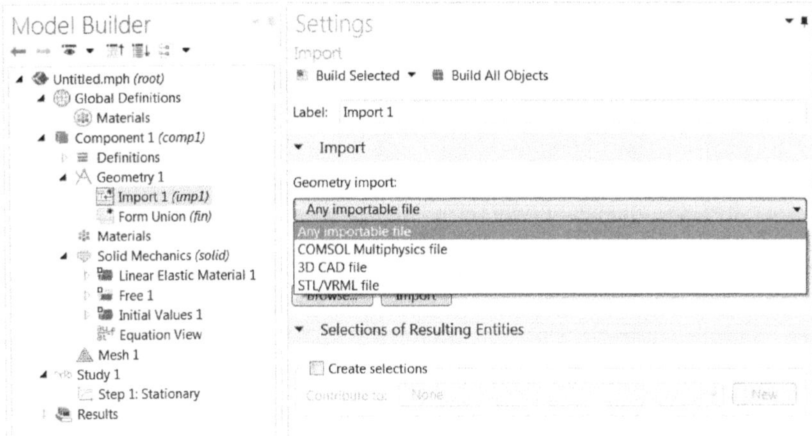

FIGURE 16.3
COMSOL import function for CAD files.

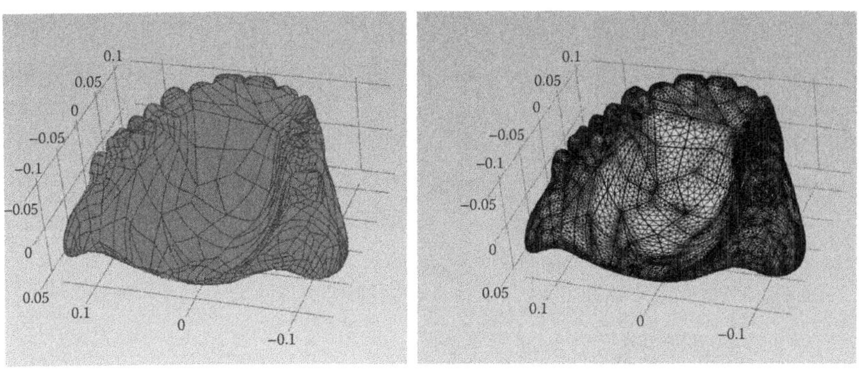

(a) (b)

FIGURE 16.4
Upper denture model built based on CT scans. The denture model is meshed with a coarse mesh (a) and with a fine mesh (b).

16.2.3 Further mechanical analysis

Next, we perform mechanical analysis of the maxillary denture through computational modeling. By referring to the procedural list given at the beginning of Chapter 14, we set the physics of the model to Solid Mechanics, the spacial dimension to 3D, the study to time-independent Stationary, and the material to Acrylic. Moreover, to the imported 3D geometry we select tetrahedral elements in quadratic order to mesh it with proper mesh density (see Figure 16.4b).

For the loading and boundary conditions, we mimic the loading and constraints experienced by the denture during mastication. Thus, for the boundary conditions, we place the denture with the tooth side down and apply a fixed boundary condition to some selected surfaces near the tips of teeth to constrain them from any motion. For the loading conditions, we apply a downward force at the top of the dome of the denture base to mimic the biting force from the upper jaw. Once all these steps are taken care of, we just click **Compute** to analyze the model.

Before we examine the modeling results, let us first have a look at the settings and outcomes of actual mechanical tests with which we will compare our results. In each of these mechanical tests, a denture is placed with the tooth side down on a platen and a point load is applied at the top of the dome of the denture base to compress the denture until it fails. This loading and support constraints situation is just like that used in the computational model.

In the upper part of Figure 16.5, we see photographs of two intact and two fractured dentures. Of these four, two represent a denture without a reinforcing wire (Figure 16.5a and b) and two with one (Figure 16.5c and d). In the wire-reinforced denture, a curved metal wire is placed inside the denture base near the teeth during the molding process of the denture. The two fractured

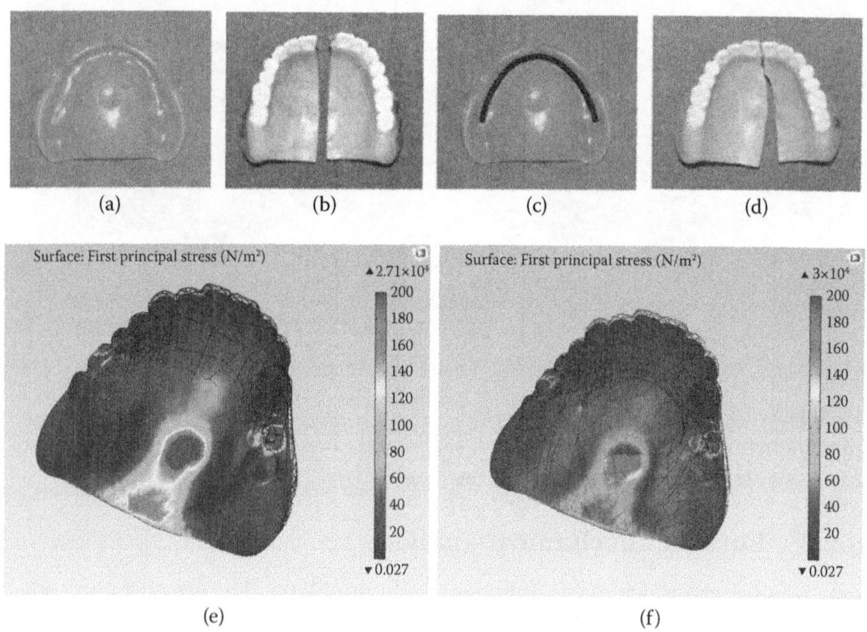

FIGURE 16.5
Photo images showing (a) the denture without wire reinforcement, (b) along with its fracture mode, and (c) the denture that with wire reinforcement, (d) along with its fracture mode. First principal stresses in the denture when wire reinforcement is (e) absent and (f) present. (Courtesy of Professor Yutaka Takahasi, Fukuoka Dental College, Fukuoka, Japan.)

dentures (Figure 16.5b and d), although one is reinforced with a wire and one is without, exhibit very similar failure modes. The one without wire reinforcement failed down right at the midline of the denture base, and the one with wire reinforcement failed in a slightly offset centerline.

Figure 16.5e and f shows some selected modeling results, in which the first principal stress in the denture without and with wire reinforcement, respectively, is shown. From the modeling results, it is clear that the first principal stress is very high along the midline of the denture base. Referring to the discussions on Mohr's circle and principal stresses in Sections A.6 and A.7 in Appendix A, we know that the first principal stress is also the maximum tensile stress in this case. Due to the brittle nature of the denture acrylic material, tensile failure is of a great concern; thus, the first principal stress should give us a good prediction on where the denture would likely fail. Looking at the fact that the highest tensile stress is reached near the midline of the denture base, it is no surprise the denture will break along the midline. The wire reinforcement does not seem to contribute to any alteration of alleviation of the maximum tensile stress; thus, a similar failure mode is expected, as is the case in the mechanical loading tests. This fact suggests that a different wire placement is necessary in order to achieve a structural strengthening effect in the dentures. The reader is encouraged to explore this issue further.

16.3 Computational Modeling for Enhancing the Test Standards and Regulatory Processes

According to the U.S. Food and Drug Administration (FDA), Class III devices are those that support or sustain human life, are of substantial importance in preventing impairment of human health, or which present a potential, unreasonable risk of illness or injury. Due to the level of risks associated with Class III devices, they require premarket approval (PMA) from the FDA, in which the safety and effectiveness of these medical devices are scientifically evaluated and regulatory reviewed.

Most of the medical implant devices are Class III devices, hence requiring PMA from FDA. To gain PMA, these implants have to go through rigorous tests per American Society for Testing and Materials (ASTM) standards and sometimes, International Organization for Standardization (ISO) standards. An integrative computational modeling approach is poised to not only enhance the standards development and improvement process but also elevate the effectiveness of FDA's PMA process.

16.3.1 Testing the femoral stem of a hip implant

In the case of partial and total hip joint prostheses, the ISO 7206-4:2010(E) standard specifies a test method for determining the endurance properties

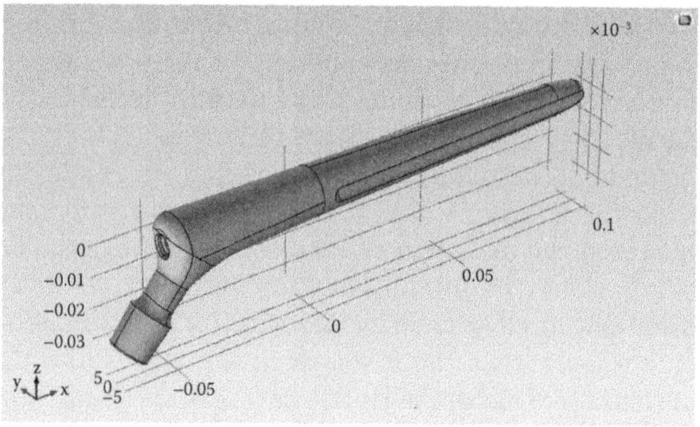

FIGURE 16.6
Imported CAD model of the hip stem.

of stemmed femoral components of total hip joint prostheses and stemmed femoral components used alone in partial hip joints under specified laboratory conditions. It also defines the test conditions and describes how the specimen is set up for the test.

In this section, we demonstrate the use of the computational modeling technique to perform mechanical testing of a femoral stem of a hip implant according to ISO 7206-4:2010(E) and compare the results with those of the ASTM round-robin test. Note that a round-robin test is a test (including measurement, analysis, and experiment) in which several participating laboratories perform their independent tests by following the same set of conditions and compare the interlaboratory testing results. The CAD geometric model for the femoral stem used here is the one used for the ASTM round-robin test that is available for download at http://www.astm.org /committee/F04.htm. Figure 16.6 shows the hip stem model after being imported into COMSOL.

16.3.2 Setting up the round-robin test

To get the model ready for mechanical analysis in COMSOL, like in the case for the denture model, we set the physics of the model to Solid Mechanics, the spacial dimension to 3D, and the study to time-independent Stationary. For the material, we use titanium with Young's modulus $E = 114$ GPa and Poisson's ratio $\nu = 0.3$.

For applying the loading and boundary conditions, we will follow the ISO 7206-4:2010(E) guidelines. Since the hip stem is oriented with its shaft axis parallel to the x axis, we apply a point load in a direction that forms a 10° angle with the x axis in the x-z plane and a 9° angle with the x axis in the x-y plane according to the ISO 7206-4:2010(E) standard. The point load with a magnitude of $P = 2300$ N is applied at the lowest point of the circular trunnion face at the neck end pointing toward the distal end of the hip stem.

For the boundary conditions, per the ISO 7206-4:2010(E) guidelines, the distal end of the hip stem is potted for movement constraints. To do so in the model, we first create a cylinder with its top surface about 95 mm away from the center of the position of the femoral head and oriented perpendicular to the direction of the point load. This cylinder is then subtracted from the hip stem geometry to result in a cut surface on the distal side, as shown in Figure 16.7. A fixed constraint boundary condition is then applied to this cut surface to secure the hip stem for mechanical loading.

Figure 16.8a shows the hip stem after the fixed boundary condition is applied at the lower cut surface, and Figure 16.8b shows the model after meshing in which tetrahedral elements in quadratic order are used. After clicking **Compute**, we analyze the model. Figure 16.8c shows some selected results.

In a close quantitative examination, we note that the highest first principal stress occurred at the bottom of the neck, as shown in Figure 16.9, with a value of approximately 79 ksi, and the highest stress in the driver hole is about 31 ksi. Note that the locations of the highest stress points are slightly off-centered to the negative y axis side, or off the upper side in the figure. The corresponding locations off to the lower side have stress values of about 57 and 25 ksi, respectively. The ASTM round-robin test reports an average value of 59 and 25 ksi for the neck region and the driver hole region, respectively, both occurring off to the lower side, indicating that the results obtained here are consistent with those of the round-robin test. The slight differences between the results shown here and from the round-robin test, however, may be attributed to the different values used for the materials properties or to the difference in the exact location where the load is applied.

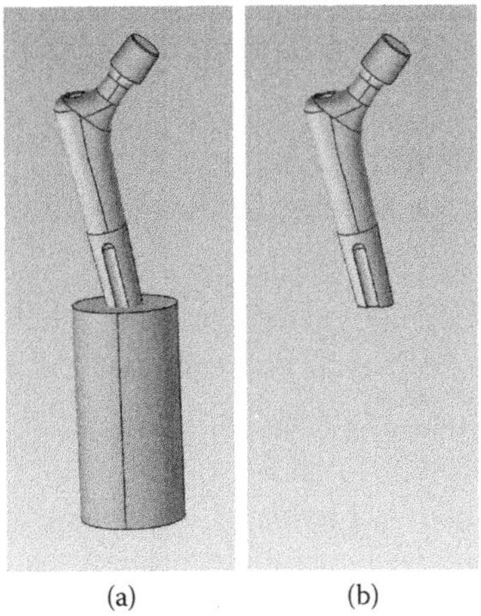

FIGURE 16.7
Cutting the distal end of the hip stem for boundary fixation. A cylinder is added to the hip stem model (a) and then subtracted from it (b).

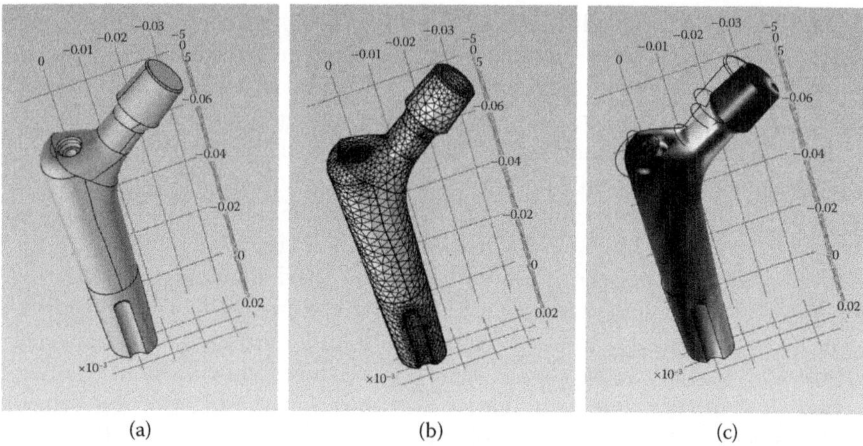

FIGURE 16.8
Modeling the hip stem for the round-robin test. The part of the hip stem modeled in the process (a), after meshing (b), and after analysis (c).

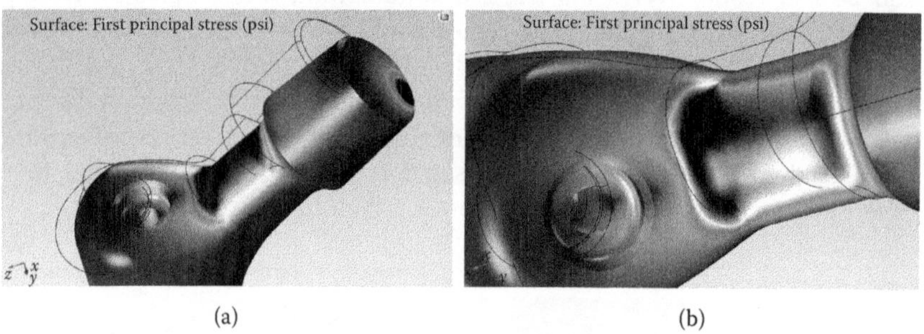

FIGURE 16.9
Close look at the first principal stress in the hip stem. The distribution of the first principal stress near the neck region in an overall view (a) and a closeup view (b).

16.3.3 Testing the femoral component of a knee implant

Following the same steps, we now briefly go through a round-robin test for a knee component. Figure 16.10 shows the imported model of the femoral component of a knee implant. Figure 16.11a shows the model after further manipulation through cutting for boundary condition application (note that the bottom part of the original CAD model shown in Figure 16.10 has been cut and removed), and Figure 16.11b shows the model after applying the meshing step with tetrahedral elements of the quadratic order. To get the model ready for mechanical analysis, we set the physics of model to Solid Mechanics, the spacial dimension to 3D, and the study to time-independent Stationary.

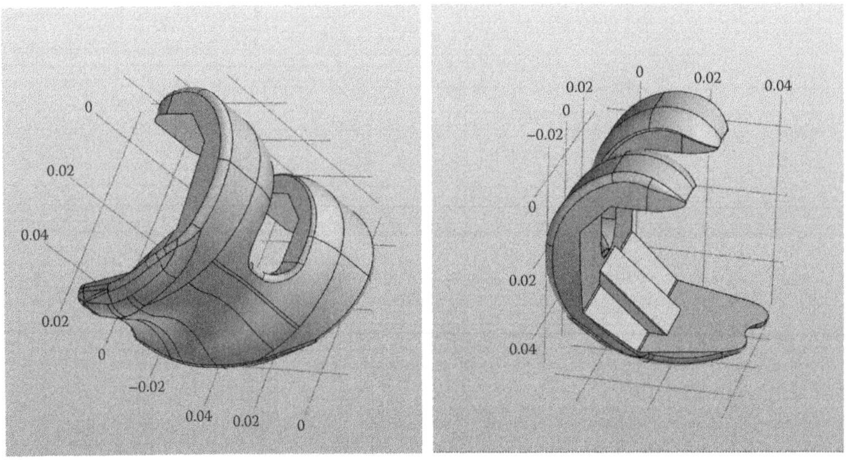

(a) (b)

FIGURE 16.10
Modeling of the femoral component of a knee implant. The femoral component before sectioning in a front view (a) and a back view (b).

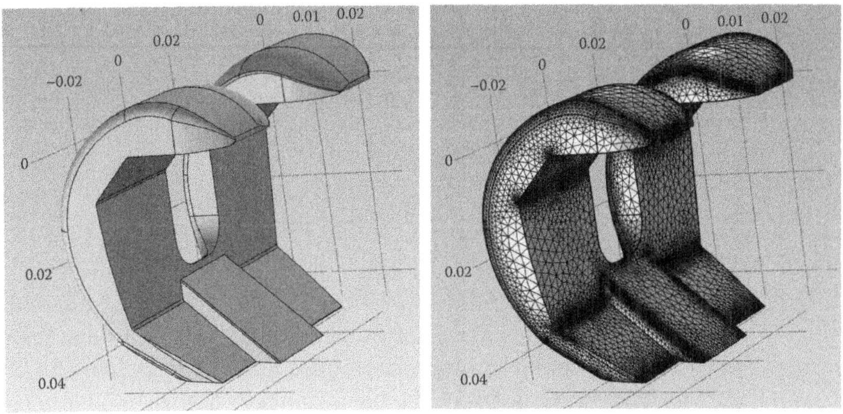

(a) (b)

FIGURE 16.11
Setting up for the round-robin test for the femoral knee implant. The femoral component after sectioning (a) and after meshing (b).

For the material, we use titanium with Young's modulus $E = 105$ GPa and Poisson's ratio $\nu = 0.33$.

For the boundary condition, a fixed constraint is applied to the cut surface (the bottom surface in Figure 16.11), and for the loading condition, a downward (in the positive x axis direction) point load of 1 N is applied at a point near the top of the medial condyle (the upper left point in Figure 16.11).

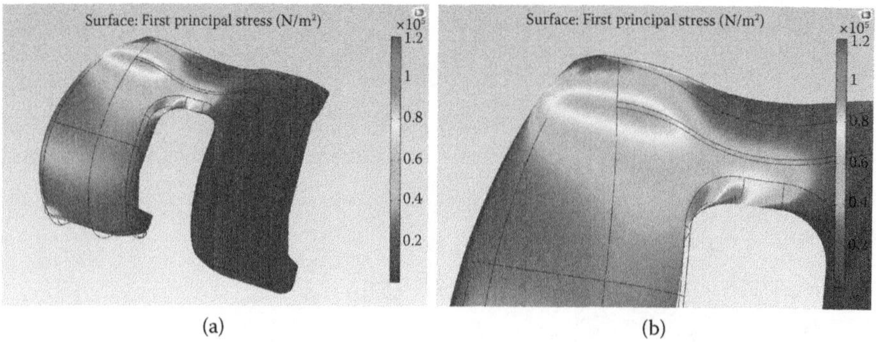

FIGURE 16.12
First principal stress in the femoral knee implant. Distribution of the first principal stress in an overall view (a) and a closeup view (b).

Figure 16.12 shows the obtained first principal stress in the femoral knee component after the loading analysis. In a close quantitative examination (see the two red regions in Figure 16.12b), we note that the highest stress is approximately 0.139 MPa in the medial condyle region and about 0.138 MPa in the anterior notch region. The ASTM round-robin test reports an average value for the first principal stress of 0.119 and 0.103 MPa for the medial condyle region and the notch region, respectively. The differences between the results shown here and the round-robin ones may be attributed to the different values used for the materials properties or to the difference in the location where the load is applied.

16.3.4 Testing of a spinal implant assembly

ASTM 1717-14 is a standard guiding the test methods for static and fatigue testing of spinal implant assemblies in a vertebrectomy model. These test methods are intended to provide a basis for the mechanical comparison among past, present, and future spinal implant assemblies and allow comparison of spinal implant constructs with different intended spinal locations and methods of application. These test methods may also apply to mechanical evaluation of cervical spinal implant assemblies, and thoracolumbar, lumbar, and lumbosacral spinal implant assemblies.

According to the ASTM 1717-14 standard, the entire test assembly should simulate a vertebrectomy model via a large gap between two ultra-high-molecular-weight polyethylene (UHMWPE) test blocks (simulating the vertebra) to facilitate static mechanical tests such as compression bending, tensile bending, and torsion and dynamic test. The spinal assembly may include anterior vertebral body screws and rods, or posterior sacral screws, hooks, rods, and transverse elements.

Here, let us briefly discuss a FEM-based computational model developed per the ASTM 1717-14 standard for elucidating the mechanical details in such

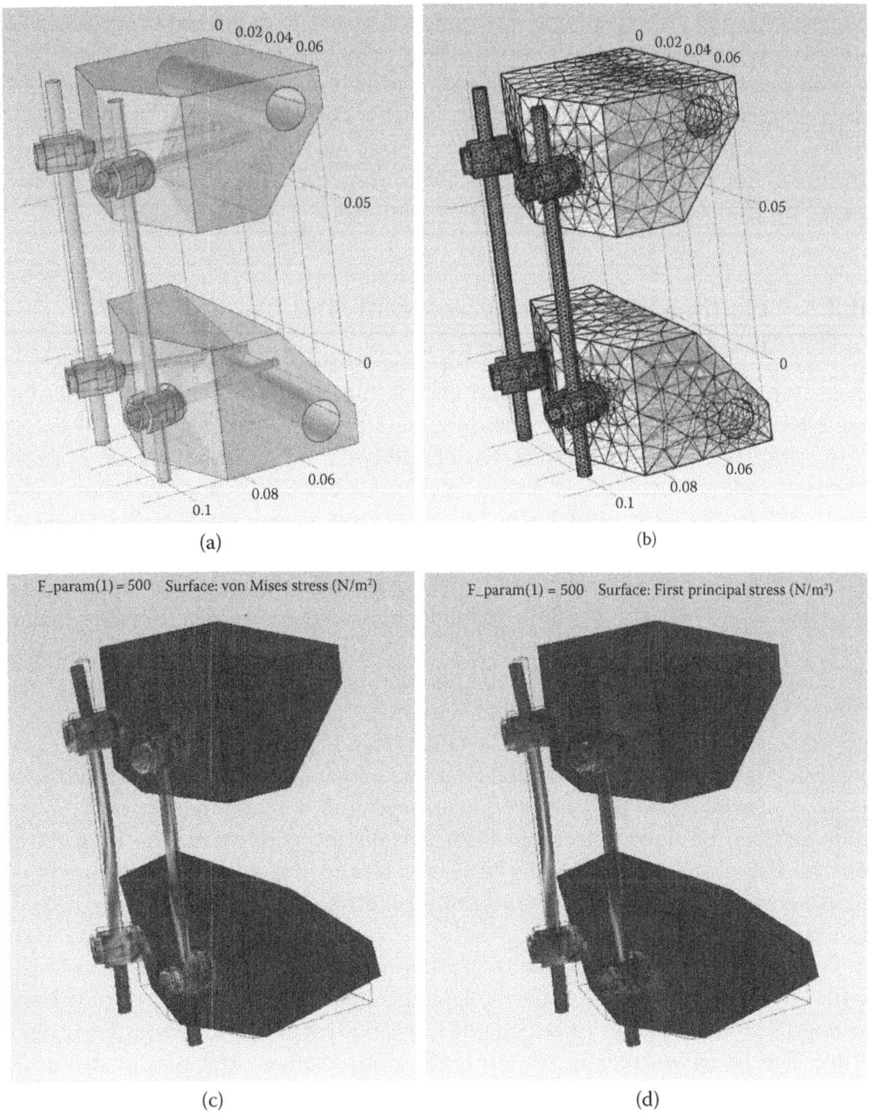

FIGURE 16.13
Modeling the test of a spinal implant assembly. 3D views of the geometry of the spine implant assembly (a) and after meshing (b). 3D views of the obtained von Mises stress (c) and first principal stress (d).

a test of the entire spinal implant assembly. Figure 16.13 shows the model developed and some selected results after mechanical analysis. More specifically, Figure 16.13a shows the imported CAD model initially developed in SolidWorks, Figure 16.13b shows the meshed model, Figure 16.13c shows the deformed test assembly and the von Mises stress in the rods, and Figure 16.13d shows the deformed assembly and the first principal stress in the rods.

This example illustrates that a computational modeling approach can shed much insight into the intricate details of such a test by providing visualization of deformations and stress distributions, and it may very well be in a position to provide innovative ideas on strategies to improve such a test standard for enhancing the test standardization and regulatory processes.

16.3.5 Calling for clinically relevant and predictive modeling

The computational modeling examples of hip, knee, and spine implants discussed in this section are of certain value in providing a reference for comparison between implants of different designs or from different manufacturers in order to identify the worst-case scenario. However, the true value of computational modeling should be in its predictive power of clinically relevant failure modes.

Referring to the discussions given in Appendix A, there are many factors that could affect the failure mode of a material or a device. From a mechanical and material perspective, these factors include the loading conditions (types of loads and rates of loading), the stress states and trajectories, the maximum stress values and stress types, and the material types and their failure tendency. From a clinical and in vivo environment's perspective, there are other combined factors, such as enzymatically induced material degradations and environment-accelerated reactions between body fluids and the implant materials. From a holistic perspective, the interplays between the mechanical and material factors and the in vivo environmental factors may lead to weakened material strengths causing compounded types of failures.

To demonstrate how the results of computational modeling can be used to predict material failure (in a mechanical and material perspective), we take a close look at the wisdom of a Brazilian tensile test using a compressive test setup. The Brazilian tensile test is designed to evaluate the tensile strength of brittle materials such as rocks and concrete, in which a specimen made of a circular disc (or cylinder) is subject to a compressive loading along one of its diameter lines. Under this test, the specimen is expected to crack into two pieces along the line of loading and the tensile strength is evaluated as $\sigma_t = P/(\pi R t)$, in which P is the compressive load applied to the point of failure, R is the diameter of the disc (or cylinder), and t is the thickness (or length) of the specimen.

Figure 16.14 shows modeling results in which a 2D circular disc (with $R = t = 1$ m) is subject to a vertical compressive load ($P = 1$ N) in a plane stress analysis. From the distribution of the max tensile stress in the disc, shown in Figure 16.14a, it is clear that the max tensile stress indeed occurs near the vertical centerline. Note that since a brittle material tends to fail first

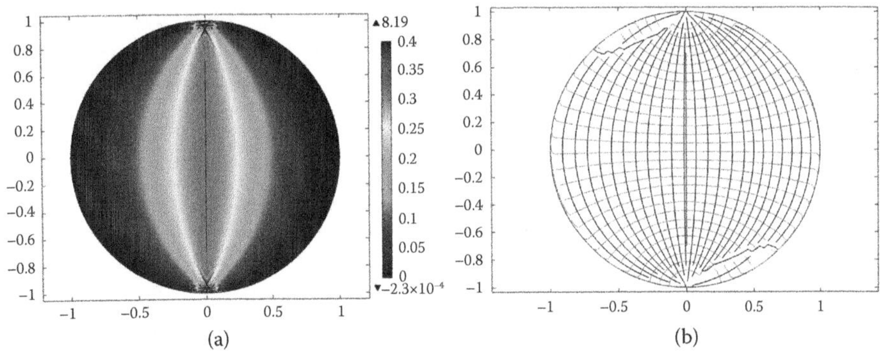

FIGURE 16.14
Modeling the Brazilian tensile test. Distribution of von Mises stress (a) and stress trajectories (b).

due to tensile breakage, it is prudent to examine the max tensile stress, its distribution and trajectories, instead of the von Mises stress. To see the orientations of the tensile stresses throughout the disc, we obtained the induced stress trajectories, that is, the tension and compression lines (see Appendix A for more discussions). As shown in Figure 16.14b, the arrangements of the tension lines (light gray) and compression lines (dark gray) show a stress state in which tensile stresses are pulling the disc along the vertical centerline on both sides, indicating that the specimen is likely to be pulled apart along its vertical centerline into two half pieces.

In a more quantitative examination, Figure 16.15 shows the distribution of the max tensile stress along the vertical centerline (Figure 16.15a) and along the horizontal centerline (Figure 16.15b), respectively. These results show that aside from the vicinity of the two loading points where stress concentration is expected to occur, the max tensile stress is fairly uniform along the vertical centerline. Figure 16.15b shows the distribution of the max stress along the horizontal centerline in which the stress peaks at the center. These results indicate that the max tensile stress reaches its highest value along the vertical centerline, with a stress value close to 0.318 N/m^2. Plugging the parameters (i.e., $R = t = 1$ m and $P = 1$ N) into the given formula, $\sigma_t = P/(\pi Rt)$, we have $\sigma_t = 0.318\ \text{N/m}^2$, agreeing very well with the modeling prediction.

This example shows that computational modeling, when performed correctly with sufficient details on the induced stress states, is capable of predicting the anticipated failure mode and failure strength of the material under testing. Along this line of argument, computational modeling of implant devices should be performed under conditions that closely resemble the actual in vivo situations with the goal of revealing the induced stress states of all intricate components to shed useful insight into the potential failure modes and fracture surfaces. Of course, as I argued throughout this book, the need for closely representing the actual situations calls for integrative consideration of the problems. Fortunately, it can be accomplished through integrative

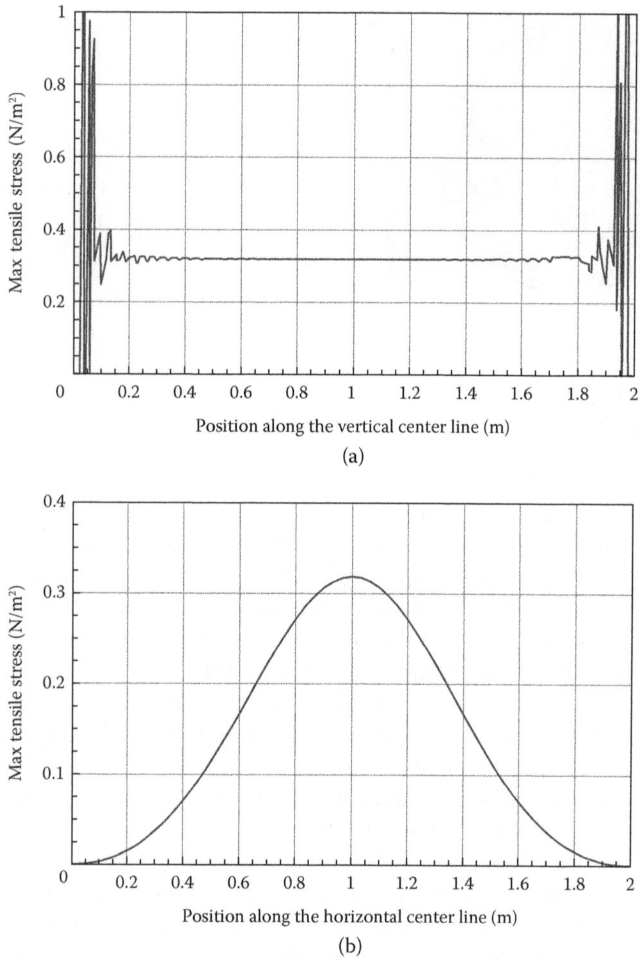

FIGURE 16.15
Max tensile stress along the vertical and horizontal centerlines (a) after vertical and (b) after horizontal.

computational modeling. Once realized, the predictive power of the computational modeling approach is expected to unleash biomedical innovation and promote the quality of life in a speedy and economical manner.

16.4 Examining the Transient Hypoxia Condition in Cornea due to Contact Lens Wear

Contact lenses have brought people of myopia or hyperopia normal vision without the inconvenience associated with wearing corrective glasses.

Wearing contact lenses is of course not without any side effects. From a physiological standpoint, contact lens wear has the potential to cause significant epithelial and stromal acidosis because the lens acts as a barrier to oxygen diffusion into the cornea, leading to corneal hypoxia, which plays an important role in affecting corneal health. The side effects of corneal hypoxia range from corneal acidosis, swelling, microcysts, and vascularization, to decreased resistance, to bacterial infection, depending on the severity. It is thus important to have a reliable metric to refer to when assessing the possible impact of contact lens wear on the oxygenation and health of corneas.

Over the years, metrics such as the oxygen transmissibility of the lens, equivalent oxygen percentage, anterior corneal oxygen flux, and total corneal consumption have been used for gaging the impact of contact lenses on corneal oxygenation. Among these metrics, transmissibility (i.e., Dk/t, where D is the oxygen diffusion coefficient in the lens, k the Henry constant of oxygen solubility, and t the thickness of the lens) is the only quantity that can be measured directly, and the rest are all indirect quantities estimated based on the Dk/t value. For this reason, Dk/t has been used extensively throughout the contact lens community.

While Dk/t is a physical property of the lens that can be measured and has made the comparison of lenses from different manufacturers possible, it is not sufficient to rely on the Dk/t value to quantify oxygen tension and flux at the posterior surface of the lens, or the distribution of the oxygen partial pressure throughout the cornea. For example, clinical data suggest that corneal swelling can occur even with silicone hydrogel lenses having very high oxygen transmissibility ($Dk/t > 175$).

A computational modeling approach is perfectly suited to providing better insight into the situation of corneal oxygenation with contact lens wear. Figure 16.16 shows a case in which oxygen diffusion into a cornea through a contact lens is investigated. Due to the axial symmetric nature in the corneal and lens geometry, we can simplify the problem by performing a 2D axisymmetric study (see more discussion on axisymmetry in Chapter 9) without losing the ability to capture the actual 3D structures of the cornea and the contact lens.

The 2D views in Figure 16.17 show the results of this 2D axisymmetric computational model of the cornea with contact lens wear. Comparing the 2D and 3D views, we can tell that the left upper edge of the 2D axisymmetric model is where the center of the contact lens and cornea is located.

In this analysis, diffusion of oxygen from the ambient environment into the cornea through the contact lens in a time-transient manner is examined. The entire model consists of a contact lens with a Dk value of 100 and diopter numbers of about -3.0 D, a thin tear-film layer, and the corneal epithelial, stromal, and endothelial tissue layers. These tissues consume oxygen at their respective rates for metabolic purposes. To consider proper constraints for the model, a partial pressure of oxygen at mmHg is applied to the lower boundary of the endothelium that borders the aqueous humor, and 55 mmHg is applied to the lower boundary of the sclera that borders the blood capillaries. For the

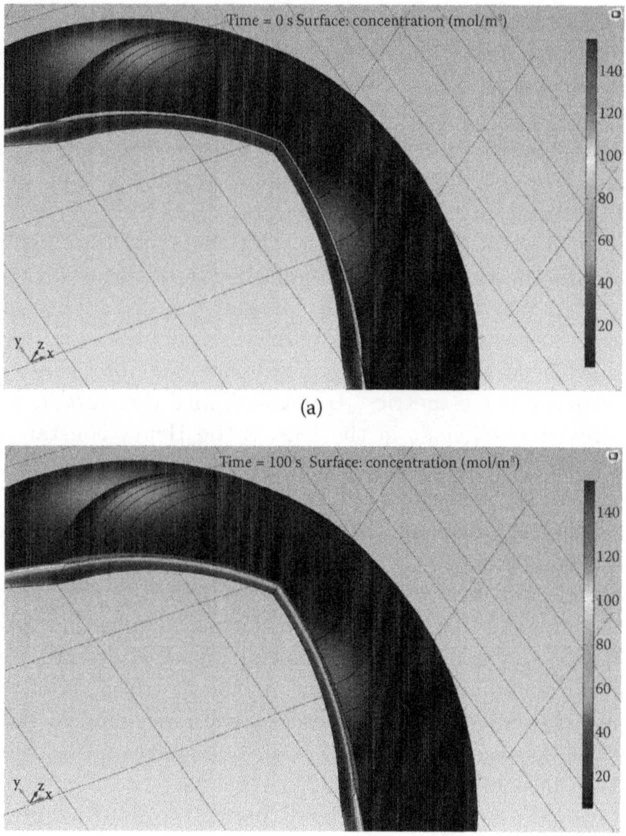

(b)

FIGURE 16.16
Oxygen diffusion into a cornea through a contact lens in 3D views at (a) time 0, the moment the eye opens after reaching the close-eye steady state, and (b) 100 seconds afterwards.

ambient oxygen partial pressure, values of 61.4 and 155 mmHg are used as the close-eye and open-eye conditions, respectively.

In this time-dependent transient diffusion analysis, the distribution of oxygen partial pressure throughout the entire cornea over time between the close-eye steady state and the open-eye steady state is determined and visualized as shown in Figure 16.17. For example, Figure 16.17a shows the oxygenation state of the cornea with contact lens wear at time 0, or the moment the eye opens after reaching the close-eye steady state. As time progresses from time 0 to 2 seconds (Figure 16.17b), 20 seconds (Figure 16.17c), 40 seconds (Figure 16.17d), 80 seconds (Figure 16.17e), and 100 seconds (Figure 16.17f) afterwards, it is clear that more oxygen reaches the corneal tissues, especially in the first 20 seconds. The change in oxygen level becomes smaller as time

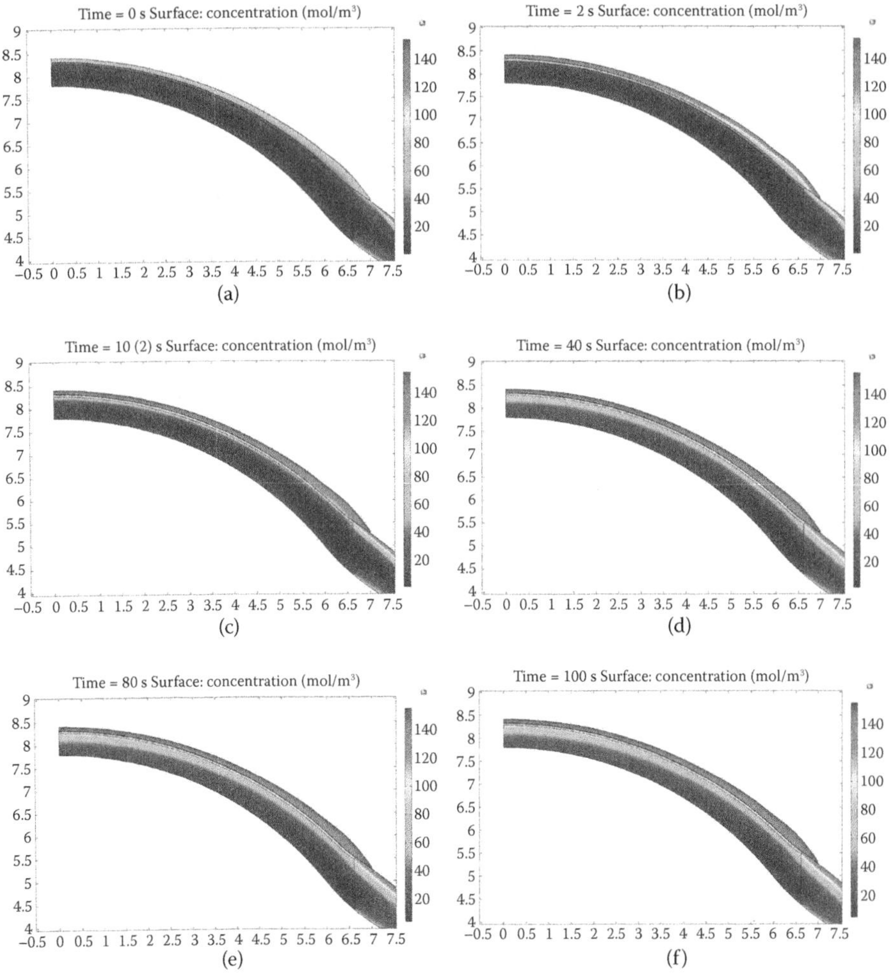

FIGURE 16.17
Oxygen diffusion into the cornea through contact lens in 2D views at times (a) 0, (b) 2, (c) 20, (d) 40, (e) 80, and (f) 100 seconds afterwards.

passes 80 seconds, an indication that the cornea is reaching its open-eye steady state in terms of oxygen diffusion. However, even in an open-eye steady-state situation, a large portion of the cornea is still under an oxygenation state, with the level of partial pressure for oxygen under 60 mmHg.

To get a different perspective of the change in corneal oxygenation with time, the transient response of the oxygen partial pressure from the close-eye to open-eye steady states at two cross sections can be closely examined. The first section cut is through the center of the cornea and contact lens, where both the contact lens and the stromal layer are the thinnest, and the second section cut is at the edge of the cornea near the limbus, where both the contact lens and the stromal layer are the thickest.

Figure 16.18 shows the results through the center (Figure 16.18a) and edge (Figure 16.18b) cuts, respectively, in which the oxygen profiles throughout the cornea and contact lens at times 0, 2, 4, 6, 8, 10, 20, 40, 60, 80, and 100 seconds, respectively, during the transition from the close-eye to open-eye steady states are plotted. The left end of the graphs marks the side of the endothelium, and the right end of the graphs marks the outer surface of the contact lens (for this reason, the distance spans of the two plots are different due to the difference in the thicknesses of the cornea and contact lens). From these profiles of oxygen partial pressure, we can clearly see that the oxygen level increases rather rapidly in the first several seconds until about 40 seconds. After that, changes slow down, and after some 60 seconds, changes are only slightly visible, indicating that oxygen diffusion into the cornea is approaching its open-eye steady state.

In the center cut (Figure 16.18a), all regions of the corneal tissues have above zero oxygen partial pressure, but overall, it is below 24 mmHg over a large span of the stromal tissue within the first 20 seconds after the eye opens. However, in the edge cut (Figure 16.18b), some span of the stroma is under a state of hypoxia, with zero oxygen partial pressure in the first 20 seconds. Even after reaching the open-eye steady state, almost two-thirds of the stroma is experiencing a partial oxygen pressure below 24 mmHg.

16.5 Examining the pH Drop in a Titanium Crevice due to Corrosion

To allow maximum flexibility during surgery for surgeons to pick and choose different combinations of parts, implant modularity has been a common practice over the years. Modular metallic implants consist of not only different parts but also different alloys. While implant modularity indeed provides great flexibility to improve personalized fits for patients, different parts coming together will create small gaps (or crevices) between parts and different alloys will cause galvanic potential differences. More and more evidence from the clinical retrieved implants shows that corrosion in the crevices of these modular implants is one major contributing factor leading to the failure of them. While crevice corrosion has been studied for many years, both experimentally and computationally, the true cause for modular implant failure remains elusive, thus hindering not only the clinical successes of these modular implants but also the regulatory approval processes.

A computational approach can be used to examine this corrosive process. Let us have a look at a computer model analyzing the corrosion process in a crevice of a commercial pure titanium based on thermodynamics by considering simultaneously electrode reactions, equilibrium reactions, and

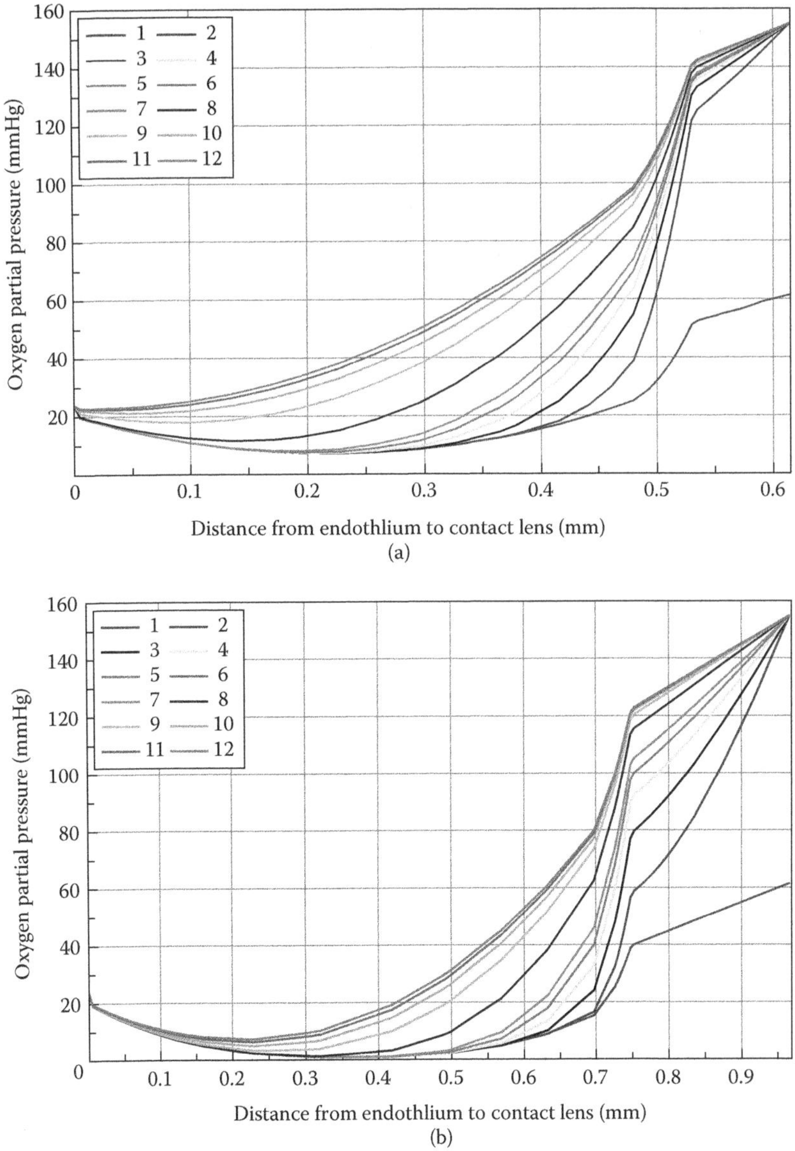

FIGURE 16.18
The changing profile of corneal oxygenation over time in a section, (a) cut through the center of the cornea and (b) cut near the limbus. Shown are graphs 1 through 12 at 0, 2, 4, 6, 8, 10, 20, 40, 60, 80, and 100 seconds during a transition from close-eye to open-eye steady states. Note that the shaded regions on the left represent the span of stromal tissue, the shaded region on the right is the span of the contact lens, and the gap in between is the span of epithelial tissue having a uniform thickness of 0.5 mm.

mass transport, coupled with electrochemical polarization, and evaluate the pH profile along the depth of a crevice with various crevice widths.

To simplify matters, a crevice is considered to be 10 mm in length with various widths from 0.5 to 50 μm. The corrosive environment is induced by experimental polarization of commercial pure titanium. Figure 16.19 shows the measured polarization curve, in which the anodic current is mainly attributed to the dissolution of titanium (or oxidation) and the cathodic current to oxygen reduction under an acid environment with pH = 6.3.

The involved oxidative and reductive electrode reactions are as follows:

$$\text{Oxidation: } \mathrm{Ti} \rightarrow \mathrm{Ti(IV)} + 4e^-$$
$$\text{Reduction: } \mathrm{O_2} + 4\mathrm{H}^+ + 4e^- \rightarrow 2\mathrm{H_2O}$$

The nonelectrode equilibrium reactions occurring during the corrosive and mass transport processes include

$$\mathrm{Ti(IV)} + \mathrm{H_2O} \leftrightarrow \mathrm{Ti(OH)}^{3+} + \mathrm{H}^+, \quad \log(K) = -1.4$$
$$\mathrm{Ti(OH)}^{3+} + \mathrm{H_2O} \leftrightarrow \mathrm{Ti(OH)}_2^{2+} + \mathrm{H}^+, \quad \log(K) = -1.7$$
$$\mathrm{Ti(OH)}_2^{2+} + \mathrm{H_2O} \leftrightarrow \mathrm{Ti(OH)}_3^{+} + \mathrm{H}^+, \quad \log(K) = -2.0$$
$$\mathrm{Ti(OH)}_3^{+} + \mathrm{H_2O} \leftrightarrow \mathrm{Ti(OH)}_4 + \mathrm{H}^+, \quad \log(K) = -4.0$$
$$\mathrm{H_2O} \leftrightarrow \mathrm{OH}^- + \mathrm{H}^+, \quad \log(K) = -13.6$$

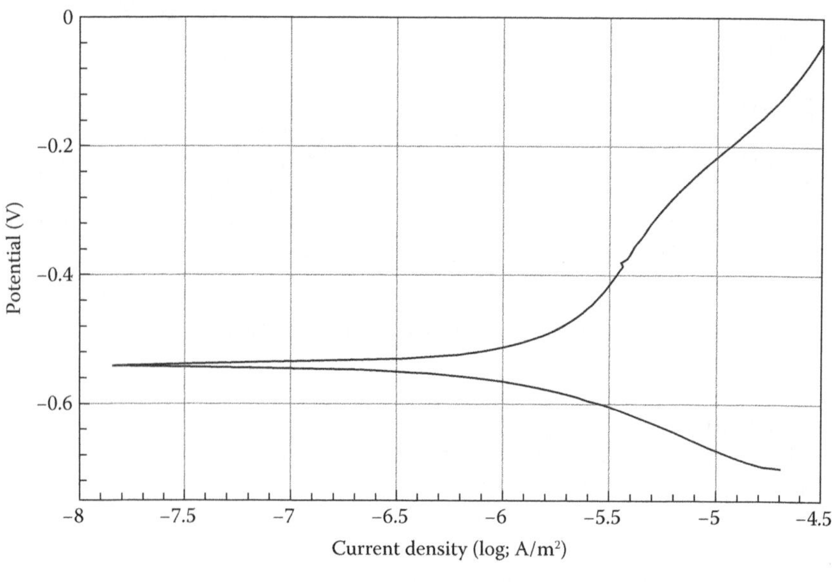

FIGURE 16.19
Polarization curve for commercial pure titanium.

In this corrosive process, while the electrode reactions are controlled by the kinetics of electrode polarization, all the reactant and product species are governed by the generalized Nernst–Planck equation in terms of transport. In the computational analysis, the polarization potential is swept from −0.7 to −0.1 V, and the resulting pH profile inside the crevice along the depth of the crevice is evaluated.

Figure 16.20 shows some selected results for the pH profiles at −0.1 V along the crevice depth, where the left end of the graphs is the crevice mouth at a solution of pH 6.3 and the right end the bottom of the crevice.

In all cases, a general trend is that pH deceases gradually in an exponential decaying pattern from the mouth to the bottom of the crevice. Comparisons between the cases show that the narrower the crevice is, the lower the pH level becomes. For example, in the case of 50 μm crevice width, the pH drops to approximately 4.4 at the bottom from 6.3 at the mouth, while in the case of 0.5 μm crevice width, it drops to about 2.6 at the bottom.

Although the corrosive environment considered here is under forced polarization, rather than a spontaneous process, the results shown should pose a warning that the thermodynamics in a tight space with poor mass transport could lead to severe pH drop. This in turn can accelerate the corrosive process, leading to possible compounded device failure and tissue damage. The obtained modeling results shed some insight into the mechanisms and consequences of crevice corrosion in commercial pure titanium driven by

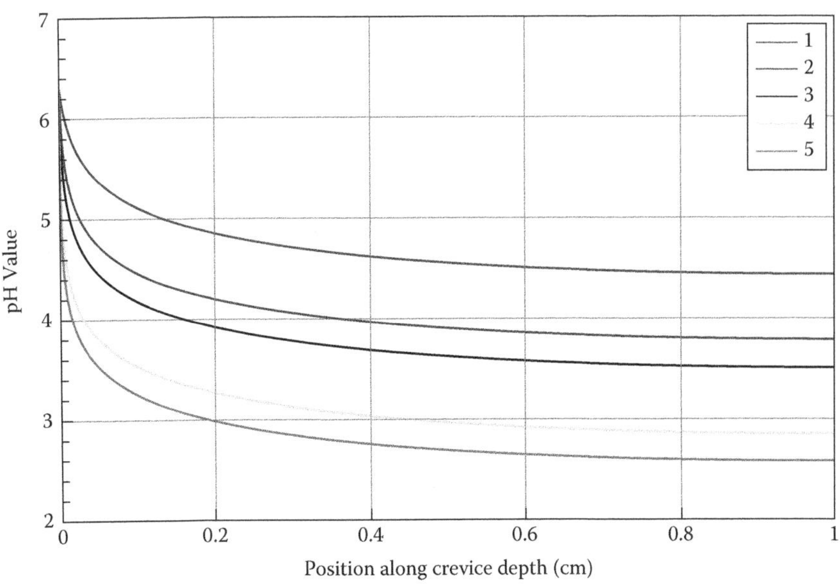

FIGURE 16.20
pH profiles along the crevice depth for crevices with various widths. Cases 1 through 5 are for widths of 50, 10, 5, 1, and 0.5 μm, respectively.

thermodynamics. The pH value in a crevice can drop very severely, especially when the width of the crevice is small. Such a significant drop in pH will only accelerate the corrosive process, leading to compounded device failure and tissue damage. For improving the clinical successes of these modular implants and their regulatory approval processes, it is necessary to quantitatively analyze the crevice environment in terms of reaction kinetics, mass transport, and the concentration of various relevant ions.

16.6 What to Expect in Future Editions

The examples given in this book (the first edition) and those in *Computational Bioengineering* are to serve as simple demonstrations that a computational approach can not only help solve biomedical problems of real-world relevance but also provide visualization of obtained results to assist the modeler to gain better scientific and engineering insights into the design or analysis problems undertaken. In future editions, I envisage that more advanced and integrated examples will be presented and discussed to help the reader see more benefits of computational modeling in advancing health care and improving quality of life, as well as general engineering for stimulating innovation.

Part IV

Useful Knowledge

A

Mechanics of Materials

A.1 Terms: *Linear*, *Nonlinear*, *Elastic*, and *Plastic*

In most design and analysis problems entailing the use of materials, a designer often needs to consider the mechanical properties of the materials used or to be used. In dealing with materials' mechanical properties, we often encounter terms like *linear* and *nonlinear* relationship, and *elastic* and *plastic* behavior, as if a linear relationship were always associated with elastic behavior and a nonlinear relationship with plastic behavior. In this section, we take a close look at these terms with the goal of helping the reader develop a clear understanding of them and be able to make right decisions in either selecting a material or analyzing one.

Let us first define these terms. On the one hand, *linear* and *nonlinear* are geometric terms often used to refer to a relationship between two variables, such as in a load–displacement curve or in a stress–strain curve. When these relationships are straight lines, we call them linear, and when they are curved lines, we call them nonlinear. On the other hand, the terms *elastic* and *plastic* refer to material or structural deformational behavior, specifically the ability to regain the original shape after the removal of loads. When a material or structure regains its original shape (all deformations vanish) after the removal of loads, we consider it deforming with elastic behavior, and when it does not regain its original shape, we call it deforming with plastic behavior.

Knowing the meanings of these different terms, we should now have a sense that a linear relationship is not necessarily always associated with elastic behavior and a nonlinear relationship with plastic behavior. In the following section, we will see that a material can behave linear elastically and nonlinear elastically, and it can also exhibit elastic yielding and plastic yielding behavior.

A.2 Describing Materials' Various Properties

Indeed, these terms are often used in combinations to describe a certain mechanical property or behavior. For example, a material or structure can exhibit elastic behavior with either a linear or nonlinear relationship

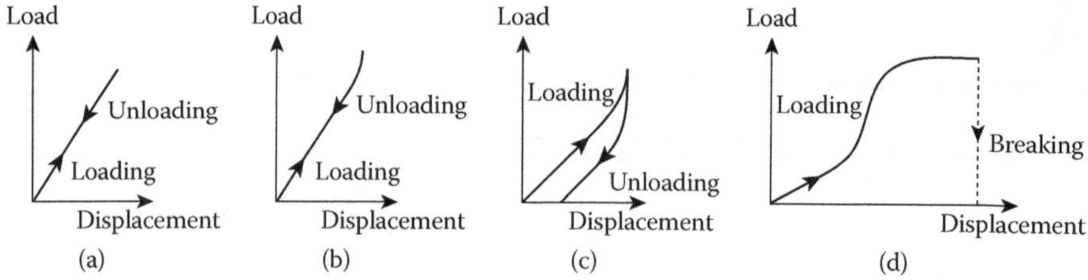

FIGURE A.1
Four types of load–displacement curves representing linear elastic (a), nonlinear elastic (b), partial plastic (c), and full plastic (d) behavior of materials.

between load and displacement or between stress and strain. As illustrated in Figure A.1a, linear elastic behavior is one in which the load–displacement curve is a straight line (hence linear) and the loading and unloading curves follow the same trace such that the displacement will vanish (hence elastic) when the applied load is removed. Nonlinear elastic behavior describes a curved (hence nonlinear) load–displacement relationship, but the displacement induced by loading will vanish (hence elastic) after the removal of the load, as illustrated in Figure A.1b.

While these two cases show elastic behavior, the difference between linear and nonlinear elastic behavior, in a practical sense, is that the former occurs when the deformation is very small (often invisible) and the latter occurs when the deformation is slightly larger (sometime visible). For instance, when one gently uses fingers to pinch an aluminum can and then let go of it without causing any permanent shape change, the deformation in the can before letting go of the fingers is nonlinear elastic deformation.

When a material is loaded to yielding, the load–displacement curve will be nonlinear. Here, yielding means that the slope of the load–displacement curve or stress–strain curve, or modulus of elasticity, decreases. Material yielding can be regarded as partial or full. Partial yielding behavior is one in which the material, although exhibiting reduced modulus of elasticity, can still carry increased loading. However, due to the endured yielding in the materials, when the applied load is gradually removed during unloading, the load–displacement curve will follow a different path. After the applied load is totally removed, part of the induced displacement will vanish due to its elastic nature, but part will remain in the form of permanent deformation. This permanent deformation is called plastic deformation, or sometimes residual deformation. The resulting load–displacement curve is a partial plastic load–displacement curve, as illustrated in Figure A.1c. If we refer to the aluminum can example, this partial plastic behavior can be observed when we pinch the fingers just a bit harder such that after letting go of the fingers, the can will recover most of the pinching deformation but with a small dent remaining in the can.

A full plastic load–displacement curve is one in which a material is loaded into the state of full yielding, where the displacement will increase continuously even without any additional loading. In such a state, the material will keep deforming plastically. This is the stage often referred to as full yielding, and once it occurs, even with the quick removal of all loads, all the induced deformation will remain (hence full plastic deformation). In most situations, this kind of full yielding will lead to material failure (e.g., breaking if under tension) quickly, as depicted in Figure A.1c. To picture this behavior, we may think of stretching a piece of plastic sheet or rod until it breaks.

A.3 Linear, Nonlinear, Elastic, and Plastic Behavior in a Single Material

It is worth noting that these four types of load–displacement curves do not necessarily originate from four different materials. They may appear in a single material at different stages of loading. Figure A.2a shows a load–displacement curve for a material undergoing linear elastic, nonlinear elastic, elastic yielding, and plastic yielding deformations. Here, elastic yielding describes the same situation as the partial yielding discussed earlier in which the elastic part of the deformation vanishes and the plastic part remains after unloading, and plastic yielding describes the same full plastic deformation behavior.

If we look closely at the curve shown in Figure A.2a, we can note that the linear elastic behavior of a material occurs at the beginning of the loading stage when the induced displacement is very small. When the displacement increases slightly, the material may exhibit nonlinear but elastic behavior. This behavior is sometimes referred to as large-deformation nonlinearity, or geometric nonlinearity. When the displacement increases further, the material will reach an elastic yielding zone in which it still exhibits elastic behavior but

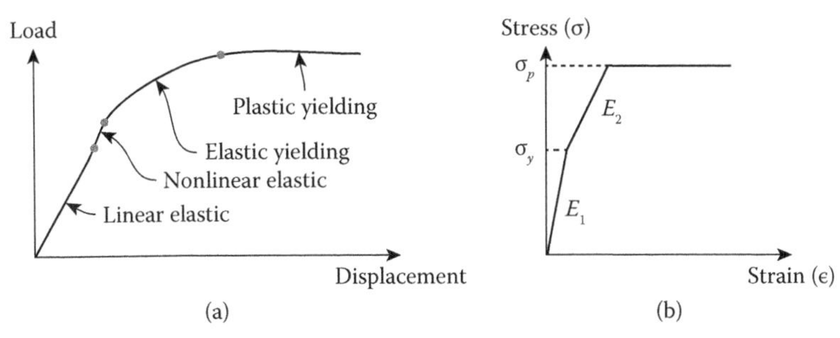

FIGURE A.2
Load–displacement curve (a) along with its corresponding stress–strain curve (b) for a given material.

with reduced modulus of elasticity (or Young's modulus). As the displacement continues to increase, the material will enter a plastic yielding zone in which the displacement or deformation keeps increasing without needing any further increase in loads.

Figure A.2b shows the corresponding stress–strain curve derived from the load–displacement curve shown in Figure A.2a. It presents another look at these mechanical properties from a pure material's perspective by eliminating all geometric-related influences. When the material behaves elastically, in both the linear and nonlinear manner, it has Young's modulus E_1. When the stress in the material reaches its elastic yielding point (σ_y), it will start to exhibit reduced elastic property with Young's modulus E_2, where $E_2 < E_1$. As the strain in the material further increases, the material will reach its plastic yielding point (σ_p), after which full plastic deformation will occur and the stress in the material will remain the same until the material breaks.

A.4 Example of Nonlinear Elastic Behavior

As we learned in the preceding section, nonlinear elastic behavior is often the result of large geometric deformation. Thus, it is sometimes referred to as large-deformation-induced nonlinearity or geometric nonlinearity. To demonstrate this geometric nonlinearity, we take a look at a wire with fixed constraints at its two ends and subjected to a transverse load (P) at its midspan, as illustrated in Figure A.3. For a thin wire, with a very small cross section area, under the given loading and constraint conditions, the wire can be assumed (in a simplified view) to deform into a triangle configuration, as depicted by the dash lines. According to the free-body diagram shown on the right in the figure, to remain in equilibrium, the tension (T) in the wire and the transverse load (P) should satisfy

$$P = 2T\cos\theta = 2T\frac{\delta}{\sqrt{\delta^2 + (L/2)^2}} \tag{A.1}$$

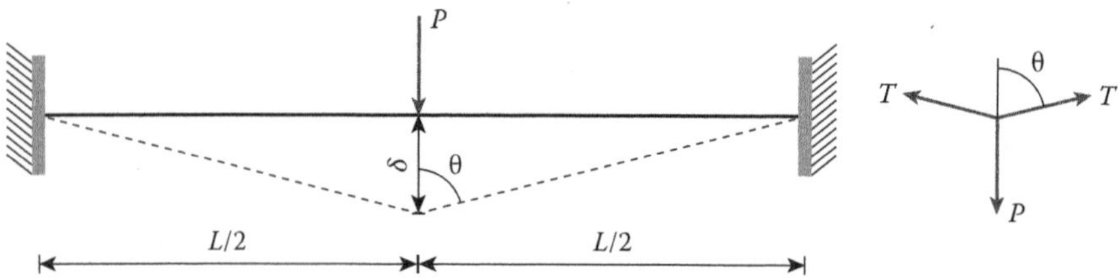

FIGURE A.3
A wire with fixed constraints at two ends is subject to a transverse load undergoing deformation simplified as a triangle shape (a) and along with a free-body diagram (b).

in which δ is the transverse deflection at the midspan and L is the length of the wire. The induced tension in the wire can be determined by multiplying the stress ($\sigma = E\epsilon$) with the cross section area (A) as $T = A\sigma = AE\epsilon$, in which E is the Young's modulus of the wire material and ϵ is the mechanical strain in the wire, which can be determined as $\epsilon = [\sqrt{\delta^2 + (L/2)^2} - L/2]/(L/2)$. With substitution of these relationships into Equation A.1, we establish the following load–deflection relationship:

$$P = \frac{4EA}{L} \frac{\delta(\sqrt{4\delta^2 + L^2} - L)}{\sqrt{4\delta^2 + L^2}} \tag{A.2}$$

Clearly, Equation A.2 describes a nonlinear relationship between the applied load (P) and the resulting deflection (δ) at the midspan. As long as the induced stress and strain in the wire are small such that the wire exhibits elastic behavior, this type of nonlinearity will be of elastic nature as well. Therefore, this type of nonlinearity is geometric. It is worth cautioning that because a simplified wire deformation of a triangle configuration is assumed, this example only serves to illustrate geometric nonlinearity and it should not be used to predict the wire performance. Recalling the discussion in Chapter 14 on a vibrating string, because such a large geometric deformation is necessary for producing sound, geometric nonlinearity needs to be activated in the software in order to capture its actual behavior.

Figure A.4 shows the load–deflection curve plotted based on Equation A.2 with constants E, A, and L all set to unity (1). Interestingly, not only the load–deflection relationship is a nonlinear curve, but the nonlinear behavior

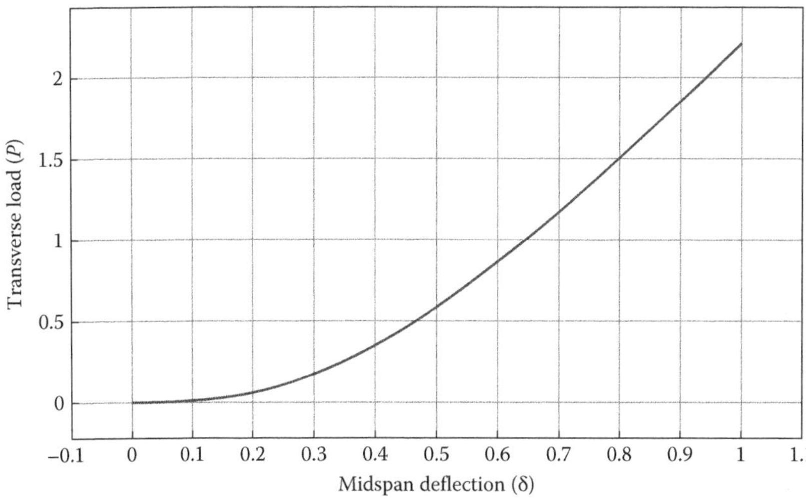

FIGURE A.4
Load–deflection curve based on Equation A.2 with E, A, and L all set to unity (1).

appears when the deflection is small. Since when the deflection of the wire is small, the induced stress and strain in the wire are also small, the observed large-deformation-induced nonlinear relationship can and will occur when the wire is still in its elastic nature.

A.5 Pseudoelastic, Hyperelastic, and Viscoelastic

The mechanical properties discussed in the preceding sections are associated with materials when they do not go through any intrinsic structural changes due to mechanical loading or other factors, like temperature variation. To provide an overview, let us also briefly get a sense of what the other elastic words, like *pseudoelastic*, *hyperelastic*, and *viscoelastic*, mean.

Some materials, like memory alloys, will undergo phase transition due to temperature changes, thereby exhibiting recoverable or reversible deformation behavior (hence elastic) as temperature changes back and forth. This type of elastic behavior is sometimes called pseudoelastic or superelastic.

Other materials, like many polymeric materials and biological tissues, will undergo polymer chain or collagen fiber reorientation under stretching, leading to the stiffening of the materials (i.e., increasing in the slope of the load–displacement curve)—a type of nonlinear relationship. When the material is in its elastic nature, the observed nonlinear stiffening behavior is called hyperelastic. A hyperelastic load–displacement curve may resemble the geometric nonlinear elastic curve shown in Figure A.4.

Viscoelastic is a term used to describe a material that possesses time (or rate)-dependent behavior, meaning that the material may exhibit different load–displacement or stress–strain curves when the loading rates are different. The main reason for this behavior is that viscoelastic materials are regarded as made of solid components that follow Hooke's law and fluidic components that follow Newton's law. Thus, for viscoelastic materials, a combined Hookean and Newtonian method is often used to evaluate these combined solid- and fluid-like characteristics with equivalent models made of springs (representing the elastic part) and dashpots (representing the viscous part). Load–displacement or stress–strain relationships of viscoelastic materials are always nonlinear, with loading and unloading curves following two different paths, known as hysteresis. But after the removal of all loads, deformations in the material will vanish (hence elastic), albeit slowly, due to the viscous components. Common viscoelastic materials include paint, catchup sauce, rubber, and many biological materials.

A.6 Loading Modes, Stress States, and Mohr's Circle

I often see that people have a tendency to associate the loading mode in a mechanical test with the failure mode of the material to be tested.

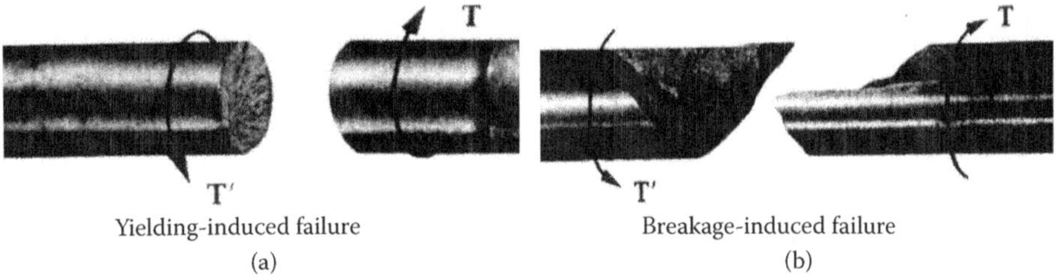

FIGURE A.5
Two fractured rods after torsional tests under yielding-induced failure (a) and breakage-induced failure (b). (Reproduced with permission from Beer F. P. et al., *Mechanics of Materials*, 6th edition, McGraw Hill, 2012.)

For example, if a material is expected to fail in tension, a tensile test is to be conducted, and if a material is expected to fail in shear, a shearing test should be performed. Although this belief is not totally incorrect, it ignores the consideration of the actual stress state induced in the material and its causal relationship with the failure modes influenced by the types of materials.

To help understand this statement better, let us take a look at the two images show in Figure A.5, in which two cylindrical rods failed in two different modes under the same torsional loading. The rod on the left has a fracture surface that resembles a perpendicular cross section cut, and the rod on the right has a fracture surface of a helical cut. The fact that these two rods, having the same geometric shape and subjected to the same type of loading, fail in two different modes indicates that the failure mode of a material is not directly related to its loading mode. Something else is at work.

This something else turns out to be one of the most important factors—the type of materials that these two rods are made of. If we look more closely at the fracture surfaces, we can note that the textures of the two fracture surfaces are also different. The one on the left shows the sign of material yielding, and the one on the right the sign of tensile breakage. So then, why will yielding and breakage failure modes cause the two rods to fracture in two different cut surfaces? To answer this question, we will need to know the stress states in these rods with the help of Mohr's circle.

Mohr's circle is a two-dimensional (2D) graphical representation of the stress state of a given point in a material using a circle (for a 2D stress state; three circles will be needed for a three-dimensional [3D] stress state) in a σ-τ coordinate system, with a pair of opposite points on the circle representing the stress state of a stress element in a given direction. To visualize this, let us look at Figure A.6, where a Mohr's circle and two stress elements in a plane stress situation (see discussion in Section 8.2.1) are sketched.

For the stress element shown in the middle, representing a viewing angle through the x-y orientation, we consider a normal stress σ_x and a shear stress τ_{xy} in the x-cut plane, and a normal stress σ_y and a shear stress τ_{xy} in the

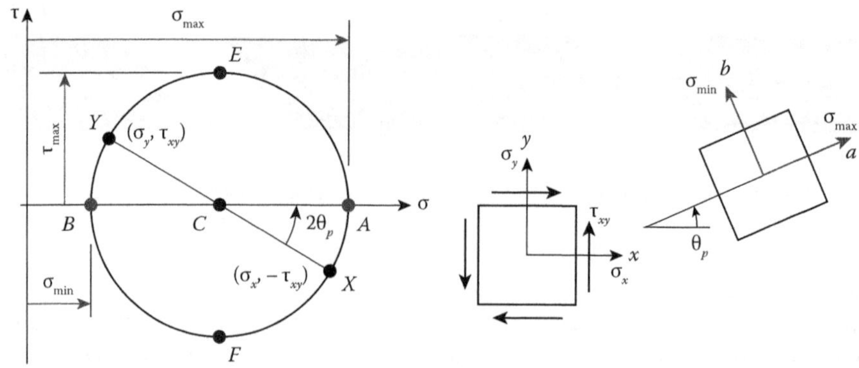

FIGURE A.6
Mohr's circle and stress elements for depicting the stress state of a given point.

y-cut plane. By using these paired stress values in each cut plane as coordinates, we mark two points, $X(\sigma_x, -\tau_{xy})$ and $Y(\sigma_y, \tau_{xy})$, in the σ-τ coordinate system shown on the left, with σ as the abscissa and τ as the ordinate. A sign convention is followed in this process in which tensile normal stresses (σ_x and σ_y) are considered positive and compressive normal stresses negative, and clockwise shear stresses (τ_{xy}) are positive and counterclockwise shear stresses negative. By linking the two points, X and Y, with a line, we find an intersection with the abscissa (the σ axis) at point C. Then, using point C as the center point, we construct a circle passing through both points X and Y. This is the so-called Mohr's circle, honoring its creator, Christian Otto Mohr (1835–1918), a German civil engineer.

On a Mohr's circle, any pair of opposite points (with respect to the center point C), like the X-Y pair, represent the stress state of the given point in a certain viewing orientation. This means that the stress state of the given point can be represented by countless different combinations of stress components depending on our viewing orientations. For the A-B pair, while still representing the same stress state of the point, because τ_{xy} is zero, it describes an orientation in which a stress element only has normal stresses acting on it. This orientation is called the principal directions, and the corresponding stresses (i.e., $\sigma_{\max}$ and $\sigma_{\min}$) are called principal stresses.

From the Mohr's circle, we can see that a counterclockwise rotation by an angle of $2\theta_p$ will transform the X-Y pair to the A-B pair. For the stress element, a counterclockwise rotation by θ_p (half of the rotation in the Mohr's circle) will transform the element in the x-y orientation to the one in the principal a-b orientation, as shown on the right in Figure A.6. With a further 90° counterclockwise rotation from the A-B orientation, we will reach the E-F orientation, where the shear stress reaches its maximum, $\tau_{\max} = (\sigma_{\max} - \sigma_{\min})/2$. This also means that with a 45° counterclockwise rotation from the a-b stress element, we will obtain a stress element, having

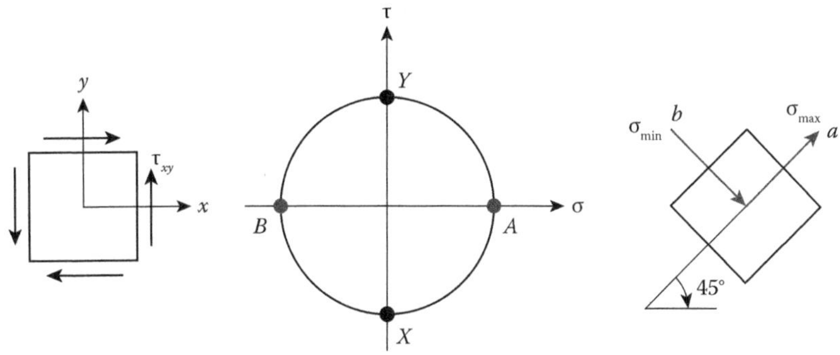

FIGURE A.7
Mohr's circle for torsional rods and two important stress elements.

maximum shear stresses. However, in this stress element both normal stresses are not only present but also equal, that is, $\sigma_x = \sigma_y = (\sigma_{\max} + \sigma_{\min})/2$.

Equipped with the knowledge of Mohr's circle, let us now return to the two torsional rods discussed earlier and analyze the cause for fracture by examining the stress states in them. Figure A.7 shows the Mohr's circle for a surface point on a cylindrical rod undergoing pure torsional loading. From this Mohr's circle, we can see that in the x-y orientation (corresponding to the X, Y points on the circle), the stress element has only shear stresses acting on it with no normal stresses. This means that the x-y stress element experiences the maximum shear stresses. On the other hand, the principal stress element, the a-b stress element (corresponding to the A, B points on the circle), is a 45° counterclockwise rotation away, because the X-Y and A-B lines are 90° apart in the Mohr's circle. In the principal stress element, the maximum principal stress is maximum tension and the minimum principal stress is maximum compression. Put together, when the two rods undergo a torsion loading test, the x-cut plane (as well as the y-cut plane) endures maximum shearing, the 45°-cut plane experiences the maximum tension, and the 135°-cut plane experiences the maximum compression.

Knowing that a ductile material tends to fail due to shear-induced material yielding and a brittle material due to tension-induced breakage, we can now say that the rod on the left failed in a shear mode due to its ductile material nature because the shear stress is the highest in the x-cut plane (incidentally, this cut plane has the smallest cross section area). It should be expected to fail in the x-cut plane due to shear-induced material yielding. For the rod on the right, it failed in a tension mode due to its brittle nature because the tensile stress reaches its maximum along a plane oriented 45°. It is thus not surprising that the fracture surface caused by tension-induced breakage is oriented at a 135° angle from the x-cut plane, perpendicular to the direction of the maximum tension. In short, the failure mode of a material is not determined by the loading mode but by the induced stress state (i.e., the maximum stresses and their orientations) and the type of materials. If the material is of the ductile type, shearing-induced yielding failure should be concerned, and if the material is of the brittle type, tension-induced breakage should be avoided.

A.7 von Mises Stress or Principal Stress?

In many design problems concerning the strength of a selected material, one of the most important questions we have to ask is how to make sure the material will not fail under the intended application. Recalling the discussions in Sections A.3 and A.6, we may ask, more pointedly, how to ensure the material does not fail due to shear-induced yielding if it is of the ductile type, or tension-induced breakage if it is of the brittle type.

To answer to this question, we can set up computational modeling to conduct a solid mechanics analysis of the designed structure or device, as demonstrated in the several cases in Chapter 16. Once the analysis is properly done, we will have access to many different types of stresses. This leads to a new question: Of all these available stresses, which one should we examine in order not to let the material fail? In most finite element method (FEM) software packages, the default setting for viewing mechanical stresses is von Mises stress. However, in Section A.6 we learned from the concept of Mohr's circle that the principal stresses are the extrema. So a simpler question then is, von Mises stress or principal stress, which one should we refer to in our design process?

To answer this question, we need to know what von Mises stress is. But before that, let us first look at the principal stresses in both 2D and 3D situations. For the principal stresses, σ_{max} and σ_{min}, shown in the Mohr's circle of a 2D plane stress situation (Figure A.6), we often call σ_{max} the first principal stress and σ_{min} the second principal stress and denote them as σ_1 and σ_2, respectively, as illustrated in Figure A.8. The maximum shear stresses are at the top and bottom of the Mohr's circle with $\tau_{\text{max}} = (\sigma_1 - \sigma_2)/2$.

By expanding this concept further to a 3D situation, we use three Mohr's circles, as shown in Figure A.9, each representing the 2D situation of one of

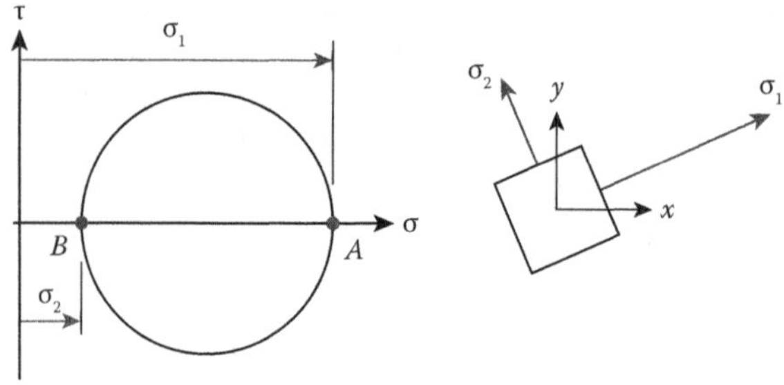

FIGURE A.8
A 2D Mohr's circle and the first and second principal stresses.

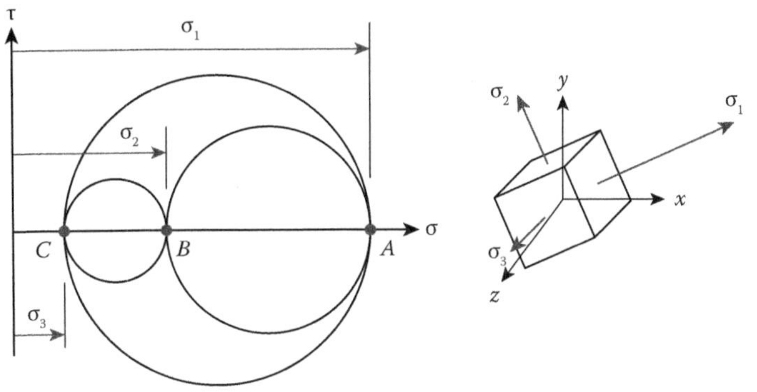

FIGURE A.9
Three-dimensional Mohr's circles and the first, second, and third principal stresses.

the three orthogonal plans, namely, the x-y, y-z, and x-z planes. For example, the circle between points A and B represents the stress state in the x-y plane with σ_1 and σ_2 as the two principal stresses, the circle between points B and C represents the stress state in the y-z plane with σ_2 and σ_3 as the two principal stresses, and the circle between points A and C represents the stress state in the x-z plane with σ_1 and σ_3 as the two principal stresses. In each of the three planes, the corresponding maximum shear stress is, respectively,

$$\tau_{\max_{(xy)}} = \frac{(\sigma_1 - \sigma_2)}{2}, \quad \tau_{\max_{(yz)}} = \frac{(\sigma_2 - \sigma_3)}{2}, \quad \text{and } \tau_{\max_{(xz)}} = \frac{(\sigma_1 - \sigma_3)}{2}$$

With this knowledge of principal and maximum shear stresses, we can now define von Mises stress. Strictly speaking, von Mises stress is not stress in a vector sense. Instead, it is a scalar representation of the distortion energy within a material using a quantity that carries the units of stresses. Mathematically, von Mises stress is calculated with the following expression:

$$\sigma_{vM} = \sqrt{\frac{(\sigma_1 - \sigma_2)^2 + (\sigma_2 - \sigma_3)^2 + (\sigma_1 - \sigma_3)^2}{2}} \tag{A.3}$$

Looking at Equation A.3, we can immediately tell that von Mises stress is actually determined based on the sum of the three maximum shear stresses. Indeed, von Mises stress is formulated as a criterion to capture the maximum shearing-induced distortion energy in a material under mechanical loading. This criterion states that for safe use of a material, its maximum von Mises stress should not exceed the yield strength of the material. Recalling the discussions in the preceding sections, we now know that von Mises stress should be examined as a quantitative guide in the design process when the material to be used is of the ductile type (metals and most polymers, etc.), because the shear-induced yielding of the material is of great concern.

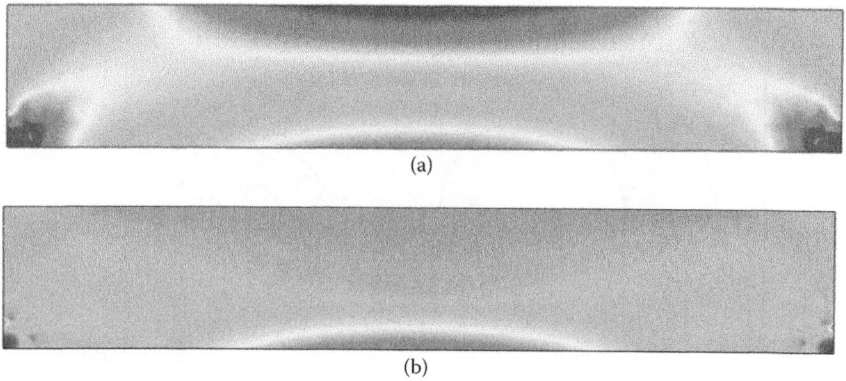

FIGURE A.10
(a) von Mises and (b) first principal stresses in a simply supported beam structure sustaining a downward distributed load at the upper edge.

On the other hand, as we can see in Figure A.9, the first principal stress σ_1 represents the maximum tensile stress in the material for almost all cases except when all these principal stresses are compressive (negative in values), like an underwater situation in which the material is under a hydrostatic compressive pressure all around. So if the material to be used is of the brittle type (ceramics, concrete, glass, etc.), the first principal stress should be used as a quantitative guide to ensure that the maximum value of the first principal stress in the material is smaller than the tensile strength of the material.

To help visualize these arguments, Figure A.10 shows the stresses in a simply supported beam structure sustaining a downward load at the upper edge, with Figure A.10a showing the distribution of von Mises stress and Figure A.10b showing that of the first principal stress. If steel is to be used for the beam, the upper edge and lower corners will be the regions of concern due to presence of the high von Mises stress (Figure A.10a). However, if concrete is to be used, the lower edge should be of grave concern because of the highest first principal tensile stress (Figure A.10b). This also explains why in practice engineers often put more reinforcing metal bars (or rebars for short) in the lower part of concrete beam structures.

A.8 Trajectories of Tension and Compression Lines

As we learned in Sections A.6 and A.7, at any given point in a structure under mechanical loading we can identify the principal directions for the stresses by constructing Mohr's circles and determining the orientation of the stress element that corresponds to the pairs of extrema with zero shear stresses, that is, the *A*-*B*, *B*-*C*, or *A*-*C* pairs on the Mohr's circles in Figure A.9.

Let us now consider a plane stress situation (see more discussion in Section 8.2.1). Referring to Figure A.9, we assume that the first principal stress (σ_1) is positive (tensile), the second one (σ_2) zero, and the third one (σ_3) negative (compressive), which is likely the case for most plane stress situations. After identifying the directions of the first (tension) and third (compression) principal stresses at some selected points across the plane structure, we mark the two directions using perpendicular crosses at these points (note that these two principal stresses are always perpendicular to each other). To distinguish the two stresses, we use red for the stroke representing the tensile direction and blue for the stroke representing the compressive direction. Finally, we link the red strokes into red lines and blue strokes into blue lines by following the orientations of these strokes. The outcome is two sets of lines representing the directions of maximum tensile stress (red lines) and maximum compressive stress (blue lines), which sometimes are also referred to as the stress trajectories. Figure A.11 shows the trajectories of tension and compression lines in the same simply supported beam structure discussed in the preceding section. With a close inspection, we note that these two sets of lines are orthogonal, meaning that at each intersection, a red line is perpendicular to a blue line, as expected.

An intuitive way to picture these stress trajectories is to superimpose a principal stress element, shown in Figure A.12, onto any of these intersection points. Assuming the beam structure is made of concrete, we should expect

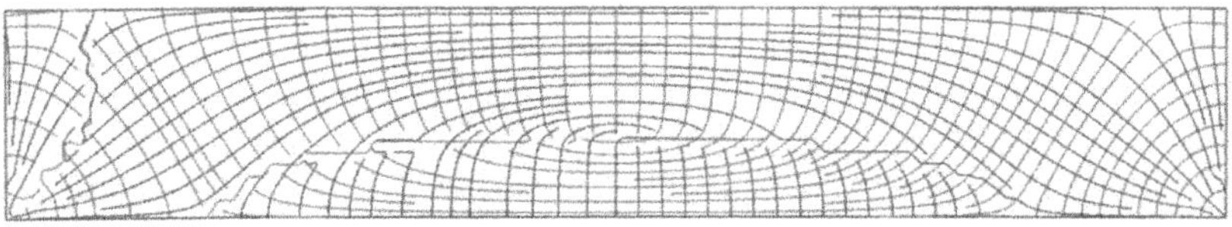

FIGURE A.11
Trajectories of tension (red) and compression (blue) lines in the beam.

FIGURE A.12
(a) Principal stress element with a marking cross at the center, and (b, c) two images of fracture lines in concrete beams. (Courtesy of Jeff R. Filler, http://reinforced-concrete.blogspot.com.)

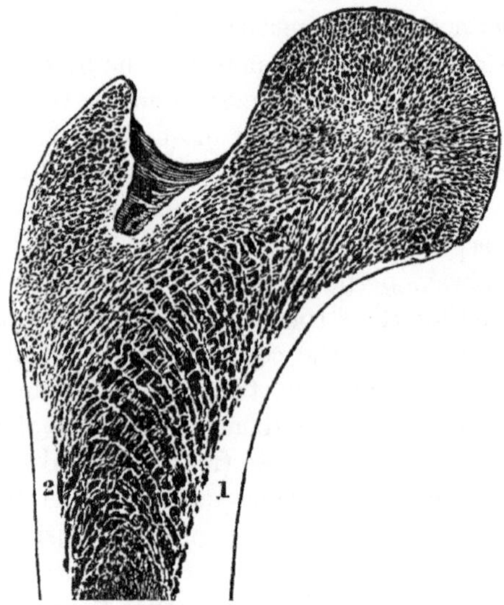

FIGURE A.13
Cross section image of a human femoral head showing the architectures of the trabecular (or cancellous, spongy) bone. (Courtesy of http://etc.usf.edu/clipart/50500/50502/50502_femur.htm)

tension-induced breakage as the failure mode. Referring to the principal stress element, a breaking line caused by tensile stresses should be perpendicular to the tensile stress, meaning that the breaking lines in the concrete will coincide with the compression lines. By comparing the images of the actual fracture lines near the corner and at the bottom shown in Figure A.12 with the stress trajectories shown in Figure A.11, we can see clearly that these fracture lines follow exactly the compression lines in these regions (caused by tensile breakage). In return, these stress trajectories also give civil engineers ideas and ways to reinforce concrete structures.

Not only civil engineers know how to take advantage of the stress trajectory information for strengthening concrete structures and other composites; nature knows it well, too. The structure of the human femoral head is one such example. Inside a thin layer of strong cortical (or compact) bone is coarsely structured trabecular (or cancellous, spongy) bony structure. Interestingly, as shown in Figure A.13, the architecture of the spongy bony structure is not random. In fact, it resembles the stress trajectories of the femoral head. According to Wolff's law, named after Julius Wolff (1836–1902), bones in a healthy person or animal will remodel in adaptation to the loads they are experiencing. Therefore, the architecture of the spongy bone is likely the result of the bone remodeling process in meeting the strengthening needs of human growth and daily activities, guided by the stress trajectories inside the femoral head. The reader is encouraged to explore this further using the computational modeling approach discussed in this book.

B

Useful Mathematic Knowledge

B.1 Dot Product

Here, we provide the mathematic derivation for the calculation of the dot product. For the two vectors

$$u = u_x\vec{i} + u_y\vec{j} + u_z\vec{k} \text{ and } v = v_x\vec{i} + v_y\vec{j} + v_z\vec{k}$$

intersecting at an angle (θ), as illustrated in Figure B.1, let us consider the triangle formed by the vectors. By vector algebra, we express the length of the side opposite of θ:

$$w = u - v = (u_x - v_x)\vec{i} + (u_y - v_y)\vec{j} + (u_z - v_z)\vec{k}$$

By the law of cosines, we can write the following relationship in terms of the lengths of the three sides of the triangle and the angle (θ) between u and v:

$$|w|^2 = |u|^2 + |v|^2 - 2|u||v|\cos\theta$$

in which

$$\begin{aligned}
|u|^2 &= \left(\sqrt{u_x^2 + u_y^2 + u_z^2}\right)^2 = u_x^2 + u_y^2 + u_z^2 \\
|v|^2 &= \left(\sqrt{v_x^2 + v_y^2 + v_z^2}\right)^2 = v_x^2 + v_y^2 + v_z^2 \\
[w|^2 &= \left(\sqrt{(u_x - v_x)^2 + (u_y - v_y)^2 + (u_z - v_z)^2}\right)^2 \\
&= (u_x - v_x)^2 + (u_y - v_y)^2 + (u_z - v_z)^2 \\
&= u_x^2 + v_x^2 + u_y^2 + v_y^2 + u_z^2 + v_z^2 - 2u_xv_x - 2u_yv_y - 2u_zv_z
\end{aligned}$$

Thus,

$$2|u||v|\cos\theta = |u|^2 + |v|^2 - |w|^2 = 2(u_xv_x + u_yv_y + u_zv_z)$$

and therefore,

$$\cos\theta = \frac{u_zv_z + u_yv_y + u_zv_z}{|u||v|}$$

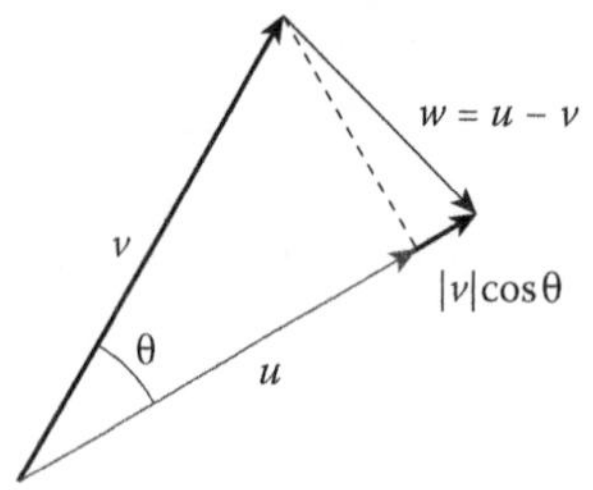

FIGURE B.1
Dot product of two vectors.

Since $0 \leq \theta < \pi$, we have

$$\theta = \cos^{-1}\left(\frac{u_x v_x + u_y v_y + u_z v_z}{|u||v|}\right)$$

By definition, the product of two vectors equals the length of the first vector (e.g., $|u|$) multiplying the projection length of the second vector on the first (e.g., $|v|\cos\theta$), as illustrated in Figure B.1. Thus, the dot product of two vectors can be expressed as

$$u \cdot v = |u||v|\cos\theta = u_x v_x + u_y v_y + u_z v_z \tag{B.1}$$

Here are some properties of the dot product, given that u, v, and w are vectors and c is a scalar:

1. $u \cdot v = v \cdot u$
2. $(cu) \cdot v = u \cdot (cv) = c(u \cdot v)$
3. $u \cdot (v + w) = u \cdot v + u \cdot w$
4. $u \cdot u = |u|^2$
5. $0 \cdot u = 0$

B.2 Cross Product

If two vectors, $u = u_x\vec{i} + u_y\vec{j} + u_z\vec{k}$ and $v = v_x\vec{i} + v_y\vec{j} + v_z\vec{k}$, are not parallel but intersect with each other at an angle (θ), they determine a plane (P), as illustrated in Figure B.2. We select a unit vector $\vec{n}$ perpendicular to the plane by the right-hand rule, which is the direction the right thumb points when the fingers curl around the angle θ from u to v.

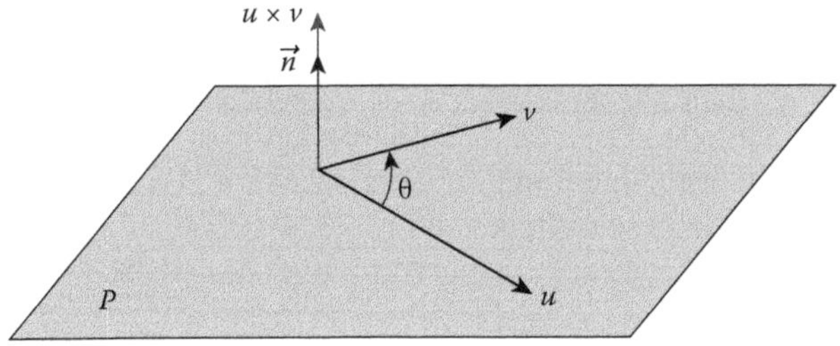

FIGURE B.2
Cross product of two vectors.

By definition, the cross product of the two vectors can be expressed as

$$u \times v = (|u||v| \sin \theta)\ \vec{n}$$

Note that $|u||v| \sin \theta$ equals the area of the parallelogram formed by vectors u and v in the P plane.

Unlike the dot product, the cross product is a vector, and its direction is represented by the unit vector $\vec{n}$. According to this definition, when vectors u and v are parallel, that is, $\theta = 0$, then $u \times v = 0$. Furthermore, we can arrive at the following properties for the cross product, given that u, v, and w are vectors and r and s are scalars:

1. $(ru) \times (sv) = (rs)(u \times v)$
2. $u \times (v + w) = u \times v + u \times w$
3. $v \times u = -(u \times v)$
4. $(v + w) \times u = v \times u + w \times u$
5. $0 \times u = 0$

Knowing these properties, we can express

$$\begin{aligned} u \times v &= (u_x\vec{i} + u_y\vec{j} + u_z\vec{k}) \times (v_x\vec{i} + v_y\vec{j} + v_z\vec{k}) \\ &= u_x v_x \vec{i} \times \vec{i} + u_x v_y \vec{i} \times \vec{j} + u_x v_z \vec{i} \times \vec{k} \\ &\quad + u_y v_x \vec{j} \times \vec{i} + u_y v_y \vec{j} \times \vec{j} + u_y v_z \vec{j} \times \vec{k} \\ &\quad + u_z v_x \vec{k} \times \vec{i} + u_z v_y \vec{k} \times \vec{j} + u_z v_z \vec{k} \times \vec{k} \end{aligned}$$

By substituting the following relationships,

$$\begin{aligned} \vec{i} \times \vec{j} &= -\vec{j} \times \vec{i} = \vec{k} \\ \vec{j} \times \vec{k} &= -\vec{k} \times \vec{j} = \vec{i} \\ \vec{k} \times \vec{i} &= -\vec{i} \times \vec{k} = \vec{j} \\ \vec{i} \times \vec{i} &= \vec{j} \times \vec{j} = \vec{k} \times \vec{k} = 0 \end{aligned}$$

into the above expression, we have

$$u \times v = (u_y v_z - u_z v_y)\vec{i} - (u_x v_z - u_z v_x)\vec{j} + (u_x v_y - u_y v_x)\vec{k}$$

The term on the right-hand side of this equation is actually the determinant of the following square matrix:

$$det \begin{bmatrix} \vec{i} & \vec{j} & \vec{k} \\ u_x & u_y & u_z \\ v_x & v_y & v_z \end{bmatrix} = (u_y v_z - u_z v_y)\vec{i} - (u_x v_z - u_z v_x)\vec{j} + (u_x v_y - u_y v_x)\vec{k}$$

Therefore, we can express

$$u \times v = det \begin{bmatrix} \vec{i} & \vec{j} & \vec{k} \\ u_x & u_y & u_z \\ v_x & v_y & v_z \end{bmatrix} \tag{B.2}$$

B.3 Taylor and Maclaurin Series

A Taylor series expands a function into a series with an infinite sum of terms determined at a specified point from the values of the function's derivatives. For example, for a one-dimensional function, $f(x)$, its Taylor series can be expressed as a series expansion about a point $x = a$ as

$$f(x) = f(a) + f'(a)(x-a) + \frac{f''(a)}{2!}(x-a)^2 + \frac{f^{(3)}(a)}{3!}(x-a)^3 + \cdots + \frac{f^{(n)}(a)}{n!}(x-a)^n + \cdots$$

where $n!$ is the factorial of n: $n! = n \times (n-1) \times (n-2) \times \cdots \times 2 \times 1$.

When $a = 0$, the expansion is known as a Maclaurin series:

$$f(x) = f(0) + f'(0)x + \frac{f''(0)}{2!}x^2 + \frac{f^{(3)}(0)}{3!}x^3 + \cdots + \frac{f^{(n)}(0)}{n!}x^n + \cdots$$

B.4 Proof of $dA = \det[J]d\xi d\eta$

In transforming two-dimensional (2D) elements in coordinates (x, y) to coordinates (ξ, η), we use the following mapping functions:

$$x = x(\xi, \eta), \quad y = y(\xi, \eta)$$

This indicates that x and y are now functions of ξ and η. By the chain rule of differentiation, we express

$$dx = \frac{\partial x}{\partial \xi} d\xi \vec{i} + \frac{\partial x}{\partial \eta} d\eta \vec{j}, \quad dy = \frac{\partial y}{\partial \xi} d\xi \vec{i} + \frac{\partial y}{\partial \eta} d\eta \vec{j}$$

where $\vec{i}, \vec{j}$ are unit vectors in the ξ, η directions, respectively.

By the definition of the cross product, we can calculate the area formed by dx and dy in coordinates x and y using the following formula:

$$dA = |dx \times dy|$$

By expanding the dx and dy expressions into

$$dx = \frac{\partial x}{\partial \xi} d\xi \vec{i} + \frac{\partial x}{\partial \eta} d\eta \vec{j} + 0\vec{k} \text{ and } dy = \frac{\partial y}{\partial \xi} d\xi \vec{i} + \frac{\partial y}{\partial \eta} d\eta \vec{j} + 0\vec{k}$$

and applying Equation B.2, we obtain

$$dA = \left\| \begin{bmatrix} \vec{i} & \vec{j} & \vec{k} \\ \frac{\partial x}{\partial \xi} d\xi & \frac{\partial x}{\partial \eta} d\eta & 0 \\ \frac{\partial y}{\partial \xi} d\xi & \frac{\partial y}{\partial \eta} d\eta & 0 \end{bmatrix} \right\| = \left(\frac{\partial x}{\partial \xi}\frac{\partial y}{\partial \eta} - \frac{\partial x}{\partial \eta}\frac{\partial y}{\partial \xi} \right) d\xi d\eta$$

$$= \det \begin{bmatrix} \frac{\partial x}{\partial \xi} & \frac{\partial y}{\partial \xi} \\ \frac{\partial x}{\partial \eta} & \frac{\partial y}{\partial \eta} \end{bmatrix} d\xi d\eta$$

Let

$$[J] = \begin{bmatrix} \frac{\partial x}{\partial \xi} & \frac{\partial y}{\partial \xi} \\ \frac{\partial x}{\partial \eta} & \frac{\partial y}{\partial \eta} \end{bmatrix}$$

be the Jacobian matrix of transformation in a 2D space; then we have

$$dA = \det \left[J\right] d\xi d\eta \tag{B.3}$$

B.5 Proof of $dV = \det[J] d\xi d\eta d\zeta$

In transforming three-dimensional (3D) elements in coordinates (x, y, z) to coordinates (ξ, η, ζ), we use the following mapping functions:

$$x = x(\xi, \eta, \zeta), \quad y = y(\xi, \eta, \zeta), \quad z = z(\xi, \eta, \zeta)$$

which make x, y, and z functions of ξ, η, and ζ. By the chain rule of differentiation, we express

$$dx = \frac{\partial x}{\partial \xi} d\xi \vec{i} + \frac{\partial x}{\partial \eta} d\eta \vec{j} + \frac{\partial x}{\partial \zeta} d\zeta \vec{k}$$
$$dy = \frac{\partial y}{\partial \xi} d\xi \vec{i} + \frac{\partial y}{\partial \eta} d\eta \vec{j} + \frac{\partial y}{\partial \zeta} d\zeta \vec{k}$$
$$dz = \frac{\partial z}{\partial \xi} d\xi \vec{i} + \frac{\partial z}{\partial \eta} d\eta \vec{j} + \frac{\partial z}{\partial \zeta} d\zeta \vec{k}$$

where $\vec{i}, \vec{j}, \vec{k}$ are unit vectors in the ξ, η, ζ directions, respectively.

Using the dot and cross product expressions, we can calculate a volume formed by dx, dy, and dz in coordinates x, y, and z by the following formula:

$$dV = |dz \cdot (dx \times dy)|$$

By the cross product formula, we know

$$dx \times dy = \begin{bmatrix} \vec{i} & \vec{j} & \vec{k} \\ \frac{\partial x}{\partial \xi} d\xi & \frac{\partial x}{\partial \eta} d\eta & \frac{\partial x}{\partial \zeta} d\zeta \\ \frac{\partial y}{\partial \xi} d\xi & \frac{\partial y}{\partial \eta} d\eta & \frac{\partial y}{\partial \zeta} d\zeta \end{bmatrix}$$

Multiplying it out, we obtain

$$dx \times dy = \left(\frac{\partial x}{\partial \eta} \frac{\partial y}{\partial \zeta} d\eta d\zeta - \frac{\partial x}{\partial \zeta} \frac{\partial y}{\partial \eta} d\eta d\zeta \right) \vec{i} - \left(\frac{\partial x}{\partial \xi} \frac{\partial y}{\partial \zeta} d\xi d\zeta - \frac{\partial x}{\partial \zeta} \frac{\partial y}{\partial \xi} d\xi d\zeta \right) \vec{j}$$
$$+ \left(\frac{\partial x}{\partial \xi} \frac{\partial y}{\partial \eta} d\xi d\eta - \frac{\partial x}{\partial \eta} \frac{\partial y}{\partial \xi} d\xi d\eta \right) \vec{k}$$

Then, by the dot product formula we calculate

$$dV = |dz \cdot (dx \times dy)| = \left(\frac{\partial x}{\partial \eta} \frac{\partial y}{\partial \zeta} - \frac{\partial x}{\partial \zeta} \frac{\partial y}{\partial \eta} \right) \frac{\partial z}{\partial \xi} d\xi d\eta d\zeta$$
$$- \left(\frac{\partial x}{\partial \xi} \frac{\partial y}{\partial \zeta} - \frac{\partial x}{\partial \zeta} \frac{\partial y}{\partial \xi} \right) \frac{\partial z}{\partial \eta} d\xi d\eta d\zeta + \left(\frac{\partial x}{\partial \xi} \frac{\partial y}{\partial \eta} - \frac{\partial x}{\partial \eta} \frac{\partial y}{\partial \xi} \right) \frac{\partial z}{\partial \zeta} d\xi d\eta d\zeta$$

which is equivalent to

$$dV = \det \begin{bmatrix} \frac{\partial x}{\partial \xi} & \frac{\partial y}{\partial \xi} & \frac{\partial z}{\partial \xi} \\ \frac{\partial x}{\partial \eta} & \frac{\partial y}{\partial \eta} & \frac{\partial z}{\partial \eta} \\ \frac{\partial x}{\partial \zeta} & \frac{\partial y}{\partial \zeta} & \frac{\partial z}{\partial \zeta} \end{bmatrix} d\xi d\eta d\zeta$$

Let

$$[J] = \begin{bmatrix} \frac{\partial x}{\partial \xi} & \frac{\partial y}{\partial \xi} & \frac{\partial z}{\partial \xi} \\ \frac{\partial x}{\partial \eta} & \frac{\partial y}{\partial \eta} & \frac{\partial z}{\partial \eta} \\ \frac{\partial x}{\partial \zeta} & \frac{\partial y}{\partial \zeta} & \frac{\partial z}{\partial \zeta} \end{bmatrix}$$

be the Jacobian matrix of transformation in a 3D space; then we have

$$dV = \det \left[J\right] d\xi d\eta d\zeta \tag{B.4}$$

B.6 Lagrange Multipliers

Lagrange multipliers are often used for imposing constraints when seeking conditional extrema (maximal or minimal values) of a given variable or function.

To see how it is done, let us examine a situation in which we wish to find the points on a hyperbolic cylinder $x^2 - z^2 = 1$ that are closest to the origin. As illustrated in Figure B.3, since the points having an equal distance to the origin in a 3D space form a sphere, let us imagine a small sphere of radius a centered at the origin: $x^2 + y^2 + z^2 - a^2 = 0$. To find the closest points on the hyperbolic cylinder to the origin, all we need to do is expand the radius of the sphere until the spheric surface touches the hyperbolic cylindrical surface. To express this mathematically, we first express these two surfaces in the following functions:

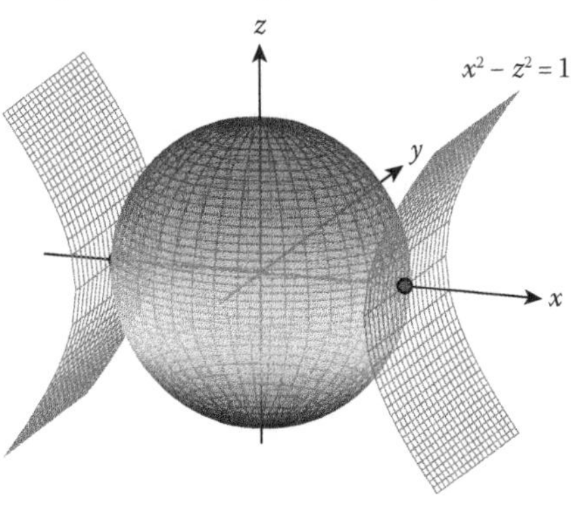

FIGURE B.3
Single-condition extrema.

$$g(x, y, z) = x^2 - z^2 - 1 = 0$$
$$f(x, y, z) = x^2 + y^2 + z^2 - a^2 = 0$$

and then find the points where the two surfaces touch.

By the definition of gradient (Section 2.2.1), $\nabla g(x, y, z)$ and $\nabla f(x, y, z)$ are the normal vectors of the tangent planes at a given point (x, y, z) in each case. Thus, when the two surfaces touch each other, they will have a common tangent plane and their normal vectors will be parallel to each other.

Thus, we have

$$\nabla f = \lambda \nabla g$$

where λ is a positive constant (a scalar variable) that is known as the Lagrange multiplier. Referring to Equation 2.9, along with the two functions given above, we calculate

$$2x\vec{i} + 2y\vec{j} + 2z\vec{k} = \lambda(2x\vec{i} - 2z\vec{k})$$

This leads to the following three algebra equations:

$$\begin{aligned} x(2-2\lambda) &= 0 \\ 2y &= 0 \\ 2z(1+\lambda) &= 0 \end{aligned}$$

Since the point at which the two functions touch cannot be $x = 0$, we have

$$x \neq 0, \quad \lambda = 1; \quad y = 0; \quad z = 0$$

This means that the points where the two surfaces touch will have the coordinates of $(x, 0, 0)$. By substituting this condition into the hyperbolic function, we find $x = \pm 1$. Therefore, there are two points on the hyperbolic cylinder that are closest to the origin (see the marked circles in Figure B.3), and they are located at

$$(1, 0, 0) \text{ and } (-1, 0, 0)$$

This example shows that to find the extrema of function $f(x, y, z) = 0$ under the constraint of $g(x, y, z) = 0$, we introduce a Lagrange multiplier, λ, to construct the following function,

$$f(x, y, z) - \lambda g(x, y, z)$$

and find its extrema by setting its gradient to zero:

$$\nabla f(x, y, z) - \lambda \nabla g(x, y, z) = 0$$

The solutions to this equation are the extrema of $f(x, y, z) = 0$ under the constraint of $g(x, y, z) = 0$.

Next, we examine a situation in which two Lagrange multipliers are used.

As shown in Figure B.4, the plane $x + y + z = 3$ cuts the cylinder $x^2 + y^2 = 9$ in an ellipse. Find the points on the ellipse that lie closest to and farthest from the origin.

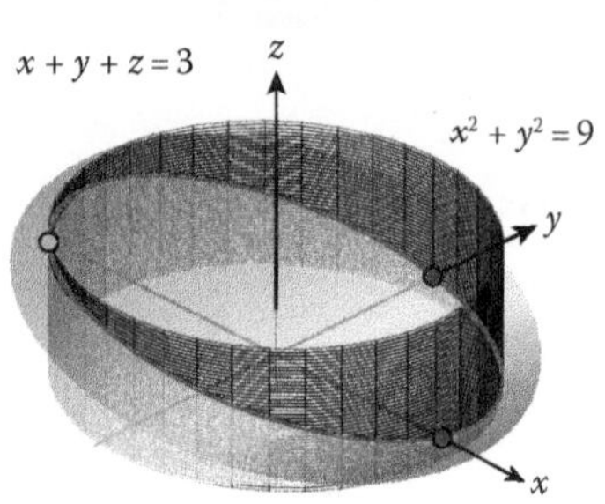

FIGURE B.4
Multicondition extrema.

Using a similar approach, we construct a sphere that captures all points with equal distance a to the origin using the following function,

$$f(x, y, z) = x^2 + y^2 + z^2 - a^2 = 0$$

and rephrase this problem as to find the extrema of $f(x, y, z)$ under the constraints of

$$g_1(x, y, z) = x^2 + y^2 - 9 = 0 \text{ and } g_2(x, y, z) = x + y + z - 3 = 0$$

To solve this problem, we introduce two Lagrange multipliers, λ and μ, and use them to construct the following function:

$$f(x, y, z) - \lambda g_1(x, y, z) - \mu g_2(x, y, z)$$

To the find its extrema we set its gradient to zero:

$$\nabla f(x, y, z) - \lambda \nabla g_1(x, y, z) - \mu \nabla g_2(x, y, z) = 0$$

By using Equation 2.9, along with the $g_1(x, y, z), g_2(x, y, z)$ functions given above, we obtain

$$2x\vec{i} + 2y\vec{j} + 2z\vec{k} = \lambda(2x\vec{i} + 2y\vec{j}) + \mu(1\vec{i} + 1\vec{k} + 1\vec{k})$$

which can be simplified to the following three algebra equations:

$$\begin{aligned} 2x(1 - \lambda) &= \mu \\ 2y(1 - \lambda) &= \mu \\ 2z &= \mu \end{aligned}$$

Of these three equations, when $\lambda = 1$ we have

$$\lambda = 1, \mu = 0, z = 0$$

Substituting these conditions into the $g_1(x, y, z), g_2(x, y, z)$ functions, we have

$$x^2 + y^2 = 9, \quad x + y = 1$$

which leads to

$$x = 3, y = 0; \quad \text{or} \quad x = 0, y = 3$$

So the first set of extrema is located at

$$(3, 0, 0) \text{ and } (0, 3, 0)$$

as marked by the two red circles in Figure B.4. The distance of both these two points to the origin is 3.

When $\lambda \neq 1$, we have

$$\lambda \neq 1, x = y = \frac{z}{1-\lambda}$$

Applying this condition to the cylinder function $(g_1(x, y, z))$, we obtain

$$x = \pm\frac{3\sqrt{2}}{2}$$

Then, with the plane function $(g_2(x, y, z))$, we find

$$z = 3 \mp 3\sqrt{2}$$

So the second set of extrema is found at

$$\left(\frac{3\sqrt{2}}{2}, \frac{3\sqrt{2}}{2}, 3 - 3\sqrt{2}\right) \text{ and } \left(-\frac{3\sqrt{2}}{2}, -\frac{3\sqrt{2}}{2}, 3 + 3\sqrt{2}\right)$$

Unlike the first set of extrema, these two points have different distances to the origin. They are 3.247 and 7.839, respectively. So only one of these points is located farthest from the origin, which is marked by the circle in the upper-left corner in Figure B.4.

Putting it all together, we find two points on the ellipse that are closest to the origin, and they are located at

$$(3, 0, 0) \text{ and } (0, 3, 0)$$

and one point that is farthest from the origin, located at

$$\left(-\frac{3\sqrt{2}}{2}, -\frac{3\sqrt{2}}{2}, 3 + 3\sqrt{2}\right)$$

In this case, because there are two constraining conditions, two Lagrange multipliers are used. As a general observation based on these two examples, it is clear that the number of Lagrange multipliers needed to determine the conditional extrema should equal the number of constraining conditions.

Index

H

I

J

K

L

Q

R

S

T

U

* 9 7 8 1 4 6 6 5 7 2 2 8 7 *
#0001 - 270217 - C0 - 234/156/24 [26] - CB - 9781466572287